D1328039

ANTIHYPERTENSIVE AGENTS

MEDICINAL CHEMISTRY
A Series of Monographs

EDITED BY

GEORGE deSTEVENS

CIBA Pharmaceutical Company
A Division of CIBA Corporation
Summit, New Jersey

Volume 1. GEORGE deSTEVENS. Diuretics: Chemistry and Pharmacology. 1963

Volume 2. RUDOLFO PAOLETTI (ED.). Lipid Pharmacology. 1964

Volume 3. E. J. ARIËNS (ED.). Molecular Pharmacology: The Mode of Action of Biologically Active Compounds. (In two volumes.) 1964

Volume 4. MAXWELL GORDON (ED.). Psychopharmacological Agents. Volume I. 1964. Volume II. 1967.

Volume 5. GEORGE deSTEVENS (ED.). Analgetics. 1965

Volume 6. ROLAND H. THORP AND LEONARD B. COBBIN. Cardiac Stimulant Substances. 1967

Volume 7. EMIL SCHLITTLER (ED.). Antihypertensive Agents. 1967

In Preparation

U. S. VON EULER AND RUNE ELIASSON. Prostaglandin.

ANTIHYPERTENSIVE AGENTS

Edited by

EMIL SCHLITTLER

CIBA Pharmaceutical Company
A Division of CIBA Corporation
Summit, New Jersey

ACADEMIC PRESS   *New York and London*   1967

ACADEMIC PRESS INC.
111 Fifth Avenue, New York, New York 10003

United Kingdom Edition published by
ACADEMIC PRESS INC. (LONDON) LTD.
Berkeley Square House, London W.1

LIBRARY OF CONGRESS CATALOG CARD NUMBER: 67-22775

PRINTED IN THE UNITED STATES OF AMERICA

Est autem alkimia operativa et practica . . . non solum expensas et alia infinita rei publicae potest dare, sed docet invenire talia quae vitam humanam possunt prolongare in multa tempora, ad quae per naturam produci potest.

But there is another alchemy, operative and practical . . . which not only can yield wealth and very many other things for the public welfare but it also teaches how to discover such things as are capable of prolonging human life for much longer periods than can be accomplished by nature.

Roger Bacon   (*c.* 1220–*c.* 1292)

Opus tertium, Chapter 12

LIST OF CONTRIBUTORS

Numbers in parentheses refer to the pages on which the authors' contributions begin.

WALTER E. BARRETT, CIBA Pharmaceutical Company, A Division of CIBA Corporation, Summit, New Jersey (331)

HUGO J. BEIN, CIBA Limited, Basle, Switzerland (191)

GEORGE DESTEVENS, CIBA Pharmaceutical Company, A Division of CIBA Corporation, Summit, New Jersey (263)

JEAN DRUEY, CIBA Limited, Basle, Switzerland (223)

WERNER E. FLACKE, Department of Pharmacology, Harvard Medical School, Boston, Massachusetts (429)

J. V. HODGE, Wellcome Medical Research Institute, University of Otago Medical School, Dunedin, New Zealand (459)

S. MORRIS KUPCHAN, Department of Pharmaceutical Chemistry, University of Wisconsin, Madison, Wisconsin (429)

G. E. LEE, May and Baker, Limited, Dagenham, Essex, England (295)

ADRIAN MARXER, CIBA Limited, Basle, Switzerland (279)

ROBERT A. MAXWELL, Burroughs Wellcome and Company Inc., Tuckahoe, New York (115)

ROBERT P. MULL, CIBA Pharmaceutical Company, A Division of CIBA Corporation, Summit, New Jersey (115)

ALBERT J. PLUMMER, CIBA Pharmaceutical Company, A Division of CIBA Corporation, Summit, New Jersey (67)

H. R. RODRIGUEZ, CIBA Pharmaceutical Company, A Division of CIBA Corporation, Summit, New Jersey (151)

OSWALD SCHIER, CIBA Limited, Basle, Switzerland (279)

EMIL SCHLITTLER, CIBA Pharmaceutical Company, A Division of CIBA Corporation, Summit, New Jersey (191)

HOLLIS G. SCHOEPKE, Abbott Laboratories, North Chicago, Illinois (393)

F. O. SIMPSON, Wellcome Medical Research Institute, University of Otago Medical School, Dunedin, New Zealand (459)

F. HORACE SMIRK, Wellcome Medical Research Institute, University of Otago Medical School, Dunedin, New Zealand (1)

T. L. SOURKES, Allan Memorial Institute of Psychiatry, McGill University, Montreal, Quebec, Canada (151)

LEO R. SWETT, Abbott Laboratories, North Chicago, Illinois (393)

JEAN TRIPOD, CIBA Limited, Basle, Switzerland (223)

LINCOLN H. WERNER, CIBA Pharmaceutical Company, A Division of CIBA Corporation, Summit, New Jersey (331)

PREFACE

Antihypertensive substances are almost exclusively the fruit of industrial research. It is a fact that the pharmaceutical industry is going through a difficult period presently and that the usefulness of its research endeavors are often questioned by many of our fellow human beings. In spite of this attitude, all of us who have been active in combatting the ill effects of elevated blood pressure are convinced that we have contributed toward alleviating the sufferings of mankind. However, it should be pointed out that in spite of considerable success the treatment of high blood pressure is still a wide open field and new possibilities for antihypertensive therapy may develop at any time. In view of the 16–18 million people (*Penn. Med.* **70**, 86, 1967) in this country afflicted with high blood pressure alone the importance of antihypertensive research cannot be overrated.

We all realize that for ultimate success it is mainly the clinicians who say the final word concerning the utility of the compounds prepared by chemists and screened for activity by pharmacologists. For this reason it may seem strange that more space has not been allocated to the clinical evaluation of antihypertensive agents. However, this decision lies within the framework of this series, which is essentially experimental and not clinical.

It is hoped that this book on "Antihypertensive Agents" will fulfill some needs, although there are a number of reasons why this might be doubted. First, there are a number of colleagues (among these some eminent ones) who think that, in general, too many books are written and published today. Second, the developments in the field of medicinal chemistry are so rapid that before long many chapters of such a book will be obsolete and will have only a documentary value.

In spite of these adverse possibilities the book on "Antihypertensive Agents" has finally materialized. A number of potential authors declined my invitation for a contribution. That their professional activities prevented them from indulging in an enterprise suffering from the above-mentioned shortcomings is thoroughly understandable. My greatest appreciation goes, therefore, to the authors who did enthusiastically share with me the burden of contributing to a common goal. It was a unique experience to closely collaborate and to extensively correspond with colleagues who in many cases were not even personally known to me previously or who were more than 10,000 miles away.

My thanks are due first to the authors who helped me with untiring enthusiasm and then to Dr. George deStevens, Editor-in-Chief of this Series, with whom I have a unique personal and professional association. I am also indebted to CIBA Pharmaceutical Company, a division of CIBA Corporation, for letting me work on this project. My gratitude also goes to Misses Rose Farina, Sonja Cardona, and Marcia Swanstrom (all of CIBA Pharmaceuticals), who never tired of typing and retyping innumerable pages of the manuscript.

EMIL SCHLITTLER

Summit, New Jersey
July, 1967

CONTENTS

LIST OF CONTRIBUTORS vii
PREFACE ix
LIST OF ANTIHYPERTENSIVE AGENTS xv

CHAPTER I

The Pathogenesis of Hypertension

F. HORACE SMIRK

   I. Introduction 2
  II. Evidence that hypertensive disease is due to blood-pressure elevation as such . 7
 III. Evidence that over-average blood pressures, though determined by the operation of physiological processes, not only predispose to the development of frank
hypertension, but are an integral component of its pathogenesis . . . 10
 IV. Evidence that, in relation to pathogenesis, the basal and supplemental parts of
the casual blood pressure deserve separate consideration 12
  V. Evidence that a genetic factor is concerned in the pathogenesis of essential hypertension and probably to some degree also in the pathogenesis of other hypertensive conditions 16
 VI. Evidence that rigidity of the arterial reservoir is concerned in elevation of the
blood pressure 20
VII. Evidence relating to the pathogenesis of renal hypertension (the relationship of
experimental to clinical renal hypertension) 21
VIII. Evidence relating to increased vascular reactivity in hypertension . . . 32
 IX. Evidence concerning the responses of hypertensive and normotensive patients
and experimental animals to pressor agencies 38
  X. Evidence concerning the relationship of the amount of renal substance to blood-
pressure elevation 46
 XI. Evidence that in chronic hypertension in man and in experimental animals the
baroceptors become set to operate at a higher level 50
XII. Summary 52
    References 58

CHAPTER II

Experimental Hypertension in Animals and Its Use in Screening for Antihypertensive Compounds

ALBERT J. PLUMMER

   I. Introduction 68
  II. Experimental hypertension 69
 III. Development of antihypertensive agents 93
 IV. Discussion 107
    References 109

CHAPTER III

Guanethidine and Related Adrenergic Neuronal Blocking Agents

ROBERT P. MULL AND ROBERT A. MAXWELL

   I. Introduction 115
  II. Pharmacology of the adrenergic neuronal blocking agents 116
 III. Chemistry of the adrenergic neuronal blocking agents 123
    References 145

CHAPTER IV

α-Methyldopa and Other Decarboxylase Inhibitors

T. L. SOURKES AND H. R. RODRIGUEZ

    I. Introduction 151
   II. Synthetic decarboxylase inhibitors 157
  III. Enzymology and biochemical pharmacology 168
  IV. Methyldopa 182
      References 186

CHAPTER V

Rauwolfia **Alkaloids**

E. SCHLITTLER AND H. J. BEIN

Part One—Hypotensive Drugs from *Rauwolfia* spp.

     I. Introduction 191
    II. Chemical classification of *Rauwolfia* alkaloids 193
   III. Chemistry of reserpine-type alkaloids. 193
   IV. Alkaloids related to reserpine 194
    V. Semisynthetic reserpine derivatives 196
   VI. Total synthesis of reserpine and reserpine analogs 197
  VII. Synthesis of model compounds 198

      Part Two—Pharmacology of Reserpine .

  VIII. Effect of reserpine on the central nervous system 206
   IX. Effect of reserpine on the sympathetic nervous system 207
    X. Effect of reserpine on the circulatory system 210
   XI. Effect of reserpine on various endocrine functions 212
  XII. Interference with the action of reserpine 214
      References 215

CHAPTER VI

Hydralazines

J. DRUEY AND J. TRIPOD

    I. Introduction 223
   II. Chemistry of hydrazinophthalazines and related compounds . . . 224
  III. Biochemistry 234
  IV. Pharmacodynamics and therapeutic use in man 239
   V. Summary and conclusions 256
     References 257

CHAPTER VII

Diuretics in the Clinical Treatment of Hypertension

GEORGE deSTEVENS

    Chemistry of Diuretics 263
    References 276

CHAPTER VIII

Quaternary Ganglionic Blockers

A. MARXER AND O. SCHIER

    I. Introduction 279
   II. Chemistry of the ganglionic blockers 279
  III. Pharmacological effects and therapeutic use of quaternary ganglionic blockers. 289
     References 293

CHAPTER IX

Non-Quaternary Ganglionic Blockers

G. E. LEE

I. Introduction 295
II. Chemistry and structure–activity relationships of amine ganglionic blocking
agents 297
III. Pharmacology 322
IV. Excretion, distribution, and metabolism 324
V. Clinical studies 326
References 328

CHAPTER X

Adrenergic Blocking Agents

L. H. WERNER AND W. E. BARRETT

I. Introduction 331
II. Phenethylamine derivatives 333
III. Derivatives of benzodioxan 334
IV. β-Haloethylamine adrenergic blocking agents 344
V. Derivatives of phenylpiperazine 353
VI. Substituted imidazolines 357
VII. Miscellaneous compounds with adrenergic blocking activity 361
VIII. Ergot alkaloids 362
IX. Adrenergic β-receptor blocking agents 364
X. Pharmacology and clinical application of α- and β-adrenergic blocking agents . 368
References 384

CHAPTER XI

Chemistry and Pharmacology of Monoamine Oxidase Inhibitors

HOLLIS G. SCHOEPKE AND LEO R. SWETT

I. Introduction 393
II. Hydrazines 394
III. Nonhydrazines 398
IV. Mechanism of action 412
V. Side effects and toxic reactions 420
References 424

CHAPTER XII

Hypotensive *Veratrum* Alkaloids

S. MORRIS KUPCHAN AND WERNER E. FLACKE

I. Introduction 429
II. Alkaloids and taxonomy of *Veratrum* and related genera . . . 430
III. Chemical classification of *Veratrum* alkaloids 430
IV. Chemistry and relative activity of the hypotensive *Veratrum* alkaloids . . 430
V. Chemistry and relative hypotensive activity of semisynthetic alkamine esters . 436
VI. Pharmacological actions and methods used for comparative evaluation . . 439
VII. *In vivo* distribution 450
VIII. Clinical uses 451
References 453

CHAPTER XIII

Use of Antihypertensive Drugs in Combinations

F. O. SIMPSON AND J. V. HODGE

I. Introduction 459
II. Combinations of antihypertensive drugs 462
III. Antihypertensive drugs combined with other drugs 475
IV. Conclusion 481
References 482

AUTHOR INDEX 487

SUBJECT INDEX 524

ANTIHYPERTENSIVE AGENTS

Generic Name	Trade Name
A	
Acetazolamide	Diamox
Acetoxatrine	—
Alkavervir	Veriloid
Allopurinol	Zyloprim
Amanozine	Renolin
Amisometradine	Rolicton
Amitriptyline	Elavil
Angiotensin amide	Hypertensin-CIBA
Atropine methylnitrate	Eumydrin, Metropine, etc.
Azamethonium bromide	Pendiomide
Azapetine phosphate	Ilidar
B	
Bendroflumethiazide	Benuron, Naturetin
Benzthiazide	Naclex, Exna
Bethanidine hydriodide	Esbatal
Bretylium tosylate	Darenthin
Butoxamine hydrochloride	—
C	
α-Chloralose	Somio
Chlorazinil hydrochloride	Daquin
Chlorisondamine chloride	Ecolid
Chlorpheniramine maleate	Chlor-Trimeton
Chlorthalidone	Hygroton
Chlorthiazide	Diuril
Clopamide	Brinaldix
Clorexolone	Nefrolan
Cortisone acetate	Cortone Acetate, Cortivite, etc.
Cyclopenthiazide	Navidrix
D	
Debrisoquin	Declinex
Deserpidine (Canescine)	Harmonyl

Generic Name	Trade Name
Deoxycorticosterone acetate	Percorten, Descotone, etc.
Diallylbarbituric acid	Dial, Diadol
Diazoxide	Mutabase
Dibozane	—
Dichlorisoproterenol	—
1-[2-(diethylamino)-ethyl] reserpine	Bietaserpin
Diethylstilbestrol	Stilbestrol, Stilbetin, etc.
Dihydralazine	Nepresol
Dimecamine	—
Dimenhydrinate	Dramamine
Diphenylmethylatropinium bromide	Gastropin
Disulfiram	Antabuse, etc.
Droperidol	Inapsine
E	
Ethacrynic acid	Edecrin
Ethylenediamine tetracetic acid (Edathamil)	Versene
Etryptamine acetate	Monase
F	
Fenfluramine hydrochloride	Ponderax
Furosemide	Lasix
G	
Gallamine tricthiodide	Flaxedil
Guanethidine	Ismelin
Guanisoquin sulfate	—
Guanoclor	Vatensol
Guanoxan sulfate	Envacar
H	
Haloanisone	—
Hexamethonium bromide	Vagolysen

Generic Name	Trade Name
Hexamethonium chloride	Methium
Hydralazine hydrochloride	Apresoline
Hydralazine + hexamethonium	Hyphex
Hydrochlorthiazide	Esidrix, Hydrodiuril, Oretic, etc.
Hydrocortisone	Cortril, Hydrocortone, etc.

I

Imipramine	Tofranil
Iproniazide	Marsilid
Isocarboxazide	Marplan
Isoproterenol hydrochloride	Isuprel, Aleudrin, etc.
Isoxsuprine	Vasodilan

L

Lidocaine hydrochloride	Xylocaine, Lignocaine

M

Mebutamate	Capla
Mecamylamine hydrochloride	Inversine
Meperidine hydrochloride	Demerol, Dolantin, etc.
Mephentermine sulfate	Wyamine
Meprobamate	Miltown, Equanil, etc.
Mepyramine = Pyrilamine maleate	Neo-Antergan, etc.
Mersalyl	Salyrgan
Metaraminol bitartrate	Aramine
Methantheline bromide	Banthine
10-Methoxydeserpidine	Decaserpyl
Methoxyisoxsuprine	—
Methylclothiazide	Enduron
Methyldopa	Aldomet
Methylphenidate hydrochloride	Ritalin
Methysergide maleate	Sansert

Generic Name	Trade Name
N	
Nialamide	Niamid
O	
Oriprenaline	—
Oxapentonium	Oxaditon, Diamonal
Oxypertine	—
Oxyphenonium bromide	Antrenyl
P	
Pargyline hydrochloride	Eutonyl
Pargyline + methyclothiazide	Eutron
Pempidine tartrate	Tenormal, Perolysen
Penbutamine	—
Penhexamine	—
Pentacynium	Presidal
Pentabarbital	Nembutal
Pentolinium tartrate	Ansolysen
Piperoxan hydrochloride	Benodaine
Pitressin	Vasopressin
Pivazide	Tersavid
Phenelzine sulfate	Nardil
Pheniprazine hydrochloride	Catron
Phenmetrazine hydrochloride	Preludin
Phenobarbital	Luminal, Liquital, etc.
Phenoxybenzamine hydrochloride	Dibenzyline
Phentolamine hydrochloride	Regitine
Phenylephrine hydrochloride	Neo-Synephrine, Synasal, etc.
Polythiazide	Renese
Prenylamine	Segontin
Probenecid	Benemide
Pronethalol	Alderlin
Propranolol hydrochloride	Inderal
Protoveratrine A	Protalba
Protoveratrine B	—
R	
Reserpine	Serpasil, Sandril, etc.

Generic Name	Trade Name	Generic Name	Trade Name
Rescinnamine	Moderil, etc.	Triamterene	Dyrenium
		Trichlormethiazide	Naqua, Flutra, etc.
S		Trimethaphan camphorsulfonate	Arfonad
Scopolamine butylbromide	Buscopan	Trimethidinium methosulfate	Ostensin
Spironolactone	Aldactone-A	Tripelennamine citrate	Pyribenzamine citrate
Spiroxamide	—	d-Tubocurarine chloride	Tubarine, Tubadil, etc.
Syrosingopine	Singoserp		
		V	
T			
Thiopental sodium	Pentothal	Vasopressin	Pitressin
Tolazoline hydrochloride	Priscoline	**Z**	
Tranylcypromine sulfate	Parnate	Zoxazolamine	Flexin

CHAPTER I

The Pathogenesis of Hypertension

F. Horace Smirk

I. Introduction, 2

II. Evidence That Hypertensive Disease Is Due to Blood-Pressure Elevation as Such, 7

III. Evidence That Over-average Blood Pressures, though Determined by the Operation of Physiological Processes, Not Only Predispose to the Development of Frank Hypertension, but Are an Integral Component of Its Pathogenesis, 10

IV. Evidence That, in Relation to Pathogenesis, the Basal and Supplemental Parts of the Casual Blood Pressure Deserve Separate Consideration, 12
    A. Evidence That the Casual Blood Pressure Is the Sum of at Least Two Almost Independent Variables, Namely, the Basal and the Supplemental Pressures, 13
    B. Evidence That the Supplemental Pressure Is Influenced by Several Factors, 14
    C. Evidence That the Basal Blood Pressure May Be Subdivided into a Neurogenically and a Nonneurogenically Maintained Part, 15

V. Evidence That a Genetic Factor Is Concerned in the Pathogenesis of Essential Hypertension and Probably to Some Degree Also in the Pathogenesis of Other Hypertensive Conditions, 16
    A. The Genetics of Hypertension in Man, 16
    B. Spontaneous Genetic Hypertension in Rats, 18
    C. Rats Genetically Susceptible to Salt Hypertension, 20

VI. Evidence That Rigidity of the Arterial Reservoir Is Concerned in Elevation of the Blood Pressure, 20

VII. Evidence Relating to the Pathogenesis of Renal Hypertension (The Relationship of Experimental to Clinical Renal Hypertension), 21
    A. Evidence That Blood-Pressure Increases of Sufficient Degree and Duration May Be Self-perpetuating or Self-augmenting, 22
    B. Factors Influencing the Liberation of Renin, 24
    C. The Interrelationships of Renin, Juxtaglomerular Granulation, Angiotensin, Angiotensinase, Aldosterone, Electrolytes, and Blood Pressure, 26
    D. Antirenin, 32

VIII. Evidence Relating to Increased Vascular Reactivity in Hypertension, 32
    A. The Reactivity of Resistance Blood Vessels in Hypertensive and in Normotensive Individuals, 33
    B. Increased Vascular Reactivity in Experimental Hypertension, 34

IX. Evidence Concerning the Responses of Hypertensive and Normotensive Patients and Experimental Animals to Pressor Agencies, 38
    A. The Relationship between the Cold Pressor Test, Age, and Supplemental Pressures in Hypertensives and Normotensives, 38
    B. The Effect of Other Pressor Stimuli in Hypertensives and Normotensives, 40
    C. Responses to Pressor Agents in Experimental Hypertension, 42

X. Evidence Concerning the Relationship of the Amount of Renal Substance to Blood-Pressure Elevation, 46
   A. Renoprival Hypertension, 47
   B. Response to Pressor Stimuli after Bilateral Nephrectomy, 48
XI. Evidence That in Chronic Hypertension in Man and in Experimental Animals the Baroceptors Become Set to Operate at a Higher Level, 50
XII. Summary, 52
   References, 58

I. Introduction

The pressure of blood in major arteries depends upon the amount of blood pumped into them by the heart and the resistance offered to the flow of blood by the numerous small branch vessels which convey blood to the tissues. The share of the blood received by particular organs varies with their current needs.

The blood pressure in health may vary considerably with change in the individual's physical, emotional, and metabolic activity, and it is affected genetically and environmentally. In hypertension, wide variations of the blood-pressure level also occur in response to endogenous and exogenous stimuli, and in essential hypertension the variations are often greater than in health. The disorder "essential hypertension" is the commonest variety of high blood pressure. It has sometimes been defined as blood-pressure elevation in the absence of any clearly identifiable cause. It has been called "primary hypertension"; and indeed, in the present state of our knowledge, blood-pressure elevation seems to be the first clear evidence of emergence of the disorder; furthermore, the clinical manifestations of the disorder appear to be due to the high blood pressure as such, and not as the direct consequence of any of the underlying causes for the blood-pressure elevation.

In health, strenuous exercise and other stimuli may elevate the blood pressure to heights which would be frankly abnormal were they to occur under resting conditions; hence, some difficulty in definition has arisen from the fact that no level of the blood pressure can be stated which defines a boundary between normal and abnormal.

There are several disorders in which hypertension occurs, and while there is evidence that the complex changes associated with blood-pressure elevation are not exactly the same in different disorders, it appears that some of the mechanisms leading to blood-pressure elevation may occur in common in hypertension from different causes. It will be shown later that, probably, one reason for this is that hypertension, as such, causes changes in the body which lead to perpetuation or further increase of the blood pressure—in other words, to a vicious circle.

Once hypertension has developed, the secondary changes which are liable to occur are held in common by disorders which have started in different ways, and in some patients at a late stage in the evolution of the disorder, it may be difficult, or at present impossible, to decide on the original cause of the hypertension. It is often overlooked that when the blood pressure rises above normal, the rise is perched on the top of the previous normal range.

The hypotensive drugs available in 1967 ordinarily are capable of reducing the blood pressure in health and, to a larger extent, in hypertension. Reduction of the blood pressure is not necessarily, or even probably, due to the neutralization of just those abnormalities which have caused the blood-pressure increase. The blood-pressure reduction sometimes may be brought about by the drug acting exclusively upon that part of the blood pressure which is maintained by entirely physiological mechanisms.

This and other features common to hypertensions of different origins go some way toward explaining the convenient fact that the sympatholytic drugs in use at the present time, if effective at all, are effective in different types of hypertension. There are occasional patients who are resistant or nearly resistant to all drugs. Most such patients have advanced renal disease; a few are encountered in association with recent severe cerebral hemorrhage. In a great majority of patients, however, the height of the blood pressure may be reduced, and the adverse effects of high pressure are brought under a measure of control.

In what follows, most attention will be given to essential hypertension. There is much evidence now that, at least when fully established, this disorder has a multifactorial pathogenesis, in the sense that many different physiological systems are concerned in the maintenance of a high blood-pressure level; possibly also it may be multifactorial in its first origins.

There is good evidence that in the later stages of its natural history, essential hypertension causes abnormalities to develop in the kidney. It seems likely that in some patients a nonrenal disorder ends up by the addition of a renal component which carries the already elevated blood pressure to a still higher level; hence, in the later stages, essential and renal hypertension may come to resemble each other very closely; therefore in discussing the pathogenesis of manifest renal hypertension one is at the same time discussing the pathogenesis of a factor which occurs—but usually at a comparatively late stage— in essential hypertension.

Other types of hypertension which occur clinically have experimental analogs. For example, an endocrine disorder, Cushing's syndrome, is due to excessive secretion of adrenal cortex hormones and is associated with blood-pressure elevation. Some of these hormones, for example cortisone, when given therapeutically or in laboratory animals, will raise the blood pressure. Some of the features of phaeochromocytoma, which is due to a catecholamine-secreting tumor, may be duplicated experimentally by the parenteral administration of the adrenal medullary hormones norepinephrine and epinephrine. Hypertension is usual in primary aldosteronism, due to excessive aldosterone secretion, usually from a tumor in the adrenal cortex.

The factors which determine the level of the blood pressure in health are numerous, and complexity arises because their activities are interdependent, so that as a general rule, a major disturbance in the activity of one factor alters the activity of the others. Although there is no sharp line dividing normal from abnormally high blood pressures, a blood pressure of 160 mm Hg systolic, 90 mm Hg diastolic is sometimes mentioned as the upper limit of normal for blood pressures taken under ordinary clinical conditions. Such a pressure, however, would be unusually high in a young person, and life insurance statistics show that blood pressures even lower than this are associated with an over-average mortality later from cardiovascular causes. Also, blood pressures which are constantly high are associated with more disabilities and a higher mortality than blood pressures which are raised only intermittently.

The relationship between the cardiac output and the peripheral resistance is influenced by many factors, including the nervous system. In hypertension some of these factors may be acting within the normal range, or acting in their usual way but outside the normal range, or their actions may be modified by frankly pathological changes. The following is a list of physiological events which may alter the blood pressure of healthy individuals, and most of them influence the blood-pressure level also in persons with hypertension.

(1) Changes in the activity of higher centers in the brain, associated with emotion, tenseness, or mental concentration.

(2) Changes in the activity of the sympathetic nervous system, arising in one or more of several sites, including the hypothalamus, medulla, cell stations in the spinal cord, sympathetic ganglia, and sympathetic nerve endings. The changes which may occur at each of these sites may be complex, thus the extent to which sympathetic nerve endings affect cardiac or vascular muscle may be influenced by the amount of the neurotransmitter, norepinephrine, released from the nerve endings, and by changes in the rate of its destruction or return to storage sites.

(3) Changes in the response to sympathetic nerve stimulation of the cardiac muscle and of the smooth muscle of blood vessels.

(4) Changes in the activity of the parasympathetic nervous system, which ordinarily decreases heart rate and output. The parasympathetic nervous system is one of the physiological mechanisms for preventing excessive blood-pressure rises, but in hypertension it is insufficiently effective.

(5) Changes in the activity of the heart or blood vessels occurring in response to the blood-pressure level and to a number of factors such as release of norepinephrine and epinephrine from the medulla of the adrenal gland.

(6) Changes in the blood volume which, by altering the rate of return of blood to the heart, may influence its output.

(7) Changes in the caliber of the veins and capillaries which serve as capacity-storage vessels, thereby influencing the amount of blood returned to the heart and the cardiac output. Such changes are sometimes due to alteration in the amount of sympathetic nervous stimulation, or they may be nonnervous in origin.

(8) Changes in the rate of secretion of certain hormones. Ordinarily, excessive secretion of the thyroid hormone, and of certain hormones from the adrenal cortex and from the pituitary gland tend to be associated with higher blood-pressure levels, and deficiencies in their secretions with lower blood-pressure levels.

(9) Changes in the release of the enzyme renin in the kidney, with consequent liberation of angiotensin and secondary release of aldosterone, occur under certain circumstances in health, especially in response to events tending to limit the circulation of blood through the kidneys. Such changes may influence the final resultant level of the blood pressure. The complexities of this system are very great, and are referred to under renal hypertension.

(10) Variations even within the normal range of the blood pressure influence the baroceptors located principally in the carotid sinus and aortic arch. These act by restricting the extent of the blood-pressure change. Thus physiological changes tending to raise the blood pressure become opposed by other physiological changes tending to lower the blood pressure, and the reverse occurs. In general, the baroceptors exert their effects by altering the activity of the sympathetic nervous system, so that when the blood pressure falls, there is an increased discharge of sympathetic nerve impulses to heart and blood vessels, and when the pressure rises, a decrease in such impulses. The carotid body which responds in particular to changes in blood composition also acts as a regulator of the blood pressure in certain circumstances.

Several physiological and pathological events can be shown, convincingly, to be associated with blood-pressure increase in experimental animals and sometimes clinically, and correspondingly numerous hypotheses as to the causes of hypertension have been based upon these findings. In most hypotheses emphasis has been laid upon one of the factors which might elevate the blood pressure, as if it were the sole, the primary, or the dominant explanation of a clinical hypertension. If, however, there is a type of high blood pressure which arises multifactorially by the sum of the contributions of many factors tending to raise the blood pressure, then any attempt to frame an explanation of it in terms of a single cause would be frustrating, because, even if that cause participates in the blood-pressure elevation, when looked at closely, it will become clear that it does not provide a sufficient explanation. It would be possible for investigators to have examined closely all of a number of participating causes for blood-pressure elevation, and rejected them one by one because they did not seem to provide a sufficient explanation, or to advance them as alternative hypotheses, making the suggestion that one of them has to be regarded as the sole or dominant cause.

The suggestion has been made by Smirk (246, 247, 249: p. 322) that in the commonest type of high blood pressure, "essential hypertension," many factors are concerned in the blood-pressure elevation, and they are not present in any constant proportion. A persistently high level of the blood pressure marks the first emergence of essential hypertension as a separate disorder, there being no single antecedent pathological process sufficient by itself to explain the blood-pressure rise in all patients.

The clinical manifestations of essential hypertension appear to be due to, or accelerated by, either the blood-pressure elevation or the associated vasoconstriction. Whatever antecedent changes cause the rise of blood pressure in essential hypertension, they appear in themselves to be symptomless, and harmless, except that they raise the blood pressure. Evidence will be presented that it is the height of the blood pressure, however produced, that gives rise to the clinical manifestations of essential hypertension.

In contrast to essential hypertension, such disorders as nephritis, Cushing's disease, or aortic coarctation exhibit the manifestations of the primary disorder as well as those secondary to the hypertension. These primary disorders have their own natural histories and may cause disabilities and sometimes death due to the primary disorder and unrelated to the hypertension.

Some, possibly many, of the factors which have been advanced as sole explanations of the pathogenesis of essential and of some other types of human hypertension are, in fact, participating in a complex system of interrelated adjustments, the resultant of which is a blood-pressure elevation.

Fortunately, a description, one by one, of the factors which might be concerned in a multifactorial hypothesis is virtually also a description of rival unifactorial hypotheses which have in common that they seek to explain hypertension (usually essential hypertension) in terms of one of the factors to be discussed later, this factor being regarded as the only, or at least the dominant, underlying cause. Recent evidence is mostly favorable to a multifactorial hypothesis, as being the best explanation of the rise of blood pressure in essential hypertension; but it seems that a disturbance of the renal circulation is at least the dominant cause of the rise of blood pressure in a variety of renal disorders in which hypertension occurs.

Inevitable complexities should not obscure an important underlying principle for which there is very strong evidence (246, 249: p. 322) namely:

hypertension is an intermediate cause, in the sense that whatever cause or causes lead to hypertension, it is the hypertension as such which leads on to hypertensive disease. This being so, anything which causes a lasting blood-pressure increase becomes at least a contributory factor in the pathogenesis of hypertensive disease, and anything which restricts blood-pressure increase is a protection against hypertensive disease.

If this statement is true, one may deduce that blood-pressure reduction in all types of hypertension, irrespective of the cause, should lessen the amount of hypertensive disease, and that this benefit should not depend on the means used, so long as there is effective blood-pressure reduction. The means used must not be uncomfortable, or harmful to the patient, but provided the drug or procedure is harmless and does not cause discomfort, it would appear that if effective, the site of action is not necessarily important.

Finally, if we consider the natural history of essential hypertension, a distinction has to be made between the causes of rise in the blood pressure and the factors which influence the degree to which rise of blood pressure leads to such manifestations of hypertensive disease as heart failure, stroke, coronary disease, and renal excretory defects. There are circumstances which influence the frequency with which particular complications (such as coronary disease and stroke) occur: for example, females tolerate hypertension better than males. Among hypertensives in Japan, stroke is much more frequent than coronary disease, and in the United States, coronary disease, relative to stroke, occurs more frequently than in Japan (143, 238, 252, 286).

Treatment by antihypertensive drugs has a much more striking effect in preventing some of the complications of hypertension than others—for example, it is easier to prevent left ventricular failure than strokes. It would appear that there are conditions which modify the liability to particular disabilities, and it is possible that measures which are ideal from the standpoint of preventing stroke may not be ideal from the standpoint of preventing heart failure or coronary artery disease. For example, the relative degrees to which systolic and diastolic pressures are reduced may have different effects upon the incidence of the various complications of hypertension.

II. Evidence that hypertensive disease is due to blood-pressure elevation as such

While there are many separate pathological conditions known to be causally associated with high blood pressure, the blood-pressure elevation, if high enough or of sufficient duration, is associated with certain clinical manifestations. These include congestive heart failure, cardiac asthma, breathlessness on exertion of cardiac origin, electrocardiographic changes indicating left ventricular preponderance and increase in heart size. There may be such retinal manifestations as papilloedema, retinal oedema, soft exudates, hard exudates (stellate figures), and hemorrhages, and changes occur in the retinal blood vessels such as waistlike narrowing of arteries and constriction of the arteriovenous crossings. Headaches, giddiness, attacks of encephalopathy and epistaxis also may occur in hypertension, irrespective of the primary cause. Cerebral vascular accidents are more frequent when hypertension is present, but they may occur when the blood pressure is normal. Patients will, of course, differ in their vulnerability to the effects of blood-pressure elevation: for example, males tolerate hypertension less well than females.

As will be mentioned later, the correlation between blood-pressure elevation and clinical manifestations is much closer when basal blood pressures are studied than when, as is usual, only casual blood pressures are considered.

The results of treatment by blood-pressure reduction have added strong evidence for the proposition that the characteristics of hypertensive disease are due to the hypertension as such. The benefits resulting from effective reduction of the blood pressure do not depend upon the cause of the blood-pressure elevation, but are found in all types of hypertension. It is not that reduction of the blood pressure necessarily removes basic causes, but it breaks a link in the chain of causation; for, whatever primary conditions have led to blood-pressure elevation, the high pressure becomes a secondary cause with its own characteristic manifestations. Reduction of the blood pressure reduces the incidence of hypertensive manifestations, whatever the cause of the hypertension may be. This subject is treated in detail elsewhere (249: p. 678).

Many clinics have found that the mortality of advanced hypertensive disease is greatly reduced by the effective use of hypotensive drugs (36, 123, 233, 240, 248, 251). Evidence along the same lines has been reported as the results of surgical sympathectomy, together with some adverse comments (18, 70, 218, 268) and clinical improvements have been observed with severe salt restriction (44, 140, 293). There has been dispute as to whether comparatively mild cases of hypertension have a lower mortality if the blood pressure is reduced. Smirk (251) compared the outlook of 270 treated and 199 untreated hypertensive patients of retinal grades I and II, similar in their basal blood pressures and clinical features. Higher levels of the basal blood pressure are correlated with a higher mortality. The 5-year mortality is considerably reduced, approximately to one half, by effective blood-pressure reduction using drugs. The degree of improvement is greater with those who presented with high basal pressures than with those whose basal pressures were comparatively low.

Aside from decrease in mortality, certain reversible clinical manifestations such as breathlessness (38, 83, 110, 139, 170, 184, 206, 229, 232, 239, 255, 265, 266) and electrocardiographic left ventricular strain pattern (60, 164, 186, 206, 229, 240, 255) show improvement when effective blood-pressure reduction is maintained. Thus in congestive heart failure, cardiac asthma, and breathlessness on exertion which is due to hypertension, the blood-pressure reduction is likely to bring effective relief, and deaths from heart failure and left ventricular failure are now exceptional in patients on effective drug treatment, whereas in untreated patients these were the commonest causes of death. It was shown by Smirk *et al.* (257) that relief of left ventricular failure and breathlessness commonly follows effective blood-pressure reduction, even though no digitalis or diuretics of any kind are given, and without more reduction in the salt intake than the withdrawal of added salt at meal times.

Such retinal manifestations as papilloedema, retinal oedema, soft exudates, hard exudates, and hemorrhages are removed when the blood pressure is reduced effectively (14, 15, 39, 184, 189, 206, 217, 225, 248, 255). Hard exudates may take a long time to disappear. Changes in the arteries such as waistlike narrowing and constriction of arteriovenous crossings do not seem to improve with treatment.

Headaches and often giddiness are relieved and attacks of encephalopathy and epistaxis become less frequent. The results of our clinic (59, 123, 249: p. 686) suggest that cerebral vascular accidents are reduced in frequency by blood-pressure reduction. Clinical improvements occur in all types of hypertension, and the improvement would appear to be due to the removal of the immediate cause of these manifestations, namely, elevation of the blood pressure arising from a variety of causes.

Additional evidence comes from experimental studies. Although the manifestations of hypertensive disease vary somewhat from one animal to another, in one and the same animal there are usually manifestations characteristic of hypertension irrespective of the means used to induce it. For example, in the rat, hypertension may lead to cardiac hypertrophy, renal damage to untouched kidneys, periarteritis nodosa, and with very high pressures, to medial necrosis of arterioles. Smirk and Phelan (259) showed that these characteristics of rat hypertension may occur spontaneously in rats from our colony of genetic hypertensives. Wilson and Byrom (296) found similar changes in renal hypertension brought about by constriction of a renal artery, and Smirk (250) described similar changes in salt hypertension.

Gaunt *et al.* (90) administered reserpine and hydralazine, singly and combined, to rats receiving deoxycorticosterone acetate (DCA) and salt. The results were compared with those obtained in rats receiving DCA and salt only. Survivals were longer and acute renal arteriolar lesions and periarteritis were much less frequent in the rats receiving hypotensive drugs.

Masson *et al.* (172), using hydralazine as a hypotensive agent, noted that it reduced the severity of extrarenal lesions in rats rendered hypertensive by ischemia of sole remaining kidneys. Gardner (87) used hydralazine injections to reduce the blood pressure of rats rendered hypertensive by a regimen of salt, and cortexone. They also noted that the hydralazine, although administered discontinuously, reduced considerably the occurrence of acute vascular disease. Gardner and Brooks (89) obtained similar results with hydralazine in adrenal regeneration hypertension, and Gardner (88) used bretylium tosylate to obtain corresponding results in uninephrectomized rats treated with sodium chloride and cortexone. McQueen and Hodge (169), using reserpine, largely prevented rises of blood pressure in rats with a unilateral renal artery clip. The rats receiving reserpine had a striking reduction in the frequency and severity of lesions in the untouched kidney.

The evidence is indeed strong that in man and in experimental animals hypertension as such leads to characteristic hypertensive manifestations whatever the original cause of the hypertension may be, and that in man and in experimental animals reduction of the blood pressure may prevent lesions, or in some instances ameliorate manifestations already present, and decrease the mortality below the level which occurs in untreated hypertensive disease. This conclusion is important, for as pointed out earlier (246, 247, 249: p. 320), if blood-pressure elevation as such causes the manifestations, certain deductions about the pathogenesis may be made, which are referred to in the following section.

III. Evidence that over-average blood pressures, though determined by the operation of physiological processes, not only predispose to the development of frank hypertension, but are an integral component of its pathogenesis

If high pressure, as such, leads to or greatly accelerates the development of hypertensive disease, we have to believe that high blood pressure due to the action of physiological processes acting to an over-average degree, being a mechanical change, will resemble in its action a similar mechanical change due to a recognizable pathological process. Also, a rise of blood pressure, due to a pathological process, perched on top of a "high normal" blood pressure, is more likely to be associated with hypertensive disease than a rise in pressure superimposed on a low starting level (246, 247).

In blood-pressure distribution curves based on population surveys, it is evident that the blood pressure may vary considerably from one individual to another. In the survey of Master *et al.* (174) the casual blood pressures of persons aged 30 years or less may cover a range of 55 mm Hg systolic, 40 mm Hg diastolic, the upper end of the casual blood pressure distribution curve reaching a level of approximately 155 mm Hg systolic, 100 mm Hg diastolic.

As age advances, there is comparatively little change in the lower end of the blood-pressure distribution curve, but the average blood pressure rises considerably, and the high pressure end of the curve is in the region of 200 mm Hg systolic, 110 mm Hg diastolic in the age group 60–64. These figures are derived from the survey (174) of a working population, which thereby eliminates many persons with very high blood pressures who would be unable to work.

As the casual blood pressures of young persons may cover a range of 55 mm Hg systolic and 40 mm Hg diastolic, a blood-pressure rise—for example, one equal in magnitude to the above range—would carry those who started at the low end of the distribution curve to a blood pressure of 150/90 mm Hg, whereas the corresponding increase superimposed upon the blood pressures of those of the upper end of the distribution curve could, theoretically, lead to pressures of 210/140 mm Hg, though in fact such a diastolic pressure would be above that ordinarily encountered with a systolic blood pressure of 210 mm Hg. This illustration is merely intended to show that the difference between the casual blood pressures of one apparently healthy young person and another, but both within the limits of a gaussian distribution curve, is important in determining the eventual height of the casual blood pressure should a rise occur, either from alterations in the physiology or from events which are demonstrably pathological.

The evidence that over-average blood pressures in comparatively young persons are associated with an increased expectation of frank hypertension and cardiovascular disabilities in later life is overwhelming. The already strong evidence from life insurance statistics of over 30 years ago (1–3, 128, 129) has been strongly reinforced in the recent Build and Blood Pressure Study of the American Society of Actuaries (269). Not only do over-average diastolic blood pressures increase the expectation of frank hypertensive disease and increase the mortality from cardiovascular causes, but at equal levels of the diastolic pressure the mortality increases with increasing height of the systolic pressure (269). Persons whose blood pressures are under average have an under-average expectation of hypertension and cardiovascular disease in later life (269).

Similar results (57, 120, 228, 271) have been obtained in follow-up studies on student health groups, in industry, and in selected communities, as in the Framingham study.

It is also of great interest that there are communities in which the average blood pressure in the various age groups is well below those of population groups in the United States, Europe, Australia, and New Zealand. In most such population groups the incidence of hypertension is low (249: p. 44).

Casual blood pressures such as 170/100 are very high for young people, and are due in many instances to frank pathology, such as narrowing of a renal artery; but in general, over-average blood pressures within the usual range probably are due to over-average activity of entirely physiological mechanisms. In young people who appear to be healthy, the blood-pressure distribution curve is gaussian, and the distribution of blood-pressure levels is compatible with normal biological variation.

The evidence that in essential hypertension blood-pressure elevation sometimes precedes the development of arteriosclerosis and arteriolosclerosis was summarized by Smirk (247, 249; p. 309), and additional evidence has since become available.

In addition to permanent elevation of the blood pressure, transient blood-pressure rises occur in almost all persons in response to tenseness or emotion and to physical exertion. There is some evidence that persons exhibiting over-average increases of blood pressure in response to such stimuli have a greater expectation of frank hypertension in later life, even though at rest their pressures subside to within normal limits. Further information is given in Section IV, B.

Although there is some difficulty in proving that over-average blood pressures which, however, lie within the limits conventionally regarded as normal are physiological, some evidence in favor of this view comes from the fact that by selective interbreeding from rats with over-average blood pressures, Smirk and Hall (256) developed a colony of rats which exhibit spontaneous hypertension. Further details are given in the section on genetic hypertension (Section V).

IV. Evidence that, in relation to pathogenesis, the basal and supplemental parts of the casual blood pressure deserve separate consideration

There is no precise level of the casual blood pressure above which it can be stated that normotension ends and hypertension begins. As regards the effect on prognosis and the development of hypertensive disease, there are no lines of demarcation between frank hypertension, over-average blood pressure, pressures close to the average, and under-average blood pressures. Statistically, the outlook worsens throughout the entire range from moderate hypotension to severe hypertension, but such findings, based as they are on the blood-pressure averages of groups of individuals, cannot be used without qualification to state the prognosis of individuals composing the group.

The blood pressure of most normotensives is highly variable, and of hypertensives more so. Single figures for the systolic and diastolic blood pressures do not adequately represent the blood pressure of an individual who, under certain circumstances, may have a blood pressure which could be regarded as high in terms of life insurance statistics, and under other conditions a blood pressure which would be considered normal or even low. Clearly, this gives some difficulty in analyzing the pathogenesis of high blood pressure. The study of basal pressures goes some way to overcoming this difficulty, and it reveals problems requiring further investigation.

A. Evidence That the Casual Blood Pressure Is the Sum of at Least Two Almost Independent Variables, Namely, the Basal and the Supplemental Pressures

Basal blood pressures taken by the technique of Smirk (245, 249: p. 15, 298) are much less variable than casual blood pressures. The casual minus the basal blood pressure we described as the "supplemental blood pressure" (245), this being the variable part of the casual blood pressure, changing from minute to minute in response to environmental and other stimuli. As Kilpatrick (142) showed, the basal blood pressure in normotensives is sufficiently reproducible to be a characteristic of the patient's cardiovascular system; in hypertensives it is more variable (142, 261), but much less so than the casual blood pressure. Smirk and Simpson (cited Smirk, 253: p. 390, 261) have shown that the basal blood pressure usually increases with age, but does not usually exhibit much variation within such periods as a year or two (261). The basal pressure in untreated persons is closely related to the subsequent mortality from hypertensive disease, but the supplemental blood pressure, if related, is not closely related (251, 262)—certainly not within an 8-year follow-up period.

Valid measurements of the basal blood pressure need to be done under defined conditions, as for a basal metabolic rate, following a night's rest in a single room with a sedative in order to ensure sleep. This is followed by repeated blood-pressure measurements at half-minute intervals by an undisturbed observer for a period of 10–15 minutes, the object of repetitive measurement being to overcome the reaction of the subject to the observer and his sphygmomanometer. Additional details have been given elsewhere (245, 249: p. 15). The basal blood pressure is not necessarily the lowest pressure in a 24-hour period. Ordinarily, if a person falls asleep while the basal blood pressure is being measured, there is little additional fall in blood-pressure level during the next few minutes (254, 264, 287). When, however, blood pressures are measured at frequent intervals during a night's sleep, we found that they may fall a little below the basal pressure, occasionally much below (253: p. 99, 254). The basal pressure, however, has the advantage that the actual measurement takes about 15 minutes, and if conditions are good, may be made by a medical practitioner in the patient's own home.

The large differences found by Richardson et al. (226) between the lowest sleeping blood pressure and the basal blood pressure, using the technique of Alam and Smirk (5), appear to be due, at least in part, to their employment of a technique of basal blood pressure measurement which we abandoned in 1940, together with errors due to failure to monitor the posture of the subjects (Smirk, 253: p. 99). In the lateral posture, when the cuff arm of the subject is uppermost, the pressure registered may be 15 mm systolic, 10 mm diastolic below the level with the patient lying on the back. The same objection will apply to intra-arterial measurements of the blood pressure. Changes of posture during sleep occur frequently in some subjects.

In a collection of normotensive individuals and also in a collection of hypertensives, it was found by Smirk and co-workers (245, 262) that the basal and supplemental pressures were almost independent variables, in the sense that the possession by an individual of a high basal pressure did not increase or much diminish the expectation of that individual's having a high supplemental blood pressure. The fact that the basal and supplemental pressures in this sense are independent variables makes it unlikely that rises in the basal and in the supplemental pressure arise from one and the same cause. This opinion is supported further by the 8-year follow-up study of the untreated hypertensive patients referred to above (262). The mortality in the 8 years was closely related to the basal pressure but unrelated to the supplemental pressure. Nevertheless, the possibility must be kept in mind that persons with high supplemental pressures may be prone eventually to develop high basal pressures.

B. Evidence That the Supplemental Pressure Is Influenced by Several Factors

It should be pointed out that although the supplemental pressure may be influenced by a wide variety of imposed stimuli (245), reference here will be restricted to those influencing the supplemental pressure under conditions ordinarily encountered in the care of patients or during investigatory procedures. For example, cold showers may produce large increases in the supplemental pressure, but the high supplemental pressures so induced do not concern the present investigation.

There is a formidable collection of evidence that emotional stimuli, such as a visit to a clinic or conversations on certain topics may cause substantial blood-pressure rises (249: p. 212).

Patients with worries or who are emotional may exhibit high supplemental blood pressures, even when they are familiar with the clinic personnel and environment (66, 85, 249: p. 212); also many patients who are not noticeably emotional do so. Recent, even moderate, physical exertion may add to the supplemental blood pressure. The supplemental pressure is often as great as 30 mm Hg systolic, 10 mm Hg diastolic, and may be much greater.

It has been stated that persons who are usually normotensive, but exhibit appreciable blood-pressure rises in response to stimuli of various kinds, have a greater expectation of developing permanent hypertension and eventually of a cardiovascular death. This statement is based on life insurance figures, which show that persons who have an over-average blood pressure at a first examination, which, however, lies within normal limits when repeated, nevertheless have an enhanced liability to sustained hypertension and a cardiovascular death. If a person whose blood pressure when first taken is over-average is then recalled and rested, and further blood pressures are taken, the final blood pressure should be compared with normotensives who have undergone the same procedure, because the blood pressure in normotensives also falls on repetition.

One might expect that frequent though intermittent rises of the supplemental blood pressure would lead ultimately to hypertensive disease (4), even if the development of pathological changes took place more slowly than those which undoubtedly occur in response to elevations of the basal blood pressure. Long-term studies are needed, for we found no positive correlation between the height of the supplemental pressure and the mortality in an 8-year follow-up of untreated hypertensives (262).

C. EVIDENCE THAT THE BASAL BLOOD PRESSURE MAY BE SUBDIVIDED INTO A NEUROGENICALLY AND A NONNEUROGENICALLY MAINTAINED PART

When hypertensive individuals are given large doses of hexamethonium in the horizontal posture, the blood-pressure level falls below the basal pressure, due to blockade of nervous impulses by the ganglion-blocking agent. Doyle and Smirk (64) investigated the extent to which the blood pressure could be reduced below the basal blood pressure by the administration of hexamethonium. An initial dose of hexamethonium, usually 25 mg, was administered and 15 mg was given subsequently at 2-minute intervals intravenously until two successive doses had produced no further fall in the blood pressure. In some patients the additional fall below basal levels was slight, and the hexamethonium floor blood pressure high; in others there was a considerable fall with hexamethonium, and the floor blood pressure was comparatively low. The extent to which the blood pressure falls below the basal after maximal doses of hexamethonium may be described as the "neurogenically maintained" part of the basal blood pressure, in that a drug which acts by blocking sympathetic nerve impulses to blood vessels has removed that part of the blood pressure. The part not so removed is described as the "nonneurogenically maintained" part.

The term "neurogenically maintained" is intended to avoid the assumption that the part of the blood pressure removed by hexamethonium is necessarily an index of the amount of nervous stimulation of blood vessels. For example, with a constant amount of nervous stimulation of the blood vessels, hexamethonium should cause a larger blood-pressure fall if the blood vessels were more reactive to nervous stimulation than if they were less reactive. Although the dose of hexamethonium used was large, it is possible that not all of the nervous impulses to blood vessels were thereby blocked. The magnitude of the neurogenically maintained part of the blood pressure might have been underestimated. But it is highly probable that the basal blood pressure is subdivisible into a neurogenically maintained part and another part which is not neurogenically maintained.

A few patients with advanced renal disease become almost completely resistant to the action of sympatholytic drugs, presumably because their blood-pressure level, unlike most of the renal hypertensives, was almost entirely nonneurogenically maintained. In such patients it has always been possible to induce large blood-pressure falls either by sublingual sodium azide or trinitrin, or by intravenously administered sodium nitroprusside (254). All three substances act directly on the smooth muscle of the blood vessels.

Experiments have been made which show (260) that in rats with different types of hypertension, the proportion of the neurogenically maintained and nonneurogenically maintained parts of the peripheral resistance varies, the former being removable by hexamethonium, and the latter, to an important extent, by sodium nitroprusside, leaving behind a part which is not removable by either, which, in the case of perfused blood vessels, presumably is structural.

It is important to recognize that in chronic renal hypertension induced by placing a clip on a renal artery, there will usually be an increase above the normal in all three of the above-mentioned components of the blood pressure. The experiment shows that in this instance, the rise of blood pressure, while arising in the first place from a single primary cause, namely, a clip on a renal artery, is eventually maintained by more than one mechanism.

V. Evidence that a genetic factor is concerned in the pathogenesis of essential hypertension and probably to some degree also in the pathogenesis of other hypertensive conditions

A. THE GENETICS OF HYPERTENSION IN MAN

The evidence that a genetic factor is concerned in determining blood-pressure levels in essential hypertension is overwhelming, but there is much dispute about the nature of the genetic factors involved. In addition to a genetic predisposition to frank hypertension and hypertensive disease, the children of hypertensive individuals commonly have higher casual blood pressures than the children of normotensives. A difficulty in interpreting the evidence comes from the fact that the casual blood pressure is the sum of at least two independent variables. As hypertensive disease is unusual in the absence of a high basal pressure, it always seemed likely to the author that the basal blood pressure would prove to be inherited, and our recent preliminary studies favor this supposition. As basal and supplemental pressures are almost independent variables, the level of the supplemental pressure, if influenced genetically, is likely to be inherited in some other way. An alternative possibility is that persons with high casual pressures may have children with high supplemental pressures, and although the high supplemental pressure favors the ultimate development of a high basal pressure in later life, so many other factors are involved that an original genetic relationship between supplemental and basal pressures becomes obscured.

When discussing the inheritance of essential hypertension, it is necessary also to consider closely whether reference is made to the inheritance of hypertensive disease, or only to the inheritance of high levels of the blood pressure which promote hypertensive disease.

Platt (216) considers that blood-pressure elevation and consequential hypertensive disease in essential hypertension is mainly of genetic origin, due or mainly due, to a single gene, the effects of which ordinarily become manifest in middle life. There is also good evidence, which we have confirmed, that the casual blood pressures of young people are related to the blood pressures of their parents, though, often, only a few mm Hg may separate the blood pressure of the children of hypertensives and normotensives. It has not yet been decided whether the tendency of the blood pressure to rise in middle life is inherited in the same way as the blood-pressure levels of young people.

Pickering (213, 214) lays emphasis on the fact that the blood-pressure level in all age groups is influenced genetically. Not only are over-average but also under-average blood pressures affected. He points out that the distribution curve of the blood pressures of young individuals is gaussian. In essential hypertension he regards the disorder as being in essence the upper end of a normal distribution curve. In this he accepts the view expressed some years before by Smirk (246, 247) that the over-average blood pressures in young people are probably, for the most part, the upper end of this distribution curve, and of physiological origin. The present author desires to stress that in middle and especially in later life, the blood-pressure distribution curve is no longer gaussian, but strongly skewed, there being a predominance of high blood pressures.

One of the difficulties in drawing conclusions about inheritance from the behavior of groups of individuals is that the average of the groups is not necessarily representative of the usual behavior of the individuals. Where casual blood pressures are concerned, it is usual for the blood pressure to rise with age, but in some individuals casual blood pressures repeated after 15 or 20 years are found to have fallen, perhaps an expression of the variability of casual blood pressures. Furthermore, rises in casual blood pressure do not necessarily advance step by step: in some individuals there is apparently a slow progression, and in others steep rises occur in middle life. When basal blood pressures are considered, the rate of rise with age varies considerably, but comparatively few individuals show a fall, and some of these may be accounted for by errors in the determination of the basal blood pressure which, while much less than the errors inherent in casual blood pressures, are nevertheless present. It is clear from casual and from near-basal (287) blood-pressure distribution curves that there must be individuals whose pressure rises are much greater than the average, and also individuals whose blood pressures do not rise with age.

The number of persons with very high blood pressures in a population survey must be considerably curtailed by the comparatively short life expectancy of individuals with very high pressures. Population surveys do not allow a fair comparison between the blood pressures of the comparatively young and comparatively old population groups, in that were a cohort of young individuals followed until they were aged 60–69, it would be found that of those who had died, many were hypertensives who, having reached the top end of the blood-pressure distribution curve, were abstracted from it by death from hypertensive disease.

The extent of the rise of blood pressure with age is therefore underestimated in distribution curves, and the underestimate is affected particularly by persons with very high blood pressures who, had they lived, would have greatly increased the positive skewing.

It is easy to underestimate the part played by heredity in hypertension which is of sufficient severity to endanger life. Thus, if the propositus is in an older age group, the surviving sibs available for comparison may contain a larger proportion of those with comparatively low blood pressures; the children are unlikely as yet to have shown much blood-pressure rise.

Gearing *et al.* (91) and Schweitzer *et al.* (242), while agreeing that there is evidence of a familial concentration of essential hypertension, stress the difficulty in distinguishing between genetic and environmental factors. While the evidence for inheritance seems to be very strong, it must be admitted that comparatively few studies have included an investigation of the effects of familial environment. The question of what is inherited is also relevant. Almost certainly this is not blood pressure as such, but one or more of the numerous mechanisms which influence the blood-pressure level.

B. Spontaneous Genetic Hypertension in Rats

A review of blood pressures in like twins (249: p. 43) reveals that in general, the casual pressures of like twins resemble each other closely, and more so than do the casual blood pressures of unlike twins (289). This observation led the present author to an attempt to establish a race of rats with genetic hypertension. The attempt was successful (256). Since the colony was established, the level of the blood pressure has increased (259) so that their average systolic blood pressure is 160 mm Hg systolic, as against 120 mm Hg systolic in our normotensive stock colony. Many of the genetic hypertensive rats reach blood pressures of 170–180 mm Hg systolic, or more. The rats with the higher pressures have a distinctly higher-than-average incidence of periarteritis nodosa (259), characteristic of very high blood pressures in rats, and in a few instances fibrinoid necrosis of the smooth muscle of arterioles may be observed. Evidently a type of genetic hypertension has been developed which is sufficient by itself to cause frank hypertensive disease.

Okamoto and his co-workers (199) have also obtained a colony of rats with genetic hypertension. Scrutiny of their results and ours suggests that there are differences in their characteristics: for example, the blood-pressure rise occurs earlier in life in our rats.

Rats with genetic hypertension have been mated with normotensive controls. The blood-pressure distribution curve in the F_2 generation shows no tendency to segregate. Our conclusion, at the present time, will be limited to the statement that the hypertension cannot be explained by the operation of a single gene (263). It would not be safe, on the evidence at present available to us, to state that the number of genes exceeds two. These rats, when young, exhibit no evidence of disease, other than cardiac hypertrophy associated with the hypertension. The kidneys in particular are histologically normal, and their injected blood vessels show no defect (259). When young, apart from blood-pressure elevation, they appear to be normal rats, and their blood-pressure distribution curve is gaussian. It appears, therefore, that this genetic hypertension is unlike experimental Goldblatt hypertension, as it is present at a time when there is no evidence of any renal disease, and therefore may resemble the early stage of essential hypertension.

The multifactorial hypothesis referred to earlier (247, 249: p. 320) makes reference to a genetic factor as concerned in the blood-pressure elevation in essential hypertension, and also to the author's view that elevations of blood pressure resulting from the overactivity of physiological mechanisms are, nevertheless, an integral part of the pathogenesis of essential hypertension, in that subsequent rises of blood pressure perched on the top of a high normal blood pressure would induce higher blood-pressure levels than a corresponding increase occurring in a person who started with a low physiological level of the blood pressure. Furthermore, blood-pressure rises due to such conditions as a renal disorder or Cushing's disease would, according to this hypothesis, tend to have higher eventual blood-pressure levels and more hypertensive disease if superimposed upon a high starting level. Our genetic hypertensive colony provides an interesting experimental model, in that when genetic hypertensive and control rats are subjected to a blood-pressure raising stimulus, the resulting mortality and morbidity are much higher in the genetic hypertensives. This has been shown to be the case when genetic hypertensives and controls are exposed to the administration of 1.4% salt solution as drinking fluid (250), unilateral nephrectomy, unilateral nephrectomy with 1% salt solution as drinking fluid, $\frac{3}{4}$-nephrectomy, and by the application of a clip to one renal artery (258). Clearly, in this experimental model the combination of a moderate degree of genetic hypertension with the application of various types of blood-pressure raising stimuli had in common the effect of producing a high incidence of hypertensive disease.

C. Rats Genetically Susceptible to Salt Hypertension

Dahl and his co-workers have selectively bred two rat colonies, one susceptible and one resistant to the development of hypertension after excess salt ingestion. Hypertensive disease occurs readily in the salt-susceptible rats. Dahl *et al.* (47) find that the salt-susceptible rats have a greater vascular reactivity to angiotensin and norepinephrine than rats which are salt-resistant. Evidently in the rat there is more than one way of influencing the blood pressure genetically.

VI. Evidence that rigidity of the arterial reservoir is concerned in elevation of the blood pressure

It is often assumed that it is only rises in the diastolic pressure which cause hypertensive disease. This assumption is inconsistent with life insurance statistics published over 30 years ago, and also with the very extensive figures from the recent Build and Blood Pressure Study of the American Society of Actuaries (269).

In our follow-up study on untreated hypertensive patients there is a clear relationship between high basal pulse pressures and high mortality (254). This provides further evidence in the same direction.

It is generally conceded that the pulse pressure is increased in older people partly as a result of increase in the rigidity of the large vessels.

Ordinarily the rigidity of large vessels is greater in hypertensives than in normotensives (19), this being almost certainly the response to the increased mechanical strains to which they are subjected.

The pulse wave velocity increases with increase in the rigidity of the arterial reservoir, and has been shown by Rahier (222) and by Simonson and Nakagawa (243) to increase with age. Miasnikov (181) showed that the pulse wave velocity increased in hypertension. Nye (196) modified the blood pressure of normotensives and hypertensives by drugs. Increase of pressure increased and decrease of pressure decreased the pulse wave velocity in both hypertensives and normotensives. At correspondingly high blood pressures the pulse wave velocity was greater in the normotensives; at correspondingly low blood pressures the pulse wave velocity was slightly greater in the hypertensives. Evidently there are difficulties in disentangling the effects of contemporaneous blood-pressure levels from structural factors modifying the rigidity of the arterial reservoir.

It seems likely, however, that this increased rigidity is one of the means by which an over-average pressure becomes further increased with advancing age, and the evidence is good that increases in the systolic blood pressure are associated with an increase in the mortality from hypertensive disease (269).

VII. Evidence relating to the pathogenesis of renal hypertension (the relationship of experimental to clinical renal hypertension)

Goldblatt and his co-workers (95) were responsible for the first clear demonstration that a type of experimental hypertension may be induced by interference with the renal circulation by such means as narrowing one or both renal arteries, or causing disturbances of the renal circulation in other ways. Narrowing of a renal artery is associated with the liberation into the circulation of the enzyme renin, which acts upon a substrate in the plasma to form a pressor agent, angiotensin. Shortly after the constriction of a renal artery, pressor activity can be detected in the circulating blood, but after several weeks it becomes difficult to demonstrate, even though the blood pressure may have risen further; hence there are arguments against the simple hypothesis that continued blood-pressure elevation depends on liberation of a pressor agent which raises the blood pressure by its direct action on small blood vessels. While there is no doubt that the kidney is responsible for the blood-pressure rise, the topic is complex. An account of some of these complexities will be given later.

Whatever the explanation of experimental renal hypertension may be, there is no doubt that clear-cut examples exist of a similar process in man. There are well-authenticated examples of lasting reductions of the blood pressure following either removal of a kidney with unilateral renal artery obstruction, or by a graft leading to improvement of its circulation. It seems very probable that hypertension associated with other types of renal disease arises because a mechanism of this kind has been evoked, either by intrarenal disturbance of the circulation, or in some other way. For example, in man, organization of an extravasation of blood around the kidney, the result of injury, may cause hypertension (46), and this resembles the blood-pressure elevation which follows the spraying of plastic on the surface of a kidney (223) or wrapping a kidney in cellophane (201). Irradiation of a kidney causes diffuse damage of the renal parenchyma, and leads to hypertension in man (50, 159) and in experimental animals (111, 302). On the other hand, very advanced disease of the renal parenchyma may be present in man (207) and in the rat (254) without any blood-pressure elevation.

For many years it was assumed that renal artery constriction caused the blood pressure to rise because the kidney became ischemic, but there are doubts, because in many instances the rise of blood pressure apparently restores the rate of flow of blood through the constricted artery, and in other instances this restoration of the blood flow may have occurred as a result of the capacity for autoregulation possessed by the renal and some other blood vessels (133). In the case of autoregulation, the explanation for restoration of blood flow would be a decrease in the peripheral resistance, due to dilatation of blood vessels beyond the obstruction. However, careful studies of the renal blood flow in man by Stamey (270) led to the conclusion that surgically curable renovascular hypertension from a unilateral renal artery narrowing occurred only when there was evidence of 23% or greater decrease in renal plasma flow compared with the opposite kidney. In many instances radiological evidence of renal artery obstruction was not accompanied by hypertension. It would appear that in man, as in laboratory animals, moderate renal artery constriction does not always elevate the blood pressure, for the constriction must be of a sufficient degree if it is to cause a blood-pressure rise; but it should not be so great as to cause infarction of the kidney. Clinical studies have greatly improved the extent to which cure by surgery can be forecast preoperatively.

A. Evidence That Blood Pressure Increases of Sufficient Degree and Duration May Be Self-perpetuating or Self-augmenting

Although it is likely that the tendency of high blood pressure to be self-perpetuating is present with hypertension of nonrenal origin, most of the evidence comes from studies in experimental renal hypertension. The topic, though it also concerns nonrenal hypertension, is referred to, therefore, in the present section.

Wilson and Byrom (296) found that in the rat, a sufficient narrowing of one renal artery gives rise, in almost all instances, to high blood pressure, which is relieved if that kidney is removed within a few weeks of creation of the obstruction. If removal is delayed, damage of the untouched kidney may perpetuate the blood-pressure rise. Also in the rat, Byrom and Dodson (37) found that when hypertension is induced by narrowing the renal artery of a sole remaining kidney, the removal of the clamp after 12 weeks was associated with a fall of blood pressure to normal within 12 hours. If, however, a renal artery is constricted without removing the opposite kidney, the removal of the clip often fails to reduce the blood pressure. Failures of the blood pressure to fall are correlated with the occurrence of arteriolar lesions in the untouched kidney. The parenchyma of the kidney with a clip on the renal artery is apparently protected from hypertensive damage by the clip.

Floyer (81) performed the experiment of clipping one renal artery in the rat for a period of 8 weeks, leaving the other kidney untouched. The clip was then removed. If the untouched kidney is removed, the blood pressure returns to normal, but if, alternately, the kidney which has had its renal artery unclipped is removed, the residual hypertension persists.

Blacket and Sellers (20) reported similar findings in the rabbit, in that, when a clip was placed on the renal artery of a sole remaining kidney, removal of the clip after 4–15 days led to a fall of blood pressure back to the original level. However, in four out of six rabbits with hypertension of 6–25 weeks' duration, there was delay of up to 23 days before the blood pressure returned to normal.

Daniel et al. (49) also worked with rabbits, leaving a renal artery clip on a sole kidney in place for 119–222 days. Removal of the clip after this long period did not usually remove the hypertension.

Evidently there exists in the rat, and probably in man (247) at least one mechanism by which high blood pressures may be self-perpetuating, even self-augmenting. This mechanism appears to depend upon the fact that in the rat, and probably in man, hypertension leads to a type of renal damage capable of maintaining a blood-pressure elevation after the original cause of the blood-pressure increase has been removed. On the other hand, the dog appears to be different. Several observers (21, 288) find that removal of the clamped kidney in the dog, the other kidney being intact, restores the arterial pressure to normal.

Unlike the rat, the dog seldom develops a permanent hypertension after constriction of one renal artery, unless either the other kidney is removed or its arterial supply is also constricted.

Schroeder (241), however, finds that by selection, dogs may be discovered which respond to unilateral clamping of a renal artery by blood-pressure elevation, even when the other kidney remains intact. By yearly biopsies of the untouched kidney he has observed the development, after several years, of renal arteriolar lesions.

There seems to be strong evidence that hypertension as such may damage previously healthy kidneys, and that at least in certain instances, this damage is capable of maintaining the blood-pressure elevation after the original primary cause has been removed.

A nonrenal self-perpetuating mechanism was described by Pickering (212) and confirmed by Fleming (80). These authors found that if, in the rabbit, hypertension of 7 weeks' or more duration is induced by placing a clip on the renal artery of a sole remaining kidney, the excision of the kidney does not remove the hypertension in the 3 or 4 days during which the animal survives. If, however, the previous hypertension is of short duration, the blood pressure falls after excision of the kidney.

Medoff and Bongiovanni (175), Yeakel et al. (300), and Farris et al. (71) showed that rats subjected for long periods to audiogenic stimulation developed elevation of the blood pressure. Restall and Smirk, cited by Smirk (247), confirmed this, and found that the blood-pressure elevations were not abolished by light ether anesthesia, and persisted for at least several months after the audiogenic stimulation had ended. There was at this time no histological evidence of renal damage. Here again is another example of a change in blood-pressure level outlasting the stimulus which induced it.

After 15 years of experience with continued drug therapy of hypertension, we find in our clinic that many severely hypertensive patients eventually become much easier to treat, in the sense that near-normal blood pressure can be maintained now with much smaller doses of hypotensive drugs than were required at the onset. In several instances when drugs were discontinued temporarily, the blood pressure rose only slowly to a level necessitating restoration of drug treatment; certainly in many instances the blood pressure was maintained well below the original level for periods which exceeded by several weeks the known duration of action of the drugs the patients were taking. In conversation with members of other hypertensive clinics we find that this experience is not unusual. Information of possible relevance is mentioned in the section on baroceptor mechanisms (Section XI).

Other mechanisms by which hypertension may be perpetuated or increased include cardiovascular hypertrophy, increased cardiovascular reactivity to pressor stimuli, and hardening of the arterial reservoir which is accelerated by hypertension.

B. Factors Influencing the Liberation of Renin

For a few days after constricting a renal artery, a pressor agent enters the renal vein blood in amounts sufficient to raise the blood pressure (94, 126, 152) and the pressor agent can be detected in the arterial blood. The renal vein blood contains the enzyme renin. A few weeks later it becomes difficult to detect pressor agents in the circulating blood, in amounts which would readily explain the rise of blood pressure (152).

Ogden (197) found at this stage that sodium pentobarbitone, yohimbine, or 883F* caused appreciably larger blood-pressure falls than they did in the first two weeks after renal artery constriction. The suggestion was made that after a time a nervous mechanism replaces the humoral mechanism. The large falls of blood pressure which are induced by hexamethonium in both experimental and human renal hypertension (254) have been mentioned as favorable to this view, but there remains firm evidence that whatever action the nervous system may have, the presence of a kidney with impaired circulation continues to be the underlying cause for the hypertension. The central problem is how the kidney controls the blood-pressure level.

Despite evident difficulties in relating renal hypertension to the discharge of the enzyme renin from the kidneys, with subsequent formation of angio-

---

* Prosympal [2(diethylaminomethyl)-1,4 benzodioxan].

tensin II, most attempts to explain renal hypertension involve the study of these substances. Indeed, at present there are few alternative approaches to the problem. It may, however, be worth mentioning that the angiotensins, vasopressin, oxytocin, and bradykinin are not the only vasoactive peptides. Braun-Menéndez and Paladini (25) mention that proteolytic enzymes other than renin may, if produced locally, exert a vasoconstrictor action, due to the formation of pressor polypeptides of the angiotensin type. Anephrotensin, prepared by the incubation of serum for 24 hours at pH 3.8–4, is also an active vasoconstrictor polypeptide which Rosas and Croxatto (231) obtained in larger amounts from the serum of DCA-treated rats than of controls; and Rosas (230) obtained larger amounts of anephrotensin from the serum of bilaterally nephrectomized rats and dogs.

Brown *et al.* (32) stress the fact that aside from difficulties inherent in the methods used, the various estimates of renin in plasma may not be of equivalent significance. Some estimates of what has been called "renin activity" depend on the incubation *in vitro* of plasma for a fixed period, and the angiotensin is then determined. The activity depends not only on the concentration of renin but also of substrate in the sample of plasma. Brown *et al.* (32, 33) and Lever *et al.* (156) eliminate the endogenous substrate and allow the renin to act on an exogenous standard substrate, after which an assay is made of the angiotensin so formed.

The concentration of renin in blood is influenced by many more factors than were envisaged a few years ago.

Some recent observations of great interest come from Veyrat *et al.* (290), Brown *et al.* (31, 32), Fasciolo *et al.* (72), and Taquini *et al.* (273). The renin activity in the blood is closely related to the sodium balance. Salt loading decreases (31, 290) and salt restriction increases the level of renin activity in the blood (31, 72, 273, 290). Thiazide treatment may lead to marked elevation of the plasma renin (32). Renin activity is increased in patients with edema (72, 290) but it is also increased in normotensives by decrease of the extracellular fluid volume. There is a large increase in renin activity in pregnancy (31, 72), as well as of the excretion of aldosterone (146, 227). There is usually little change in renin activity in essential hypertension (31, 72, 290) and no change is detected in as many as 50% of patients with hypertension from renal artery stenosis (31, 72, 290). Increase in renin activity in the blood is often associated with increased excretion of aldosterone (31, 32, 290).

Primary aldosteronism is associated with abnormally low plasma renin activity (31).

Adrenal insufficiency is associated with a high plasma renin (31). Severe loss of blood (205), thirst (107), and exercise in normotensives (115) may all cause an increase in the plasma renin activity. An increased liberation of renin from the kidney is also encountered in shock (127).

Such observations show clearly that the activities of renin involve alterations in, and are affected by, several physiological systems. For example, pregnancy may induce far larger changes in the plasma renin activity than clipping a renal artery.

Gross *et al.* (108) found that the renin content of the rat kidney is reduced when DCA is given in doses which do not produce hypertension, and whether a renal artery is or is not constricted. With a unilateral renal artery clamp Blaquier *et al.* (22) found that in rats the renin content of the clamped kidney was normal or reduced, and that of the untouched kidney was reduced to a greater degree (22). The angiotensinase concentration was unaltered by clipping. Mostly it is reported that the renin content of the kidney with the clamp is increased.

Taquini *et al.* (273) found that nephrectomy led to a rapid disappearance of renin from the blood in normal and renal hypertensive dogs. Normally there is a secretion of renin which maintains the blood levels ordinarily found.

C. The Interrelationships of Renin, Juxtaglomerular Granulation, Angiotensin, Angiotensinase, Aldosterone, Electrolytes, and Blood Pressure

As a pressor agent in man, angiotensin II (valine 5) has over six times (by weight) the potency of norepinephrine (51) and is liberated under some of the conditions which lead to renal hypertension,-but close study shows one cannot explain renal hypertension satisfactorily by assuming that in renal hypertension angiotensin acts directly on blood vessels and raises the blood pressure by increasing the peripheral resistance. Genest *et al.* (92) found that the amounts of angiotensin which raise the diastolic pressure of normal subjects by as much as 30 mm Hg cause concentrations of angiotensin in blood which are four or five times those encountered in essential or renal hypertension. It seems that the amount of angiotensin in the blood is insufficient to cause hypertension by a simple direct action. Of course it might have been taken out of the blood and concentrated in blood vessels. While this last explanation deserves further study, so also do the many other factors, renal and extrarenal, which influence or are influenced by renin and angiotensin—as for example, the relation between angiotensin and the liberation of aldosterone from the adrenal glands, with resulting changes in the electrolytes.

There is evidence that the enzyme renin is to be found mainly in the cortex of the kidney, and it is probably either formed or stored in the juxtaglomerular apparatus, as was originally suggested by Goormaghtigh (97). The juxta-glomerular apparatus is a collection of cells surrounding the afferent arterioles to glomeruli. Tobian (280, 281) suggested that the apparatus may respond to afferent arteriolar pressure changes, decreases in pressure leading to a release of renin from the characteristic granules found in the cells of the apparatus. The renin then acts as a circulatory regulator to maintain the level of the blood pressure and the supply of blood to the kidneys. Alternatively, juxtaglomerular response may be determined by changes of intrarenal pressure. But there are some odd findings. When a renal artery is constricted, the other kidney remaining intact, there is an increase in the granulation of the clamped kidney together with degranulation of the untouched kidney (283); but if the renal artery is clamped in a sole remaining kidney, increase in juxtaglomerular granulation does not take place, even though removal of the other kidney increases the degree of blood-pressure elevation.

Furthermore, Gross et al. (108) and Regoli et al. (224) have shown that there is no rise above normal in the renin content of a sole kidney with a renal artery clip or of the animal's blood. Nolla-Panades and Simpson (194) showed that when a clip was placed on the aorta above the two renal arteries, there was no change in the renal granulation index as compared with a dummy-operated group. When the clip was placed between the renal arteries, a marked decrease in the granulation index was found in the kidney above the clip and an increase in the kidney below the clip. The rise in blood pressure was greater when the clip was placed above both kidneys than when it was placed between them. Nolla-Panades and Simpson (194) concluded that the changes in granulation of the juxtaglomerular apparatus are not directly dependent on the level of the blood pressure in the renal arteries, and renal hypertension can develop without any change in the granulation index. The lack of correlation between blood-pressure level and juxtaglomerular granulation is exemplified also in the observation of Tobian (280) that rats with a unilateral clip on a renal artery, which fail to become hypertensive, showed an increase of the granulation index in the clamped kidney, and degranulation in the untouched kidney. Blaquier et al. (22) raised an objection to the concept of decreased juxtaglomerular cell granulation and decreased renin content of the kidneys being a response to stretch. In rats with a unilateral renal artery clip the extent to which the renin content of the untouched kidney was diminished was the same irrespective of the animal's blood pressure.

These remarkable but well-authenticated findings suggest that while the juxtaglomerular cells may be the source or storage site of renin, they have so far failed to support the idea that juxtaglomerular changes have a close association with the occurrence of renal hypertension.

A number of investigations summarized by Tobian (282) lead to the conclusion that the amount of juxtaglomerular granulation commonly changes in parallel with the renin content of the kidney.

Although there has been much difficulty in measuring the renin and angiotensin concentration in blood, and some disparate results have arisen from defects in the methodology, there are now conclusions which appear to have gained acceptance.

Renin may be estimated in plasma by allowing the renin to act under standard conditions upon substrate, thereby liberating angiotensin. The angiotensin is then determined by bioassay as, for example, by its pressor effect in bilaterally nephrectomized rats. The amount of angiotensin liberated in this way is considerable and not difficult to assay, and it is possible to assay the renin content of 0.2 ml of plasma, whereas 20 ml of plasma, or more, are needed for determination of the plasma angiotensin.

Although most of the actions of the enzyme renin appear to be due to the liberation of angiotensin, it cannot be assumed that a change in the concentration of renin in the plasma will always be associated with a corresponding change in the amount of angiotensin released. Unknown as well as known influences may modify the amount of angiotensin formed. It has been suggested, for example, that one factor to be considered is the amount of the substrate, an α_2 globulin, available for the renin to act upon. Additionally, the substance first formed by the action of renin is considered to be the decapeptide, angiotensin I, which is almost inactive (113) and is converted to the more active angiotensin II by the so-called plasma-converting enzyme. This intermediate step may also be modified by conditions which have not yet been defined sufficiently. The angiotensin II is broken down rapidly by angiotensinase, normally present in blood, to less active or inactive residues, but it would appear from the experiments of Helmer *et al.* (116) that the so-called "angiotensinase" may represent a group of different enzymes which in common inactivate angiotensin. As already mentioned, the amount of angiotensin measured in the plasma may not be firm evidence of the amount of angiotensin reaching and acting either directly on blood vessels or indirectly through the adrenal gland. Dickinson and Lawrence (55) find that continued subthreshold infusions of angiotensin in rabbits cause larger blood-pressure rises than infusions of comparatively short duration. In either case the blood pressure falls soon after stopping the infusion. Brown *et al.* (30) made a similar investigation, the infusion of angiotensin being maintained for periods up to 3 months. The greatest mean rise of blood pressure was 34 mm Hg. The blood pressure fell rapidly when the infusion was stopped. Doses in excess of 0.25 μg per kilogram per minute induced a rise of blood pressure followed by a fall. The smaller doses of 0.06–0.2 μg per kilogram per minute usually induced long-continued rises of blood pressure.

These many variables make the interpretation of results difficult, yet observations of great interest and importance have been made. The general impression is that in chronic renal hypertension, due to narrowing of a renal artery, or of both renal arteries, some patients may show a slight increase in the amount of renin and angiotensin in the circulating blood, particularly when it has been clearly demonstrated that there is a sufficient pressure difference between the parts of a renal artery proximal and distal to the obstruction. In other patients no increase in the concentration of renin in plasma has been found. This applies to venous samples of systemic blood, to venous samples from a renal vein, and to arterial samples. Helmer (114), however, using spirally cut thoracic aortas of rabbits, has been able to detect vasoconstrictor substances in the renal vein blood of a large proportion of hypertensive patients. His figures include 14 out of 17 positives in essential hypertension (3 malignant) and all of 7 with occlusive renal disease.

It is generally considered that the concentrations of angiotensin found in the plasma in cases of chronic benign renal hypertension in man are also well below the concentrations of angiotensin found in the plasma after administration of sufficient angiotensin to raise the blood pressure in normotensives. It must be freely admitted that the response to acute administration is not necessarily a satisfactory guide to the results which follow the long-term administration and, as has been mentioned, the infusion of subthreshold doses of angiotensin II, if long continued, will raise the blood pressure.

Doyle and Smirk (64) showed in man that when the blood pressure is increased acutely by injections of angiotensin, norepinephrine, or S-methyl isothiourea, the blood-pressure rise is nonneurogenically maintained, in the sense that it is not removable by a large dose of a ganglion-blocking drug such as hexamethonium, whereas in essential hypertension and in chronic renal hypertension in man the blood pressure rise is, to an important extent, but not exclusively, neurogenically maintained.

In acute human and experimental studies, angiotensin has been found to constrict the pulmonary blood vessels and to raise the pulmonary artery pressure (84, 86, 190, 294). In essential hypertension, there is no rise in pulmonary artery pressure except when heart failure has occurred (84, 190, 237, 292, 294, 301). As pointed out by Chimoskey *et al.* (41), this does not altogether exclude the possibility of a causal relationship between angiotensin and essential hypertension. However, it adds to the already strong evidence against any direct or simple interrelationship.

In rats, Laverty and Smirk (152) showed that cross-perfusion of blood from a rat with chronic renal hypertension into a hind limb of a control rat does not reveal the presence of any significant amount of renal pressor agent in the arterial blood. A renal pressor agent was detected readily in arterial blood from a rat with acute renal hypertension (152).

Rats with chronic renal hypertension have large falls of blood pressure after intravenous hexamethonium, but the hexamethonium floor, the lowest level attained after maximal doses, is higher than in our genetic hypertensives or normotensives.

It is clear, therefore, that there are important difficulties in attempting to explain chronic renal hypertension in terms of the direct pressor action of angiotensin. Furthermore, the action of angiotensin appears to be complex.

Angiotensin II acts directly on minute blood vessels, and causes contraction of aortic strips. This action has usually been attributed to a direct effect on the smooth muscle, but Distler *et al.* (58) consider that the effect is indirect and mediated by liberation of norepinephrine from the sympathetic nerve endings. Their suggestion is based on poor responses of norepinephrine-depleted vascular smooth muscle to angiotensin.

In a preparation in which a rat hind limb was separately perfused and connected to the upper part of the animal only by nerves, Laverty (151) showed that injection of angiotensin into the upper part of the animal led to a discharge down the nerves which caused vasoconstriction in the vascularly isolated hind limb.

It has been shown since by Lewis and Reit (157) that angiotensin causes stimulation at least of the superior cervical sympathetic nerve ganglia of the cat, and this may explain Laverty's observations. Additionally, however, it has been reported (34) that an injection of angiotensin into the blood vessels supplying the brain causes a rise of blood pressure. It may be that angiotensin II has some direct action on higher sympathetic centers, but constriction of blood vessels supplying the nervous tissue may be an alternative explanation. It has been shown by Feldberg and Lewis (75) that angiotensin liberates catecholamines from the adrenal medulla, one molecule of angiotensin liberating several thousand of catecholamines. Evidently, therefore, the action of angiotensin II as a promptly acting pressor agent may be highly complicated.

Laragh *et al.* (149), Genest *et al.* (93), and Mulrow and Ganong (188) showed that angiotensin infusion leads to increase in the aldosterone concentration in blood.

All these complications affecting the concentration of circulating renin, the several factors influencing the resulting concentration of angiotensin in the blood stream, the possibility that the concentration of angiotensin at its sites of action does not run parallel to the concentration in the blood stream, and the fact that angiotensin II has several sites of action, make it an impossible task to control all the factors concerned, and most difficult to draw firm conclusions about the relation of renin and angiotensin to renal hypertension.

Aldosterone, by its action on the kidney, leads to retention of sodium and water and excretion of potassium. Hypertension may follow, perhaps due in part to the electrolyte disturbance. It has been shown quite clearly by Conn *et al.* (42, 43) that ordinarily the blood pressure is elevated in cases of primary aldosteronism arising from the secretory activity of certain adrenal tumors. But even when there is frank aldosteronism with gross depletion of the plasma potassium, the blood pressure is not as a rule raised to great heights, and there is difficulty in attributing the very large blood-pressure increase which may follow constriction of one or both renal arteries solely to increased secretion of this hormone.

Mulrow (187) found increased aldosterone production in a few patients with hypertension and renal vascular lesions, but mostly their aldosterone excretion and plasma angiotensin II were within normal limits. He thinks that in most patients the renin–angiotensin system is not the mechanism causing the hypertension associated with renal-vascular lesions. Moreover, Laragh *et al.* (149) consider that most patients with essential hypertension do not secrete excessive quantities of aldosterone. On the other hand, in experimental animals, Morris *et al.* (183) find angiotensin II is often present in renal-vascular hypertension and disappears from the blood on removal of the affected kidney or of the renal artery occlusion.

In cases of malignant hypertension, however, aldosterone is commonly present to an increased extent in the blood (149). Some estimates of high angiotensin concentration in the blood of patients with malignant hypertension are inconclusive, in that the patients were in congestive heart failure (92).

The association of a renal artery narrowing with secondary hyperaldosteronism has been demonstrated (100). Whether renin-angiotensin and secondary aldosterone increase are responsible for blood-pressure increase or not, it is clear that there are well-authenticated examples of hypertension due to renal artery constriction which are associated with manifestations of secondary hyperaldosteronism, including hypopotassemia. Usually there is a raised concentration of renin and angiotensin in the blood.

In contrast, in cases of Conn's syndrome of primary aldosteronism and in Cushing's syndrome, Brown *et al.* (32) noted an abnormally low plasma renin. This may have been due to the aldosterone causing sodium retention. Their highest renin concentrations were encountered in patients characterized by malignant hypertension, renal disease, hyperaldosteronism, and hyponatremia.

It is generally assumed that where there is aldosterone excess, it acts by retention of sodium and increase of extracellular volume. In experimental renal hypertension, Tobian (280) has shown that the sodium content of the arterial wall is increased. This observation is consistent with the hypothesis that the amount of aldosterone liberated in experimental renal hypertension is sufficient to modify electrolyte metabolism. Nolla-Panades (193) found that in rats with experimental renal hypertension from an aortic clip above the renal arteries, the increase in sodium and potassium of the aorta affected the abdominal aorta which was exposed to a near normal blood pressure as well as the thoracic aorta which was exposed to a high blood pressure. According to Peterson (208) the rat is exceptional in that angiotensin does not enhance aldosterone secretion. In our New Zealand strain of rats with genetic hypertension the sodium and water content of large arteries did not, however, differ much from that of control normotensive rats.

Bartter *et al.* (16) consider that in man, despite the increase of aldosterone in edematous states, there is a regulatory process whereby an increase of extracellular fluid volume normally inhibits and a deficit increases the aldosterone secretion. It was possible to demonstrate the effect of changing the extracellular fluid volume independently of changes in electrolyte concentration.

An important suggestion by Ledingham and Cohen (154) is that the balance between peripheral resistance and cardiac output has been altered as the result of changes in sodium and water balance.

Wilson (295) has expressed the view that an increase in the cardiac output may play an important role in the initial blood-pressure rise in experimental renal hypertension. This may be due to an increase in the tone of capacity blood vessels, or may be influenced by increased contractility of the heart. He raises the possibility that the increase in the blood-pressure level is due to autoregulatory, myogenic constriction of the arterioles.

The author's impression is that while changes in the secretion of aldosterone may add to or subtract from the level of the blood pressure, these by themselves do not yet seem sufficient to explain the blood-pressure level in many hypertensive patients other than those with Conn's syndrome.

D. ANTIRENIN

The discovery of antirenin by Johnson and Wakerlin (132) started a long series of investigations in which it was shown, especially in the dog, that even chronic experimental renal hypertension could be counteracted by preparations containing antirenin. Early on, doubts were raised about the specificity of the materials injected, but with the use of purer preparations there remains little doubt that antirenins are effective even in chronic renal hypertension. Recently Deodhar *et al.* (53) have shown that homologous renins of the rat, rabbit, and dog, though not antigenic, could be rendered antigenic by acetylation. In a dog, hypertensive for 6 years, immunization with acetylated dog renin not only induced a high titre of antirenin to dog renin, but led to progressive lowering of the blood pressure.

Such results argue for the continuation of participation of renin in the pathogenesis of experimental renal hypertension even into the chronic stages.

VIII. Evidence relating to increased vascular reactivity in hypertension

There has been much interest in the question of whether, in hypertension of various kinds, the cardiovascular system reacts to pressor stimuli more vigorously than in normotension. An increase in cardiovascular reactivity might be a factor in the pathogenesis of hypertension. Cardiovascular responses are complicated, for they involve changes in the activities of the heart, resistance blood vessels, capacity vessels, and the baroceptors; hence the result obtained is much influenced by the precise conditions under which experiments are performed. It is proposed, therefore, to refer to the responses of resistance blood vessels first, since the number of variables here are fewer.

A. THE REACTIVITY OF RESISTANCE BLOOD VESSELS IN HYPERTENSIVE AND IN NORMOTENSIVE INDIVIDUALS

The term "increased reactivity" is employed here to refer to an increase above the normal in the response of peripheral blood vessels to stimulation, such that either they show a larger increase in perfusion pressure when perfused at a constant rate, or a larger decrease in the flow of blood through them when exposed to a constant pressure. The expression "increase in the reactivity of blood vessels," as used here, makes no assumption as to the reason why blood vessels react to a particular stimulus by larger-than-average increase in peripheral resistance. In some instances it could be due to enhanced responsiveness of otherwise unaltered vascular smooth muscle; in others it might be due to hypertrophy of the muscle or to some other structural change which makes the normal response of vascular muscle more effective. Used in this sense, there is general agreement that in hypertension in man, the small systemic blood vessels of such anatomical regions as have been examined show an increase above the normal in their responsiveness to a variety of stimuli (12, 35, 48, 62, 64, 65, 101, 130, 155, 176–178, 185, 191). Authors have not always specified the etiology of the hypertension patients studied, but mostly they appear to have been of the the essential type.

An increase in the responsiveness to epinephrine has been demonstrated in the blood vessels of the hand and forearm by Duff (65) and Daly and Duff (48).

Enhanced reactivity of the hand or forearm blood vessels of human hypertensives to norepinephrine has been shown to occur by Doyle et al. (62, 63) and by Daly and Duff (48); both used intra-arterial injections of the drug. Greisman (101) and Mendlowitz and collaborators (177) found an enhanced reactivity in the nail-fold blood vessels of hypertensives; they also noted (176) enhanced reactivity in patients with Cushing's syndrome and in patients treated with adrenocorticotropic hormone (ACTH). Barany and James (12) reported enhanced reactivity to norepinephrine in the heel skin of hypertensives, and Moulton et al. (185) demonstrated an enhanced response of blood vessels in the quadriceps muscle of hypertensives, using the effect of the vasoconstrictor action of topically administered norepinephrine upon the clearance from the muscle of ^{24}Na.

Doyle *et al.* (62, 63) demonstrated an increased reactivity of the forearm blood vessels of hypertensives to 5-hydroxytryptamine creatinine sulfate injected into a brachial artery. There was also a slight but not statistically significantly greater response in the hypertensives to angiotensin II. Mendlowitz *et al.* (179), using digital vessels, demonstrated an enhanced reactivity to angiotensin II.

Increased reactivity of blood vessels to a variety of central nervous system stimuli such as the character of the examination room, pin pricks, pistol shots, electric shocks, etc., have been reported (35, 191). Pfeiffer and Wolff (209) noted that psychological stimuli caused a greater decrease in renal blood flow and larger blood-pressure rises in hypertensives than in normotensives.

B. Increased Vascular Reactivity in Experimental Hypertension

In animals an increase has been demonstrated in the reactivity of blood vessels taken from experimental hypertensives and compared with blood

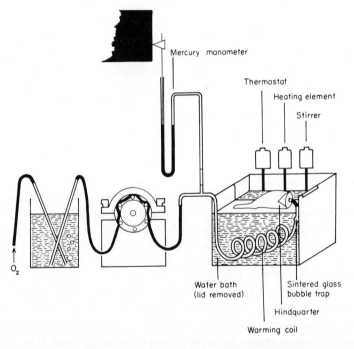

Fig. 1. From left to right in the diagram: oxygenated perfusion fluid is taken up from the reservoir, passed through a rotary pump, and delivered to a warming coil immersed in a water bath at 40°C. It is connected by a rubber tube to a cannula inserted into the abdominal aorta. The perfusion is at constant rate, hence the perfusion pressure recorded by the mercury manometer is a measure of the peripheral resistance. (Courtesy of Professor E. G. McQueen.)

vessels from the corresponding vascular territory of normotensives. Blood vessels have been perfused with either a physiological saline, or with blood. Mostly, the experiments have been made in the rat, which readily allows comparison of the responses of perfused blood vessels from hypertensives and controls.

Preparations we have found useful for this purpose have been described by Fastier and Smirk (74), Field and Laverty (79), Laverty and Smirk (152) and McGregor (162).

For perfusion with oxygenated physiological saline (e.g., Kreb's solution), a rotary pump is used in which rollers propel fluid along a rubber tube of suitable dimension (Fig. 1). The saline is taken up from a reservoir, passed through a coil immersed in a water bath, warmed to a suitable temperature, and delivered at a constant rate into the aorta of a severed pithed rat hind quarter. The hind quarter lies on a shelf, just above the water bath which has a removable lid. The perfusion pressure is recorded kymographically. Injections may be made into the rubber tubing close to the rat hind quarter, or may be added to the reservoir. Alternately, to perfuse a single limb, the fluid may be delivered into a femoral artery.

Preparations for the blood perfusion of a rat hind limb, through a femoral artery, have been described by Field and Laverty (79) and by Laverty and Smirk (152), using the blood pump described by Field et al. (78); the apparatus is shown in Fig. 2. Blood may be taken from one femoral artery of a rat,

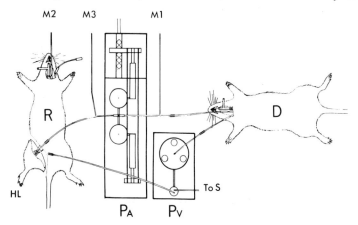

Fig. 2. Arterial blood is taken from the donor rat (D), led by polyethylene tubing to the constant output arterial pump (Pa) which delivers blood into the femoral artery of the hind limb (HL) of the recipient rat (R). Blood is returned from the hind limb to the venous pump (Pv) and thence to the donor (D). Filling of the venous pump reservoir is assisted by a two-bottle suction device (S) which maintains a negative pressure. The arterial pressure of the donor is recorded in manometer M1, of the recipient (R) in manometer M2, and manometer M3 records the perfusion pressure of blood entering the hind limb (HL).

passed through the pump and delivered into the opposite femoral artery so as to perfuse the hind limb at a constant rate. The hind limb may be either innervated or denervated. The venous blood may be returned to the rat either through normal channels or with the assistance of a venous pump. The perfused limb may be separated from the rest of the rat except for nervous connections.

Alternately, blood may be taken from a donor animal, passed through the constant output pump into the femoral artery of the recipient, collected from the femoral vein, and returned by a venous pump to the donor. Once again, the recipient hind limb may be separated from the upper part of the animal, preserving only the nervous connections and the femur for mechanical support.

A preparation using the same principle has been devised recently by McGregor (162), making it possible to perfuse mesenteric blood vessels at a constant rate, and to subject them, when desired, to stimulation of the splanchnic nerves.

Using the rat hind quarter preparation, perfused at a constant rate with physiological saline, Restall and Smirk, cited by Smirk (247), showed that the blood vessels of renal hypertensive rats, prepared by narrowing a renal artery, showed enhanced reactivity to epinephrine, in that larger-than-normal rises of perfusion pressure were obtained on injecting epinephrine into the perfusion fluid. McQueen (165, 166), using the same preparation, greatly extended this preliminary work, using norepinephrine, 5-hydroxytryptamine, and Pitressin (vasopressin) as pressor agents. It was shown that hind limb vessels from hypertensive rats were more reactive to norepinephrine than the blood vessels of normotensive control rats. The hypertension in these experiments was induced either by a unilateral clip on a renal artery, or by a unilateral clip on a renal artery together with contralateral nephrectomy.

The placing of a unilateral clip on a renal artery, together with contralateral nephrectomy and bilateral adrenalectomy, however, was not regularly associated with any increase in the vascular reactivity.

McQueen (167) showed that with a unilateral constricting clip on a renal artery, and the other kidney intact, the increase in reactivity progresses over about 2 weeks, and appears to be related to the development of hypertension.

An increase in the reactivity to serotonin (5-hydroxytryptamine) and to Pitressin (166) was demonstrated in rats with a clip on the renal artery of a sole remaining kidney. The increase in the reactivity was demonstrable also in rats with hypertension due to unilateral perinephritis (167). In rats developing hypertension after subtotal adrenalectomy and drinking 1.5% salt solution (244), there was no evidence of an increase in the norepinephrine responsiveness (167). In the moderate degree of hypertension induced by 9α-fluorohydrocortisone with 1% salt solution in the drinking water, there was no significant change in the response to norepinephrine (167). As will be mentioned later, McQueen and Hodge (169) found that by preventing the blood-pressure rise after clipping a renal artery, by reserpine, it was possible to prevent or greatly reduce some of the manifestations secondary to hypertension, such as periarteritis; and also (168) the associated increase in the reactivity of the blood vessels of the perfused rat hind quarter was decreased significantly.

Using the innervated blood-perfused but vascularly isolated rat hind limb preparation (152), our New Zealand strain of genetic hypertensive rats was shown by Laverty (150) to exhibit a slightly increased response to norepinephrine when compared with stock rats. When, however, the perfused hind limb was functionally denervated by the administration of hexamethonium to the upper part of the animal, there was a significant increase in the reactivity of the hind limb to norepinephrine as compared with similarly treated controls. In similar experiments an enhanced vascular reactivity after sympathetic block with hexamethonium was noted in the innervated hind limb preparation of rats with chronic renal hypertension due to the application of a clip on a renal artery.

Using the preparation of rat mesenteric blood vessels devised by McGregor (162), McGregor and Smirk (163) found that blood-perfused mesenteric vessels of rats from the New Zealand strain with genetic hypertension showed an enhanced reactivity to norepinephrine when compared with controls.

It should be pointed out that the reactivity of blood-perfused blood vessels is much greater than that of saline-perfused vessels, and may reveal features of interest which are not displayed when the vessels are saline-perfused.

As enhanced reactivity of perfused blood vessels to a variety of vaso-constrictor drugs is characteristic of several types of hypertension, one must consider the possibility that the increase is secondary to the raised blood pressure, for example, due to hypertrophy of the vascular muscle. This may be a part of the explanation when the hypertension has lasted long enough. An experiment of Nolla-Panades (192), however, shows that an increase in the reactivity of perfused blood vessels may occur when they are protected from any important blood-pressure elevation. Nolla-Panades (192) induced hypertension in rats by placing a clip on the aorta above both renal arteries. This led to hypertension in the upper part of the rat, but below the clip the blood pressure was shown not to have risen appreciably. The reactivity of the saline-perfused hind quarter blood vessels, taken from this preparation, and compared with controls, showed an increase in the responsiveness to norepinephrine, despite the fact that the vessels had not been exposed to any significant elevation of the blood pressure.

The experiments on vascular reactivity show that in certain types of hypertension, notably Goldblatt hypertension, and in the spontaneous hypertension of our New Zealand genetic hypertensive rat colony, there is an increase in the

*reactivity of the blood vessels to a variety of stimuli. In man this appears to be
true also, at least in essential hypertension.* More experimental studies are
needed using other animals, other types of hypertension, and other stimuli. It
will be seen in the next section that comparisons of the reactivity of the whole
cardiovascular system of hypertensives and normotensives to pressor stimuli
have yielded divergent results, both in human subjects and in experimental
animals. Some of the disparity depends on the methods used.

IX. Evidence concerning the responses of hypertensive and normotensive patients and experimental animals to pressor agencies

Whereas in man and in experimental animals increased reactivity of resistance blood vessels to vasoconstrictor stimuli is reported by almost all observers, the situation is quite different when blood pressures are studied. Although
comparisons of the reactions of hypertensives and controls to pressor agencies
have yielded some very confusing results in man and animals, experiments will
be cited later which appear to explain some of them. In the whole animal,
blood pressure changes involve responses from the baroceptors, and changes in
the activity of the heart and capacity vessels may occur, as well as changes in
the resistance blood vessels.

A. The Relationship between the Cold Pressor Test, Age, and Supplemental Pressures in Hypertensives and Normotensives

Much of the interest in cardiovascular reactivity stems from the report of
Hines and Brown (121) that when an arm is plunged into ice-cold water (4°C),
the rise of blood pressure is greater in hypertensives than in normotensives,
and is greater in the children of hypertensive parents than in the children of
normotensives. Hines and Brown considered increased reactivity to the cold
pressor test to be an indication of future hypertension. Most who have worked
in the field find an increase in the response of hypertensives as compared with
the controls.

Unfortunately, some research groups used young normotensives as controls,
apparently unaware that normotensives of the same age grouping as essential
hypertensives are generally more reactive to the cold pressor test than young
persons. Normotensive controls should therefore be of the same age grouping
as the essential hypertensives.

Evidence that the cardiovascular reactivity to the cold pressor test increases
with age has been published by Alam and Smirk (4), Feldt and Wenstrand (77),
Russek and Zohman (236), Russek (235), Pickering and Kissin (215), and
Hines (119). The increase with age in the pressor response to cold is associated
also with an increase in the pressor response to carbon dioxide inhalation

(219, 220). Age, therefore, may influence the responses to other pressor agents. Yates and Wood (299), however, found little difference in the responses of young and old persons.

Among authors who compared the responses in essential hypertension or borderline hypertension with controls in the same age groups, and found larger pressor responses in those with over-average pressures are: Alam and Smirk (4), Feldt and Wenstrand (76), Russek and Zohman (236), Thacker (274), Briggs and Oerting (27), and Ayman and Goldshine (11).

Others who found enhanced reactivity to the cold pressor test in hypertensives but did not necessarily employ controls of a similar age group include Smithwick and Robertson (267), Windesheim et al. (297).

Miller and Bruger (182) confirmed the report of Alam and Smirk (4) that renal hypertensives in general do not show hyperreactivity to the cold pressor test.

Authors who found no hyperreactivity in the cold pressor responses of hypertensives or prehypertensives include Armstrong and Rafferty (8), Pickering and Kissin (215), and Todd (284).

There is considerable dispute about whether hyperreactivity to the cold pressor test is inherited and whether it predicts a tendency to hypertension. Briggs and Oerting (28) found it valuable in the prediction of pregnancy toxemia.

Hines (119), Thomas (276), Dieckmann and Michel (56), and Briggs and Oerting (28) studying in the aggregate large numbers of persons believe the response to the cold pressor test is inherited.

Feldt and Wenstrand (77) found no relationship between the reactivity and family history of hypertension; neither did Chesley and Chesley (40).

Some of the authors who found no enhanced reactivity to the cold pressor test in hypertensives—for example, Armstrong and Rafferty (8)—did not follow the technique of Hines and Brown (121).

The level to which the blood pressure is allowed to fall before the application of cold is important. Hines (119) rested his subjects till their blood pressures had settled to a steady level, which often took 15 or 20 minutes in normotensives, and ordinarily longer in hypertensives. The stimulus of cold was then applied for a period of 1 minute, and the difference between the baseline pressure and the maximum height to which the blood pressure rose in association with the stimulus was taken as the degree of reactivity.

While the application of cold, as such, raises the blood pressure, it is also raised by any condition or environment which induces tenseness or even alerts the subject. When in preparation for the test the subject is rested and allowed to become familiar with the observer and the procedure of blood-pressure measurement, the level of the blood pressure may fall to a near-basal level (249: p. 29, 287, 298). Any stimulus which then alerts the individual is likely to cause a larger rise of pressure in hypertensives than in normotensives. Consequently, the rise of pressure is partly due to cold and partly the response of the subject's supplemental pressure to a psychological stimulus. If cold is applied without attempting first to obtain a near-basal state, then the difference between the responses of normotensives and hypertensives will be smaller.

B. THE EFFECT OF OTHER PRESSOR STIMULI IN HYPERTENSIVES AND NORMOTENSIVES

Differences in method of the kind described in connection with responses to the cold pressor test may account for some of the divergent reports relating to the effects of other pressor agencies in hypertensives and normotensives.

1. *Epinephrine*

Hetényi and Sümegi (118) and Hess (117) reported an increase in the pressor responses of hypertensives to epinephrine, but this result was not confirmed by Pickering and Kissin (215), Kylin (147), Deicke and Hülse (52), Jansen (131), Gordon and Levitt (98), and Elliot and Nuzum (67). Judson *et al.* (134) studied in detail 5 normals and 13 hypertensives. In some instances (98, 134) there was a slight increase in the pressor response to epinephrine in the hypertensives when expressed in mm Hg but no increase when expressed as a percentage of the original blood pressure.

2. *Norepinephrine*

Increase in the response of hypertensives to norepinephrine expressed in mm Hg rises of pressure were noted by Doyle and Black (61) using age-matched controls. A similar result was reported by Goldenberg *et al.* (96) but their controls were younger than their hypertensives; and by Judson *et al.* (135) who did not mention the ages of their controls. The latter studied 5 normotensive and 6 hypertensive patients. The blood-pressure increase was slightly greater in the hypertensives but expressing the results as a percentage of the original blood pressure, they found no increase in the reactivity of the hypertensives.

Barany and James (12) employed controls of the same age grouping as their hypertensives. They found no significant difference in their pressor responses to norepinephrine.

3. *Posterior Pituitary Hormone*

No difference in the responses of hypertensives and controls to injections of posterior pituitary hormone was noted by Elliot and Nuzum (67).

4. *Carbon Dioxide*

Raab and Redlich (221), Ludwig (158), and Hardgrove *et al.* (109) all found an increase above the normal in the pressor responses of hypertensives to carbon dioxide inhalation, and the difference observed by Hardgrove *et al.* did not appear to depend on age differences of hypertensives and normotensives.

Raab and Redlich (221) also found that elderly persons gave, as an average, larger responses to carbon dioxide inhalation than young persons. The figures published by Hardgrove *et al.* did not show this.

5. *Effect of Smoking*

The use of tobacco is associated with greater rises of blood pressure in hypertension than in normotension, according to Hines and Roth (122).

6. *Emotion and Tenseness*

A very extensive literature exists relating the emotional state of individuals to the height of the blood pressure. There is not the slightest doubt that emotional stimuli may cause a rise in the level of the blood pressure in normotensives and in hypertensives. In general, it is thought that the increases of blood pressure observed in the hypertensives are larger than those reported in normotensives. Sometimes such results are interpreted as indications of an enhanced reactivity of the cardiovascular system in hypertension, such that an emotional stimulus will produce a larger rise in the blood pressure in hypertension, or in one predisposed thereto, than it does in normotension. Alternately, some authors favor the explanation that many hypertensives are individuals whose emotions are stronger, and that the larger responses often encountered in hypertensives are the result of the larger amounts of emotion which they generate. An important difficulty in reaching any conclusion is the difficulty in deciding about the amount of emotion which is supposed to have given rise to the increase of blood pressure. The topic has been reviewed elsewhere (249: p. 212). The following general statement may be made: many hypertensives appear to be entirely normal in their emotional responses, and others have emotional difficulty, and on the whole exhibit more aggressive tendencies than do normotensives. *It may well be that a part of the larger rises of blood pressure in response to emotional situations encountered in most hypertensives is the result of more emotion, and in others that it is the result of a greater reactivity of the cardiovascular system. The high probability is that both of these explanations are correct ones in different individuals, and that no generalization can be found which covers all the widely differing circumstances.*

7. *Breath-Holding*

This led to larger pressor responses in hypertensives than in normotensives of a similar age grouping in the experiments of Ayman and Goldshine (10, 11) and by Feldt and Wenstrand (76), whose normotensives, however, were as an average 37.1 years, and hypertensives 52 years of age. Additionally, Feldt and

Wenstrand (76) used men and women as normotensives, but only men as hypertensives.

8. *Controlled Muscular Work*

Controlled muscular work seems to be associated regularly with an increased rise of the systolic blood pressure in hypertensives, according to Barath (13), Eppinger and Kisch (68), Eppinger and Schwarz (69), and Bauer and Neuberger (17). Thacker (275) found exercise induced larger rises of blood pressure in university students with over-average blood pressures than in those with average or under-average pressures. Norris *et al.* (195) found older patients experienced larger blood-pressure rises than the young. The effects on diastolic pressure were variable.

9. *Comment on the Study of Pressor Responses*

It is fundamental to recognize that pressor stimuli inevitably involve complex secondary adjustments throughout the circulatory system. It is not surprising, therefore, that experiments involving responses from the entire circulatory system yield less uniform results than those which study the responses of a single vascular bed.

When comparisons are made of the responses of hypertensives and normotensives to pressor stimuli, it is important that they should be matched for age and sex, and it should be realized that casual blood pressures are subject to emotional and environmental change in normotensives, and more so in hypertensives. Also, it is important to note that the application of a stimulus, for example, an injection, may induce psychological rises of blood pressure as well as any changes brought about by administered drugs. Emotional rises of blood pressure are usually larger if they occur in a person whose blood pressure has been allowed to subside to a near-basal level. But in any case, as will be illustrated by experimental studies, the magnitude of pressor responses to a variety of agents is related to the starting level of the blood pressure.

C. Responses to Pressor Agents in Experimental Hypertension

The term "increased reactivity of the cardiovascular system" is sometimes taken to imply a cardiovascular state—for example, in hypertension—in which exaggerated pressor responses follow the administration of most pressor agencies. Clinical experiences show that such generalizations may be difficult to justify. It has already been pointed out that the response of the cardiovascular system to pressor agencies is complicated, in that it involves change in the activities of the heart, resistance blood vessels, capacity vessels, and the baroceptors.

The number of conflicting reports concerning responses to pressor stimuli clinically and in experimental animals led Phelan *et al.* (211) and Phelan (210) to seek an explanation. Some information was obtained by a study of the relationship between the initial blood pressure and the rise in blood pressure following injection of various drugs; comparing, in the first place, normotensive rats with other normotensives, genetic hypertensive rats with other genetic hypertensives, and renal hypertensive rats with renal hypertensives; and afterwards hypertensives with normotensives.

Regressions of blood pressure rises on initial blood pressure were studied separately in normotensive rats and in rats from our genetic hypertensive colony using as pressor drugs biological angiotensin, synthetic angiotensin II, vasopressin, and *S*-methylisothiourea. In normotensives and genetic hypertensives, regression analysis showed that with all these drugs lower initial blood pressures were associated with larger pressor responses. Using synthetic angiotensin and vasopressin, the same result was obtained in rats with chronic renal hypertension induced by placing a clip on a renal artery.

When, however, the pressor drug used was norepinephrine, high initial blood pressures were no longer associated with smaller pressor responses; and this result held for normotensives, for genetic hypertensives, and for chronic renal hypertensives provided the initial blood pressure did not exceed 170 mm Hg. Above 170 mm Hg the renal hypertensives showed a decreased pressor response. As norepinephrine is considered to be the sympathetic neuro-transmitter, this last result was subjected to a confirmatory study, involving in all 59 controls and 42 hypertensive rats.

The relationship between hypertensives and normotensives is, therefore, best studied by comparison of the regression lines of blood-pressure rise on initial blood pressure. With several pressor drugs it is found that at levels of the initial blood pressure between about 135–145 mm Hg systolic, representing over-average levels for our normotensive colony and under-average levels for genetic and renal hypertensives, the pressor responses are larger in the hypertensives.

Where genetic hypertensives are concerned, the regression lines for pressor responses on initial blood pressures were significantly higher than the corresponding regression line of controls; in the case of epinephrine ($P < 0.01$), biological angiotensin ($P < 0.01$), vasopressin ($P < 0.01$) (Fig. 3), and *S*-methyl-isothiourea ($P < 0.01$). In the chronic renal hypertensives (210), the regression line for the renal hypertensive using vasopressin was also above those for controls (Fig. 4).

In contrast, when the pressor drugs used were synthetic angiotensin or norepinephrine the regression lines of the hypertensives did not lie significantly above the controls neither in the genetic nor in the chronic renal hypertensives.

It may explain some of the confusion in the literature to mention, as will be made clear from Fig. 4, that whereas rats with severe renal hypertension and

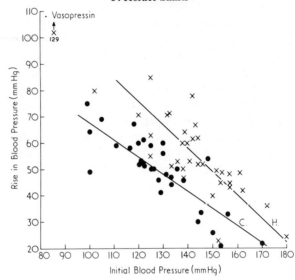

Fig. 3. Relation between initial blood pressure and rise in blood pressure with injected vasopressin. The regression lines for genetic hypertensive (H) rats ($r = -0.811$, P < 0.001) and control (C) rats ($r = -0.832$, P < 0.001) are both significant. (Reproduced from *Circulation Research*, Vol. X, 1962.)

high initial blood pressures would show a smaller response to vasopressin than normotensives, such rats with only a moderate blood-pressure increase show an increase above the normal in their response to pressor drugs.

Some further clarification may be derived by comparing the pressor responses of hypertensives and normotensives after maximal doses of hexamethonium; (5 mg intravenously for rats weighing 300 g). The hexamethonium renders the preinjection blood pressures more nearly equal and blocks baroceptor control over blood pressure levels. After hexamethonium, the responses of genetic and renal hypertensive rats to several drugs exceed those of normotensives.

Thus, after hexamethonium, genetic hypertensives exhibit larger blood-pressure rises than normotensives in response to norepinephrine (211), 5-hydroxytryptamine, tyramine, and Pitressin (254).

It would appear therefore that in our genetic hypertension of rats there is not only an increase in the reactivity of the resistance blood vessels to several vasoconstrictor agents, but also that this increased pressor reactivity may be demonstrated in the whole animal when the blood pressure has been lowered and baroceptor action blocked by means of hexamethonium.

It seems likely that such an increase in reactivity, when present, is concerned in the rise and maintenance of high blood pressure even though there is no proof that it is concerned in the initial rises of the blood pressure.

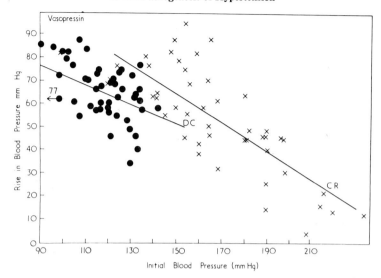

Fig. 4. Relation between initial blood pressure and rise in blood pressure with injected vasopressin for chronic renal hypertensive (CR) rats and dummy-operated control (DC) rats. The regression lines for CR rats ($r = -0.789$, $P < 0.001$) and DC rats ($r = -0.459$, $P < 0.01$) are both significant. (Reproduced from *American Heart Journal*, vol. 71, 1966.)

The above-mentioned results may explain some of the disparities in the results of comparisons of the pressor responses of hypertensive and normotensive animals, a summary of which follows:

1. *Epinephrine*

In hypertensive rabbits an increased response to epinephrine was reported by Brown and Maegraith (29). Rothman (234) also found an enhanced response to epinephrine in renal hypertensive rabbits, but a decrease in rabbits made hypertensive by ligature of cerebral arteries. Olsen *et al.* (200) found an enhanced response in renal hypertensive rats. A slightly increased response was noted by Masson *et al.* (173) in rats treated with DCA. Verney and Vogt (288) found an increase in the response to epinephrine in some renal hypertensive dogs. Page and Taylor (204) found no great difference between the responses of renal hypertensive dogs and controls.

2. *Norepinephrine*

Olsen *et al.* (200) found an increase in the response of renal hypertensive rats to norepinephrine. Conway (45) found no large difference in the response to norepinephrine of rabbits after they were made hypertensive by the application of latex to the surface of a sole remaining kidney; but after pretreatment with large doses of hexamethonium, the response to norepinephrine was greater in the hypertensive than in the normotensive state. This corresponds with the results obtained by Phelan *et al.* (211) on genetic hypertensive rats to which reference was made earlier. Rothman (234) reported an increase in the sensitivity of renal hypertensive rabbits to norepinephrine but a decrease in the response of cerebral hypertensive rabbits.

3. *Posterior Pituitary Hormone*

Ogden *et al.* (198) found a markedly increased response to posterior pituitary hormone in renal hypertensive rabbits, and this was present even in the prehypertensive stage. Brown and Maegraith (29) also reported an increased pressor response above the normal in rabbits made hypertensive by a clip on a renal artery.

4. *Tyramine*

In studies with tyramine, Olsen *et al.* (200) found no difference between the responses of renal hypertensive rats and controls, but Brown and Maegraith (29) noted an increase above the normal in the response of rabbits made hypertensive by renal artery obstruction. Verney and Vogt (288) found an increased response in renal hypertensive dogs, usually from bilateral renal artery obstruction.

5. *Renin and Angiotensin*

Several observers have studied the effects of renin and angiotensin on hypertensive and control animals. Pickering (212) noted an enhanced response to renin in rabbits made hypertensive by renal artery constriction. Kapp *et al.* (136) found a slightly increased response to renin in hypertensive animals, whereas Taggart and Drury (272) found a somewhat similar response in hypertensive and normotensive animals. Page (202) found a slight increase in the response to renin, but no increase in the response to angiotensin in renal hypertensive dogs. Katz and Friedberg (137) found no exaggerated response to renin in hypertensive dogs. Masson *et al.* (173) found only a slight increase in the response to angiotensin and to renin in rats treated with DCA.

6. *Carotid Artery Occlusion*

Carotid artery occlusion may cause a greater rise of pressure in dogs with renal hypertension, according to Bouckaert *et al.* (23) and Grimson (102), but Verney and Vogt (288) found no difference in the responses of their renal hypertensive dogs and controls.

7. *Cold Pressor Test*

The cold pressor test applied to renal hypertensive dogs by Thomas and Warthin (277) produced similar results in hypertensives and controls, but Alexander *et al.* (7) found an increase in the response of families of rabbits with spontaneous hypertension, as compared with controls.

8. *Phenylethylamine*

The responses to phenylethylamine were found to be similar in renal hypertensive rats and controls by Olsen *et al.* (200).

9. *Isoamylamine*

The responses of renal hypertensive rats were found by Olsen *et al.* (200) to be smaller than those of controls.

X. Evidence concerning the relationship of the amount of renal substance to blood-pressure elevation

Though the cause of Goldblatt hypertension remains unknown, almost certainly it results from the discharge into the circulation of a substance or substances taking their origin within the kidney. It is uncertain whether these raise the blood pressure in chronic renal hypertension by providing a pressor stimulus; by inhibiting an extrarenal depressor mechanism; by exerting an action on the adrenal cortex, modifying salt and water metabolism through the intermediation of aldosterone release; or by some altogether undisclosed mechanism.

A. RENOPRIVAL HYPERTENSION

It is clear that normal renal tissue has a restraining influence on the development of Goldblatt hypertension (73, 138). When hypertension is produced by placing a clip on one renal artery in the rat, the extent to which the blood pressure rises is greatly increased if the opposite normal kidney is removed. In the dog, narrowing of one renal artery may fail to produce significant hypertension unless the opposite kidney is removed. The removal of one or both kidneys favors a rise of the blood pressure in response to a variety of pressor agencies. For example, measures used to produce experimental hypertension, such as the administration of salt, or of DCA, are more effective if unilateral nephrectomy has been done beforehand.

In the few days' survival following bilateral nephrectomy, the blood pressure may rise appreciably (26, 105, 112), but in the absence of the kidneys the normal control over blood volume and the sodium content of body fluids is lost, and some authors consider that when rises of blood pressure occur in bilaterally nephrectomized rats and dogs, it is due to the animals' having access to water and salt, and without this, hypertension does not develop (279).

Attempts by peritoneal and other kinds of dialysis to obtain a longer period of survival have had a measure of success, yet when the blood pressure is increased, there remain uncertainties as to the part played by changes in the blood volume, extracellular fluid volume, and sodium and electrolyte concentration.

In contrast to the bilateral nephrectomy, the removal of half of one kidney and all of the other ($\frac{3}{4}$-nephrectomy) is moderately well tolerated in rats, but with the eventual development of hypertension in most instances (254). Gross histological changes develop in the half-kidney remaining, so that the resulting hypertension cannot be confidently ascribed to reduction in the amount of normally functioning renal tissue; the abnormal half-kidney may be discharging into the blood some agency leading to blood-pressure increase.

Merrill et al. (180) reported observations on four patients deprived of all renal tissue for 10–62 days. Hypertension did not occur when the diet was low in protein and there was no over-hydration. Merrill has also relieved hypertension in a patient with malignant hypertension by homotransplantation of a kidney with subsequent removal of a sole diseased kidney.

It seems highly probable that in renal hypertension, and probably in some cases in the late stages of essential hypertension, the level of the blood pressure depends in part upon the release of substances from the kidneys which directly or indirectly lead to blood-pressure elevation, and partly, or at least in some instances, upon reduction in the amount of healthy renal tissue, which enhances the responses of blood vessels to a number of pressor agencies, including those responsible for Goldblatt hypertension.

Floyer (82) showed that the ability of renal tissues to antagonize some blood-pressure increases is independent of its excretory function, and takes place when the cut end of the ureter is implanted into the inferior vena cava.

Grollman and Rule (106), Ledingham (153), and Turiaf *et al.* (285) found that the nephrectomized member of a parabiotic pair of rats developed hypertension, whereas the other rat of the pair ordinarily remained normotensive.

Against the view that hypertension due to the placing of a clip on the renal artery and renoprival hypertension are fundamentally similar is the observation by Kolff and Page (145) that antirenin does not prevent renoprival hypertension.

Grollman (103) considers that a deficiency of renal tissue is the main factor responsible for the blood-pressure elevation in chronic experimental renal hypertension. He has obtained a renal extract which lowers the blood pressure in experimental renal hypertension when given by mouth (104).

Braun-Menéndez (24) proposed the hypothesis that the amount of kidney substance required for body needs is controlled by a substance, renotropin, which is under the influence of the anterior pituitary and thyroid hormones. In the presence of renal damage the kidney may be unable to respond to the stimulus of renotropin and hypertension results.

B. Response to Pressor Stimuli after Bilateral Nephrectomy

Investigations in which blood vessels, taken from rats some days after bilateral nephrectomy, are studied by perfusion techniques, provide interesting results, even if a relation to clinical hypertension is hard to prove. McQueen (165) found the perfused blood vessels of the rat hind quarter removed from renoprival rats were more reactive to norepinephrine than the corresponding blood vessels of controls.

Within several hours, after bilateral nephrectomy, and before there is much deterioration of the rat, the responses to several pressor agencies are exaggerated to such an extent that the preparation is used routinely for the detection or assay of certain pressor agents.

1. *Epinephrine*

Houssay and Dexter (125) found increases in the response to epinephrine in bilaterally nephrectomized dogs.

2. *Norepinephrine*

McCubbin and Page (161) found a moderate increase in the response of bilaterally nephrectomized dogs to norepinephrine.

3. *Renin and Angiotensin*

Tigerstedt and Bergman (278) found an increased response in bilaterally nephrectomized animals to injections of renin. Using bilaterally nephrectomized dogs, Govaerts (99) observed an increase in the response to renin. Pickering (212) noted an increased response in bilaterally nephrectomized rabbits, as did also Page and Helmer (203). McCubbin and Page (161) found a definite increase in the response to renin and to angiotensin in dogs after bilateral nephrectomy, this coming on within 24 hours, and being complete in 48 hours. Houssay and Dexter (125) found an increase in the response to angiotensin in bilaterally nephrectomized dogs. Masson *et al.* (171) noted an increased response to renin in bilaterally nephrectomized rats.

4. *5-Hydoxytryptamine (Serotonin)*

McCubbin and Page (161) found the response to 5-hydroxytryptamine (serotonin) to be greater in most bilaterally nephrectomized dogs than in controls.

5. *Tryptamine*

Using bilaterally nephrectomized dogs, McCubbin and Page (161) usually found some increased reactivity to tryptamine.

6. *Pitressin*

Some increases in the response to Pitressin in bilaterally nephrectomized dogs were also reported by McCubbin and Page (161), but the results were variable.

7. *Barium Chloride*

McCubbin and Page (161) found there was usually a decrease in the response to barium chloride after bilateral nephrectomy.

8. *Comment*

Clinically, gross histological changes in the kidney, especially those affecting the renal cortex, may be associated with elevation of the blood pressure, and loss of the protective function of renal tissue, as well as the liberation of substances which raise the blood pressure directly or indirectly, may be involved in disorders of the renal parenchyma, particularly those which restrict renal circulation.

When renal parenchymal defects and hypertension occur in comparatively young people, at an age when essential hypertension is unusual, it is likely that the blood-pressure increase is due to the renal defect. It is the author's experience, however, that gross abnormalities in renal histology, involving cortical as well as medullary structures, may occur in aged men and rats without elevation of the blood pressure. In a number of such rats the application of a renal artery clip was still capable of raising the blood pressure (254).

Although the number of clinical experiences bearing on the relationship between the amount of renal tissue and the blood pressure are comparatively few, there are instances in which the removal of the relatively healthy kidney has been associated with considerable increase in the level of the blood pressure, especially when the renal artery of the remaining kidney was found to be constricted.

It is clear in the renoprival state that overhydration is likely to be associated with hypertension, and that reduction in the fluid load may restore a normal blood pressure. The renoprival state, or even unilateral nephrectomy, may render an animal more susceptible to a variety of pressor stimuli, but definite proof that bilateral removal of the kidneys without overhydration is sufficient by itself to cause hypertension is difficult to obtain.

Additional evidence on renal hypertension is likely to emerge from the results of renal transplantation in man. Kolff et al. (144) state, "We consider renal hypertension to have two components: renal and renoprival. When the renal component is dominant, the management of the hypertension by means of the regulation of salt and water is difficult. When the renal component is removed by bilateral nephrectomy, the resultant renoprival hypertension responds easily to water and sodium restriction. A successful kidney homotransplant will then convert the renoprival hypertension to normotension. The blood pressure reducing function of the kidney, which was demonstrated many years ago in dogs, is now confirmed in man."

XI. Evidence that in chronic hypertension in man and in experimental animals the baroceptors become set to operate at a higher level

As much has been written about the baroceptors in hypertension, the subject will be treated briefly, for there is little dispute about the facts. The carotid sinus in human hypertension remains active, and mechanical compression of the carotid sinus region reduces the blood pressure as it does in normotension. When chronically hypertensive persons are subjected to procedures which in normotensives would call for a homeostatic adjustment of the circulation, the same appropriate adjustment appears to occur in hypertensives (249: pp. 253 and 342). Measures which should cause blood-pressure falls are antagonized by an increase in the neurogenically maintained stimulation of heart and blood vessels, whereas those tending to raise the blood pressure are associated with decreases in the neurogenically maintained activity. Thus, in hypertension as in health, appropriate homeostatic adjustments are made in response to the upright posture, blood loss, gain or decrease in body fluid, and a variety of other measures referred to elsewhere.

McCubbin *et al.* (160), using electroneurographic techniques, showed experimentally in chronically hypertensive dogs that the threshold of the carotid sinus buffer mechanism had been reset to operate at a higher level, thus maintaining the arterial pressure at the high level rather than operating so as to return it toward normal. Even so, the blood pressure in hypertensive persons is often highly variable.

Lampen (148) and Kezdi (141) blocked the inhibitory action of the baroceptors in man by injection of procaine into each carotid sinus region, and found the blood pressure rose considerably both in normotensives and hypertensives. Volhard (291) and Kezdi (141) suggested that the rigidity of the walls of the carotid sinuses might interfere with this normal inhibitory function, and lead to a rise in the blood pressure, and in conformity with this idea, Asteroth and Kreunziger (9) reported that in old persons, and in hypertensives, rigidity in the wall of the carotid sinus was sometimes demonstrable. Hence, under such conditions, rises of blood pressure should cause less deformation of the carotid sinuses, thereby interfering with the effective action of the baroceptors.

The idea that the common types of hypertension are due primarily to an altered baroceptor function is, however, not sufficiently supported by evidence. It is characteristic, for example, of hypertension due to denervation of the carotid sinuses in experimental animals that the pulse rate is increased, and that the blood pressure may fall even to normal when the animal is quiescent or asleep. These are not the characteristics of substantial essential or renal hypertension. On the other hand, Alam and Smirk (4) found that whereas blood-pressure raising reflexes from the application of cold, or from exercised voluntary muscle in man were associated with slowing of the pulse rate in normals, the slowing was not observed in hypertensives. Apparently, therefore, although it is generally admitted that in hypertension the baroceptors continue to operate, and at a high level, it would appear that the homeostatic mechanisms do not operate in exactly the same way as in health. There is another argument against hypertension in man being sufficiently explained in terms of diminished restraint by the baroceptors. After hexamethonium, which blocks baroceptor activity, the pressor responses to angiotensin, norepinephrine, and *S*-methyl isothiourea are increased to a greater extent in hypertension than in normotension. If baroceptor activity were more active in normotension than in hypertension, hexamethonium should increase the responses of normotensives more than those of hypertensives.

It is to be anticipated, however, that relatively weak baroceptor activity will allow the blood pressure to rise to higher levels, and this might be a contributory factor.

XII. Summary

There is good evidence that such manifestations of hypertensive disease as heart failure, stroke, acceleration of renal impairment, and acceleration of coronary disease may follow blood-pressure elevation, no matter what its cause, but there are variations in the capacity of individuals to withstand high blood pressure: for example, women tolerate hypertension better than men. Probably the susceptibility to various types of disease induced or accelerated by hypertension may be modified: for example, the Japanese have more strokes but less coronary disease than is found in Great Britain, the United States, Australia, or New Zealand.

The casual blood pressure is variable; measured without special precautions, it is made up of the basal blood pressure, which is obtained under standard basal conditions, and the supplemental blood pressure (casual minus basal), which represents the rise of the blood pressure above the basal level, in response to a variety of environmental stimuli. The basal pressure is relatively constant for the individual, in the sense that under ordinary living conditions the basal blood pressure does not usually change much on repetition at such intervals as a week, a month, or even a year; but when repeated after 5 or more years it is usually found to have risen, whereas the supplemental pressures may have risen or fallen.

Patients whose blood pressures are high only intermittently sustain less damage to the cardiovascular system and the kidneys than patients whose blood pressures are persistently at a high level. Our follow-up studies show that such intermittent rises of the supplemental pressure, if unaccompanied by elevation of the basal blood pressure, do not appear to influence prognosis adversely in periods such as 5–8 years. But there is some evidence that high supplemental pressures, when encountered in young people, may be followed after many years by abnormally high basal pressures. Hence, high supplemental pressures may prove to be disadvantageous and cause illness in follow-up periods of 15–30 years' duration.

In some individuals the blood pressure during continued deep sleep falls well below the level of the basal blood pressure; in others it shows little additional fall. Perhaps sleeping pressure may be as good or a better guide to prognosis than the basal pressure, but as patients requiring treatment cannot be left untreated for long periods, an investigation to demonstrate this would be difficult to arrange.

As with most biological phenomena, the blood pressure is not the same in all healthy young persons. In young adults the blood-pressure distribution curve is gaussian, and the differences between those whose casual blood pressures are over or under average are generally presumed to represent the normal range of variation in the activities of those physiological processes which determine the blood pressure level. But it has been shown that persons whose blood pressures lie in the upper end of the distribution curve have, on an average, a lower life expectancy and a higher expectation of a cardiovascular death than those whose blood pressures lie in the lower end of the distribution. Indeed, blood pressures close to the average are not the ideal: the ideal is the under-average. Furthermore, young adults with one or both parents having essential hypertension have, on an average, higher blood pressures than persons of the same age with normotensive parents, and in time the children of hypertensives have a higher incidence of frank hypertension. We might refer to these healthy persons who are predisposed to eventual hypertensive disease as having a hypertensive diathesis.

The author's view for many years (246, 247, 249: p. 320) has been that the intracardiovascular pressures, as such, lead to hypertensive disease and therefore lasting elevations of blood pressure, even when resulting from the operation of physiological processes, become an integral part of the pathogenesis of frank hypertension and hypertensive disease. It is seldom in young adults that the blood pressure in the earliest stages of "essential hypertension" is high enough to cause symptoms, but blood-pressure rises, when perched on top of high physiological levels, may carry the final height of the blood pressure to levels which are associated frequently with hypertensive disease.

Pickering's hypothesis (212–214), though expressed differently, includes the fundamental part of the hypothesis I put forward in 1946, 1949, and 1957, which is stated above. There are other features held in common but also some important differences: for example, I do not exclude the possibility of genetic factors being concerned in the rise of blood pressure with age.

The over-average casual blood pressures in first-degree relatives, mostly children, of substantial hypertensives have been dissected further. The average basal and the average supplemental blood pressures are both greater in the under 40 first-degree relatives of hypertensives than in controls of a similarly young age group, but in the individuals composing the groups there is no close relationship between the heights of the basal and supplemental pressures.

It has been shown that in a group of untreated persons, judged to be hypertensive on the basis of their casual blood pressures, the rise of blood pressure with age over periods of 5–15 years is more usually due to rise in the basal blood pressure; the supplemental pressure may rise or fall.

In a few large families, the number of sibs with substantial hypertension, the occurrence of hypertension in three generations, and the absence of appreciable blood-pressure elevation in young members of the family make it likely that these are families in which the rise with age is strongly influenced genetically. While it is possible to argue that the rise with age in such families is due to a common environment, it is not unusual to find that during the period when the blood pressure must have risen, the environments of the sibs have differed considerably. However, the present author differs from Platt in believing that the underlying components which raise the blood pressure in essential hypertension vary from case to case.

A multifactorial hypothesis seems to offer the best explanation for established essential hypertension, in the sense that many factors are concerned in the rise of blood pressure, leading thereby to the occurrence of hypertensive disease. It seems likely that this will be found to be true even if further investigation reveals that a single factor occurs more frequently or plays a larger part than other factors.

In the colony of rats which we have bred to develop a spontaneous genetic hypertension at an early age, we find that a variety of blood-pressure raising stimuli such as salt administration or subtotal nephrectomy carry the blood pressure to heights which are associated much more frequently with hypertensive disease than they are in the corresponding experiments on normotensive control rats. Here we see the effect of a combination of a genetic factor with an external stimulus. Rats which develop systolic blood pressures of 160 mm Hg or more without being subject to experiments often develop frank hypertensive disease spontaneously, such as periarteritis nodosa, advanced renal damage, and occasionally medial arteriolar necrosis. Evidently, in this experimental model, inherited hypertension may be sufficiently high by itself to cause hypertensive disease, but the severity and incidence of such disease is increased by environmental conditions tending to raise the blood pressure further.

It is now apparent that certain well-defined types of human hypertension may occur, as, for example, renal hypertension due to narrowing of a renal artery; phaeochromocytoma due to a catecholamine-secreting tumor, usually located in the adrenal medulla; excessive secretion of the adrenal cortex in Cushing's disease; aldosterone-secreting tumors of the adrenal cortex; and hypertension may occur which persists for a time after denervation of one or both carotid sinuses. Even in the aggregate, such well-defined types of hypertension are a minority. Dickinson (54) has given a full and valuable account of evidence which supports his belief that narrowing of arteries supplying the brain may be responsible for elevation of the blood pressure. Hypertension may occur in such renal diseases as nephritis, pyelonephritis, radiation nephritis, and so on. It is often assumed, but without definite proof, that this renal hypertension is fundamentally of the same kind as that which in animals results from interference with the renal circulation by placing a clip on a renal artery.

Although there is no doubt that sufficient interference with the renal circulation can usually be relied upon to induce hypertension, the manner in which it does so remains uncertain. But it is very highly probable that it is due to the action of some substances, not necessarily directly pressor, leaving the abnormal kidney and entering the general circulation.

It is difficult to believe that substances with the high potency of renin and angiotensin, which, under certain circumstances, are discharged from the kidney when its circulation is impaired, are not participating in the establishment of renal hypertension. However, the biochemistry following a renal artery clip is extraordinarily complicated, and the possibility cannot be excluded that renin and angiotensin are more concerned with the regulation of electrolyte and water metabolism than with the blood pressure. Such a supposition involves the assumption that another substance or substances—so far undetected—cause the renal hypertension, or that it is due to change in the water and electrolytes of the body.

Some workers think that essential hypertension and renal hypertension are basically similar in origin. It is possible that a factor or factors discharged from the kidney after a renal artery is clipped may also be discharged from the kidneys by some alternative mechanism, and be a factor in the causation of essential hypertension, even at a stage before there are structural changes in the kidneys. It has now been shown conclusively that extra renin may be released from the kidneys under a variety of experimental conditions unassociated with elevation of the blood pressure, and until we know the cause of renal artery clip hypertension, there remains the possibility that conditions other than impaired renal circulation, and even unassociated with structural change, may lead to a renal type of hypertension, fundamentally similar to clipped renal artery hypertension.

In the early stages of essential hypertension, there may be no detectable structural defects in the kidney. This is an argument, but not a conclusive one, against there being a renal component in the hypertension in its early stages.

There is, however, very good evidence that high blood pressure of sufficient degree and duration is often self-perpetuating, even self-augmenting. One important mechanism by which this occurs is by hypertensive damage to previously normal kidneys. If this is accepted as a general principle, it may be anticipated that a variety of causes for blood-pressure elevation may go on to a stage when renal mechanisms and possibly other secondary mechanisms play their part in maintaining blood-pressure elevations which may have started in a variety of ways. Not only so, but the rise of blood pressure by a variety of mechanisms which are associated with aging is unlikely to be prevented from so doing by the presence of a degree of previous blood-pressure elevation from some disorder such as nephritis or pyelonephritis. Hence there are several reasons why cases of chronic hypertension from a number of different starting causes come to resemble each other, and often enough are almost indistinguishable and react to drugs in a similar manner.

For some of the features of human essential hypertension, we have an experimental model in our colony of rats with spontaneous genetic hypertension. These rats have their hypertension at least as early as the third week of life, but up to the third month of life we have been unable to detect any difference from normotensive rats in the renal structure by light microscopy, and no difference in the injected renal blood vessels; therefore while there might be some esoteric renal mechanism responsible for the high blood pressure, there is so far no evidence of it. Here, therefore, is an example of a genetic, apparently nonrenal hypertension, resembling in this respect human essential hypertension in its early stages.

The author's preference is for the view that in the early stages of essential hypertension, it is usual for the blood-pressure rise to be determined solely by the over-activity of physiological processes, and there is no reason to believe there is any renal abnormality, or in fact any qualitative defect. Many years ago Alam and Smirk (4) expressed the view that a high degree of reactivity of the blood pressure to sensory stimuli does not, by itself, lead to an increase in the level of the blood pressure at rest. It is possible, however, that a high degree of reactivity of the blood pressure to blood-pressure raising reflexes may express itself in daily life by abnormally strong and frequent blood-pressure variations, and it is even possible that this may lead sometimes to the development of permanent hypertension. In most cases of essential hypertension the natural relationship between pulse rate and blood pressure is reversed, rise of blood pressure being accompanied by increased pulse rate.

Recently Hoobler (124) in his admirable review on the mechanism of essential hypertension, summarized recent evidence. He concluded, quoting Brod and others, that the first identifiable physiological defect in the labile hypertensive person is the failure to accommodate peripheral resistance so as to maintain normal blood pressure under environmental stress.

There is ample evidence that the children of patients with essential hypertension, even when under age 30, tend to have casual blood pressures which, as a group, are above the average for unselected children of similar ages. My preliminary studies indicate that as an average, the basal blood pressure is only a little higher in the children of hypertensives under age 30 than in unselected persons of the same age group. Although the supplemental pressure is highly variable, the average level appears to be raised also, and the rise above the average in the casual pressures of the children of hypertensives appears to be influenced more by the supplemental than by the basal blood pressure.

There may be difficulties in distinguishing between factors which are genetic and factors which are familial but not genetic. One cannot, for example, rule out the possibility that the supplemental pressure may be influenced by the children of known hypertensives being less relaxed at the time of blood-pressure measurement than children who have no knowledge of parental hypertension.

For this reason there might be some difficulty also in obtaining a fully basal state.

It is clear, however, that although some of this early rise of blood pressure above the average for their age group is likely to affect the level of their blood pressures in later life, the actual level attained by the children of hypertensives before they reach age 30 is rarely high enough to be of concern, were there not the expectation of a further rise of blood pressure with age.

With advancing age, a wide variety of changes take place which are likely to be associated with degrees of elevation of the blood pressure; thus, fibrotic changes may occur in the kidney, hardening occurs in the major blood vessels of the arterial reservoir. Increase in cardiovascular reactivity to some pressor stimuli occurs as age advances, and increase in vascular responsiveness to a variety of vasoconstrictor agents is associated with several types of hypertension and may lead to further increase of the blood pressure. An over-average level of the blood pressure both accelerates such changes and becomes associated with cardiovascular hypertrophy. Obesity which tends to increase in the middle and later years of life is associated with a modest blood-pressure increase not accounted for by errors in cuff blood pressures due to arm dimensions (6).

Atherosclerosis with narrowing of a renal artery may occur in previously normotensive individuals, and such cases are examples of renal hypertension and are to be distinguished from essential hypertension. In other instances the atherosclerosis may have been accelerated by the hypertension, and the narrowing of one or both renal arteries, or of a number of small arteries, is, in some measure at least, a part of the evolution of essential hypertension, and constitutes one way in which a renal component may be added on to a disorder which probably is not renal at its outset.

The fact, mentioned earlier, that hypertension in some countries, for example, Japan, is very common, whereas atherosclerosis in Japan is much less frequent than in most Western countries, favors the view that atherosclerosis, for example, in a renal vessel, is not a main cause for hypertension in the Japanese.

It is not suggested that all such factors influence the blood pressures of all patients whose blood pressures rise with age to frankly hypertensive levels. Many whose blood pressures rise with age attain levels in the upper range of pressures usual at their age. Such pressures are disadvantageous, in that they increase the liability to cardiovascular disorders, though to a smaller degree than in those who are frankly hypertensive and have important rises in the basal blood pressure. So it seems to the author that established essential hypertension is a multifactorial disorder in which many physiological and pathological processes combine to elevate the blood pressure, and cause, or predispose to, hypertensive disease. Some factors elevating the blood pressure are already operating in persons under the age of 30, but not usually raising the blood pressure—basal or supplemental—

to a great degree. Many of the factors causing the blood pressure to rise are associated with advancing age, but in some persons a rise of blood pressure with age does not occur or is of unimportant magnitude; in others the rise is great, and the main determinant of an eventually fatal hypertension. The unity of the clinical picture in essential hypertension is due to the fact that virtually all the clinical manifestations are due to the high blood pressure as such, and because the various body changes—some physiological, others pathological—which, in combination, cause hypertension, only lead to hypertensive disease because they raise the blood pressure.

Future studies will surely reveal that there are individuals with definable pathological changes which will make it possible to describe subgroups or entirely remove some classes of patient from the category of essential hypertension. On the other hand, it should be recognized that a high starting level of the blood pressure and rises of blood pressure with advancing age are likely to influence the occurrence of hypertensive disease in persons who have some easily recognized, if not easily explained cause, such as nephritis or Cushing's disease.

If established essential hypertension is a multifactorial disorder, it is likely that no drug or procedure will be found which neutralizes at once all the various underlying factors concerned in high blood pressure from these causes. But as blood-pressure elevation represents the first emergence of the disorder, essential hypertension as a recognizable entity, and is the cause of hypertensive disease in secondary hypertension, it follows that reduction of the blood pressure represents the logical means by which deterioration is avoided or postponed.

References

1. Actuarial Society of America and the Association of Life Insurance Medical Directors, "Blood Pressure," Report of the Joint Committee on Mortality, 1925.
2. Actuarial Society of America and the Association of Life Insurance Medical Directors, Blood Pressure Study, 1939.
3. Actuarial Society of America and the Association of Life Insurance Medical Directors, Supplement to Blood Pressure Study, 1941.
4. Alam, G. M., and Smirk, F. H., *Clin. Sci.* 3, 259 (1938).
5. Alam, G. M., and Smirk, F. H., *Brit. Heart J.* 5, 152 (1943).
6. Alexander, J. K., Amad, K. H., and Cole, V. W., *Am. J. Med.* 32, 512 (1962).
7. Alexander, N., Tibbs, W. J., and Drury, D. R., *Proc. Soc. Exptl. Biol. Med.* 95, 356 (1957).
8. Armstrong, H. G., and Rafferty, J. A., *Am. Heart J.* 39, 484 (1950).
9. Asteroth, H., and Kreunziger, H., *Z. Kreislaufforsch.* 40, 11 (1951).
10. Ayman, D., and Goldshine, A. D., *New Engl. J. Med.* 219, 650 (1938).
11. Ayman, D., and Goldshine, A. D., *A.M.A. Arch. Internal Med.* 63, 899 (1939).
12. Barany, F. R., and James, P., *Clin. Sci.* 18, 543 (1959).
13. Barath, E., *A.M.A. Arch. Internal Med.* 42, 297 (1928).
14. Barnett, A. J., *Brit. J. Ophthalmol.* 36, 593 (1952).

15. Barnett, A. J., and Fraser, J. R. E., *Alfred Hosp. Clin. Rept.* (*Melbourne*) **4**, 35 (1954).
16. Bartter, F. C., Liddle, G. W., Duncan, L. E., Jr., Barber, J. K., and Delea, C., *J. Clin. Invest.* **35**, 1306 (1956).
17. Bauer, J., and Neuburger, F., *Z. Klin. Med.* **120**, 628 (1932).
18. Bechgaard, P., and Hammarström, S., *Acta Chir. Scand. Suppl.* 155 (1950).
19. Beyerholm, O., *Acta Med. Scand.* **67**, 323 (1927).
20. Blacket, R. B., and Sellers, A. L., *Clin. Sci.* **10**, 177 (1951).
21. Blalock, A., and Levy, S. E., *Ann. Surg.* **106**, 826 (1937).
22. Blaquier, P. C., Bohr, D. F., Taquini, A. C., Jr., and Hoobler, S. W., *Proc. Soc. Exptl. Biol. Med.* **108**, 711 (1961).
23. Bouckaert, J. J., Elaut, L., and Heymans, C., *J. Physiol.* (*London*) **89**, 3P (1937).
24. Braun-Menéndez, E., *Acta Physiol. Latinoam.* **2**, 1 (1952).
25. Braun-Menéndez, E., and Paladini, A. C., *Circulation* **17**, 668 (1958).
26. Braun-Menéndez, E., and von Euler, U. S., *Nature* **160**, 905 (1947).
27. Briggs, J. F., and Oerting, H., *Minn. Med.* **16**, 481 (1933).
28. Briggs, J. F., and Oerting, H., *Minn. Med.* **20**, 382 (1937).
29. Brown, G. M., and Maegraith, G. G., *J. Physiol.* (*London*) **99**, 304 (1941).
30. Brown, J. J., Chapuis, G., and Robertson, J. I. S., *Lancet* I, 1356 (1963).
31. Brown, J. J., Davies, D. L., Lever, A. F., and Robertson, J. I. S., *Can. Med. Assoc. J.* **90**, 201 (1964).
32. Brown, J. J., Davies, D. L., Lever, A. F., and Robertson, J. I. S., *Brit. Med. J.* II, 144 (1965).
33. Brown, J. J., Davies, D. L., Lever, A. F., Robertson, J. I. S., and Tree, M., *Biochem. J.* **93**, 594 (1964).
34. Buckley, J. P., and Bickerton, R. K., *Federation Proc.* **20**, 112 (1961).
35. Burch, G. E., Cohn, A. E., and Neumann, C., *J. Clin. Invest.* **21**, 655 (1942).
36. Burnett, C. F., Jr., and Evans, J. A., *New Engl. J. Med.* **253**, 395 (1955).
37. Byrom, F. B., and Dodson, L. F., *Clin. Sci.* **8**, 1 (1949).
38. Campbell, A., and Robertson, E., *Brit. Med. J.* II, 804 (1950).
39. Campbell, A. J. M., Graham, J. G. and Maxwell, R. D. H., *Brit. Med. J.* I, 251 (1952).
40. Chesley, L. C., and Chesley, E. R., *Surg., Gynecol. Obstet.* **69**, 436 (1939).
41. Chimoskey, J. E., Blaquier, P. C., Taquini, A. C., Jr., and Bohr, D. F., *Am. J. Physiol.* **202**, 690 (1962).
42. Conn, J. W., *J. Lab. Clin. Med.* **45**, 3 (1955).
43. Conn, J. W., Knopf, R. F., and Nesbit, R. M., *Am. J. Surg.* **107**, 159 (1964).
44. Contratto, A. W., and Rogers, M. B., *New Engl. J. Med.* **239**, 531 (1948).
45. Conway, J., *J. Physiol.* (*London*) **127**, 69 (1955).
46. Corry, D. C., *Brit. Med. J.* I, 433 (1946).
47. Dahl, L. K., Heine, M., and Tassinari, L., *Circulation* **30**, Suppl. 2, 11 (1964).
48. Daly, J. J., and Duff, R. S., *Clin. Sci.* **19**, 457 (1960).
49. Daniel, P. M., Prichard, M. M. L., and Ward-McQuaid, J. N., *Quart. J. Exptl. Physiol.* **39**, 101 (1954).
50. Dean, A. L., and Abels, J. C., *J. Urol.* **52**, 497 (1944).
51. de Bono, E., Lee, G. de J., Mottram, F. R., Pickering, G. W., Brown, J. J., Keen, H., Peart, W. S., and Sanderson, P. H., *Clin. Sci.* **25**, 123 (1963).
52. Deicke, E., and Hülse, W., *Verhandl. Deut. Ges. Inn. Med.* **36**, 277 (1924).
53. Deodhar, S. D., Haas, E., and Goldblatt, H., *Can. Med. Assoc. J.* **90**, 236 (1964).
54. Dickinson, C. J., "Neurogenic Hypertension." Blackwell, Oxford, 1965.
55. Dickinson, C. J., and Lawrence, J. R., *Lancet* I, 1354 (1963).
56. Dieckmann, W. J., and Michel, H. L., *A.M.A. Arch. Internal Med.* **55**, 420 (1935).

57. Diehl, H. S., and Hesdorffer, M. B., *A.M.A. Arch. Internal Med.* **52**, 948 (1933).
58. Distler, A., Liebau, H., and Wolff, H. P., *Nature* **207**, 764 (1965).
59. Douglas, R. M., *Med. J. Australia* **2**, 525 (1964).
60. Doyle, A. E., *Am. Heart J.* **45**, 363 (1953).
61. Doyle, A. E., and Black, H., *Circulation* **12**, 974 (1955).
62. Doyle, A. E., and Fraser, J. R. E., *Circulation Res.* **9**, 755 (1961).
63. Doyle, A. E., Fraser, J. R. E., and Marshall, R. J., *Clin. Sci.* **18**, 441 (1959).
64. Doyle, A. E., and Smirk, F. H., *Circulation* **12**, 543 (1955).
65. Duff, R. S., *Brit. Heart J.* **19**, 45 (1957).
66. Dustan, H. P., Corcoran, A. C., Schneckloth, R., and Page, I. H., *Circulation* **12**, 698 (1955).
67. Elliot, A. H., and Nuzum, F. R., *Am. J. Med. Sci.* **189**, 215 (1935).
68. Eppinger, H., and Kisch, F., cited by Raab, W., *Ergeb. Inn. Med. Kinderheilk.* **46**, 452 (1934).
69. Eppinger, H., and Schwarz, H., cited by Raab, W., *Ergeb. Inn. Med. Kinderheilk.* **46**, 452 (1934).
70. Evelyn, K. A., Alexander, F., and Cooper, S. R., *J. Am. Med. Assoc.* **140**, 592 (1949).
71. Farris, E. J., Yeakel, E. H., and Medoff, H. S., *Am. J. Physiol.* **144**, 331 (1945).
72. Fasciolo, J. C., de Vito, E., Romero, J. C., and Cucchi, J. N., *Can. Med. Assoc. J.* **90**, 206 (1964).
73. Fasciolo, J. C., Houssay, B. A., and Taquini, A. C., *J. Physiol. (London)* **94**, 281 (1938).
74. Fastier, F. N., and Smirk, F. H., *J. Pharmacol. Exptl. Therap.* **89**, 256 (1947).
75. Feldberg, W., and Lewis, G. P., *J. Physiol. (London)* **171**, 98 (1964).
76. Feldt, R. H., and Wenstrand, D. E. W., *A.M.A. Arch. Internal Med.* **67**, 1157 (1941).
77. Feldt, R. H., and Wenstrand, D. E. W., *Am. Heart J.* **23**, 766 (1942).
78. Field, L. W., de Graaf, W., and Wallis, A. T., *J. Appl. Physiol.* **12**, 142 (1958).
79. Field, L. W., and Laverty, R., *J. Physiol. (London)* **143**, 213 (1958).
80. Fleming, H. A., *J. Pathol. Bacteriol.* **65**, 441 (1953).
81. Floyer, M. A., *Clin. Sci.* **10**, 405 (1951).
82. Floyer, M. A., *Clin. Sci.* **14**, 163 (1955).
83. Ford, R. V., and Spurr, C. L., *Am. Practitioner Dig. Treat.* **5**, 251 (1954).
84. Forman, S., May, L. G., Bennett, A., Kobayashi, M., and Gregory, R., *Proc. Soc. Exptl. Biol. Med.* **83**, 847 (1953).
85. Freis, E. D., *Med. Ann. District Columbia* **23**, 363 (1954).
86. Freis, E. D., Stanton, J. R., Culbertson, J. W., Kitter, J., Halperin, M. H., Burnett, C. H., and Wilkins, R. W., *J. Clin. Invest.* **28**, 353 (1949).
87. Gardner, D. L., *Brit. J. Exptl. Pathol.* **41**, 60 (1960).
88. Gardner, D. L., *Brit. J. Exptl. Pathol.* **43**, 88 (1962).
89. Gardner, D. L., and Brooks, P. W., *Brit. J. Exptl. Pathol.* **44**, 31 (1963).
90. Gaunt, R., Antonchak, N., Miller, G. J., and Renzi, A. A., *Am. J. Physiol.* **182**, 63 (1955).
91. Gearing, F. R., Clark, E. G., Perera, G. A., and Schweitzer, M. D., *Am. J. Public Health* **52**, 2058 (1962).
92. Genest, J., Boucher, R., de Champlain, J., Veyrat, R., Chretien, M., Biron, P., Tremblay, G., Roy, P., and Cartier, P., *Can. Med. Assoc. J.* **90**, 263 (1964).
93. Genest, J., Koiw, E., Nowaczynski, W., and Sandor, T., *Acta Endocrinol. Suppl.* 51, p. 173 (1960).
94. Glenn, F., Child, C. G., and Heuer, G. J., *Ann. Surg.* **107**, 618 (1938).
95. Goldblatt, H., Lynch, J., Hanzal, R. F., and Summerville, W. W., *J. Exptl. Med.* **59**, 347 (1934).

96. Goldenberg, M., Pines, K. L., Baldwin, E. de F., Greene, D. G., and Roh, C. E., *Am. J. Med.* **5**, 792 (1948).
97. Goormaghtigh, N., *Proc. Soc. Exptl. Biol. Med.* **42**, 688 (1939).
98. Gordon, W., and Levitt, G., *J. Clin. Invest.* **14**, 367 (1935).
99. Govaerts, P., *Ciba Found. Symp. Hypertension Humeral Neurogenic Factors*, p. 136, London, (1954).
100. Gowenlock, A. H., and Wrong, O., *Quart. J. Med.* **31**, 323 (1962).
101. Greisman, S. E., *J. Clin. Invest* **33**. 975 (1954).
102. Grimson, K. S., *J. Physiol. (London)* **95**, 45P (1939).
103. Grollman, A., *Am. J. Physiol.* **142**, 666 (1944).
104. Grollman, A., *Perspectives Biol. Med.* **2**, 208 (1959).
105. Grollman, A., Muirhead, E. E., and Vanatta, J., *Am. J. Physiol.* **157**, 21 (1949).
106. Grollman, A., and Rule, C., *Am. J. Physiol.* **138**, 587 (1943).
107. Gross, F., Brunner, H., and Ziegler, M., *Recent Progr. Hormone Res.* **21**, 119 (1965).
108. Gross, F., Schaechtelin, G., Brunner, H., and Peters, G., *Can. Med. Assoc. J.* **90**, 258 (1964).
109. Hardgrove, M., Roth, G. M., and Brown, G. E., *Ann. Internal Med.* **12**, 482 (1938).
110. Harington, M., and Rosenheim, M. L., *Lancet* **I**, 7 (1954).
111. Hartman, F. W., Bolliger, A., and Doub, H. P., *J. Am. Med. Assoc.* **89**, 1936 (1927).
112. Hartwich, A., *Z. Ges. Exptl. Med.* **69**, 462 (1930).
113. Helmer, O. M., *Am. J. Physiol.* **188**, 571 (1957).
114. Helmer, O. M., *Med. Clin. N. Am.* **45**, 309 (1961).
115. Helmer, O. M., *Can. Med. Assoc. J.* **90**, 221 (1964).
116. Helmer, O. M., Kohlstaedt, K. G., and Page, I. H., *Federation Proc.* **1**, 114 (1942).
117. Hess, F. O., *Verhandl. Deut. Ges. Inn. Med.* **36**, 262 (1924).
118. Hetényi, S., and Sümegi, S., *Klin. Wochschr.* **4**, 2298 (1925).
119. Hines, E. A., Jr., *Am. Heart J.* **19**, 408 (1940).
120. Hines, E. A., Jr., *J. Am. Med. Assoc.* **115**, 271 (1940).
121. Hines, E. A., Jr., and Brown, G. E., *Ann. Internal Med.* **7**, 209 (1933).
122. Hines, E. A., Jr., and Roth, G. M., *Proc. Staff Meetings Mayo Clinic* **13**, 524 (1938).
123. Hodge, J. V., McQueen, E. G., and Smirk, F. H., *Brit. Med. J.* **I**, 1 (1960).
124. Hoobler, S. W., *in* "Hypertension: Second Hahnemann Symposium on Hypertensive Disease" (A. N. Brest and J. H. Moyer, eds.), p. 59. Lea & Febiger, Philadelphia, Pennsylvania, 1961.
125. Houssay, B. A., and Dexter, L., *Ann. Internal Med.* **17**, 451 (1942).
126. Houssay, B. A., and Fasciolo, J. C., *Compt. Rend. Soc. Biol.* **127**, 147 (1938).
127. Huidobro, F., and Braun-Menéndez, E., *Am. J. Physiol.* **137**, 47 (1942).
128. Hunter, A., *J. Inst. Actuaries* **70**, 60 (1939).
129. *Trans. Intern. Congr. Life Assurace Med. London, 1935.*
130. Jackson, W. B., *Am. Heart J.* **56**, 222 (1958).
131. Jansen, W. H., *Deut. Arch. Klin. Med.* **147**, 339 (1925).
132. Johnson, C. A., and Wakerlin, G. E., *Proc. Soc. Exptl. Biol. Med.* **44**, 277 (1940).
133. Johnson, P. C., *Circulation Res.* **15**, I-2 (1964).
134. Judson, W. E., Culbertson, J. W., Tinsley, C. M., Litter, J., and Wilkins, R. W., *J. Clin. Invest.* **29**, 1405 (1950).
135. Judson, W. E., Epstein, F. H., and Wilkins, R. W., *J. Clin. Invest.* **29**, 1414 (1950).
136. Kapp, F., Friedland, C. K., and Landis, E. M., *Am. J. Physiol.* **131**, 710 (1941).
137. Katz, L. N., and Friedberg, L., *Am. J. Physiol.* **127**, 29 (1939).
138. Katz, L. N., Mendlowitz, M., and Friedman, M., *Proc. Soc. Exptl. Biol. Med.* **37**, 722 (1938).

139. Kelley, R. T., Freis, E. D., and Higgins, T. F., *Circulation* 7, 169 (1953).
140. Kempner, W., *Ann. Internal Med.* 31, 821 (1949).
141. Kezdi, P., *A.M.A. Arch. Internal Med.* 91, 26 (1953).
142. Kilpatrick, J. A., *Brit. Heart J.* 10, 48 (1948).
143. Kimura, N., *in* "World Trends in Cardiology" (A. B. Keys and P. D. White, eds.), pp. 22–33. Harper (Hoeber), New York, 1956.
144. Kolff, W. J., Nakamoto, S., Poutasse, E. F., Straffon, R. A., and Figueroa, J. E., *Circulation* 30, Suppl. 2, 23 (1964).
145. Kolff, W. J. and Page, I. H., *Am. J. Physiol.* 181, 575 (1955).
146. Kumar, D., Feltham, L. A. W., and Gornall, A. G., *Lancet* I, 541 (1959).
147. Kylin, E., *Klin. Wochschr.* 3, 1175 (1924).
148. Lampen, H., *Verhandl. Deut. Ges. Kreislaufforsch.* 15, 88 (1949).
149. Laragh, J. H., Angers, M., Kelly, W. G., and Lieberman, S., *J. Am. Med. Assoc.* 174, 234 (1960).
150. Laverty, R., *Proc. Univ. Otago Med. School* 39, 23 (1961).
151. Laverty, R., *J. Pharm. Pharmacol.* 15, 63 (1963).
152. Laverty, R., and Smirk, F. H., *Circulation Res.* 9, 455 (1961).
153. Ledingham, J. M., *Clin. Sci.* 10, 423 (1951).
154. Ledingham, J. M., and Cohen, R. D., *Can. Med. Assoc. J.* 90, 292 (1964).
155. Lee, R. E., and Holze, E. A., *J. Clin. Invest.* 30, 539 (1951).
156. Lever, A. F., Robertson, J. I. S., and Tree, M., *Biochem. J.* 91, 346 (1964).
157. Lewis, G. P., and Reit, E., *J. Physiol. (London)* 179, 538 (1965).
158. Ludwig, W., *Arch. Exptl. Pathol. Pharmkol.* 160, 302 (1931).
159. Luxton, R. W., *Quart. J. Med.* 22, 215 (1953).
160. McCubbin, J. W., Green, J. H., and Page, I. H., *Circulation Res.* 4, 205 (1956).
161. McCubbin, J. W., and Page, I. H., *Circulation Res.* 2, 35 (1954).
162. McGregor, D. D., *J. Physiol. (London)* 177, 21 (1965).
163. McGregor, D. D., and Smirk, F. H., unpublished work (1966).
164. McMichael, J., *Brit. Med. J.* I, 933 (1952).
165. McQueen, E. G., *Clin. Sci.* 15, 523 (1956).
166. McQueen, E. G., *Proc. Univ. Otago Med. School* 35, 32 (1957).
167. McQueen, E. G., Ph.D. Thesis, University of Otago, Dunedin, New Zealand (1960).
168. McQueen, E. G., *Clin. Sci.* 21, 133 (1961).
169. McQueen, E. G., and Hodge, J. V., *Quart. J. Med.* 30, 213 (1961).
170. McQueen, E. G., and Trewin, E., *Med. J. Australia* 2, 425 (1952).
171. Masson, G. M. C., Del Greco, F., Corcoran, A. C., and Page, I. H., *Am. J. Physiol.* 180, 337 (1955).
172. Masson, G. M. C., Hazard, J. B., Corcoran, A. C., and Page, I. H., *A.M.A. Arch. Pathol.* 49, 641 (1950).
173. Masson, G. M. C., Page, I. H., and Corcoran, A. C., *Proc. Soc. Exptl. Biol. Med.* 73, 434 (1950).
174. Master, A. M., Garfield, C. I., and Walters, M. B., "Normal Blood Pressure and Hypertension." Lea & Febiger, Philadelphia, Pennsylvania, 1952.
175. Medoff, H. S., and Bongiovanni, A. M., *Am. J. Physiol.* 143, 300 (1945).
176. Mendlowitz, M., Gitlow, S. E., and Naftchi, N. N., *J. Appl. Physiol.* 13, 252 (1958).
177. Mendlowitz, M., and Naftchi, N. N., *Circulation* 16, 915 (1957).
178. Mendlowitz, M., Naftchi, N. N., Wolf, R. L., and Gitlow, S. E., *Circulation* 22, 788 (1960).
179. Mendlowitz, M., Naftchi, N. N., Wolf, R. L., and Gitlow, S. E., *in* "Hypertension: Second Hahnemann Symposium on Hypertensive Disease" (A. N. Brest and J. H. Moyer, eds.), p. 53. Lea & Febiger, Philadelphia, Pennsylvania, 1961.

180. Merrill, J. P., Giordano, C., and Heetderks, D. R., *Am. J. Med.* **31**, 931 (1961).
181. Miasnikov, A. L., *Am. J. Cardiol.* **5**, 692 (1960).
182. Miller, J. H., and Bruger, M., *Am. Heart J.* **18**, 329 (1939).
183. Morris, R. E., Jr., Robinson, P. R., and Scheele, G. A., *Can. Med. Assoc. J.* **90**, 272 (1964).
184. Morrison, B., *Brit. Med. J.* I, 1291 (1953).
185. Moulton, R., Spencer, A. G., and Willoughby, D. A., *Brit. Heart J.* **20**, 224 (1958).
186. Moyer, J. H., Miller, S. I., and Ford, R. V., *J. Am. Med. Assoc.* **152**, 1121 (1953).
187. Mulrow, P. J., *Can. Med. Assoc. J.* **90**, 277 (1964).
188. Mulrow, P. J., and Ganong, W. F., *Yale J. Biol. Med.* **33**, 386 (1961).
189. Murphy, E. A., *Lancet* II, 899 (1951).
190. Nelson, R. A., May, L. G., Bennett, A., Kobayashi, M., and Gregory, R., *Am. Heart J.* **50**, 172 (1955).
191. Neumann, C., Cohn, A. E., and Burch, G. E., *J. Clin. Invest.* **21**, 651 (1942).
192. Nolla-Panades, J., *Circulation Res.* **12**, 3 (1963).
193. Nolla-Panades, J., unpublished work (1964).
194. Nolla-Panades, J., and Simpson, F. O., *Clin. Sci.* **27**, 393 (1964).
195. Norris, A. H., Shock, N. W., and Yiengst, M. J., *Circulation* **8**, 521 (1953).
196. Nye, E. R., *Brit. Heart J.* **26**, 261 (1964).
197. Ogden, E., *Bull. N. Y. Acad. Med.* [2] **23**, 643 (1947).
198. Ogden, E., Brown, L. T., and Page, E. W., *Am. J. Physiol.* **129**, 560 (1940).
199. Okamoto, K., and Aoki, K., *Japan. Circulation* [*English Ed.*] *J.* **27**, 282 (1963).
200. Olsen, N. S., Schroeder, H. A., and Menhard, E. M., *Proc. Soc. Exptl. Biol. Med.* **74**, 581 (1950).
201. Page, I. H., *J. Am. Med. Assoc.* **113**, 2046 (1939).
202. Page, I. H., *Am. J. Physiol.* **134**, 789 (1941).
203. Page, I. H., and Helmer, O. M., *J. Exptl. Med.* **71**, 495 (1940).
204. Page, I. H., and Taylor, R. D., *Am. J. Physiol.* **156**, 412 (1949).
205. Paladini, A. C., and Scornik, O. A., *Proc. Soc. Endocrinol., Cambridge, 1962*, p. 265.
206. Palmer, A. J., *Med. J. Australia* **2**, 428 (1952).
207. Peart, W. S., *Brit. Med. J.* II, 1353 (1959).
208. Peterson, L. H., *Proc. Joint W.H.O.-Czech. Cardiol. Soc. Symp., Prague, 1960*, p. 295. State Medical Publishing House, Prague, 1961.
209. Pfeiffer, J. B., and Wolff, H. G., *J. Clin. Invest.* **29**, 1227 (1950).
210. Phelan, E. L., *Am. Heart J.* **71**, 50 (1966).
211. Phelan, E. L., Eryetishir, I., and Smirk, F. H., *Circulation Res.* **10**, 817 (1962).
212. Pickering, G. W., *Clin. Sci.* **5**, 229 (1945).
213. Pickering, G. W., *Proc. Joint W.H.O.-Czech. Cardiol. Soc. Symp., Prague, 1960*, p. 43. State Medical Publishing House, Prague, 1961.
214. Pickering, G. W., *Brit. Med. J.* II, 959 and 1021 (1965).
215. Pickering, G. W., and Kissin, M., *Clin. Sci.* **2**, 201 (1936).
216. Platt, R., *Quart J. Med.* [*N.S.*] **16**, 111 (1947).
217. Platt, R., *Quart. J. Med.* [*N.S.*] **23**, 441 (1954).
218. Platt, R., and Stanbury, S. W., *Lancet* I, 651 (1950).
219. Raab, W., *Ann. Internal Med.* **14**, 1981 (1941).
220. Raab, W., "Hormonal and Neurogenic Cardiovascular Disorders." Williams & Wilkins, Baltimore, Maryland, 1953.
221. Raab, W., and Redlich, F. K., *Z. Klin. Med.* **129**, 455 (1936).
222. Rahier, J. P., *Acta Cardiol.* **16**, 425 (1961).
223. Rau, G. C., *Science* **111**, 229 (1950).

224. Regoli, D., Hess, R., Brunner, H., Peters, G., and Gross, F., *Arch. Intern. Pharmacodyn.* **140**, 416 (1962).
225. Restall, P. A., and Smirk, F. H., *New Zealand Med. J.* **49**, 206 (1950).
226. Richardson, D. W., Honour, A. J., Fenton, G. W., Stott, F. H., and Pickering, G. W., *Clin. Sci.* **26**, 445 (1964).
227. Rinsler, M. G., and Rigby, B., *Brit. Med. J.* **II**, 966 (1957).
228. Robinson, S. C., *New Engl. J. Med.* **223**, 407 (1940).
229. Rønnov-Jessen, V., and Bech, V., *Ugeskrift Laeger* **115**, 589 (1953).
230. Rosas, R. B., *Circulation Res.* **12**, 573 (1963).
231. Rosas, R. B., and Croxatto, H., *Circulation Res.* **10**, 880 (1962).
232. Rosenheim, M. L., *Proc. Roy. Soc. Med.* **45**, 269 (1952).
233. Rosenheim, M. L., *Brit. Med. J.* **II**, 1181 (1954).
234. Rothman, S., *Am. J. Physiol.* **180**, 61 (1955).
235. Russek, H. I., *Am. Heart J.* **26**, 398 (1943).
236. Russek, H. I., and Zohman, B. L., *Am. Heart J.* **29**, 113 (1945).
237. Sancetta, S. M., *Circulation Res.* **8**, 616 (1960).
238. Sassa, K., *Japan. Heart J.* **3**, 203 (1962).
239. Saville, S., *Lancet* **II**, 358 (1950).
240. Schroeder, H. A., *Am. J. Med.* **17**, 540 (1954).
241. Schroeder, H. A., *Proc. Joint W.H.O.-Czech. Cardiol. Soc. Symp., Prague, 1960*, p. 436. State Medical Publishing House, Prague, 1961.
242. Schweitzer, M. D., Clark, E. G., Gearing, F. R., and Perera, G. A., *J. Chronic Diseases* **15**, 1093 (1962).
243. Simonson, E., and Nakagawa, K., *Circulation* **22**, 126 (1960).
244. Skelton, F. R., *Proc. Soc. Exptl. Biol. Med.* **90**, 342 (1955).
245. Smirk, F. H., *Brit. Heart J.* **6**, 176 (1944).
246. Smirk, F. H., *Roy. Australasian Coll. Physicians Pamp.* (1946).
247. Smirk, F. H., *Brit. Med. J.* **I**, 791 (1949).
248. Smirk, F. H., *Brit. Med. J.* **I**, 717 (1954).
249. Smirk, F. H., "High Arterial Pressure." Blackwell, Oxford, 1957.
250. Smirk, F. H., *Proc. Univ. Otago Med. School* **41**, 29 (1963).
251. Smirk, F. H., *New Zealand Med. J.* **63**, 413 (1964).
252. Smirk, F. H., *Japan. Heart J.* **6**, 289 (1965).
253. Smirk, F. H., *Ciba Found. Symp., Antihypertensive Therapy Principles and Practice*, pp. 99 and 390.
254. Smirk, F. H., unpublished work.
255. Smirk, F. H., and Alstad, K. S., *Brit. Med. J.* **I**, 1217 (1951).
256. Smirk, F. H., and Hall, W. H., *Nature* **182**, 727 (1958).
257. Smirk, F. H., Hamilton, M., Doyle, A. E., and McQueen, E. G., *Am. J. Cardiol.* **1**, 143 (1958).
258. Smirk, F. H., and Hodge, J. V., unpublished work (1966).
259. Smirk, F. H., and Phelan, E. L., *J. Pathol. Bacteriol.* **89**, 57 (1965).
260. Smirk, F. H., and Phelan, E. L., unpublished work (1966).
261. Smirk, F. H., and Simpson, F. O., unpublished work (1966).
262. Smirk, F. H., Veale, A. M. O., and Alstad, K. S., *New Zealand Med. J.* **58**, 711 (1959).
263. Smirk, F. H., Veale, A. M. O., and Phelan, E. L., unpublished work (1966).
264. Smirk, F. H., and Wallis, A. T., unpublished work (1966).
265. Smith, K. S., and Fowler, P. B. S., *Lancet* **I**, 417 (1955).
266. Smith, K. S., Fowler, P. B. S., and Edmunds, V. *Brit. Med. J.* **II**, 1243 (1954).
267. Smithwick, R. H., and Robertson, C. W., *Angiology* **2**, 143 (1951).

268. Smithwick, R. H., and Thompson, J. E., *J. Am. Med. Assoc.* **152**, 1501 (1953).
269. Society of Actuaries, "Build and Blood Pressure Study." Chicago, Illinois, 1959.
270. Stamey, T. A., "Renovascular Hypertension." Williams & Wilkins, Baltimore, Maryland, 1963.
271. Symonds, B., *J. Am. Med. Assoc.* **80**, 232 (1923).
272. Taggart, J., and Drury, D. E., *J. Exptl. Med.* **71**, 857 (1940).
273. Taquini, A. C., Blaquier, P. C ., and Taquini, A. C., Jr., *Can. Med. Assoc. J.* **90**, 210 (1964).
274. Thacker, E. A., *Am. Heart. J.* **20**, 89 (1940).
275. Thacker, E. A., *Ann. Internal Med.* **14**, 415 (1940).
276. Thomas, C. B., *Am. J. Med. Sci.* **224**, 367 (1952).
277. Thomas, C. B., and Warthin, T. A., *Am. Heart J.* **19**, 316 (1940).
278. Tigerstedt, T., and Bergman, P. C., *Acta Physiol. Scand.* **8**, 223 (1898).
279. Tobian, L., Jr., *J. Clin. Invest.* **29**, 849 (1950).
280. Tobian, L., Jr., *Physiol. Rev.* **40**, 280 (1960).
281. Tobian, L., Jr., *Am. J. Caridol.* **8**, 684 (1961).
282. Tobian, L., Jr., *Can. Med. Assoc. J.* **90**, 160 (1964).
283. Tobian, L., Jr., Thompson, J., Twedt, R., and Janecek, J., *J. Clin. Invest.* **37**, 66 (1958).
284. Todd, R. L., *J.-Lancet* **64**, 410 (1944).
285. Turiaf, J., Zizine, L., and Sors, C., *Presse Med.* **62**, 57 (1954).
286. Ueda, H., *Am. J. Cardiol.* **10**, 371 (1962).
287. Veale, A. M. O., Hamilton, M., Irvine, R. O. H., and Smirk, F. H., *New Zealand Med. J.* **61**, 65 (1962).
288. Verney, E. B., and Vogt, M., *Quart. J. Exptl. Physiol.* **28**, 253 (1938).
289. Verschuer, O., and Zipperlen, V., *Z. Klin. Med.* **112**, 69 (1922).
290. Veyrat, R., de Champlain, J., Boucher, R., and Genest, J., *Can. Med. Assoc. J.* **90**, 215 (1964).
291. Volhard, F., *Verhandl. Deut. Ges. Kreislaufforsch.* **15**, 40 (1949).
292. von Lichtlen, P., Buhlmann, A., and Schaub, F., *Cardiologia* **35**, 139 (1959).
293. Watkin, D. M., Froeb, H. F., Hatch, F. T., and Gutman, A. B., *Am. J. Med.* **9**, 428 (1950).
294. Werko, L., and Lagerlof, H., *Acta Med. Scand.* **133**, 427 (1949).
295. Wilson, C., *Ciba Found. Symp., Antihypertensive Therapy*, p. 584 (1965).
296. Wilson, C., and Byrom, F. B., *Lancet* I, 136 (1939).
297. Windesheim, J. H., Roth, G. M., and Hines, E. A., Jr., *Circulation* **11**, 878 (1955).
298. *World Health Organ., Tech. Rept. Ser.* **231** (1962).
299. Yates, M. R., and Wood, J. E., *Proc. Soc. Exptl. Biol. Med.* **34**, 560 (1936).
300. Yeakel, E. H., Shenkin, H. A., Rothballer, A. B., and McCann, S. McD., *Am. J. Physiol.* **155**, 118 (1948).
301. Yu, P. N., Luria, M. N., Finlayson, J. K., and Stanfield, C. A., *Circulation* **22**, 835 (1960).
302. Zollinger, H. U., *Circulation* **5**, 950 (1952).

Acknowledgments

The author acknowledges the financial assistance of the N.Z. Medical Research Council and the Life Insurance Medical Research Fund of Australia and New Zealand.

CHAPTER II

Experimental Hypertension in Animals and Its Use in Screening for Antihypertensive Compounds

Albert J. Plummer

I. Introduction, 67

II. Experimental Hypertension, 69
  A. Hypertension of Renal Origin, 69
  B. Neurogenic Hypertension, 82
  C. Endocrine-induced Hypertension, 85
  D. Dietary Hypertension, 92
  E. Hereditary Hypertension, 92

III. Development of Antihypertensive Agents, 93
  A. Blood Pressure Regulatory Function of the Sympathetic Nervous System, 95
  B. Antihypertensive Substances Suppressing the Sympathetic Nervous System, 98
  C. Antihypertensive Substances Acting on Vascular Smooth Muscle, 104
  D. Miscellaneous Antihypertensive Compounds, 105

IV. Discussion, 107

  References, 109

I. Introduction

Although many techniques have been devised for causing a sustained rise in the blood pressure in various species since the original observations by Tigerstedt and Bergman (194) in 1898 of the pressor properties of extracts of the cortex of the kidney of the rabbit, none has duplicated in every detail the picture of human hypertension. This is readily comprehensible when it is considered that despite intensive clinical study the etiology of the disease in man remains obscure, though much has been learned about the nature of the disorder.

The several factors sustaining the blood pressure include the pumping action of the heart, the volume and viscosity of the blood, the elasticity of the blood vessels, and the resistance of the arterioles. Elevation of the resistance of the arteriolar bed is generally agreed to be the physical factor responsible for the clinical entity called essential hypertension. But whether the increase in the peripheral resistance is due to nervous or humorally mediated vasoconstrictor effects upon the arterioles is an unanswered and provocatively controversial question.

Much of the work in the first half of the century was oriented principally toward the production of a persistent hypertensive state in animals in order to produce a prototype of the human disease and thus to clarify its etiological nature. The first exciting progress resulting from this effort was the observation by Goldblatt (57) in 1932 that a lasting elevation could be produced in the blood pressure of the dog by interfering with the blood supply to the kidney. In 1937 Page (137) caused hypertension in dogs by wrapping the kidneys occlusively in cellophane or silk. This success was followed in sequence over the next two decades by similar observations by Wilson and Byrom (202) following renal ischemia in the rat, and by Selye (171) in 1954 following combined high sodium chloride and deoxycorticosterone acetate administration to the rat. In 1931 Heymans (83) had produced hypertension in the dog by division of the so-called baroceptor nerves from the carotid sinus and aortic arch. As a result of the combined efforts of these investigators, therefore, evidence was at hand that renal, endocrine, or neurogenic factors alone or in combination might play a functional role in the elevation of human blood pressure; and even today this probably represents a fair statement of the existing viewpoint on the problem.

Although the use of drugs for the management of hypertension was not without its proponents, a lapse of 17 years followed the availability of the Goldblatt type of hypertensive dog and the appearance of hexamethonium, the first useful antihypertensive agent prepared by Barlow and Ing (4) and studied by Paton and Zaimis (145). The detection of the hypotensive and ganglionic blocking activity of this substance was carried out in normotensive animals. Delay in earlier attempts to develop specific drugs for the management of human hypertension was in great part due to a generally accepted premise that elevated blood pressure was a protective mechanism in certain individuals who required, for some ill-defined reason, a high perfusion pressure to preserve the function and viability of essential organ systems. Such a philosophy did not provide a favorable environment for the search for antihypertensive agents, if such indeed might exist, and dissenters were not afforded an opportunity to test the hypothesis since the drugs available for use in hypertension as listed in a standard text of medicine of less than 20 years ago comprised phenobarbital and the bromides. But dissenters there were, and the collaboration of such from the clinic and the experimental laboratory over the intervening years has resulted in a substantial armamentarium of effective antihypertensive agents.

Two main themes will form the basis of this presentation, the first part consisting of a discussion of the various methods for producing hypertension in animals, commonly described as experimental hypertension, and the second dealing with the use of various experimental approaches for the detection and evaluation of potential antihypertensive agents in animals.

II. Experimental hypertension

Experimental hypertension has been the subject of a number of reviews including those by Goldblatt (56), Braun-Menéndez (20), Pickering (148), and Smirk (182). Although most of the existing clinically active hypotensive agents have been detected in normotensive animals, most have also been found to be effective in animals with various forms of experimental hypertension. Efficacy in the hypertensive animal confers an added measure of optimism in the ultimate effectiveness of an agent in the human hypertensive state. It is generally not feasible to use hypertensive animals for routine detection of drug activity. Rather, in the interest of economy of time and effort, hypertensive preparations are generally reserved for additional developmental study of agents whose hypotensive activity has been revealed in the normotensive animal.

The various methods for the production of persistent experimental hypertension in animals can be classified in five main categories, depending upon the responsible factor. These are: (A) renal, (B) neurogenic, (C) endocrine, (D) dietary and (E) hereditary.

A. HYPERTENSION OF RENAL ORIGIN

1. *Renal Hypertension in the Dog*

Of the many methods available for producing experimental hypertension, the most well known and widely studied is probably the original technique of Goldblatt, based upon constriction of the renal artery. Many years before, Richard Bright (21) had been impressed by the common occurrence of a massive left ventricle in patients with fatal renal disease and had suggested that "the altered quality of the blood ... so affects the minute and capillary circulation as to render greater action necessary to force the blood through the distant subdivisions of the vascular system." This discerning observation in 1836 and sage opinion worthy of a great physician were made almost three-quarters of a century before measurements of blood pressure were carried out in man. When this became possible in 1905 through the Korotkov (98) auscultatory method, utilizing the brachial artery occluding pressure cuff and stethoscope still in routine clinical use, it was soon realized that the enlargement of the heart described by Bright was a consequence of the elevated pressure against which the left ventricle was required to work. Despite many efforts in the early part of this century to demonstrate a link between the diseased kidneys of Bright's disease and the high incidence of elevated blood pressure, the results were variable and equivocal at best.

In 1934 Goldblatt (58) first reported a technique for consistently producing lasting renal hypertension to substantiate Bright's hypothesis by experiment. In this procedure the main renal artery of a dog was partially constricted by means of an adjustable silver clamp placed around the artery. It was early noted that the degree of constriction of the artery was critical. When the clamp was too loose hypertension did not develop, and when too tight, especially if both renal arteries were occluded, a fulminating course with an acutely developing hypertension and failure of renal excretory function with fatal uremia ensued within a few weeks. This latter state has been likened to the malignant state of essential hypertension by Goldblatt (58). Undoubtedly the ingeniously devised silver clamp contributed greatly to the success of an experiment where so many others had failed for (1) it was well tolerated by tissue and could be left on the artery for a prolonged period, (2) constriction of the artery could be precisely adjusted, (3) increase or decrease of the constriction of the artery was possible during the course of the experiment, and (4) the clamp could be removed at any time without injury to the vessel.

An unexpected observation was a temporary elevation of the blood pressure when only one renal artery was constricted. This rise in blood pressure began in 2–3 days but returned to the pre-existing level within 6 weeks to a few months. When the clamped kidney was removed during the hypertensive period, the blood pressure fell to normal within 2 days. In order to produce a permanent hypertension it was necessary to constrict the renal artery of each kidney or to constrict the main artery of one kidney and remove the other kidney a week later. In some dogs persistent hypertension lasting more than 6 years, with elevation of both systolic and diastolic pressures, was achieved with the latter procedure. With properly adjusted clamps the hypertension was not accompanied by any decrease of renal excretory function. In this so-called benign phase, by analogy with essential hypertension, Goldblatt (55) reported minimal changes in the circulatory system with moderate enlargement of the heart and thickening of the medial layer of the large and small arteries due to hypertrophy of the smooth muscle fibers but without sclerotic or degenerative changes in these blood vessels. In more severe hypertension associated with more tightly clamped renal arteries, sclerosis admixed with necrosis of the arterioles was a prominent feature. It was of interest that lesions of the arterioles were absent in the clamped kidneys even in the presence of advanced lesions elsewhere. If only one renal artery was constricted, lesions occurred only in the unclamped kidney (29), suggesting that the clamp protected the kidney against the systemic hypertension.

The principal functional change in the Goldblatt type of renal hypertension was a rise in peripheral resistance (89) with no change in cardiac rate (58), cardiac output (89), or blood volume. Such drastic procedures as renal denervation, destruction of the spinal cord, and cardiac denervation neither prevented nor abolished the hypertension resulting from constriction of the main renal artery, suggesting that a humoral mechanism was probably the causative factor. Even thiopental anesthesia did not lower the blood pressure in this disorder. It was early realized that the adrenal cortex played a role in the maintenance of renal hypertension in the dog (53, 59) since the blood pressure promptly fell to normal when both adrenals were removed from a hypertensive animal and that the hypertensive state could be restored by the injection of an adrenal cortical extract. Another link in the chain of evidence that a humoral mechanism residing in the kidney itself was involved in renal hypertension was provided by the observation that tying off the renal veins of hypertensive animals resulted in a prompt fall in blood pressure, presumably by preventing the humor from leaving the kidney. Even more direct demonstration of the probability that a renal humoral mechanism was responsible for the initiation of renal hypertension was afforded (1) by the production of hypertension by Houssay and Fasciolo (90), following transplantation of a graft of an ischemic kidney to the neck of a recently nephrectomized dog, and (2) by the detection by Prinzmetal *et al.* (153) of a pressor substance in the perfusate from the vein of an ischemic kidney.

The task of the elucidation of the details of this renal humoral mechanism, which was carried on independently by two groups of workers headed by Braun-Menéndez (18) in Argentina and by Page (143) in the United States, is fully described in two thorough reviews by these investigators. Tigerstedt and Bergman (194) had shown in 1898 that crude saline extracts of rabbit kidneys caused a rise in the blood pressure when injected into anesthetized rabbits. They named this hypothetical substance "renin." The availability of the Goldblatt renal hypertensive dog provided a reproducible type of hypertension and spurred the search for a possible renal pressor factor such as renin as the cause of the attendant vasoconstriction. Page and his associates had begun work on the purification of renin as early as 1931. The substance showed the properties of a protein. Although it became more pressor for the intact animal, upon purification it lost its constrictor activity when perfused in Ringer's solution through the tail of the dog. When it was noted that the activity was restored by the substitution of plasma for Ringer's solution, it was suggested (95) that renin was an enzyme which was not pressor itself but required activation by a component in the plasma. The plasma component ultimately proved to be the substrate for renin and was independently identified by Page and Helmer (140) and by Braun-Menéndez (19). It was named "renin substrate" by the former and "hypertensinogen" by the latter. The reaction product of renin and renin substrate, which was an extremely potent pressor substance with the properties of a polypeptide, was also independently discovered in 1939 and named "angiotonin" by Page and Helmer (140) and "hypertensin" by Braun-Menéndez *et al.* (19). In order to eliminate confusion, the composite name "angiotensin" was agreed upon by the two investigators. There is also an enzyme named hypertensinase, which inactivates angiotensin. Subsequent work has shown that the situation is more complex than at first realized. Elliott and Peart (40) showed that the initial product obtained by rabbit renin on bovine plasma was a decapeptide, and Skeggs (174) found that a two-stage process was involved with the liberation of the decapeptide (angiotensin I) by renin, followed by the further splitting of the chain by a protein designated as plasma-converting enzyme, yielding an octapeptide (angiotensin II). The octapeptide proved to be the active pressor substance, angiotensin, while the decapeptide was practically inactive. Renin substrate was shown to be an α_2-globulin. The sequence of the first 14 amino acids in the substrate and of the 10 amino acids in angiotensin I was determined by Skeggs *et al.* (175). The final proof for the order of the 8 amino acids in angiotensin II was reached with the synthesis of the polypeptide by Rittel *et al.* (160) and by Schwarz *et al.* (166) in 1957. The sequence of the amino acids in angiotensin II in hog and horse blood is the following:

$$\text{Asp–Arg–Val–Tyr–Ileu–His–Pro–Phe}$$
$$\quad 1 \quad\quad 2 \quad\quad 3 \quad\quad 4 \quad\quad 5 \quad\quad 6 \quad\quad 7 \quad\quad 8$$

In beef blood the sequence is the same, with the exception that valine is substituted for isoleucine in the fifth position as reported by Elliott and Peart (40).

It is now generally agreed that renin has no pressor activity of its own and that the pressor action following its injection or endogenous production by reduction of renal blood flow is due to the angiotensin which is ultimately synthesized by the following scheme of the renin–angiotensin system:

Renin substrate in blood (terminal tetradecapeptide of α_2-globulin)

| renin (enzyme)
↓

Angiotensin I (inactive decapeptide)

| plasma-converting enzyme (from liver)
↓

Angiotensin II (active pressor octapeptide)

The importance of angiotensin, the most potent naturally occurring vasoconstrictor in the genesis of elevated blood pressure, has given rise to much discussion and speculation. Despite its great pressor potency, it is not known with certainty how it may be involved in the regulation of blood pressure, nor is there evidence that its concentration is elevated in the blood in the chronic stage of renal hypertension in dogs. Helmer and Judson (81) have found evidence of increased pressor activity in the femoral vein blood of trained unanesthetized dogs following clamping of the renal artery, on the basis of (1) an assay of the pressor effect of the plasma (dialyzed overnight in the cold at pH 5.5) on a pithed nephrectomized rat, and of (2) the constrictor effect of the dialyzed plasma on a spirally cut strip of rabbit aorta (81). The pressor activity was most marked from the second to the eighth day after clamping, and returned to the base line by the sixteenth day despite the persistence of hypertension in the dog. Dogs with chronic hypertension of 2 years' duration exhibited elevations in pressor activity in the systemic blood of three of seven such animals. Morris et al. (130) similarly noted an elevation of the level of angiotensin II in the blood of dogs following partial occlusion of the renal artery with a disappearance of the polypeptide and a return to normotension following removal of the partial occlusion. Scornik and Paladini (168) observed that angiotensin levels in dogs with chronic renal hypertension produced by partial clamping of the renal arteries, were in all cases within normal limits in chronic hypertension, though levels in most instances increased acutely soon after severe clamping of the renal artery. Fasciolo et al. (41) found no significant change in the blood levels of renin or angiotensin after unilateral ischemia followed by contralateral nephrectomy in the dog, though blood pressure was elevated. An observation by Hickler (86) that clamping of the renal artery of the rat elevates the angiotensinase activity of the serum could well interfere with the persistence of angiotensin in the plasma in renal hypertension.

McCubbin et al. (121) have shown that after a period of several days the carotid baroceptor mechanism is reset to the hypertensive pressure levels of dogs with experimental renal hypertension. The buffer reflexes initiated by pressure-sensitive receptors in the carotid sinus then tend to maintain rather than prevent the chronic phase of hypertension. Such an adaptation would explain the persistence of renal hypertension, though the elevated renin of the clamped kidney reverted to normal after the acute stage. According to this postulate, a humoral mechanism might initiate the hypertension while the continuing disorder would depend upon a neurogenic component. Taking the positive view that the renin-angiotensin system may be involved in the production of renal hypertension, it was logical to attempt to examine synthetic polypeptide analogs as inhibitors of angiotensin, as Page (139) and Schwyzer (167) have done. However, up to the present no inhibitors of this type have been found. It may be more than a coincidence that Barrett et al. have found that the hypotensive agent, hydralazine, which increases renal blood flow (5), is also a rather effective antagonist of the pressor effect of intravenously administered angiotensin in the anesthetized dog.

Wakerlin et al. (199) obtained immunologic evidence suggesting that renin was involved in the development of renal hypertension in dogs. Although it was not possible to produce antibodies to homologous renin in the dog, antibodies were produced to hog renin by the dog. A course of intramuscular injections of hog renin in chronic renal hypertensive dogs produced an antihypertensive effect which was well correlated with the antirenin titer of the serum, while hog renin similarly was reported to prevent the development of an elevation of blood pressure after renal artery clamping. Unfortunately, antibodies to hog renin produced by injections of hog renin in the human did not neutralize human renin. The intervening literature is discussed in detail by Smirk (182). Deodhar *et al.* (38) have found that acetylation made homologous renins antigenic in the rat, rabbit and dog, and that their antibodies neutralized not only the acetylated renin but also the naturally occuring renin of each species. Immunization with acetylated dog renin progressively lowered the blood pressure of a dog, hypertensive for 6 years after renal artery clamping, to the prehypertensive level. Interestingly, the antirenin produced in the dog to acetylated dog renin also inactivated human renin, while the corresponding antibodies of the rat and rabbit were inactive. It was concluded that the acetylation of dog renin altered its configuration so as to make it resemble that of human renin. Studies with acetylated human renin may provide information as to the importance of renin in the production of human hypertension as well as an approach for ameliorating the disorder.

In addition to its direct vasoconstrictor action, there is another mechanism by which angiotensin may participate in the elevation of the blood pressure. This is through its capacity to release the potent mineralocorticoid, aldosterone, from the adrenal in both animals and man, as proposed by Laragh (104). According to this hypothesis, renin secretion by the kidney is initiated by sodium loss or by lowered blood pressure. Renin produces angiotensin, which in turn causes sodium retention by the direct stimulation of aldosterone secretion and also by a direct renal tubular action of hypertensin. The resultant sodium retention tends to increase blood volume and to elevate blood pressure. Laragh has observed an increased excretion of aldosterone in the urine of patients with malignant hypertension, and, similarly, Carpenter (26) found a hypersecretion of aldosterone, coupled with a 10-fold elevation of the renin content of the kidney, in dogs with a malignant form of experimental renal hypertension. It is uncertain whether a deranged renin-angiotensin-aldosterone mechanism is responsible for or a consequence of malignant hypertension in both the dog and man. Evidence has been provided by Hartroft (77) and Cook and Pickering (32) that the juxtaglomerular cells within the kidney are the source of renin secretion, and Tobian (195) has suggested that the stimulus for activating the secretion of these cells, located in the walls of the afferent glomerular arteriole, is a decreased stretch due to lowered renal perfusion pressure. In the experimental situation this could be due to a clamp placed on the renal artery, but in the more physiological situation it might be due to a moderate fall in blood pressure. Gross (70) postulated a control mechanism for aldosterone secretion which was close to the concept proposed by Davis (36), who provided the initial experimental evidence that the kidney played a role in the control of aldosterone secretion. This hypothesis suggests that a decrease in renal blood flow activates the juxtaglomerular cells to cause a secretion of renin and that through the renin-angiotensin system aldosterone is secreted by the adrenal cortex; aldosterone causes a retention of sodium by the renal tubular cells with a resultant increase in blood volume, blood pressure, and renal blood flow; the increased sodium and blood flow act as a negative feedback upon the juxtaglomerular cells to reduce the secretion of renin. If such a balanced mechanism plays a crucial role, as has been premised, in the regulation of electrolyte balance and blood pressure level, its derangement by appropriate experimental procedures would be expected to lead to an altered blood pressure. Presumptive support of this thesis is provided by the observation of Jones et al. (92) that the total water and sodium content of the aorta are significantly elevated along its entire course in dogs with renal hypertension produced by wrapping the kidneys with cellophane (137). More direct support of the above thesis has been afforded by Skinner et al. (180). Employing a sensitive analytical procedure, they have observed a small, continuous output of renin in the renal vein of the dog, with an increased renin level in the vein when the renal perfusion pressure was lowered and a decreased level when the perfusion pressure was elevated. These investigators have suggested that a renal baroceptor, which is delicately regulated to the prevailing mean arterial blood pressure, is, in turn, also capable of influencing the systemic pressure by the reciprocal mechanism just described. They have further postulated that arterial pressure tends to stabilize at a level at which renin secretion is minimal. The identification of the pressor-sensitive receptor would constitute a great advance in the understanding of the mechanism of renal hypertension. The suggestion by Tobian (195) that the juxtaglomerular cells may subserve this function, though reasonable, has not yet been established experimentally.

Skinner et al. (179) have also recently reported increased levels of pressor material with the properties of angiotensin appearing within 5 minutes in the renal vein and later in arterial blood following a 60-minute period of renal arterial clamping in the dog. Within 15 minutes of release of the clamp, the pressor material disappeared from both arterial and renal venous blood. Since incubation of the active plasma increased its angiotensinlike pressor activity while similar treatment of the control plasma did not, the presence of an increased amount of renin was indicated.

There appears to be no longer any question as to the presence of renin in the general circulation even under basal conditions as recently noted by Lever and Robertson (110), who have detected reninlike activity in the peripheral plasma of normal rabbits, employing a sensitive, quantitative enzyme kinetic method (111) based upon the initial velocity of angiotensin formation when renin was incubated with angiotensinase-free substrate prepared from ox serum. Higher renin levels were found in the peripheral plasma of rabbits during the first month of hypertension caused by the clamping of one renal artery and the removal of the opposite kidney. The reninlike activity of the plasma of normal rabbits was greatly reduced or eliminated within 24 hours of bilateral nephrectomy. These investigators have adopted the conservative view that the increased quantities of renin are not necessarily responsible for the development of the hypertension, suggesting rather the need for more detailed investigation of the matter. It is clear, however, that the analytical tools are steadily becoming available for a concerted attack on a problem which, until the present, has been hindered by the lack of precise methodology. The early methods for renin and hypertensin assay have been reviewed by Braun-Menéndez (18) in 1956, by Page (143) in 1961, while more recent developments have been included in a review by Peart (146) in 1965. In addition to the method mentioned above, Boucher et al. (14) have devised an extremely sensitive method with a high degree of specificity and accuracy, which can measure amounts of angiotensin as low as 10 nanograms added to whole blood. Amounts of renin less than 0.0004 dog unit can be detected. Helmer and Judson (82) have also provided a very sensitive quantitative method for the assay of renin in plasma. In studies with human plasma, evidence was obtained which suggested considerable variation of renin-substrate levels. With this method, elevated renin levels were found in the blood of hypertensive patients which fell to near normal levels upon effective antihypertensive therapy. With the application of these newer techniques, the question of the place of angiotensin in experimental and human hypertension may be answered. Page (144) views such a possibility positively, thinking it unlikely that a substance of such potency, so strategically located, would prove to have no part in the regulation of the circulation. He feels that the difficulty in the detection and measurement of the minute amounts of angiotensin are impeding a final answer. In support of this view is the work of De Moura et al. (37), who have recently found that the blood pressure of unanesthetized dogs does not begin to rise for several weeks following the continuous infusion of subpressor amounts of angiotensin, but that the pressure falls to normal when the dogs are placed in a completely quiet room or when they are asleep. It is suggested that the increased cardiovascular reactivity induced by angiotensin may be related to its capacity to enhance the effectiveness of endogenous norepinephrine (122). If this were the case, it would provide a bridge between the humoral and neurogenic factors involved in renal hypertension. Peart (146) feels that since the renin-angiotensin system is so complex, and is fraught with so many uncertain variables in its dynamics, it would be premature to take a firm stand implicating angiotensin directly in renal hypertension. In the same frame of reference, Peart, however, points out the general unreliability of plasma levels of angiotensin as such, noting that it would be quite possible for a low level of angiotensin to be present in the plasma as a result of being taken up avidly on smooth muscle receptors so that its biological activity on the arteriolar smooth muscle could be very marked. This emphasizes the need for better information concerning the rate of angiotensin production. The recent observation by Gould *et al* (74) of the presence of renin activity in the walls of blood vessels of the hog is most provocative, since it provides a possible mechanism by which angiotensin could be formed at the target smooth muscle cell itself. Whatever differences of opinion may exist, there is agreement that further experiment is necessary. A specific antagonist of angiotensin could provide a pharmacological approach to the elucidation of the role of angiotensin in the control of the blood pressure in both normal and hypertensive animals.

2. *Renal Hypertension in the Rat*

The rat has been an animal widely employed for the production and study of the mechanisms of experimental renal hypertension. Wilson and Byrom (202) first demonstrated that the rat differed from the dog in that it was possible to produce a persistent elevation of the blood pressure by the constriction of only one renal artery with a silver wire, or, more reliably, with a clip of silver ribbon as developed by Pickering and Prinzmetal (150) for use in the rabbit. In some animals blood pressures began to mount within the first 24 hours after clipping, while in others hypertension did not appear for a month, a variability which is probably related to biological difference in individual response as much as to differences in renal artery occlusion. Wilson and Byrom were able to produce elevations in blood pressure from a control mean level of 106 mm Hg to 160–180 mm Hg. The degree of constriction of the renal artery is critical, since hypertension does not develop if the reduction in blood flow is either too great or too small. With experience, the proper degree of arteriolar constriction can be achieved in 90% of the rats. The rat offers the advantage as an experimental animal in that it permits a comparison of the functional and morphological changes in the constricted and nonconstricted kidney. The vascular damage associated with the hypertension consists of a hypertrophy of the media or middle layer of the medium and small arteries, and necrotic foci with thickening of the intimal layer of the arterioles, especially within the kidney (147). The lesions are especially prominent in the unclamped kidney which is directly exposed to the heightened blood pressure.

If the clamp is removed during the first few weeks from the unilaterally clamped rat, there is a prompt restoration of the normal blood pressure, but after the unclamped kidney has developed lesions, it can maintain hypertension even after extirpation of the constricted kidney. This is in contrast to the experience in unilateral renal disease, with prolonged hypertension in man, where removal of the diseased kidney is sometimes followed by a return to a normal blood pressure level. Similarly, the edema, hemorrhages, and focal vascular spasms of the pial vessels of the rat brain, observed through a transparent window in the skull, were seen to revert to a normal appearance when the renal arterial clamp was removed sufficiently early to normalize the blood pressure, according to Byrom (22). Also, spasm with narrowing of the retinal blood vessels disappeared upon removal of the clamp sufficiently early (23).

As with the dog, various modifications of the arterial clamping procedure have led to the development of renal hypertension in the rat. Wrapping one or both kidneys of the dog in cellophane or silk was shown by Page (137) to be effective. This has led to the view that reduction of rhythmic vascular pulsation in the kidney, rather than ischemia, may be the causative factor in the production of hypertension. Compression of the kidney with a figure-of-eight ligature of cotton was employed by Grollman (64) to raise the blood pressure of the rat. Kempf and Page (93) found that if hypertension did not develop within 3 weeks after renal clamping or silk wrapping, removal of the normal kidney led to hypertension, suggesting a protective function of normal renal tissue. According to Proosdij-Hartzema and de Jongh (154), who compared the various available procedures, the most reliable method for inducing long-lasting blood pressure elevation consisted in the combination of arterial clamping of one renal artery, combined with contralateral nephrectomy in a single operation, as described by Wilson and Byrom (202).

The renin angiotensin system is present in the rat as well as in the dog, and it has been shown by Gross et al. (73) that renin activity is present in the peripheral blood of the normal rat. In contrast to most species, however, angiotensin does not enhance aldosterone secretion in the rat and Gross et al. (73) have raised some valid objections to the importance of the renin-angiotensin system as a causative factor in persistent experimental renal hypertension in the rat. Clamping of one kidney while leaving the other untouched leads to an increase in renin concentration in the clamped kidney, an increase in circulating renin in the blood, and hypertension, suggesting the possible active participation of the renin-angiotensin system. When, however, one kidney is removed and the artery to the remaining kidney is constricted to the same extent, no change occurs in the concentration of renin in this kidney nor in the blood, despite the production of persistent hypertension. These observations indicate that clamping of one renal artery can induce hypertension independently of increases in renal or blood renin concentrations. Gross feels that the renin-angiotensin system serves primarily in the regulation of renal tubular function and the control of sodium and water balance in the rat.

Blaquier (13) reported the results of cross-circulation experiments in rats which also minimize the importance of the renin-angiotensin mechanism in experimental renal hypertension. He adapted a technique of Rondell *et al.* (162) in which a femoral artery and vein of one of a pair of rats was connected by polyethylene tubing to the femoral vein and artery respectively of the other. In order to maintain a stable, normal blood volume, the animals were arranged on the two pans of a balance sufficiently sensitive to detect a weight change of 0.1 g. By adjusting the clamps on the polyethylene tubing, the flow rate in the two directions was kept equal. When hypertension was produced in the donor rat by the release of clamps which had occluded one or both renal pedicles for 4 hours, the blood pressure of the recipient animal also rose. However, when the procedure was applied to rats with renal hypertension of 1 week's duration, neither hypertension nor increase in circulating pressor substances could be detected in the recipient. From these experiments it appeared that the renin-angiotensin pressor mechanism may be operative in the initial stage but not in the chronic state of renal hypertension in the rat. Koletsky and Pritchard (97) have come to the same conclusion on the basis of transfer of blood from rats with renal hypertension to normal recipient rats, since a pressor effect was noted during the first 2 weeks after renal manipulation but not thereafter, even though the donor animals had much higher blood pressures after several weeks. These investigators suggested an altered electrolyte content of the peripheral vessels or the development of organic peripheral vascular disease as alternative factors which may be responsible for the chronic hypertensive state.

As early as 1947 Ogden (136) had suggested that the vasopressor substance present in acute renal hypertension of rats was replaced in the chronic stage by a neurogenic mechanism. This view has received recent support in the report of the work of McCubbin *et al.* (121), mentioned in the earlier discussion of renal hypertension in the dog.

Masson *et al.* (117) have provided evidence that another factor, in addition to renin, produced by the ischemic kidney of the rat, may be involved in the production of renal hypertension. By constriction of the aorta between the two renal arteries sufficiently to lower the blood pressure below the filtration pressure required for urine formation, the excretory function of the left (lower) kidney was lost, and it was transformed into an organ with only secretory capacity. This organ was originally styled by Selye and Stone (173) as an "endocrine kidney". Secretions of such an ischemic kidney caused a malignant type of hypertension, and extracts also caused severe hypertension with vascular lesions, when injected into uninephrectomized rats. Since renin alone raised the blood pressure but did not cause vascular lesions, it was postulated that an additional substance which either activated the enzymic production of angiotensin or potentiated its activity was liberated by the endocrine kidney. The nature of the vasculotoxic substance is not yet known.

Wilson (201) has proposed that an injured kidney causes the elevation of blood pressure by influencing some extrarenal factor which is concerned with body water or electrolyte distribution. This hypothesis was based on experiments by Floyer (42) showing that after total adrenalectomy in rats, renal hypertension could be maintained or restored by increasing the sodium intake. In support of this concept the work of Byrom and Dodson (24) showed that the provocative mechanism in renal hypertension still resided in the kidney even in the chronic phase. These investigators showed that in the rat rendered hypertensive by the removal of one kidney and the clipping of the artery of the other, the removal of the clip even after 3 months restored the blood pressure to normal within 12 hours, thus ruling out irreversible extrarenal factors such as organic narrowing of the arteries due to hypertrophy or degeneration as a necessary prerequisite for the development of hypertension. In contrast, when the hypertension was produced by clipping one renal artery, leaving the other kidney intact, the blood pressure did not fall when the clipped kidney was removed, indicating that hypertension can produce some change such as residual lesions in a normal kidney, which enables it to sustain chronic hypertension. Observations by Ledingham are in harmony with the concept proposed by Wilson. As early as 1953 Ledingham (106) observed that the extracellular fluid volume and the plasma volume expanded initially after renal artery clamping in the rat, but fell to the normal range in the hypertensive stage. In recent studies in the rat by means of an electromagnetic flow transducer implanted on the ascending aorta, Ledingham and Cohen (107) have measured an early increased cardiac output during the development of renal hypertension following clamping of the right renal artery and left nephrectomy. The increased cardiac output reached a maximum between the fifth and tenth days following operation. Based on this observation, it has been suggested that the increase of cardiac output may be the primary disturbance responsible for the onset of renal hypertension, since accommodation of the nervous baroceptors to an elevated blood pressure is rapid. It is postulated that the next event would be an increased constriction of the vascular smooth muscle in response to the elevated intravascular pressure, as described by Bayliss (8) in 1902, causing the pressure to rise still further. The resulting rise in pressure distal to the clip would remove the stimulus for the original increased cardiac output. The end result, with normal cardiac output and raised peripheral resistance as found in chronic renal hypertension, would thus be achieved. The cause of the early increased cardiac output is not certain, but it could be related to the action of the renin-angiotensin system in causing sodium retention and increased circulatory volume.

The experimental observation that chronic renal hypertension may be explicable on the basis of the common mechanism of an altered electrolyte and water balance is supported by the work of Tobian and Redleaf (197).

They have shown that the hypertension which persists in the rat after the excision of an ischemic kidney was accompanied by an increase in the intracellular sodium, potassium, and water content of the aorta, but that in those animals whose blood pressure returns to normal upon removal of the clipped kidney, the electrolyte and water content of the aorta was within the normal range (196). Tobian has suggested that the increased water content by "waterlogging" the walls of the arterioles could restrict the lumens, increase resistance to flow, and thereby raise blood pressure. The experiments by Floyer (42) demonstrating the necessity of the presence of the adrenal or of sodium substitution after adrenalectomy in order to maintain the renal hypertensive state in the rat suggests that the adrenal must play a part which is at least permissive. The demonstrated importance of the adrenal in the maintenance of renal hypertension and the observation by Gross that the renin-angiotensin system is primarily responsible for the tubular handling of sodium in the rat are not inconsistent with the above concept since endogenous aldosterone secretion by the adrenal may be governed by the changes in sodium and water caused by the tubular diuretic action of hypertensin in the rat. It may well be that the importance of the sodium-retaining action of aldosterone in renal hypertension in the rat is, in the final analysis, not less important in the rat than in the dog and man.

Great advances in methodology in the determination of renin in body fluids have been made recently by Lever et al. (111) and by Boucher et al. (14). The methods have been made exceedingly sensitive and more specific. In addition, the interfering action of hypertensinase has been inhibited successfully by the use of ethylenediaminetetraacetic acid or removal by acid treatment. Using the methods of Lever et al., Anchini and Gross (2) in 1965 showed the presence of a reninlike substance in the urine of the rat with certainty for the first time and found that after clamping of one renal artery the activity more than doubled for a period up to 4 weeks. After removal of the clamp, the renin activity decreased to barely measurable values and then gradually rose to the control level over a 3-week period. The fluctuations of the renin concentration in the urine paralleled closely those previously reported in the plasma by Schaechtelin et al. (164) in 1963. The application of these methods in chronic renal hypertensive unanesthetized animals should help clarify many present uncertainties.

3. Renal Hypertension in Other Species

Pickering and Prinzmetal (149) produced renal hypertension in the rabbit by the bilateral placing of silver clips upon each renal artery. The rabbit resembles the dog in that it was necessary to constrict both renal arteries or to constrict one artery and remove the other kidney in order to produce hypertension. Persistent hypertension developed over a period of a year in about one-third of the animals, an incidence somewhat below that achievable with rats.

Goldblatt (54) developed a lasting hypertension in *Rhesus* monkeys by constricting both renal arteries with silver clamps as in the dog.

4. *Renoprival Studies*

In 1943 Grollman and Rule (66) observed a rise in blood pressure in rats following removal of both kidneys. The hypertension was attributed to the removal of a protective action of the kidneys which served to maintain normal vascular tone. Grollman (64) extended this hypothesis by suggesting that renal hypertension was also due to the removal of the same protective renal factor rather than to the liberation of pressor substances.

In 1949 Grollman (67) produced hypertension in bilaterally nephrectomized dogs kept alive by an artificial kidney. Further studies reviewed by Smirk (182) have not established the exact basis of the protective action of the kidney. Since then there have been several reports of an antihypertensive principle extracted from the normotensive kidney. Muirhead *et al.* (132) found that extracts of the renal medulla interfered with the development of renoprival hypertension in the rat, while Sokabe and Grollman (187) have evidence that a protective principle is present in the cortical region of the kidney. Hamilton and Grollman (76) have reported whole kidney extracts which lower the blood pressure in renoprival hypertension but not in normotensive animals. Gordon (60) has suggested that the activity of the extracts from whole kidney is due to short-acting but potent adenosine nucleotides. On the other hand, medullary extracts prepared by Muirhead *et al.* (133) and Lee *et al.* (108) are sustained in their effect and are of relatively low molecular weight. The material examined by Lee, (soluble in ethanol), which was active in normotensive rats, was resistant to a mixture of peptide hydrolases and was destroyed by heating for an hour at 100°C. It appears to have the properties of a lipid. There are no reports on the oral activity of these renal principles.

B. Neurogenic Hypertension

1. *Baroceptor Denervation*

The arterial pressure which is exerted by the blood against the walls of the large arteries is characterized by a systolic pressure, the crest induced by the systolic contraction of the left ventricle, and by a diastolic pressure, the trough of which is achieved during the diastolic rest of the heart occurring between each heart beat. The systolic blood pressure in the large arteries is the product of the cardiac output and the peripheral vascular resistance and is accordingly a function of each. The diastolic pressure is maintained by the contraction of the large elastic arteries during the heart diastole and by the peripheral vascular resistance. In spite of the numerous influences which cause variations in pressure in a dynamic system such as the cardiovascular system, fluctuations are extremely limited. The nicety of homeostatic balance, which maintains such constancy, is treated in detail in a review by Heymans (84). From the standpoint of the present discussion, it is of importance to note that pressure-sensitive nervous receptors are located in the walls of the aortic arch and in the walls of the carotid sinus at the bifurcation of the internal and external carotid arteries in the neck. These pressor sensors, known as baroceptors, are connected by nerves with the vasomotor and vagus centers of the medulla. The afferent pathway for the carotid sinus nerve is by the glosso-pharyngeal or ninth cranial nerve, while the aortic arch nerves are carried centrally in the vagus nerves. Variations in blood pressure acting on the pressoceptors of the aortic arch or the carotid sinus produce reflex alterations in heart rate and degree of arteriolar constriction which oppose the changes and readjust the arterial blood pressure to its pre-existing or normal level. The efferent portion of the reflex arc is carried in the vagus and sympathetic nerves.

The heart rate is normally set by the balance of vagal and sympathetic tone exerted over the respective nerves from the vagal and sympathetic centers in the medulla. The tone is reflexly produced by the impulses reaching the medullary centers from the carotid sinus and the aortic arch baroceptors. Similarly, the degree of constriction of the arterioles is controlled by the degree of sympathetic tone activated by the same reflex mechanism. A rise in arterial pressure activates the baroceptors, and, in turn, increases the rate at which nervous impulses are sent to the vagal and sympathetic centers, thereby augmenting the cardioinhibitory tone of the vagus, and decreasing sympathetic cardioaccelerator and vasoconstrictor tone. The resulting reduction in heart rate, relaxation of the arterioles, and decrease in cardiac output lowers the blood pressure. Conversely, a lowered blood pressure produces the opposite reflex cardiovascular changes, with elevation of sympathetic predominance and reduced vagal activity, leading to an increase of the peripheral resistance, heart rate, and cardiac output, resulting inevitably in an elevated blood pressure.

It is thus seen that the nerves from the carotid sinus and the aortic arch are buffer or moderator nerves of the arterial pressure and that the baroceptors of these areas play an important role in the regulation of normal blood pressure. Stimulation of these nerves, as might be anticipated from the above discussion, by inhibiting the vasomotor center, causes a fall in blood pressure, while dividing these nerves leads to a persistent rise in the blood pressure in the dog, cat, and rabbit. Blood pressure elevation by this technique is known as "neuro-genic hypertension." Since this hypertension is caused by increased sympathetic tone, it is characterized by an increase in cardiac output and tachycardia, which differentiates it from renal hypertension and essential hypertension in the human, both of which are associated with increased peripheral resistance.

Heymans (83) produced persistent hypertension in the dog by section of all four buffer nerves. Bilateral vagotomy in order to sever all the regulatory nerve fibers from the aortic arch was too drastic a procedure for effecting chronic hypertension since dogs survived the operation but a short time, according to Kremer *et al.* (99). Grimson (63) devised a technique which has given good results in our experience. In a one-stage operation, both carotid bifurcations are extirpated; the left vagus and the medial two-thirds of the right vagus are divided. This has led to persistent hypertension with survival in good condition in two-thirds of the animals operated on. Boura and Green (16) have recently reviewed in some detail various denervation procedures. Since this type of hypertension is dependent upon the functional activity of the sympathetic nervous system, it is eliminated by total bilateral sympathectomy as reported by Heymans and Bouckaert (85).

The extensive damage to the arterioles and the cardiac hypertrophy seen with renal hypertension are not a common sequel to neurogenic hypertension. Heymans and Bouckaert (85) have suggested that this may be due to the fact that after section of the buffer nerves, the blood pressure is raised only when the animal is awake or excited. This intermittent type of hypertension might be expected to be less stressful than the continually elevated type of renal origin. Although neurogenic hypertension provides the advantage of a variety whose etiology is clearly established, its relationship to human hypertension is less definite. A possible relationship of the neurogenic to the chronic renal type of hypertension has been postulated by McCubbin *et al.* (121), with the suggestion that the baroceptors may be reset at a higher pressure level in the later phase of renal hypertension.

Neurogenic hypertension can be readily produced in the rabbit because the aortic depressor nerve is separate from the vagus and may be divided without cutting efferent vagus tracts. However, the lability of the blood pressure is so great that it is difficult to obtain reliable measurements. For this reason the rabbit has not been used extensively in experiments on neurogenic hypertension.

Within the past year the first report of the production of neurogenic hypertension in the rat was given by Krieger (100). Since the baroceptor fibers from the aorta travel in the sympathetic trunk and in the superior laryngeal nerves rather than in the vagus as in the dog, it was necessary to cut these pathways rather than the vagus. It was also necessary to denervate both carotid sinus areas by stripping the nervous structures from the carotid bifurcation and to paint the area with 10% phenol in ethanol. All animals thus operated on showed some degree of persistent hypertension which lasted up to a year in those with the highest pressure and tended to normalize in a few months in those in the lowest pressure range. Less tachycardia was noted in the rats than in neurogenic hypertensive dogs, possibly because the vagus was not disturbed. Bilateral adrenalectomy, after hypertension had developed, did not lower the blood pressure. There are no reports as yet of studies on the effect of drugs in this type of hypertension.

2. *Miscellaneous Nervous Mechanisms*

So-called audiogenic hypertension has been produced in rats by Medoff and Bongiovanni (124) who showed that rats exposed to intermittent loud noise for long periods developed hypertension. The noise was produced repeatedly by an air blast over a prolonged period up to 900 days. A hypertension, which persisted under ether anesthesia, resulted. Smirk (181) confirmed this observation by subjecting rats to the blast of motor horns and stated significantly that if emotional disturbances were primarily responsible, it was of note that the hypertension persisted at a time when conscious cerebral processes were suppressed by the anesthetic. The blood pressure increase lasted for several months after the audiogenic stimulation ended, but subsided in all cases at the end of a year. No evidence of renal damage was seen in the animals studied by Smirk. The mechanism of development of audiogenic hypertension is not known. Hudak and Buckley (91) exposed rats to various combinations of stressful auditory and visual stimuli at repeated intervals for periods up to 28 weeks, with varying combinations of stimuli to prevent acclimatization. The blood pressure of the rats gradually rose from 110 mm Hg to reach a maximum of 150 mm Hg. It was suggested that animals used in psychopharmacological tests might be found to have become hypertensive and of use in tests for antihypertensive effects (91).

Hypertension was produced by Dixon and Heller (39) by elevation of the intracranial tension. Kaolin was injected into the cisterna magna of dogs, producing hypertension which was thought to be secondary to obstruction of the subarachnoid space and the free drainage of the cerebrospinal fluid. A renal connection was suggested by Braun and Samet (17), since denervation of the kidneys prevented the rise of blood pressure from the injection of kaolin.

Taylor and Page (193) reported on the production of hypertension in the dog by ligature of the arteries supplying the head, but a high mortality and low incidence of hypertension resulted. When the procedure was combined with the insertion of a tantalum wire into the floor of the fourth ventricle and heating of the wire by diathermy, a much higher incidence of persistent hypertension resulted.

C. ENDOCRINE-INDUCED HYPERTENSION

1. *Deoxycorticosterone Hypertension*

Selye (170) observed that the administration of deoxycorticosterone acetate (DCA) daily for a 3-week period produced a condition in chicks which shared six of the major features of Bright's disease in the human. These included (1) sclerosis of the kidneys, (2) enlargement of the heart muscle, (3) thickening and hardening of the arteries, (4) high blood pressure, (5) generalized edema, and (6) albumin in the urine. These observations led him to suggest an adreno-cortical factor in nephrosclerotic hypertension. Further studies with the chick revealed that the administration of sodium chloride in the drinking water markedly sensitized the birds to the effect of DCA.

Studies performed in rats by Selye *et al.* (171) showed that in this species also, hypertension, nephrosclerosis, cardiac hypertrophy, and extensive vascular damage could be produced, provided that one of the kidneys was removed and 1% sodium chloride was given as drinking water. The hypertension was salt-dependent, since on a low-salt diet, DCA even in large doses did not produce hypertension. Among the mammals, the rat was peculiarly sensitive to DCA-salt induced hypertension, while the dog and the rabbit did not develop elevated blood pressure (114).

Hypertension due to DCA becomes irreversible and continues after the prolonged administration of the steroid and salt are discontinued. This fixed chronic state, which is known as metacorticoid (postcorticoid) hypertension, has been reviewed by Sturtevant (192). It is of interest that hypophysectomy prevents the development of DCA-induced hypertension and also restores the blood pressure to normal even in the metacorticoid state (61). The DCA is commonly administered in the form of implanted pellets. Friedman (44) found that removal of 75 mg pellets up to 51 days after implantation was followed by return of normal blood pressure within a week. DCA caused sodium accumulation and potassium depletion, notably in arterial walls (196), while the ability of the rat kidney to handle sodium loads was impaired (62).

DCA-induced hypertension differs fundamentally in mechanism from renal hypertension, since DCA-hypertension ensues before there is any demonstrable renal damage and even in the absence of kidneys (75, 101). Moreover, trans-planted kidneys from animals with metacorticoid hypertension are capable of lowering the blood pressure in renal hypertensive animals. In addition, adrenalectomy, which lowers the blood pressure in renal hypertension, is without effect in DCA hypertension (80).

An interesting action of DCA reported by Gross (70) is its property of reducing the renin content of the rat kidney in nonhypertensive doses whether or not the renal artery is clamped; the granules of the juxtaglomerular cells which are thought to secrete renin were reduced in intensity in this study. The relationship between this action and the hypertensive effect of DCA is not clear, and it is possible that the decreased renin content may be due to the elevated sodium content of the tissues.

Since DCA is probably not a naturally occurring steroid, sweeping generali-zations based on its actions cannot be made concerning the role of adrenocortical dysfunction in the hypertensive state. From the standpoint of the present interest, it should be noted that Gaunt *et al.* (49) have found DCA hypertension to be a stable form which lends itself to the evaluation of the hypotensive actions of reserpine and hydralazine.

2. *Aldosterone Hypertension*

This aspect of the action of aldosterone has been the subject of a thorough review by Gross (72), who presents strong evidence that its circulatory actions are mediated through its capacity for causing sodium retention. It is the most potent known mineralocorticoid and is elaborated by the adrenal cortex. The primary function of aldosterone is to modulate the transport and distribution of sodium, potassium, and hydrogen ions across cellular membranes (102). Its most important action is on renal tubular cells, where by a direct action it promotes the retention of sodium and augments the elimination of potassium ions. By virtue of its sodium-retaining action, aldosterone is indirectly involved in the maintenance of blood pressure and volume. In view of the qualitative similarity between the effects of aldosterone and DCA on electrolyte balance, Gross *et al.* (72) carried out studies on the possible hypertensive action of aldosterone. In rats made sensitive by unilateral nephrectomy and the administration of 1% sodium chloride as drinking water, it was found that the daily administration of 0.5 mg of *d-l*-aldosterone produced the same magnitude of hypertensive response as that achieved with 2.5 mg of DCA. Since 0.5 mg of the racemate was equivalent to 0.25 mg of the active isomer, *d*-aldosterone, the potency of aldosterone to DCA was 10 to 1. The equivalent dose of aldosterone was higher than would be expected on the basis of the sodium-retaining capacity of aldosterone compared with DCA, which in adrenalectomized rats and dogs is approximately 25 or 30 to 1. From this it appears that aldosterone has about one-third the hypertensive action of DCA, based on relative sodium-retaining capacities.

As was the case with DCA, hypertension was not produced in dogs or rabbits by aldosterone in spite of the production of considerable sodium retention. The vascular lesions produced in the kidney, heart, and blood vessels were much less marked in the aldosterone-treated rats than in those receiving DCA. In this connection, the amount of sodium chloride consumed by the DCA-treated animals was double that taken by those receiving aldosterone, furnishing support to the importance of the role of sodium in aldosterone hypertension. The adrenals are not essential for the development of aldosterone hypertension, nor does adrenalectomy cause any greater sensitivity to exogenous aldosterone. Aldosterone has a distinctly shorter duration of action than does DCA, and this property may also play a part in its less marked effect on the blood pressure and blood vessels (72). Using a nephrectomized rat, which is exquisitely sensitive to the reninlike pressor activity of kidney extracts, it was shown that the pressor activity found in extracts of normal kidneys was depleted from the kidneys of rats treated with either aldosterone or DCA as a result of sodium retention and increased blood volume and renal blood flow. The hypertensive effect of aldosterone may therefore be linked to sodium retention with its resulting expanded plasma volume and increased sodium and water content of the walls of the arteries and arterioles, which decrease their lumina and distensibility and increase their resistance to flow.

Although exogenous aldosterone administered in large doses results in hypertension, the occurrence of elevated levels of endogenous aldosterone does not necessarily give rise to elevated blood pressure. Primary hyperaldosteronism, first reported by Conn (30), which is the result of an aldosterone-secreting tumor of the adrenal cortex, is characterized by hypertension, potassium loss in the urine, hypokalemic alkalosis, and much reduced renin plasma levels. In fact, Conn (31) considers the combination of elevated aldosterone output and absence of renin in the peripheral plasma to be pathognomonic of primary aldosteronism with an aldosterone-secreting tumor of the adrenal cortex. Secondary hyperaldosteronism is present in malignant hypertension, where Laragh (103) feels that it is a result rather than the cause of the disorder. In this state the excess aldosterone is probably due to the excessive renin secretion from damaged kidneys, which leads in turn to the secretion of angiotensin. The latter has been shown to be a potent stimulant of aldosterone secretion upon administration to either man or dog (26) as well as when given by direct perfusion of the adrenal cortex of the dog. The action of angiotensin is specific, since equipressor doses of epinephrine and norepinephrine do not increase the secretory rate. Moreover, angiotensin can be infused intravenously for several days into normal dogs in nonpressor doses at a rate which augments urinary aldosterone excretion (26). The following concise exposition of the role of angiotensin has been proposed by Laragh (102), who suggested that a renal-adrenal mechanism may exist for the control of sodium balance in which renin, released by the kidney when its perfusion is reduced, generates angiotensin, which, in turn, stimulates aldosterone secretion by the adrenal cortex. Aldosterone, by promoting salt retention, increases blood volume which serves to restore renal perfusion and to suppress further renin release. Beyond such a cyclic "feedback" mechanism, there are the additional considerations that angiotensin is itself a potent pressor substance, and that increases in the potassium plasma level can also elicit increased secretion of aldosterone. The situation is further complicated by the observation of McCubbin and Page (122) that angiotensin appears to intensify the response of the blood vessels to norepinephrine released by sympathetic vasoconstrictor nerves.

Hyperaldosteronism secondary to edematous states including cirrhosis, nephrosis, and heart failure, is characterized by elevated plasma renin levels and by an absence of hypertension. The elevated renin level in this case is a consequence of a reduced blood volume or a reduced renal perfusion pressure. The fluid and sodium chloride retained by the action of aldosterone on the renal tubule normally remains in the circulation and tends to raise the renal perfusion pressure and stop the secretion of renin by the kidney. Since in the edematous state the retained fluid and electrolyte are filtered into the tissues, the renal perfusion is not improved, renin secretion continues unchecked, and edema becomes progressively worse as the accumulation of fluid goes on unchecked.

The aldosterone secretion rate in benign chronic renal hypertensive dogs is within normal limits, according to Carpenter *et al.* (26), indicating that the renin-angiotensin-aldosterone sequential mechanism is not overactive in this state. In contrast, these investigators noted an increased secretion of aldosterone in the malignant form of experimental renal hypertension accompanying severe renal damage such as that reported by Laragh (103) in the malignant form in the human. Gross (72) postulates that aldosterone plays a permissive role in the development of experimental renal hypertension to explain the decrease of the hypertension upon the removal of the adrenals and its restoration by the increased administration of sodium. Even though the role of aldosterone may be merely permissive, the availability of an appropriate antagonist might theoretically exert a salutary influence in experimental renal hypertension as well as in human essential hypertension.

3. Adrenal Regeneration Hypertension

In 1955 Skelton (176) produced a severe hypertension in uninephrectomized, salt-treated rats during regeneration of the enucleated adrenal cortex, an observation which served to focus attention on the role of the adrenal in hypertension. The nature of adrenal regeneration hypertension has been the subject of reviews by Gaunt *et al.* (50) and by Skelton (177). Enucleation of the adrenal was performed by making a small incision in the capsule of the adrenal gland and expressing the mass of glandular tissue through the capsular opening by the application of gentle pressure with forceps. Hypertension developed as the residual cells of the zona glomerulosa of the adrenal proliferated and the gland regenerated. It was necessary to remove the opposite adrenal, since the presence of one intact adrenal prevented both regeneration of the contralateral enucleated gland and the occurrence of hypertension, even though the intact gland underwent considerable compensatory hypertrophy. Reduction of the renal cell mass by removal of one kidney and the use of 1% salt as drinking water were necessary adjuncts. The blood pressure usually rose from about 120 to 160 mm Hg in 2 weeks and as high as 220 mm Hg within 7 weeks of the enucleation. The associated hypertensive vascular disease resembled closely that produced by DCA administration, with enlargement of the heart, kidney, and brain, with lesions in the blood vessels of these organs and generalized polyarteritis. The resemblance between adrenal regeneration hypertension and that produced by DCA administration suggested the importance of altered secretory activity of the adrenal cortex. The appearance of hypertension during the course of regeneration of the adrenal cortex is the most significant factor indicative of the pathogenic importance of regenerating cortical tissue. Since the zona glomerulosa of the adrenal is considered to be the site of aldosterone formation (51), it has been suggested that the hypertension may be due to an imbalance between the secretion of aldosterone and corticosterone. Excessive secretion of aldosterone does not appear to be responsible, for, as mentioned earlier, its administration does not produce the severe lesions which are typical of adrenal regeneration hypertension, and increased sodium in the diet would tend to decrease aldosterone secretion. Although there is no definite evidence to implicate any of the known adrenal steroids directly as the etiological agent in the experimental hypertension, Skelton considers that the concurrence of elevated plasma-free corticosterone levels, presumably cortisone, and the onset of hypertension between the second and third weeks after enucleation may be of significance. Masson *et al.* (115) have suggested that the period of adrenocortical insufficiency which follows adrenal enucleation might produce an increased sensitivity to the existing hypertensive action of corticosterone. Regeneration of the adrenal cortex appears to be regulated by the adrenocorticotropic (ACTH) hormone of the anterior pituitary, since removal of the pituitary or inhibition of ACTH production by steroid hormones prevents adrenal regeneration and the characteristic hypertension. Substances such as amphenone B (27) and stilbestrol (178), which block the synthesis of adrenal steroids, are capable of inhibiting or reversing adrenal regeneration hypertension. Re-enucleation of the regenerated adrenal after hypertension has ensued resulted in a temporary fall in blood pressure to a level above that prior to enucleation. However, when hypertension has been established, neither excision of the regenerated adrenal nor removal of salt from the drinking water was sufficient to cause a fall in blood pressure. The existence of severe renal vascular damage at this stage has prompted the suggestion that the persistent hypertension may be supported by a renal mechanism.

Despite the uncertainty as to its precise etiology, adrenal regeneration hypertension may be modified by hypotensive agents. Chart *et al.* (28) have shown that hydralazine lowered the blood pressure without influencing the salt intake of the rats. Reserpine and syrosingopine were also effective in lowering the blood pressure in this disorder. The action of reserpine was accompanied by a reduction of the salt intake of the animals, but the acute effect of reserpine appeared to be due to its known pharmacological actions on the autonomic nervous system. Syrosingopine, a weakly sedative analog of reserpine, had much less influence on salt intake but was equally effective in reducing the blood pressure.

4. *Glucocorticoid Hypertension*

Hypertension can be produced in rats by the administration of the glucocorticoids, cortisone and hydrocortisone. This form of hypertension, which has been reviewed by Gaunt (50), differs from that following DCA administration in a number of its characteristics: (1) it does not require excess sodium in the diet and is, in fact, intensified by sodium excretion; (2) there are no changes in serum sodium and potassium levels; (3) there is no renal or vascular damage; (4) the hypertension is not heightened by removal of a kidney or the addition of salt to the drinking water; (5) hypertension develops faster but is not as intense as after DCA; (6) serum cholesterol levels are not elevated as they are with DCA administration (45, 69, 94). The fundamental difference between the hypertensive action of the glucocorticoids and that of other adrenal steroids is the independence of the former of sodium ion.

Gaunt *et al.* (48) have found this form of hypertension to be more responsive to reserpine than that induced by DCA.

5. *Salt-induced Hypertension*

The relationship between sodium chloride and hypertension in both experimental animals and man has been the subject of considerable study. It has been mentioned that the administration of excess salt is obligatory for the production of hypertension with DCA, aldosterone, or during adrenal regeneration. However, it is also possible to produce hypertension in rats solely by the prolonged administration of excessive amounts of salt. This subject has been reviewed by Rodbard (161), Meneeley and Ball (127), and Sapirstein (163). In 1943, Selye and Stone (172) demonstrated nephrosclerosis in chicks fed 2% saline, and in 1948 Lenel *et al.* (109) reported hypertension in chickens drinking 1% saline. In 1950 Saperstein noted the hypertensive effect of the administration of 2% saline to normal rats. Meneeley (128) has carried out extensive studies on the hypertensive effect of excess salt ingestion by the rat and has found that the blood pressure rose slowly over a period of 12 months or longer and that the height of the blood pressure was a function of the amount of salt in the diet. A mild hypertension developed after 2.8–5.6% salt, while a moderate to severe hypertension was produced by 7–9.8% salt. Damage to the arteries, arterioles, and glomeruli of the kidney developed in animals receiving 7% or more salt in their diet. These observations have been confirmed by Koletsky (96), who found hypertension with similar lesions in rats drinking 1% salt for a period of a year. Meneeley (126) also reported electrocardiographic changes similar to those seen in human hypertension in his studies in rats. The changes were proportional to the amount of salt in the diet and to the severity of the hypertension. The animals on the higher salt ration also showed reduction in survival rate. Interestingly, the addition of potassium chloride to the diets of the latter group markedly increased survival time without affecting the hypertension.

By selective inbreeding, Dahl (33) has developed two strains of rats which differed markedly in their susceptibility to the development of experimental hypertension from excess salt ingestion. In subsequent studies Dahl (34, 35) has shown that animals from the strain which was more susceptible to developing hypertension after excess salt were also more prone to develop DCA hypertension and renal hypertension after renal artery clamping. Similarly, the more sensitive strain had significantly greater vascular reactivity to both angiotensin and norepinephrine than did the resistant strain. The combination of increased tendency to develop renal hypertension, heightened sensitivity to pressor agents, and augmented reactivity to excessive salt ingestion in the same animal strain suggests that a single aberration may be responsible for the several effects. Such a strain of animals might provide useful information in the evaluation of antihypertensive agents.

D. DIETARY HYPERTENSION

Hartroft and Best (78) produced hypertension in rats by feeding weanlings a diet deficient in choline intermittently on several 5-day periods separated by 2-day periods when choline was supplied. A marked hypertension characterized by renal tubular lesions, cardiac hypertrophy, and arteriolar lesions developed over the next several months.

Grollman and White (68) studied the effect of diets low in choline and potassium in weanling rats and newly weaned puppies and were able to regulate the severity of the hypertension by varying the duration of feeding the deficient diets. In rats the severity of the hypertension could be intensified by using 1% salt solution as drinking water or by removing one kidney. There are no reports on the use of such hypertensive animals in the study of antihypertensive drugs.

E. HEREDITARY HYPERTENSION

Elevated arterial pressure appears to be an inheritable characteristic in man, according to Pickering (148). Smirk and Hall (184) studied this aspect of experimental hypertension in the rat and succeeded by prolonged inbreeding in developing several strains of animals with elevated blood pressure. The hypertension in these animals became progressively higher with successive generations, for in 1958 about 25% of the males had blood pressures over 140 mm Hg, and in 1961 over 50% of the males exhibited blood pressures over 150 mm Hg (105). There was no difference between the response of the control and of the hypertensive animals to the pressor effect of norepinephrine administered intravenously under light anesthesia. Hexamethonium reduced the blood pressure of inherited hypertensive and control rats to the same level, suggesting that the elevated blood pressure is neurogenically maintained. Bilateral adrenalectomy lowered the blood pressures of the hypertensive and the control rats but did not alter the pressure differential which existed preoperatively between the two groups (134). Recent observations have led Smirk to believe that as the hypertension progresses, a renal factor may come into play in maintaining the hypertensive state. This type of hypertensive preparation deserves broader application in the evaluation of hypertensive substances, since he (185) has established that the absolute fall in the blood pressure was greater and hence more readily demonstrable in such hypertensive rats than in normotensive control rats in response to a variety of agents, including reserpine, guanethidine, bethanidine, and α-methyldopa. In contrast, rats with hereditary hypertension and normal controls as well were refractory to bretylium tosylate and 2-(hexahydro-1-azepinyl) ethyl guanidine, a compound closely related to guanethidine. This last observation serves to emphasize that no single experimental subject can be depended upon exclusively to reveal potential antihypertensive action.

III. Development of antihypertensive agents

Ideally, the action of an antihypertensive agent should be focused on the specific aberration responsible for the occurrence of essential hypertension. Despite intensive study, however, the etiological factors inducing this pathological state are not known with certainty. As mentioned earlier, essential hypertension in man is associated with an increased peripheral resistance due to an increased state of constriction of the arterioles, the specific cause of which remains a baffling mystery. Smirk (182) has proposed that the cause of human essential hypertension is multifactorial and that the observed blood pressure level represents the summation of a number of independent factors, one or more of which are exaggerated in hypertension. The mosaic theory of Page (138) similarly ascribes the cause of essential hypertension to multiple factors. Whatever primary causes are responsible for the rise in pressure, it is the height of the blood pressure which is responsible for the deleterious clinical manifestations, according to Smirk. Hollander (88) has provided experimental support for this view, noting that the water and electrolyte content of the arteries was elevated in the hypertensive portion but was normal in the normotensive portion of the aorta on either side of a mechanical constriction or coarctation. Wilkins (200) has expressed the same view, stating that the blood pressure elevation, however produced, if repeated often or continuously enough and high enough, results in cardiovascular disease. The opinions of various investigators are quite divergent as to the relative importance of the roles played by renal, adrenal, or nervous influences in the initiation of increased vascular tone and the elevated diastolic blood pressure typical of essential hypertension. From the viewpoint of one interested in the development of drugs, the multifactorial theory is especially attractive, since a substance acting to dampen increased pressor activity of renal, endocrine, or nervous origin or to decrease the responsivity of the arterioles to any of these influences, might be considered to possess potential as an antihypertensive agent. In practice in the laboratory, of course, one usually first becomes cognizant of the hypotensive properties of an agent in a general screening test, while the mechanism of action is evolved only as the result of more detailed study. Aside from the scientific interest, the study of mechanism is important in that any substance with a novel hypotensive effect provides the possibility of a more effective treatment of hypertension.

It would appear reasonable that in the search for antihypertensive drugs the use of hypertensive animals would be more likely to yield better results. This may well be the case, but an insufficient number of controlled studies have been carried out to establish this as a fact. Most of the experience with the effects of drugs in hypertensive animals consists of extensions of studies with substances whose hypotensive properties have been revealed in experiments in normotensive animals. It has been reported that the fall in blood pressure in renal hypertensive dogs is greater than that in normotensive animals after various hypotensive substances, but it is not certain as to whether this difference denotes a specific antihypertensive effect or merely represents a greater absolute fall which is comparable on a percentage basis. In any case, the search for antihypertensive agents has been carried out in the majority of laboratories almost exclusively with normotensive animals, since their use, which was simpler technically, has been adequate for the discovery of the majority of the drugs presently employed in the treatment of hypertension. This might be anticipated if the hypertensive state is due to the exaggeration of a function supporting the blood pressure in the normotensive state. Spontaneously occurring hypertension, which might be desirable, is rare in animals except for that recently reported by Smirk (184) with inbred strains of rats. Hypertension in this strain appears to be converted to a renal mechanism after beginning on a neurogenic basis. Also, the methods required for the production of experimental hypertension in animals have been rather time-consuming and subject to such individual variability in rate of onset and intensity of hypertension as to preclude their use in the initial evaluation of large numbers of chemical compounds. It may be that the ultimate wider availability of spontaneously hypertensive animals such as the inbred strain developed by Smirk and Hall (184) will permit their use to advantage in the search for agents which can influence the very factors peculiar to and responsible for naturally occurring hypertensive disease. Theoretically such an agent should constitute a therapeutic advance. Only such factors as are present in both normotensive and hypertensive animals can be expected to be favorably modified by existing test methods.

Regardless of the method by which a drug is evaluated, a potentially valuable hypotensive agent should cause a gradual rather than a precipitate fall of blood pressure at a practical and safely administered dosage. The fall should not be excessive and preferably the duration, rather than the intensity of the decrease, should be a function of the dose. The action should be sufficiently prolonged and steady over the effective interval. Tolerance to the drug should not be marked. Oral activity, with regular absorption from the gastrointestinal tract, is a most important requirement. Side effects should be minimal and not of a serious nature. Generally speaking, a definite and lasting drop in blood pressure should be produced consistently in several animals by doses of 5.0 mg/per kilogram or less in acute experiments to warrant serious consideration. However, arbitrary standards are always dangerous, especially when dealing with substances which exhibit a gradual onset of action or have a tendency to be cumulative. Substances which lower the blood pressure upon administration to an experimental animal are legion, but only a small fraction of these hypotensive agents meet the exacting standards required of an antihypertensive agent. For example, despite the marked hypotensive potencies of histamine and acetylcholine, their transiency of effect alone excludes them from consideration. In addition, their intensity rather than their duration of effect is increased by elevating the dose—an undesirable characteristic. Lastly, each substance produces many uncomfortable and serious side effects because of diverse effects on other organ systems. Other substances which lower the blood pressure acutely may be merely cardiac depressants, an action which can be easily detected by direct cardiac studies.

A. Blood Pressure Regulatory Function of the Sympathetic Nervous System

The sympathetic vasoconstrictor nerves were long known to regulate the peripheral resistance of the arterioles, primarily in the splanchnic area and in the skin, and hence it was logical that compounds which inhibited the sympathetic nervous system should be studied early for antihypertensive activity. Further, though there was no evidence that the increased arteriolar resistance of essential hypertension was due to exaggerated sympathetic nervous activity, it had been demonstrated by Smithwick (186) that surgical removal of a portion of the sympathetic pathways by bilateral excision of the thoracolumbar ganglionic chains lowered the blood pressure in essential hypertension by restoring the peripheral resistance toward the normal range. This observation suggested the possibility and served as an impetus to secure

this therapeutic effect with drugs through a so-called "chemical sympathectomy." In fact, drugs can produce a more effective sympathectomy than could
ever be managed surgically, since they are capable of affecting all sympathetic
pathways, central as well as peripheral, many of which are beyond the reach
of the surgeon. Another advantage is that the pharmacological sympathectomy,
by its nature, is a reversible procedure which affords the physician an opportunity to vary the duration and magnitude of the effect to the requirement of
each patient.

In view of the fact that the investigation of agents which reduce or block the
activity of the sympathetic nervous system at different levels has been most
fruitful in the area of antihypertensive therapy, a consideration of the organization and integration of this system as it regulates arterial blood flow and
pressure is appropriate at this point. The highest recognized centers of the
system are located in the hypothalamus, in the midbrain region. Descending
nervous pathways connect these centers and the various lower levels of the
system through junctions at the ganglionic and nerve-muscle regions. Over
these connecting pathways volleys of impulses pass down the spinal cord along
vasoconstrictor nerve tracts through the ganglia, ultimately reaching the
smooth muscle effector cells of the blood vessels whose caliber they regulate.
Electrical stimulation of the hypothalamic center which dominates the
system results in a general rise in blood pressure. Similarly, tension, appre-
hension, and excitement, acting from higher cortical centers which impinge
on the hypothalamus, may elicit constrictor nerve impulses which result in
an elevation of blood pressure. Although the cortical pathways involved are
not precisely defined, it is truly said that man by his thoughts alone can raise
his blood pressure. It can be further visualized that in certain cases the reduced
blood flow to the kidney, thus induced, may promote the liberation of pressor
substances which further narrow the blood vessels, thereby initiating a vicious
cycle. Although the sympathetic nervous system is subject to the influence of the
prevailing mental attitude or emotional state of an individual, fortunately this
influence does not usually interfere with the primary role of the autonomic
nervous system in the regulation of heart rate, blood pressure, digestion, body
temperature regulation, sexual function, excretion, endocrine and exocrine
glandular activity, visual efficiency, and other bodily functions, in a manner
conducive to maximum efficiency. These functions just enumerated are not
under control of the will, but are apparently mediated in an orderly fashion
without conscious action. Hence this branch of the nervous system has been
described as being autonomic or involuntary in its control. There is an essential
anatomic difference between the arrangements of the voluntary system, which
is utilized consciously, and that of the autonomic nervous system, which is of
sufficient importance to require detailed description.

The motor nerve cells of the voluntary nervous system lie entirely within the confines of the central nervous system, and terminal axons pass out of the spinal cord to end in skeletal muscles, while in the autonomic or sympathetic nervous system, a neuronal cell body is interposed between the spinal cord and the gland, vascular smooth muscle, or heart tissue which it innervates. The interposed neuron has, in fact, migrated outward from the spinal cord during the embryological development of the nervous system, and its position outside the limits of the central nervous system is, in a certain sense, symbolic of the degree of autonomy peculiar to this system. These neurons are assembled in clusters (which constitute the sympathetic ganglia) beside each thoracic and lumbar vertebra. A chain, formed by the connection of 23 such ganglia, lies on either side of the spinal cord in the lumbar and thoracic regions. The surgical removal of these chains, together with the adjacent splanchnic nerves, by Smithwick (186) reduced vasoconstriction and peripheral resistance sufficiently to lower significantly elevated blood pressure in essential hypertension.

Within each ganglion are the fibers of the preganglionic nerve emanating from the spinal cord, the cell body of the postganglionic nerve and its efferent postganglionic fibers coursing toward the peripheral blood vessels. The pre- and postganglionic neurons are in communication across a synaptic space over which impulse transmission is effected by the liberation of acetylcholine at the preganglionic cell terminals. Depolarization of the postganglionic neuron by the acetylcholine initiates trains of impulses which are propagated along the postganglionic nerve to peripheral loci such as blood vessels. Ganglionic blocking agents interfere competitively with the actions of acetylcholine formed at the ganglia and thus interrupt constrictor nerve impulses at that point.

Impulses arriving at the termini of the sympathetic nervous system cause the release of a neurohumor, norepinephrine, which acts upon a receptor site of the arteriolar smooth muscle to evoke a contraction of the smooth muscle of the blood vessel wall with a resulting increase in the resistance to the flow of blood. Since adrenaline had earlier been thought to be the neuromediator, the terms adrenergic system and sympathetic system are used interchangeably in the literature and, similarly, compounds which block the stimulatory action of norepinephrine or of sympathetic nerves on blood vessels are called adrenergic blocking or sympathetic blocking substances. More recently, adrenergic inhibitory agents have been subclassified into alpha and beta adrenergic blocking agents. The alpha type refers to those inhibiting the effects of the constrictor fibers as described above, while the beta type comprises those substances which suppress sympathetically mediated cardioaccelerator, vaso- dilator, and bronchorelaxant effects. The terms alpha and beta are derived from the discrete alpha and beta receptor substances which are present at the effector sites in the heart and in the vascular smooth muscle and which control the nature of the response of the cell to the released catecholamine.

The autonomic nervous system is not a homogeneous unit but contains another division known as the parasympathetic or cholinergic division. This system, which is a counterpart of the sympathetic division, has a center in the hypothalamus adjoining the sympathetic center and controls the identical organs innervated by the sympathetic system typically in a reciprocal manner, producing an antagonistic effect. The pharmacological nature of the two divisions is identical at the preganglionic level. This division, therefore, assumes importance in a discussion of antihypertensive agents because of the side effects produced when its actions are blocked within the ganglia. For example, the activity of the parasympathetic system causes generally dilation of the blood vessels of the abdominal viscera and cardiac slowing, which is the reverse of the effect of the sympathetic system. Since acetylcholine is the neuromediator liberated by the postganglionic nerves, it is also referred to as the cholinergic division of the autonomic system. Substances which block the action of sympathetic nerves at postganglionic sites have, in general, greater specificity of effect, since the pharmacological nature of the postganglionic nerves in the two is dissimilar rather than identical as in the case of the ganglia. The ganglia of the parasympathetic division are not arranged in chains segmentally along the vertebrae, but are spread diffusely and generally lie buried within the structure of the organs which they innervate.

Important as the adrenergic system obviously is, it was demonstrated by Cannon (25) that its complete surgical removal, with survival, was possible in animals, and more recently this has been shown to be the case in the human, where large parts of the system have been successfully removed in sympathectomies designed for the relief of hypertension. In contrast, the removal of the parasympathetic ganglia, if such were desirable, is not feasible because of anatomic considerations. Fortunately, blockade of this system by peripherally acting anticholinergic drugs is readily achieved.

B. Antihypertensive Substances Suppressing the Sympathetic Nervous System

Based on the architecture of the sympathetic nervous system as described above, there are at least three regions at which blocking drugs may act. Starting peripherally and progressing centrally, these are: (1) the junction between the sympathetic nerve and the blood vessel, (2) the junction within the sympathetic ganglia, and (3) the region of the hypothalamic sympathetic center. Even more peripherally, the responsiveness of the smooth muscle of the peripheral blood vessels to sympathetic nervous stimulation, or to other pressor factors as well, may be reduced. Substances which act at these sites have been detected by the use of normotensive anesthetized animals, although they are generally also effective in experimental hypertensive preparations as well. Animals most commonly used include the dog, cat, rabbit, and the rat under pentobarbital, α-chloralose, or diallylbarbituric acid anesthesia. Practice varies in different laboratories. In our case, the primary study has been largely restricted to the use of dogs under pentobarbital anesthesia, with supplemental study of active substances in various types of experimental hypertension. Blood pressure was recorded kymographically from a cannulated femoral artery by means of an Anderson (3) glass capsule manometer following intravenous administration of graded doses of the test substance. Blood pressure was followed for at least 4 hours in order to detect action of gradual onset. Incidental observations were made during the course of the experiment on the effect of the test substance on the hypertensive effects of epinephrine, norepinephrine, angiotensin amide, and amphetamine, in view of the possible participation of the first three of these compounds in human hypertension. Amphetamine was included because its action appears to be mediated by the release of endogenous norepinephrine.

The use of an anesthetic has much to recommend it. In the first place, it is a humane procedure and prevents discomfort, which can ensue inadvertently in the testing of new compounds of unknown activity or toxicity. In addition, there is generally a tendency of the anesthetic to augment the hypotensive effect of a substance, thus reducing the likelihood of overlooking a subtly acting compound. This action appears to be related to the depressant action of a barbiturate on the compensatory cardioaccelerator and pressor reflexes evoked by a fall in blood pressure. The choice of animals, anesthetic, and methods for the determination of blood pressure are many and varied. This aspect has been the subject of a most comprehensive recent review by Boura and Green (16), which can be consulted to advantage for description of detailed procedures.

1. Sympathetic Nervous Blockade Below the Ganglia

a. *Adrenergic Blockade.* The discussion of this group and others to follow is intended to emphasize those tests used in the laboratory to reveal such activity and to compare their effects on the blood pressure and vascular reactivity of normotensive and hypertensive animals. Their detailed pharmacology will be found in the chapter devoted to this subject.

Substances of this class, typified by phentolamine and piperoxan, inhibit the augmentory effects of exogenous epinephrine and norepinephrine upon the alpha receptors of vascular smooth muscle and thus upon the blood pressure of the dog; in sufficiently large doses they invert the pressor effect of epinephrine, and, in somewhat larger doses antagonize the pressor effect of direct sympathetic nervous stimulation. Since the beta receptors escape the inhibition, reflex tachycardia in response to the hypotension is not checked. As a result, substances of this type, though of theoretical interest, have not gained a place in antihypertensive therapy. Prior administration of reserpine reduces the associated tachycardia, but this combination has not been applied clinically.

Phentolamine lowers the blood pressure of anesthetized dogs, cats, and rabbits upon intravenous administration, in our experience, while in contrast, it has been reported to cause an elevation of the blood pressure of unanesthetized renal hypertensive rats (155). This serves to emphasize the importance of anesthesia and animal species in the evaluation of cardiovascular drugs. Extensive studies have not been carried out with this type of compound in other animal species with experimental hypertension, primarily because of general inapplicability in essential hypertension.

b. *Adrenergic Neuron Blockade*. On the basis of the pharmacological actions of guanethidine as described by Maxwell *et al.* (120) and Page and Dustan (142), the substance is best described as a specific peripheral sympathetic suppressant which impedes sympathetic efferent nervous transmission. As with other substances being considered, this discussion will deal with the pharmacological methods of detecting guanethidinelike activity in experimental animals. Its detailed pharmacology and mechanism of action will be treated in the chapter devoted to guanethidine.

The typical hypotensive effect of guanethidine is slow in onset and persistent and is accompanied by a bradycardia. Upon intravenous administration to the barbiturate-anesthetized dog, the hypotensive effect is not marked and is often preceded by an early rise in blood pressure which tends to obscure the subsequent delayed fall. Actually, guanethidine was discovered in the course of a study of the antagonism of amphetamine by some derivatives of methylphenidate rather than in a search for hypotensive activity as such. The observation of Maxwell of the antagonism of the pressor effect of amphetamine by an analog of guanethidine which had been administered a week previously provided the initial clue to the unusually long duration of its cardiovascular effects.

The hypotensive action may be more readily demonstrated by administration of the drug into the lumen of the small intestine of the anesthetized dog. As shown by Barrett (6), the initial pressor effect of guanethidine is minimized when this route is employed. The fall in blood pressure produced by guanethidine is definitely greater and more prolonged in the unanesthetized neurogenic or renal hypertensive dog than in the normotensive animal (120). Renal hypertension in the rat is also suppressed by the daily administration of guanethidine (10). Stanton (190) has recently reported that guanethidine, administered subcutaneously, elicited an initial acute fall in blood pressure in unanesthetized metacorticoid hypertensive rats but not in normotensive animals. Results with chronic administration of the drug were less consistent, with some suggestion of tolerance appearing, suggesting that this preparation might not accurately portray guanethidine activity.

In acute blood pressure experiments in anesthetized dogs, the pressor effect of norepinephrine is enhanced, while that due to amphetamine, ephedrine, or phenylethylamine is reduced. The pressor effects following bilateral occlusion of the carotid arteries and stimulation of the central end of the vagus are also antagonized. Typical of guanethidine is the antagonism of the pressor effects of amphetamine for a period of weeks after a single large dose or after the chronic daily administration of smaller doses.

The detection of activity characteristic of guanethidine is feasible in normotensive dogs on the basis of the criteria mentioned above, and should be considered when moderate hypotensive activity is preceded by a hypertensive effect upon administration of a substance to the anesthetized dog. Antagonism of amphetamine and potentiation of norepinephrine in addition, especially if demonstrable on the day following drug administration, are strongly indicative of the persistent nature of such action. The absence of sedative action readily serves to differentiate guanethidine from reserpine.

The hypotensive activity of bretylium is due to inhibition of sympathetic vasoconstrictor activity brought about by interference with the release of norepinephrine from the postganglionic nerve. Its detailed pharmacological profile will be treated in the section devoted to this topic. Upon intravenous administration to the chloralosed normotensive cat, the blood pressure usually rose temporarily and then fell gradually (15). The fall was slight but prolonged. The subtle effect could easily be mistaken for the gradual deterioration occurring in the course of an acute experiment in an anesthetized animal. However, the potentiation of the pressor effects of epinephrine and norepinephrine in the cat provided a valuable clue to the possibility that peripheral sympathetic inhibition had been produced. Relaxation of the nictitating membrane in the anesthetized cat also provided a preliminary clue that hypotension might be expected to occur in the anesthetized preparation.

2. *Ganglionic Blockade*

Substances of this category which inhibit the transmission of vasoconstrictor impulses through the ganglia include hexamethonium, chlorisondamine, mecamylamine, and pentolinium; these act by lessening the constrictor tone of the arterioles and venules, with a resulting decrease in cardiac output.

Such substances produce a prompt and marked fall in the blood pressure of dogs and rats under barbiturate anesthesia but cause only a slight reduction in the pressure of normotensive unanesthetized animals of each species (119). On the other hand, the normotensive unanesthetized rabbit and monkey exhibited a substantial fall in blood pressure after administration of ganglionic blocking agents.

The blood pressure level of the unanesthetized benign renal hypertensive dog and of the unanesthetized neurogenic hypertensive dog was only briefly depressed by ganglionic blockade while, interestingly, the conscious dog in the malignant phase of hypertension responded with a sustained systolic and diastolic decline following the injection of chlorisondamine. Apparently even in the presence of a potent ganglionic blocking agent the unanesthetized dog is capable of considerable peripheral arteriolar constriction, suggesting that certain efferent nerve pathways are not affected by ganglionic blockade or that ganglionic blockade is incomplete. This is supported by the observation of Maxwell (118) that splanchnic nerve stimulation still elevates the blood pressure after strong ganglionic blockade. These pressor mechanisms are apparently abolished by barbiturate anesthesia.

The blood pressure of anesthetized renal hypertensive rats is lowered by ganglionic blockade, while, in sharp contrast, it has been reported that the blood pressure of unanesthetized renal hypertensive animals is raised (155). In studies with pempidine, Spinks (189) found extremely variable effects on the blood pressure of conscious renal hypertensive and normotensive animals and resorted to the use of chloralosed animals.

Ganglionic blocking agents potentiate the pressor effect of epinephrine and norepinephrine in the anesthetized dog. This effect, combined with a prompt fall in blood pressure, is strongly suggestive of ganglionic blocking activity. The bradycardia produced by ganglionic blocking agents in the anesthetized dogs helps to differentiate them from the adrenergic blocking substances which regularly cause tachycardia. More specific tests for ganglionic blockade will be treated in the chapter devoted primarily to this topic.

Again, the need for the selection of the proper species for hypotensive testing is seen. It is apparent that the presence of barbiturate anesthesia is a valuable adjunct for detecting ganglionic blockade in normotensive or hypertensive animals, except for dogs with malignant renal hypertension which are responsive even in the conscious state.

3. *Central and Adrenergic Neuron Blockade*

The action of reserpine is due to a dampening of the sympathetic nervous system at all levels, centrally as well as peripherally. Its detailed mechanism of action will be discussed in the chapters devoted to the rauwolfia derivatives.

The hypotensive activity of reserpine is demonstrable in the normotensive dog, cat, or rabbit under barbiturate anesthesia. The unique features of the action of this substance are a bradycardic action in the face of a falling blood pressure, a subtle onset of action over a period of several hours, a marked potency and a prolonged action. Following a moderate single oral dose of 0.3 mg/per kilogram orally to the unanesthetized dog, the sedative and hypotensive action of the drug does not become apparent until the following day. Initially, the modest hypotensive effect of reserpine is often preceded by an equally subtle hypertensive action which tends to mask the delayed action of the drug. It was not known for several years after its discovery (131) that this was due to the release of norepinephrine from the central and peripheral sympathetic system. With the meager information available in the field in 1952, it was fortunate for the development of antihypertensive therapy that Bein (9) was able to assess correctly the pharmacological profile of reserpine.

Doses of the order of 20–50 μg/per kilogram administered orally daily cause a fall in blood pressure of 25 mm Hg, coupled with sedation only after 7–10 days, and upon cessation of treatment these effects tend to linger for a week or two. On such a chronic regime it has been found in our laboratories that reserpine is effective in lowering the blood pressure in unanesthetized renal hypertensive and neurogenic hypertensive animals. In fact, neurogenic hypertensive dogs prepared by the ablation of both carotid sinuses, the section of the left vago-sympathetic trunk and of the medial third of the right vagal trunk as recommended by Grimson (63), are more susceptible to the cardiovascular actions of reserpine. The elevated blood pressure in this case, after a latent period of several days, is lowered 50–60 mm Hg by 10–20 μg/per kilogram of reserpine orally each day (151). Reserpine has an ameliorating effect on the hypertension induced in rats by DCA and salt or by cortisone (49), and it also prevents to a considerable extent the development of adrenal regeneration hypertension in the rat (28). In rats with experimental renal hypertension, reserpine exerted a hypotensive effect within 24 hours (65), while the daily administration of reserpine for several weeks reduced the blood pressure and decreased the severity of the vascular lesions in the kidney and other organs (123) in animals with renal hypertension. Gross et al. (71) also found reserpine to exert a palliative effect in renal hypertension in the rat.

Reserpine markedly reduces the acute hypertensive episodes caused by stimulation of the central end of the divided vagus or sciatic nerves or by reduction of the pressure in the carotid sinus by bilateral carotid occlusion. The blood pressure rise after the injection of epinephrine or norepinephrine or after electrical stimulation of the efferent splanchnic nerve is increased by reserpine, in all probability by a common mechanism, indicating that the regulatory function of the sympathetic system is still intact although its level of activity may be depressed (9).

Alteration of the pressor effect of norepinephrine by effective antihypertensive agents is common; any change in the effect of this neurohumor by a substance furnishes an important clue which should be fully explored as to mechanism and bearing on ultimate utility of the compound.

It is evident that the hypotensive action of reserpine can be demonstrated experimentally both in normotensive anesthetized animals acutely, and in a wide variety of experimental hypertensive preparations upon chronic daily administration. Deserpidine and rescinnamine are quite similar pharmacologically to reserpine and respond identically to reserpine in the above tests, with the exception that rescinnamine is slightly less potent.

Syrosingopine (152) is an interesting derivative of reserpine which shares its hypotensive effects but is much less active as a sedative. The hypotensive properties of syrosingopine are readily demonstrable by the same techniques as described for reserpine.

C. Antihypertensive Substances Acting on Vascular Smooth Muscle

When administered to the anesthetized normotensive dog, hydralazine causes a fall in blood pressure which is gradual in onset and is sustained. The pharmacological behavior of the closely related dihydralazine is identical to that of hydralazine. The duration rather than the intensity of the fall increases as larger doses are given. A speeding of the heart generally accompanies the fall in blood pressure. The hypotensive action of hydralazine, which is due to reduced peripheral resistance, is manifest in various experimental hypertensive states including the renal hypertensive rat and dog (65). Gaunt et al. (49) showed that hydralazine reduced the blood pressure and increased the survival time of rats rendered hypertensive with DCA and salt administration or with cortisone; the combination of hydralazine with reserpine was even more effective. Gardner (47) similarly noted that hydralazine prevented the appearance of arterial lesions for as long as 3 months in rats made hypertensive with a combination of DCA, high salt diet, and unilateral nephrectomy. Renzi and Gaunt (157) demonstrated that the severe eclampsialike syndrome in rats produced by Masson et al. (113) by a combination of renin, high salt diet, and DCA combined with uninephrectomy, could be largely obviated, with survival of the animal, by the administration of hydralazine, with correction of the edema, sodium retention, and the hypertension. Masson et al. (116) provided evidence that the maintenance of the blood pressure of renal hypertensive rats within a normal range by chronic administration of hydralazine largely prevented the development of arterial lesions, which, however, developed when the drug was withdrawn, and severe hypertension supervened. The logical presumption was that the arteritis was related directly to the elevated blood pressure, emphasizing the value of controlling it adequately.

In acute experiments in the normotensive dog, hydralazine inhibits the effects of a group of peripherally acting endogenous pressor substances including epinephrine (12), serotonin (141), vasopressin (11), and renin (79). Recently Barrett (5) has shown that hydralazine also reduces the pressor effect of angiotensin in the dog, an action which may be related to its known capacity to augment renal blood flow (159). This broad spectrum of antipressor actions suggests a very peripheral action of the drug which has been further corroborated by the observations (a) that the vasoconstrictor action of barium chloride, which acts directly on smooth muscle, is antagonized by hydralazine (125), and (b) that it causes vasodilation of the vessels of the human forearm in doses less than those required to antagonize the vasoconstrictor effect of norepinephrine (1). The rarity of postural hypotension with hydralazine indicates that the effector cells rather than the sympathetic system are involved in the therapeutic as well as in the experimental situation.

It may be seen that the activity characteristic of hydralazine is readily detected by straightforward laboratory techniques but that the elaboration of its mechanism of action, about which there is still not complete unanimity, is a more complex matter. This aspect of the problem will be discussed in detail in the chapter devoted to the hydralazine derivatives.

D. Miscellaneous Antihypertensive Compounds

1. *Hypotensive Diuretics*

Various diuretics including the organic mercurials, chlorothiazide, hydrochlorothiazide, and spironolactone, lower the blood pressure in human hypertension. Although it is widely assumed that their blood-pressure lowering action is dependent upon the excretion of sodium, Hollander (87) has provided evidence that sodium depletion may not be the sole or even the principal causative factor. With suitable animal preparations, it appears to be possible to demonstrate the mild hypotensive effect of this class of compounds.

Renzi *et al.* (158) found that the chronic daily administration of 5.0 mg/per kilogram of hydrochlorothiazide to rats inhibited the development of adrenal regeneration hypertension, which is salt related, but did not reduce hydrocortisone-induced hypertension, which is not salt dependent. Acute administration was not effective against either form of hypertension.

In experiments by Barrett *et al.* (7), hydrochlorothiazide had no significant effect on the arterial blood pressure upon intravenous administration of up to 9.0 mg/per kilogram intravenously to the anesthetized dog, but the hypotensive effect of a subsequent injection of hydralazine was potentiated. Friedman *et al.* (46) observed the hypotensive activity of hydrochlorothiazide in rats with DCA hypertension but not in normal animals. Fregly (43) found that hydrochlorothiazide lowered the blood pressure in renal hypertension in rats, while the effect of spironolactone was not as definite. Scriabine *et al.* (169) observed that polythiazide was hypotensive in renal hypertensive rats, while Tobian and Coffee (198) found methyclothiazide ineffectual in the same experimental preparation. These investigators also noted that a low sodium intake was ineffective in alleviating the hypertension produced in rats by narrowing one renal artery (156). Stanton and White (190) have recently demonstrated that the daily administration of hydrochlorothiazide in a dose range of 2.5–20 mg/per kilogram subcutaneously to unanesthetized metacorticoid hypertensive rats produced a hypotensive effect of 20–25 mm Hg. By the oral route, 5.0 mg/per kilogram twice daily produced a comparable effect in hypertensive animals, but not in normotensive animals.

It appears therefore, that the hypotensive effects of the diuretics are both subtle and of gradual onset in animals as well as in humans and that they are more marked in hypertensive states in both instances. Given a substance with known diuretic activity, it should be possible to assess its hypotensive potential by the use of rats with adrenal regeneration or metacorticoid hypertension.

2. *Methyldopa*

The hypotensive activity of methyldopa was first reported in the human by Oates *et al.* (135) in 1960. Although Sourkes (188) had demonstrated that it inhibited the decarboxylation of dihydroxyphenylalanine (dopa) *in vitro* in 1954, it is rather unlikely that this action plays any part in its antihypertensive effect. The dog is not a suitable test animal for detecting the action of methyldopa, since large doses are required and consistent results are not obtained. Although Goldberg *et al.* (52) described a hypotensive effect in the dog after large intravenous doses, Stone (191) found no hypotensive activity in trained renal or neurogenic hypertensive dogs after the acute or subacute administration of doses up to 100 mg/per kilogram of the racemate. Minimal hypotensive effects were noted by Stone in the renal hypertensive rat after the intraperitoneal administration of 50 mg/per kilogram of the racemate, while more definite hypotension was seen after 100 mg/per kilogram. The unanesthetized rat with chronic metacorticoid hypertension appears to be more sensitive to the action of methyldopa according to Stanton and White (190), since oral administration of 100 mg/per kilogram twice daily for several days caused a persistent blood pressure fall of about 20 mm Hg. It would still appear, however, to be a difficult matter to detect with surety the methyldopa type of activity in an unknown compound by blood pressure studies in either normotensive or hypertensive animals without a prior suggestion of activity on a biochemical or chemical structural basis.

3. *Veratrum viride*

Veratrum-induced hypotension with its typical bradycardia is quite definite and prompt in onset when administered intravenously to dogs anesthetized with pentobarbital. The mechanism of action of this group of alkaloids will be discussed separately. Maison *et al.* (112) used the hypotensive action in the dog as the basis of an assay of the potency of fifteen pure alkaloids and of several mixtures of alkaloids obtained from *Veratrum viride.*

4. *Monoamine Oxidase Inhibitors*

Several monoamine oxidase inhibitors, including iproniazid, pheniprazine, and pargyline have been reported to have antihypertensive action in human hypertension. The cause of the lowering of the blood pressure is uncertain. As yet it has not been possible to show a clear relationship between cardio-vascular action and the enzymic effect.

In experiments in rats Schoepke and Wiegand (165) observed a modest fall of 17 mm Hg in the blood pressure of rats after the intraperitoneal adminis-tration of 20 mg/per kilogram of pargyline for 4 consecutive days. A dose of 10 mg/per kilogram similarly administered was ineffective. In cats the daily administration of 20 mg/per kilogram intraperitoneally for 4 consecutive days produced an average fall of 29% in the mean arterial pressure on the fourth day. This was preceded by a rise in blood pressure on the first and second days. The anesthesia may have intensified the hypotensive effect of the drug, since the cats were anesthetized with pentobarbital on 6 consecutive days in order to make blood pressure determinations.

The subtle action of these enzyme inhibitors would probably go undetected in acute animal studies because of the slow onset of effect. Studies in hyperten-sive animals have not been reported.

IV. Discussion

In the search for more effective antihypertensive agents it would appear reasonable by analogy that there would be a certain advantage in employing hypertensive animals for testing purposes. This has been done, as just described, with a representative number of compounds whose hypotensive activity in experimental animals was also manifested in human patients with hypertension. In these studies it was established that those substances which were effective in hypertensive animals were also effective in human hypertension. In fact, hypertensive animals were even more sensitive to the blood-pressure lowering properties of guanethidine and reserpine. In the case of the thiazide diuretics and also of methyldopa, hypotensive activity was demonstrated in hypertensive but not in normotensive animals. The effect of the diuretics on the blood pressure was most apparent when given orally twice daily for a few days to rats with metacorticoid hypertension, while methyldopa required the adminis-tration of large doses to renal hypertensive rats to produce significant hypo-tension. Admittedly, such subtle effects might have been overlooked in an acute test if prior knowledge of their activity in human hypertension was not available. However, it is an inescapable fact that substances do exist which may be overlooked if tested only in normal animals. It follows, therefore, that hyper-tensive preparations should play an increasingly prominent part in the com-plete evaluation of the antihypertensive potential of a substance. If the use of normotensive animals had not been so productive of effective therapeutic agents over the past 15 years, investigators would undoubtedly have made much broader use of experimental hypertensive animals than has been the case generally. Although it is quite possible that significant advances in therapy can still be achieved by the continued application of currently established procedures, there is a real likelihood that expanded studies with hypertensive animals may lead to more specific substances and to an improved understanding of the etiology of hypertension.

Acceptance of the concept that hypertensive animals should be employed in a primary test system poses certain questions to which there are not definitive answers. These include a decision as to the species of animal, the desirability of anesthesia, the type of hypertension, the method of estimating blood pressure, the route of drug administration, the duration of the experiment, and the choice of the acute or chronic study. It would not be feasible to attempt to cover all possibilities for each substance being tested because of the enormity of the task. There are wide differences in the responses of different animal species to the same compound. For example, the dog and cat are very sensitive to reserpine, while the rat and monkey require large doses. There are obvious arguments for the use of unanesthetized animals, but the use of an anesthetic serves to intensify hypotensive effects in normotensive animals and ensures that the reaction of the animal is to the drug rather than to the environment or the procedure. Since there may be multiple causes of human hypertension and since even experimental renal hypertension may be transformed into a neurogenic type in its chronic state, it is probable that complete reliance cannot be placed on any single experimental type or design, for an individual test substance. In the determination of blood pressure, a direct method in which the sensor is inserted or implanted in an artery is certainly more reliable than an indirect auscultatory technique. Parenteral methods of administration are convenient and rapid, but if activity by this route cannot be duplicated orally, additional study has little practical purpose. The duration of an acute experiment should cover a period of at least 4 hours in an anesthetized animal and even longer, with intermittent measurements of blood pressure, in conscious animals. Chronic studies, which are usually based on a lead obtained from acute experiments or other prior experience, should be extended for a few weeks on a daily basis in order to observe any tolerance or cumulation which may result with repeated administration of a drug. If an exact course cannot be prescribed in this area, by the same token it can be stated that, as always, individual judgment and imagination are indispensable requirements. With the steady pace of improving electronic technology, a final evaluation of a potential preparation should eventually be possible through the measurement of blood pressure and flow in trained, unanesthetized, hypertensive animals by means of implanted sensors and telemetry devices whereby the animal is unrestrained and totally unaware of the experimental procedure. However, such a procedure would hardly be feasible as a rapid primary test.

In a sense, experimental hypertension, albeit of a very transient nature, has been widely employed for many years in the assessment of antihypertensive possibilities of compounds. Transient hypertension has been produced in animals by the use of substances whose pressor activity might be construed even remotely to contribute to the elevation of human blood pressure. Antagonism of the pressor effect of epinephrine was early employed in the estimation of adrenergic blockade. As awareness of the role of norepinephrine became available, it supplemented or supplanted epinephrine for estimation of sympathetic dampening. Antagonism of renin, serotonin, vasopressin or amphetamine has been employed for more refined clues to hypotensive mechanisms. With realization of the potential importance of the renin-angiotensin system in the regulation of blood pressure, interest has been extended to a study of antagonists of angiotensin as well. Observation of antagonism or potentiation of these agents has the great advantage of being a direct, simple, and informative adjunct which can be incorporated into the routine blood pressure experiment.

There is little doubt that lowering of the blood pressure in hypertension is a worthwhile procedure, as evidenced by a drop of 52% in the deaths related to high blood pressure between the periods of 1950 to 1953 and 1960 to 1963 (129).

A recent report by Smirk (183) indicates salutary results from antihypertensive treatment in even more moderate forms of hypertension. Such encouraging news serves as a challenge to provide even more effective and specific drugs. Agents acting solely in hypertensive animals, or a specific peripherally acting antagonist of angiotensin, are most exciting possibilities.

References

1. Ablad, B., Johnsson, G., and Henning, M., *Acta Pharmacol. Toxicol.* **19**, 165 (1962).
2. Anchini, M., and Gross, F., *Naunyn-Schmiedberg's Arch. Exptl. Pathol. Pharmakol.* **251**, 171 (1965).
3. Anderson, F. F., *J. Lab. Clin. Med.* **26**, 1520 (1941).
4. Barlow, R. B., and Ing, H. R., *Brit. J. Pharmacol.* **3**, 298 (1948).
5. Barrett, W., personal communication (1965).
6. Barrett, W., personal communication (1965).
7. Barrett, W. E., Rutledge, R. A., Sheppard, H., and Plummer, A. J., *Toxicol. Appl. Pharmacol.* **1**, 333 (1959).
8. Bayliss, W. M., *J. Physiol. (London)* **28**, 220 (1902).
9. Bein, H. J., *Experientia* **9**, 107 (1953).
10. Bein, H. J., *Ciba Found. Symp., Adrenergic Mechanisms* p. 162 (1960).
11. Bein, H. J., Tripod, J., and Meier, R., *Experientia* **8**, 74 (1952).
12. Bein, H. J., Gross, F., Tripod, J., and Meier, R., *Schweiz. Med. Wochschr.* **83**, 336 (1953).
13. Blaquier, P., *Univ. Mich. Med. Bull.* **27**, 176 (1961).
14. Boucher, R., Veyrat, R., de Champlain, J., and Genest, J., *Can. Med. Assoc. J.* **90**, 194 (1964).
15. Boura, A. L. A., Copp, F. C., and Green, A. F., *Nature* **184**, B.A. 70 (1959).

16. Boura, A. L. A., and Green, A. F., *in* "Evaluation of Drug Activities" (D. R. Laurence and A. L. Bacharach, eds.), Vol. 1, Part 2, p. 443. Academic Press, New York, 1964.
17. Braun, L., and Samet, B., *Wien. Klin. Wochschr.* **48**, 940 (1935).
18. Braun-Menéndez, E., *Pharmacol. Rev.* **8**, 25 (1956).
19. Braun-Menéndez, E., Fasciolo, J. C., Leloir, L. F., and Munoz, J. M., *J. Physiol. (London)* **98**, 283 (1940).
20. Braun-Menéndez, E., Fasciolo, J. C., Leloir, L. F., Munoz, J. M., and Taquini, A. C., "Renal Hypertension", p. 3 ,Thomas, Springfield, Illinois, 1946.
21. Bright, R., *Guy's Hosp. Rept.* 1, 380 (1836).
22. Byrom, F. B., *Lancet* **II**, 201 (1954).
23. Byrom, F. B., *Lancet* **I**, 516 (1963).
24. Byrom, F. B., and Dodson, L. F., *Clin. Sci.* **8**, 1 (1949).
25. Cannon, W. B., and Rosenblueth, A., *Am. J. Physiol.* **104**, 557 (1933).
26. Carpenter, C. C. J., Davis, J. O., and Ayers, C. R., *J. Clin. Invest.* **40**, 2026 (1961).
27. Chappel, C. I., Charest, M. P., Cahill, J., and Grant, G. A., *Endocrinology* **60**, 677 (1957).
28. Chart, J. J., Ulsamer, G., Quinn, L., Howie, N., Sullivan, B., and Gaunt, R., *Endocrinology* **61**, 692 (1957).
29. Child, C. G., *J. Exptl. Med.* **67**, 521 (1938).
30. Conn, J. W., *J. Lab. Clin. Med.* **45**, 3 (1955).
31. Conn, J. W., and Conn, E. S., *Recent Progr. Hormone Res.* **17**, 389 (1961).
32. Cook, W. F., and Pickering, G. W., *Biochem. Pharmacol.* **9–10**, 165 (1962).
33. Dahl, L. K., Heine, M., and Tassinari, L., *J. Exptl. Med.* **115**, 1173 (1962).
34. Dahl, L. K., Heine, M., and Tassinari, L., *J. Exptl. Med.* **118**, 605 (1963).
35. Dahl, L. K., Heine, M., and Tassinari, L., *Circulation* **30**, Suppl. II, 11 (1964).
36. Davis, J. O., *Physiologist* **5**, 76 (1962).
37. De Moura, R. S., Olmsted, F., and McCubbin, J. W., quoted by I. H. Page in "Antihypertensive Therapy, Principles, Practice. International Symposium (F. Gross, ed.), p. 607, Springer, Berlin (1965).
38. Deodhar, S. D., Haas, E., and Goldblatt, H., *Can. Med. Assoc. J.* **90**, 236 (1964).
39. Dixon, W. E., and Heller, H., *Arch. Exptl. Pathol. Pharmakol.* **166**, 265 (1932).
40. Elliott, D. F., and Peart, W. S., *Biochem. J.* **65**, 246 (1957).
41. Fasciolo, J. C., DeVito, E., Romero, J. C., and Cucchi, J. N., *Can. Med. Assoc. J.* **90**, 206 (1964).
42. Floyer, M. A., *Clin. Sci.* **10**, 405 (1951).
43. Fregly, M. J., *Am. J. Cardiol.* **8**, 890 (1961).
44. Friedman, S. M., and Friedman, C. L., *J. Exptl. Med.* **89**, 631 (1949).
45. Friedman, S. M., Friedman, C. L., and Nakashima, M., *Endocrinology* **53**, 633 (1953).
46. Friedman, S. M., Nakashima, M., and Friedman, C. L., *Am. J. Physiol.* **198**, 148 (1960).
47. Gardner, D. L., *Brit. J. Exptl. Pathol.* **41**, 60 (1960).
48. Gaunt, R., Renzi, A. A., Antonchak, N., Miller, G. J., and Gilman, M., *Ann. N.Y. Acad. Sci.* **59**, 22 (1954).
49. Gaunt, R., Antonchak, N., Miller, G. J., and Renzi, A. A., *Am. J. Physiol.* **182**, 63 (1955).
50. Gaunt, R., Gross, F., Renzi, A. A., and Chart, J. J., *in* "Hypertension: First Hahnemann Symposium on Hypertensive Disease" (J. H. Moyer, ed.), p. 219, Saunders, Philadelphia, Pennsylvania, 1959.
51. Giroud, C. J. P., Stachenko, J., and Venning, E. H., *Proc. Soc. Exptl. Biol. Med.* **92**, 154 (1956).
52. Goldberg, L. I., DaCosta, F. M., and Ozaki, M., *Nature* **188**, 502 (1960).

53. Goldblatt, H., *Ann. Internal* [N.S.] *Med.* **11**, 69 (1937).
54. Goldblatt, H., *J. Exptl. Med.* **65**, 671 (1937).
55. Goldblatt, H., *J. Exptl. Med.* **67**, 809 (1938).
56. Goldblatt, H., "The Renal Origin of Hypertension." Thomas, Springfield, Illinois, 1948.
57. Goldblatt, H., Lynch, J., Hanzal, R. F., and Summerville, W. E., *Bull. Acad. Med.* (*Cleveland*) **16**, 6 (1932).
58. Goldblatt, H., Lynch, J., Hanzal, R. F., and Summerville, W. W., *J. Exptl. Med.* **59**, 347 (1934).
59. Goldblatt, H., Gross, J., and Hanzal, R. F., *J. Exptl. Med.* **65**, 233 (1937).
60. Gordon, D. B., *Am. J. Physiol.* **196**, 1340 (1959).
61. Green, D. M., Saunders, F. J., Wahlgren, N., McDonough, F. J., and Clampit, J. M., *Am. J. Physiol.* **170**, 107 (1952).
62. Green, D. M., Johnson, A. D., Bridges, W. C., and Lehman, J. H., *Circulation* **9**, 416 (1954).
63. Grimson, K. S., *Arch. Surg.* **43**, 1 (1941).
64. Grollman, A., *Am. J. Physiol.* **142**, 666 (1944).
65. Grollman, A., *J. Pharmacol. Exptl. Therap.* **114**, 263 (1955).
66. Grollman, A.. and Rule, C., *Am. J. Physiol.* **138**, 587 (1943).
67. Grollman, A., Muirhead, E. E., and Vanatta, J., *Am. J. Physiol.* **157**, 21 (1949).
68. Grollman, A., and White, F. N., *Am. J. Physiol.* **193**, 144 (1958).
69. Gross, F., *Arch. Exptl. Pathol. Pharmakol.* **232**, 161 (1957).
70. Gross, F., *Klin. Wochschr.* **36**, 693 (1958).
71. Gross, F., Noelpp, B., Sulser, F., Doebelin, R., and Kundiz, H., *Klin. Wochschr.* **33**, 372 (1955).
72. Gross, F., Loustalot, P., and Meier, R., *Acta Endocrinol.* **26**, 417 (1957).
73. Gross, F., Schaechtelin, G., Brunner, H., and Peters, G., *Can. Med. Assoc. J.* **90**, 258 (1964).
74. Gould, A. B., Skeggs, L. T., and Kahn, J. R., *J. Exptl. Med.* **119**, 389 (1964).
75. Hall, C. E., and Hall, O., *Proc. Soc. Exptl. Biol. Med.* **71**, 690 (1949).
76. Hamilton, J. G., and Grollman, A., *J. Biol. Chem.* **233**, 528 (1958).
77. Hartroft, P. M., *Circulation Res.* **12**, Part 2, 525 (1963).
78. Hartroft, W. S., and Best, C. H., *Brit. Med. J.* **I**, 423 (1949).
79. Haynes, F. W., and Dexter, L., *Am. J. Physiol.* **196**, 502 (1959).
80. Helmer, O. M., and Griffith, R. S., *Endocrinology* **49**, 154 (1951).
81. Helmer, O. M., and Judson, W. E., *Univ. Mich. Med. Bull.* **27**, 212 (1961).
82. Helmer, O. M., and Judson, W. E., *Circulation* **27**, 1050 (1963).
83. Heymans, C., *Compt. Rend. Soc. Biol.* **106**, 469 (1931).
84. Heymans, C., "Introduction to the Regulation of Blood Pressure and Heart Rate," Thomas, Springfield, Illinois, 1950.
85. Heymans, C., and Bouckaert, J. J., *Compt. Rend. Soc. Biol.* **117**, 252 (1934).
86. Hickler, R. B., *Proc. New Engl. Cardiovascular Soc.* **22**, 14 (1964).
87. Hollander, W., Chobanïan, A. V., and Wilkins, R. W., *in* "Hypertension: First Hahnemann Symposium on Hypertensive Disease" (J. H. Moyer, ed.), p. 570. Saunders, Philadelphia, Pennsylvania, 1959.
88. Hollander, W., Kramsch, D. M., Yagi, S., and Madoff, I. M., International Club on Arterial Hypertension (P. Milliez and P. Tcherdakoff), Vol. 1, p. 305, Expansion Scientifique Francaise, Paris, 1966.
89. Holman, D. V., and Page, I. H., *Am. Heart J.* **16**, 321 (1938).
90. Houssay, B. A., and Fasciolo, J. C., *Rev. Soc. Arg. Biol.* **13**, 284 (1937).
91. Hudak, W. J., and Buckley, J. P., *J. Pharm. Sci.* **50**, 263 (1961).

92. Jones, A. W., Feigl, E. O., and Peterson, L. H., *Circulation Res.* **15**, 386 (1964).
93. Kempf, G. F., and Page, I. H., *J. Lab. Clin. Med.* **27**, 1192 (1942).
94. Knowlton, A. I., Loeb, E. N., Stoerck, H. C., White, J. P., and Heffernan, J. F., *J. Exptl. Med.* **96**, 187 (1952).
95. Kohlstaedt, K. G., Helmer, O. M., and Page, I. H., *Proc. Soc. Exptl. Biol. Med.* **39**, 214 (1938).
96. Koletsky, S., *Lab. Invest.* **7**, 377 (1958).
97. Koletsky, S., and Pritchard, W. H., *Circulation Res.* **13**, 552 (1963).
98. Korotkov, N. S., *Izv. Voenno-Med. Akad.* **11**, 365 (1905).
99. Kremer, M., Wright, S., and Scarff, R. W., *Brit. J. Exptl. Pathol.* **14**, 281 (1933).
100. Krieger, E. M., *Circulation Res.* **15**, 511 (1964).
101. Langford, H. G., Snavely, J. R., and Turner, D. M., *Clin. Res. Proc.* **5**, 98 (1957).
102. Laragh, J. H., and Kelly, W. G., *Advan. Metab. Disorders* **1**, p. 217 (1964) (ed. R. Levine and R. Luft), Academic Press, New York.
103. Laragh, J. H., Ulick, S., Januszewicz, V., Deming, Q. B., Kelly, W. G., and Lieberman, S., *J. Clin. Invest.* **39**, 1091 (1960).
104. Laragh, J. H., Cannon, P. J., and Ames, R. P., *Can. Med. Assoc. J.* **90**, 248 (1964).
105. Laverty, R., and Smirk, F. H., *Circulation Res.* **9**, 455 (1961).
106. Ledingham, J. M., *Clin. Sci.* **12**, 337 (1953).
107. Ledingham, J. M., and Cohen, R. D., *Can. Med. Assoc. J.* **90**, 292 (1964).
108. Lee, J. B., Hickler, R. B., Saravis, C. A., and Thorn, G. W., *Circulation Res.* **13**, 359 (1963).
109. Lenel, R., Katz, L. N., and Rodbard, S., *Am. J. Physiol.* **152**, 557 (1948).
110. Lever, A. F., and Robertson, J. I. S., *J. Physiol.* (*London*) **170**, 212 (1964).
111. Lever, A. F., Robertson, J. I. S., and Tree, M., *Biochem. J.* **91**, 346 (1964).
112. Maison, G. L., Gotz, E., and Stutzman, J. W., *J. Pharmacol. Exptl. Therap.* **103**, 74 (1951).
113. Masson, G. M. C., Corcoran, A. C., and Page, I. H., *J. Lab. Clin. Med.* **38**, 213 (1951).
114. Masson, G. M. C., Lewis, L. A., Corcoran, A. C., and Page, I. H., *J. Clin. Endocrinol.* **13**, 300 (1953).
115. Masson, G. M. C., Corcoran, A. C., and Page, I. H., *Endocrinology* **61**, 409 (1957).
116. Masson, G. M. C., McCormack, L. J., Dustan, H. P., and Corcoran, A. C., *Am. J. Pathol.* **34**, 817 (1958).
117. Masson, G. M. C., Kashii, C., and Panisset, J. C., *Can. Med. Assoc. J.* **90**, 231 (1964).
118. Maxwell, R. A., Plummer, A. J., Ross, S. D., and Osborne, M. W., *Proc. Soc. Exptl. Biol. Med.* **92**, 225 (1956).
119. Maxwell, R. A., Plummer, A. J., Ross, S. D., Daniel, A. I., and Schneider, F., *J. Pharmacol. Exptl. Therap.* **123**, 238 (1958).
120. Maxwell, R. A., Plummer, A. J., Schneider, F., Povalski, H., and Daniel, A., *J. Pharmacol. Exptl. Therap.* **128**, 22 (1960).
121. McCubbin, J. W., Green, J. H., and Page, I. H., *Circulation Res.* **4**, 205 (1956).
122. McCubbin, J. W., and Page, I. H., *Circulation Res.* **12**, 553 (1963).
123. McQueen, E. G., and Hodge, J. V., *Quart. J. Med.* [N.S.] **30**, 213 (1961).
124. Medoff, H. S., and Bongiovanni, A. M., *Am. J. Physiol.* **143**, 300 (1945).
125. Meier, R., Bein, H. J., Gross, F., Tripod, J., and Tuchmann-Duplessis, H., *Compt. Rend.* **238**, 413 (1954).
126. Meneeley, G. R., *in* "Hypertension: First Hahnemann Symposium on Hypertensive Disease" (J. H. Moyer, ed.) p. 250. Saunders, Philadelphia, Pennsylvania, 1959.
127. Meneeley, G. R., and Ball, C. O. T., *Proc. Ann. Meet. High Blood Pressure Res. Am. Heart Assoc.* **6**, 65 (1957).

128. Meneeley, G. R., and Ball, C. O. T., *Am. J. Med.* **25**, 713 (1958).
129. *Metropolitan Life Ins. Statist. Bull.* **45**, 3 (1964).
130. Morris, R. E., Robinson, P. R., and Scheele, G. A., *Can. Med. Assoc. J.* **90**, 272 (1964).
131. Mueller, J. M., Schlittler, E., and Bein, H. J., *Experientia* **8**, 338 (1952).
132. Muirhead, E. E., Jones, F., and Stirman, J. A., *J. Lab. Clin. Med.* **56**, 167 (1960).
133. Muirhead, E. E., Hinman, J. W., Daniels, E. G., Kosinski, M., and Brooks, B., *J. Clin. Invest.* **41**, 1387 (1962).
134. Nolla-Panades, J., and Smirk, F. H., *Australasian Ann. Med.* **13**, 320 (1964).
135. Oates, J. A., Gillespie, L., Udenfriend, S., and Sjoerdsma, A., *Science* **131**, 1890 (1960).
136. Ogden, E., *Bull. N. Y. Acad. Med.* **23**, 643 (1947).
137. Page, I. H., *Science* **89**, 273 (1939).
138. Page, I. H., "Essential Hypertension, An International Symposium" (K. D. Bock and P. T. Cottier, ed.), p. 1. Springer, Berlin, 1960.
139. Page, I. H., *Arch. Internal Med.* **111**, 103 (1963).
140. Page, I. H., and Helmer, O. M., *J. Exptl. Med.* **71**, 29 (1940).
141. Page, I. H., and McCubbin, J. W., *Am. J. Physiol.* **174**, 436 (1953).
142. Page, I. H., and Dustan, H. P., *J. Am. Med. Assoc.* **170**, 1265 (1959).
143. Page, I. H., and Bumpus, F. M., *Physiol. Rev.* **41**, 331 (1961).
144. Page, I. H., and Bumpus, F. M., *Clin. Pharmacol. Therap.* **3**, 758 (1962).
145. Paton, W. D. M., and Zaimis, E. J., *Brit. J. Pharmacol.* **4**, 381 (1949).
146. Peart, W. S., *Pharmacol. Rev.* **17**, 143 (1965).
147. Pickering, G. W., *Clin. Sci.* **5**, 229 (1945).
148. Pickering, G. W., "High Blood Pressure." Churchill, London, 1955.
149. Pickering, G. W., and Prinzmetal, M., *Clin. Sci.* **3**, 211 (1938).
150. Pickering, G. W., and Prinzmetal, M., *Clin. Sci.* **3**, 357 (1938).
151. Plummer, A. J., *in* "Hypertension: First Hahnemann Symposium on Hypertensive Disease" (J. H. Moyer, ed.), p. 319. Saunders, Philadelphia, Pennsylvania, 1959.
152. Plummer, A. J., Barrett, W. E., Maxwell, R. A., Finocchio, D., Lucas, R. A., and Earl, A. E., *Arch. Intern. Pharmacodyn.* **119**, 245 (1959).
153. Prinzmetal, M., Lewis, H. A., and Leo, S. D., *J. Exptl. Med.* **72**, 763 (1940).
154. Proosdij-Hartzema, E. G., van, and de Jongh, D. K., *Acta Physiol. Pharmacol. Neerl.* **4**, 37 (1955).
155. Proosdij-Hartzema, E. G. van, and de Jongh, D. K., *Acta Physiol. Pharmacol. Neerl.* **4**, 160 (1955).
156. Redleaf, P. D., and Tobian, L., *Circulation Res.* **6**, 343 (1958).
157. Renzi, A. A., and Gaunt, R., *Am. J. Physiol.* **175**, 313 (1953).
158. Renzi, A. A., Chart, J. J., and Gaunt, R., *Toxicol. Appl. Pharmacol.* **1**, 406 (1959).
159. Reubi, F., *Helv. Med. Acta* **16**, 297 (1949).
160. Rittel, W., Iselin, B., Kappeler, H., Riniker, B., and Schwyzer, R., *Helv. Chim. Acta* **40**, 614 (1957).
161. Rodbard, S., *Proc. Ann. Meet. High Blood Pressure Res. Am. Heart Assoc.* **6**, 7 (1957).
162. Rondell, P. A., McVaugh, R. B., and Bohr, D. F., *Circulation* **17**, 708 (1958).
163. Sapirstein, L. A., *Proc. Ann. Meet. High Blood Pressure Res. Am. Heart Assoc.* **6**, 28 (1957).
164. Schaechtelin, G., Regoli, D., and Gross, F., *Am. J. Physiol.* **205**, 303 (1963).
165. Schoepke, H. G., and Wiegand, R. G., *Ann. N. Y. Acad. Sci.* **107**, 924 (1963).
166. Schwarz, H., Bumpus, F. M., and Page, I. H., *J. Am. Chem. Soc.* **79**, 5697 (1957).
167. Schwyzer, R., *Chimia (Aarau)* **12**, 53 (1958).
168. Scornik, O. A., and Paladini, A. C., *Am. J. Physiol.* **201**, 526 (1961).

169. Scriabine, A., Korol, B., Kondratas, B., Yu, M., P'An, S. Y., and Schneider, J. A., *Proc. Soc. Exptl. Biol. Med.* **107**, 864 (1961).
170. Selye, H., *Can. Med. Assoc. J.* **47**, 515 (1942).
171. Selye, H., Hall, C. E., and Rowley, E. M., *Can. Med. Assoc. J.* **49**, 88 (1943).
172. Selye, H., and Stone, H., *Proc. Soc. Exptl. Biol. Med.* **52**, 190 (1943).
173. Selye, H., and Stone, H., *J. Urol.* **56**, 399 (1946).
174. Skeggs, L. T., Marsh, W. H., Kahn, J. R., and Shumway, N. P., *J. Exptl. Med.* **99**, 275 (1954).
175. Skeggs, L. T., Kahn, J. R., Lentz, K., and Shumway, N. P., *J. Exptl. Med.* **106**, 439 (1957).
176. Skelton, F. R., *Proc. Soc. Exptl. Biol. Med.* **90**, 342 (1955).
177. Skelton, F. R., *Physiol. Rev.* **39**, 162 (1959).
178. Skelton, F. R., Guillebeau, J., and Nichols, J., *Proc. 21st Ann. Meeting Can. Physiol. Soc.*, *1957* p. 56.
179. Skinner, S. L., McCubbin, J. W., and Page, I. H., *Circulation Res.* **13**, 336 (1963).
180. Skinner, S. L., McCubbin, J. W., and Page, I. H., *Circulation Res.* **15**, 64 (1964).
181. Smirk, F. H., *Brit. Med. J.* **I**, 791 (1949).
182. Smirk, F. H., "High Arterial Pressure," p. 289. Thomas, Springfield, Illinois, 1957.
183. Smirk, F. H., *Antihypertensive Therapy, Principles Pract. Intern. Symp.* (F. Gross, ed.), p. 360. Springer, Berlin, 1966.
184. Smirk, F. H., and Hall, W. H., *Nature* **182**, 727 (1958).
185. Smirk, F. H., personal communication (1965).
186. Smithwick, R. H., *Surgery* **7**, 1 (1940).
187. Sokabe, H., and Grollman, A., *Am. J. Physiol.* **203**, 991 (1962).
188. Sourkes, T. L., *Arch. Biochem. Biophys.* **51**, 444 (1954).
189. Spinks, A., Young, E. H. P., Farrington, J. A., and Dunlop, D., *Brit. J. Pharmacol.* **13**, 501 (1958).
190. Stanton, H. C., and White, J. B., *Arch. Intern. Pharmacodyn.* **154**, 351 (1965).
191. Stone, C. A., Porter, C. C., Watson, L. S., and Ross, C. A., *in* "Hypertension, Recent Advances: Second Hahnemann Symposium on Hypertensive Disease" (A. N. Brest and J. H. Moyer, eds.), p. 417. Lea & Febiger, Philadelphia, Pennsylania, 1961.
192. Sturtevant, F. M., *Ann. Internal Med.* [N.S.] **49**, 1281 (1958).
193. Taylor, R. D., and Page, I. H., *Circulation* **3**, 551 (1951).
194. Tigerstedt, R., and Bergman, P. G., *Skand. Arch. Physiol.* **8**, 223 (1898).
195. Tobian, L., *Physiol. Rev.* **40**, 280 (1960).
196. Tobian, L., and Binion, J., *J. Clin. Invest.* **33**, 1407 (1954).
197. Tobian, L., and Redleaf, P. D., *Am. J. Physiol.* **192**, 325 (1958).
198. Tobian, L., and Coffee, K., *Proc. Soc. Exptl. Biol. Med.* **115**, 196 (1964).
199. Wakerlin, G. E., Bird, R. B., Brennan, B. B., Frank, M. H., Kremen, S., Kuperman, I., and Skom, J. H., *J. Lab. Clin. Med.* **41**, 708 (1953).
200. Wilkins, R. W., *Boston Med. Quart.* **16**, 57 (1965).
201. Wilson, C. W., *Symp. Pathogenesis Essential Hypertension, Prague, 1960* p. 405. Pergamon Press, Oxford, 1962.
202. Wilson, C., and Byrom, F. B., *Lancet* **I**, 136 (1939).

CHAPTER III

Guanethidine and Related Adrenergic Neuronal Blocking Agents

Robert P. Mull

Robert A. Maxwell

I. Introduction, 115
II. Pharmacology of the Adrenergic Neuronal Blocking Agents, 116
    A. Consequences of Adrenergic Neuronal Blockade, 119
    B. Consequences of Direct Release of Norepinephrine from Stores, 120
    C. Consequences of Inhibition of the Capacity of the Nerve Terminal to Take Up and Bind Norepinephrine, 120
    D. Consequences of Depletion of Norepinephrine Stored in Effector Organs, 121
    E. Consequences of Inhibition of Drug-induced Release of Norepinephrine from Stores, 121
    F. Additional Pharmacological Actions, 121
    G. Absorption, Fate, and Excretion, 122
    H. Tolerance, 122
    I. Side Effects, 122
    J. Therapeutic Uses, 122
III. Chemistry of the Adrenergic Neuronal Blocking Agents, 123
    A. Bretylium, 123
    B. Amidoximes and Amidines, 125
    C. Guanethidine, 128
    D. Other Heterocyclic Guanidine Derivatives, 131
    E. Aromatic Guanidine Derivatives, 140
    F. Aliphatic Guanidines, 144
    References, 145

I. Introduction

A significant advance in the management of human hypertension was initiated with the synthesis of guanethidine, an effective antihypertensive agent which acts by preventing the release of the sympathetic transmitter and by producing a depletion of tissue stores of norepinephrine. Guanethidine was found to be as potent as the ganglionic blocking agents while not sharing many of their disadvantages. The use of xylocholine and bretylium, although they inhibit the release of neurohormones from the postganglionic sympathetic nerve endings, was hampered by untoward muscarinic side effects and gradual clinical refractoriness, respectively. Guanethidine, because of its favorable clinical reception and novel structural aspects, is a prototype that has led to the preparation of numerous compounds embodying the guanidine moiety.

This survey proposes to deal mainly with the large number of guanidines possessing hypotensive activity; structurally related agents such as amidoximes and amidines, although relatively small in number, are likewise included for completeness. Bretylium, because of certain similarities of action, falls logically within the framework of this review and serves to introduce the pharmacology and chemistry of adrenergic neuronal blocking agents.

II. Pharmacology of the adrenergic neuronal blocking agents

Medical opinion has favored the view that overactivity of the sympathetic nervous system is implicated in several serious pathological conditions, e.g., essential arterial hypertension, peripheral vascular disease, and hyperthyroidism. As a consequence, medicinal chemists and pharmacologists have sought to develop compounds which would selectively inhibit the sympathetic nervous system.

The first compounds reported to produce specific inhibition of the responses of organs to sympathetic nerve activity were the adrenergic blocking drugs (84, 108). Synthetic adrenergic blocking drugs have been known since the late 1930's. They are derivatives of β-haloalkylamine, benzodioxane, imidazoline, dibenzazepine, and isopropylnorepinephrine. Adrenergic blocking agents inhibit the transmission of neuronal activity across the junction between sympathetic nerve terminals and the effector cells. Typical effectors are cardiac pacemaker cells, cardiac muscle fibers, smooth muscle cells, and cells of exocrine glands. Adrenergic blocking drugs unite with the effector cells and render them unresponsive to the transmitter substance, norepinephrine, which is released from the nerve ending as a consequence of sympathetic neuronal activity. There are two distinct sites of combination for norepinephrine and the adrenergic blocking drugs in the effector cells. These are designated as alpha adrenergic "receptors" and beta adrenergic "receptors" (78). In general, alpha receptor activation by transmitter leads to excitatory responses, e.g., augmented smooth muscle contractions, increased glandular secretion, while beta receptor activation leads to inhibitory responses, e.g., smooth muscle relaxation, cessation of glandular secretion. In order to achieve complete abolition of all the responses to sympathetic nerve activity, blockade of both receptor types is required. This can be accomplished by combining one of the derivatives of β-haloalkylamine, benzodioxane, imidazoline, or dibenzazepine which block alpha receptors with one of the derivatives of isopropylnorepinephrine which block beta receptors. Such a combination of blocking agents is experimentally feasible but is not practical from a therapeutic point of view since each of the blocking agents may exert considerable side effects. The combination of two types of blocking agents generally would make a bad situation worse.

The class of blocking agents reviewed in this chapter have the capacity to inhibit the transmission of neuronal activity across the junction between sympathetic nerve terminals and the effector cells. In this way they superficially resemble the adrenergic blocking agents. By way of contrast, however, adrenergic neuronal blocking agents, as the name implies, act within the sympathetic nerve terminals to prevent the release of transmitter substance. In reasonable doses they do not impair conduction of impulses along sympathetic nerve trunks. They do not inhibit the association of norepinephrine with effector cells as do the adrenergic blocking drugs. Effector cells are fully responsive or hyperresponsive to norepinephrine and other related catecholamines. The adrenergic neuronal blocking agents produce only a fleeting impairment of parasympathetic nerve function. (See 14, 40, 49, 50, 75, 87, 90, 128 for the general pharmacology of these agents.) Blockade of the sympathetic nervous system with neuronal blocking agents is more effective than blockade with either of the two types of adrenergic blocking agents. Since it is the release of norepinephrine from nerve terminals which is inhibited by neuronal blocking agents, both alpha and beta stimulant actions of the transmitter are simultaneously dampened.

Practically the full range of pharmacological activity of the more specifically acting adrenergic neuronal blocking agents can be understood in terms of their action at the sympathetic nerve terminal. These drugs exert several or all of the following actions at sympathetic nerve terminals:

(a) They inhibit the release by action potentials of a fraction of the norepinephrine stored in the nerve ending. By release is meant the rapid passage out of the store of enough physiologically active norepinephrine to produce a response in effector cells. The amount of transmitter which is released usually does not detectably diminish the magnitude of the store of norepinephrine. This inhibition of neuronally induced release is the primary useful action of these drugs and is called adrenergic neuronal blockade.

(b) They release norepinephrine from stores in nerve endings (61). This is a direct action of the drug at nerve endings and is independent of neuronal activity. This effect is very short lasting as compared to (a).

(c) They inhibit the capacity of the nerve terminal to take up and/or to bind norepinephrine from the extracellular fluid surrounding the nerve terminals and effector cells (42, 63, 66). Uptake and binding into nerve terminals apparently is a primary method of terminating the physiological actions of norepinephrine. This is so regardless of the route by which the norepinephrine reaches this area, i.e., by release from nerve endings or as a consequence of injection.

Table I

PROFILE OF THE ACTIONS OF SOME ADRENERGIC NEURONAL BLOCKING AGENTS AT THE SYMPATHETIC NERVE TERMINALS, *in Vivo*

Blocking agent	Block release of norepinephrine by nerve action potentials[a]	Direct, transient release of norepinephrine[b]	Inhibit uptake and/or binding of norepinephrine from extracellular fluid[c]	Deplete norepinephrine stores — In heart	In brain	Inhibit release of norepinephrine by other drugs[a]	References
Guanethidine	+	+	+	+	–	+	(87)
Bretylium	+	+	+[e]	+[e]	–	–	(14)
Bethanidine	+	+	+[e]	+[e]	–	–	(21)
Debrisoquin	+[f]	+	–	–	–	(±)	(90)
Guanisoquin	+[f]	+	+[e]	+[e]	–	+	(128)
Guanoxan	+[f]	+	+[e]	+[e]	+[e]	+	(40)
Guanoclor	+	+	+	+[e]	+[e]	+	(75)

[a] + = Phenomenon observed. – = Phenomenon not observed.

[b] As judged by occurrence of sympathomimetic effects following administration of the drug.

[c] As judged by an increase in the responsiveness of effectors to norepinephrine injection.

[d] As judged by inhibition of response of effectors to injected tyramine.

[e] Observed only after repeated administration of blocking drug. Not observed following a single dose which produces significant neuronal blockade.

[f] A part of this blockade may be alpha adrenergic blockade in addition to adrenergic neuronal blockade (see text).

(d) They deplete norepinephrine stored in nerve endings within effector organs. That is to say, they bring about a measurable diminution in the amount of stored norepinephrine. Depletion is relatively slow in onset and long lasting as compared to release. Depletion may be due in part to release of active material as described in (b), and in larger part to enhanced metabolism of the stored transmitter within the nerve terminals without concurrent replacement of the transmitter by synthesis or by uptake (c) (31, 130).

(e) They inhibit drug-induced release of the norepinephrine stored in nerve endings. This is a prolonged action.

A profile of the activity of several of the more specific adrenergic neuronal blocking agents with respect to the five actions outlined above is presented in Table I. As can be seen, the drugs have many actions in common and exhibit only a few differences. The exact molecular mechanisms whereby these five actions are mediated are controversial. The reader is referred to the following articles for more information concerning mechanisms (22, 30, 79).

A. Consequences of Adrenergic Neuronal Blockade

1. *Circulation*

Blockade of the sympathetic nervous system leads to hypotension especially in hypertensive man and animals. These drugs have greater hypotensive effect when the recipient is in the erect position than when the recipient is in the supine position. Such postural, or orthostatic, hypotension is characteristic of agents or procedures which block the sympathetic nervous system. The fall in pressure is due in large part to a reduced cardiac output which occurs secondarily to reduced return of blood to the heart from the systemic veins. Reduced venous return is a consequence of blockade by the drug of sympathetically mediated venoconstrictor reflexes which support the circulation during the maintenance of erect posture.

Sympathetic blockade leads to a slowing of the heart rate, presumably because the heart is dually innervated; the parasympathetic innervation which operates to slow the heart is left unopposed after inhibition of the sympathetic innervation has been accomplished.

2. *Central Nervous System*

Most of the neuronal blocking agents are strong bases and are therefore highly charged at physiological pH. Bretylium (II)* is highly charged because it is a quaternary ammonium compound. Therefore these compounds do not readily penetrate the blood-brain barrier and have little adrenergic neuronal

---

* Structural formulas for compounds designated by Roman numerals will be found in the chemical section of this review (Section III).

blocking activity within the central nervous system. Guanoxan (LV) and guanoclor (LXXXIII) may be exceptions to these statements since both compounds can deplete stores of norepinephrine from the hypothalamus during chronic administration (Table I).

3. *Gastrointestinal Tract*

Dampening of sympathetic impulses to the parotid glands frequently leads to parotid pain. This has been occasionally observed with guanethidine and has been particularly troublesome with bretylium.

Sympathetic impulses elicit relaxation of the muscular coats of the intestine while parasympathetic impulses are motor to these effectors. Hence, adrenergic neuronal blockade results in intestinal hyperactivity and leads to loose stools, frequent movements, or mild diarrhea in man.

4. *Genitourinary System*

Sympathetic inhibition causes failure of ejaculation. Potency however is not generally affected. Kidney function as measured by glomerular filtration rate and renal plasma flow may be reduced in man, especially when profound hypotension occurs. Progressive renal deterioration does not occur if renal impairment has not existed prior to administration of the drugs.

B. CONSEQUENCES OF DIRECT RELEASE OF NOREPINEPHRINE FROM STORES

Most of the adrenergic neuronal blockers when administered intravenously to man and animals elicit an initial period of sympathomimesis. That is, they produce signs of sympathetic excitation. This is exhibited as tachycardia, hypertension, piloerection, retraction of the nictitating membrane, and mydriasis. These actions are usually very brief in comparison to the subsequent periods of sympathetic atony.

C. CONSEQUENCES OF INHIBITION OF THE CAPACITY OF THE NERVE TERMINAL TO TAKE UP AND BIND NOREPINEPHRINE

Those agents which are potent in this respect also enhance the reponse of the effectors to injected norepinephrine. For this reason these drugs are contraindicated in treating phaeochromocytoma, where excessive secretion of norepinephrine occurs. Presumably the hyperresponsiveness occurs because the drug-induced reduction in binding leads to a larger accumulation of norepinephrine in the vicinity of the receptors in effector cells. Debrisoquin (XLV) appears to be an exception since it did not influence the retention of norepinephrine-^{3}H and its metabolites in rat hearts following intraperitoneal injection of the amine (90).

D. Consequences of Depletion of Norepinephrine Stored in Effector Organs

Severe depletion of neurotransmitter can in itself produce adrenergic neuronal blockade. Hence, this effect supports the primary adrenergic neuronal blocking action. Guanethidine (XX) and guanisoquin (XLVI) readily deplete norepinephrine stores in the heart following single injections. All of the other neuronal blocking drugs deplete only during repeated administration (Table I). It is possible that depletion during repeated administration is secondary to the "chemical denervation" produced by these drugs. It is known that surgical sympathetic denervation will produce a slow depletion of norepinephrine.

E. Consequences of Inhibition of Drug-induced Release of Norepinephrine from Stores

Phenylalkylamines such as tyramine or amphetamine which presumably act indirectly by releasing norepinephrine from neuronal stores are rendered inactive by most neuronal blocking drugs.

It has been observed that several of the neuronal blocking drugs which do not deplete norepinephrine stores following single injections, e.g., bretylium, bethanidine (LXXI) and debrisoquin, have been reported to inhibit the depleting action of reserpine and in some cases guanethidine (22). Hence, there is reason to avoid combined usage of these agents.

F. Additional Pharmacological Actions

Guanoxan has been reported to exhibit alpha adrenergic blocking actions (40). Adrenergic blockade probably results from the fact that this compound is a benzodioxane derivative and closely resembles piperoxan which is one of the earliest known alpha adrenergic blocking agents.

Guanisoquin may also have some adrenergic blocking actions (128). Furthermore, this substance as well as debrisoquin are N-substituted tetrahydroisoquinolines and are therefore chemically related to papaverine, an isoquinoline alkaloid. Papaverine is a potent dilator of smooth muscles. The suggestion has been made that part of the action of guanisoquin may be due to a papaverinelike action (128). Guanoclor effectively inhibits the enzyme dopamine β-oxidase (75). This enzyme catalyzes the hydroxylation of dopamine to yield norepinephrine in the normal synthesis of this transmitter in nerve endings. It is unlikely that inhibition of this step in the synthetic pathway increases the sympathetic neuronal block since this enzyme is probably not rate-limiting in the synthetic sequence.

G. Absorption, Fate, and Excretion

Bretylium, since it is a quaternary ammonium compound, is erratically and poorly absorbed from the gastrointestinal tract (65). The guanidine derivatives are not quantitatively absorbed, but their absorption is adequate and is considerably more predictable than is the case with bretylium (46). Bretylium is not metabolized in the body and is largely excreted in the urine. Guanethidine is rapidly metabolized and excreted during the first hour after administration. However, considerable amounts are localized in tissues, especially the heart. Once localized, guanethidine is metabolized very slowly (129). Bretylium, guanethidine, and bethanidine are apparently selectively taken up by sympathetic nerve fibers. Little is known about the fate of the other neuronal blocking agents.

H. Tolerance

Tolerance to the action of neuronal blocking agents is common. Tolerance to bretylium is so rapid and so complete that the compound is useless for prolonged administration (45). Tolerance to guanethidine is minimal and the compound has been successfully administered for years. Bethanidine falls intermediate between these drugs in respect to development of tolerance, as do the other agents.

I. Side Effects

The side effects produced in man by these agents are largely the result of their primary pharmacological action—blockade of sympathetic nerves. Morning orthostatic weakness, weakness upon exertion, and occasionally syncope are largely due to excessive blockade of reflexes which normally augment the circulation when the standing position is assumed or when exercise is taken. Impotence occurs infrequently. Loss of ejaculation without impotence occurs more frequently. Epigastric discomfort may occur as well as mild diarrhea. Slowing of the heart is customary.

J. Therapeutic Uses

These agents have been established as useful in the treatment of arterial hypertension in man. Their greatest application is in the treatment of moderate to severe forms of this disorder. The durations of action of these drugs following a single effective dose vary considerably—from several hours with bretylium and bethanidine to several days following guanethidine. Guanethidine, at present, is the agent of choice. There is no convincing evidence that the newer agents possess therapeutic superiority over this drug. Bethanidine is more rapid in onset and shorter in duration than guanethidine. This has been considered to be both an advantage and a disadvantage. The advantage gained in terms of more sensitive control over drug action is offset by the disadvantage that bethanidine must be given frequently with inevitable peaks and valleys in the intensity of the hypotensive effect (59). Bethanidine produces diarrhea with much less frequency than guanethidine.

Guanoxan elicites lassitude and nausea (114) and guanethidine does not. This suggests that any advantage that may accrue in terms of increased hypotensive action because of the incorporation of the benzodioxane ring system into the molecule may be offset by troublesome side effects which frequently accompany use of benzodioxane blocking agents.

III. Chemistry of the adrenergic neuronal blocking agents

A. BRETYLIUM

Xylocholine (I), to which reference has been made in Chapter 8 on quaternary ganglionic blockers, may be considered a predecessor to the adrenergic neuronal blocking agent bretylium, (o-bromobenzyl)ethyldimethylammonium p-toluene sulfonate (II).

(I)   (II)

Xylocholine   Bretylium

Although selectively blocking the peripheral sympathetic nervous system, xylocholine manifests certain undesirable cholinergic side effects, such as vomiting, salivation, and lachrymation, which precludes its use in the human. Further studies by Boura et al. (15) of a series of benzylquaternary ammonium compounds, however, revealed that some of these compounds were capable of lowering blood pressure by a similar mechanism (23) but with only slight parasympathomimetic action (20).

These compounds could be readily prepared by quaternization of a tertiary amine with a benzylating agent such as o-bromobenzyl p-toluene sulfonate or by quaternization of a tertiary benzylamine with an excess of a reactive derivative of the aliphatic group to be introduced (35, 36).

The large number of such compounds studied by these investigators has permitted some structure-activity relationships to be deduced.

The initial discovery that (III) is a potent sympathetic nervous system inhibitor with very few side effects was followed by studies that showed it to be less active than the benzylethyldimethylammonium compound (IV). The latter compound, unfortunately, proved to be toxic and had undesirable muscarinic properties.

$$\text{—CH}_2\overset{\oplus}{\text{N}}(\text{CH}_3)_2[\text{CH}_2]_2\text{OH} \quad X^{\ominus} \qquad\qquad \text{—CH}_2\overset{\oplus}{\text{N}}(\text{CH}_2)_2\text{C}_2\text{H}_5 \quad X^{\ominus}$$

(III)   (IV)

Using (IV) as a model, certain ring substitution studies were then undertaken in the hope of obtaining a more active and less toxic product. It was found that substitution in the o-position (notably by methyl, chloro, bromo, and iodo) gave some compounds with high activity; other substituents (such as ethyl, fluoro, trifluoromethyl, and nitro) in this position produced less active compounds. In all these cases, however, the muscarinic effects were diminished. The o-methoxy compound, while slightly active, still possessed these unwanted toxic properties.

On the basis of activity, specificity, and low toxicity, bretylium (II) was considered to be the most promising of all these and was selected for clinical investigation. The *meta* and *para* as well as disubstituted isomers of bretylium failed to give compounds with worthwhile activity. Alteration of the cationic head of the bretylium molecule (18), e.g., the trimethylammonium homolog, gave less active compounds except for the pyrrolidinium analogs which were about as potent as bretylium but shorter acting and more toxic. When the benzyl group was replaced, for example, by phenyl or 2-picolyl, the products so obtained were found to possess poor activity. More recently the benzyl quaternary ammonium compounds (V) and (VI) have been described by Dóda et al. (43, 44) as possessing sufficient activity and low toxicity to warrant clinical trials.

Boura and Green (20) studied the pharmacology of bretylium and found that it acts by producing a blockade of the postganglionic sympathetic nervous system resulting from inhibition of the release of the transmitter at the adrenergic nerve endings. It would seem that bretylium may specifically affect catecholamine storage and release mechanisms; ^{14}C-labeled material indicates a selective accumulation of the drug in the sympathetic ganglia and adrenergic nerves (14, 15, 18). An extensive review of the pharmacology of bretylium has been written by Green (61).

Initial favorable clinical results, which showed that bretylium exhibited selective antiadrenergic effects in man, were later found to be hampered by the occurrence of tolerance to the drug; its clinical usefulness too was limited by erratic absorption in the human (45, 46).

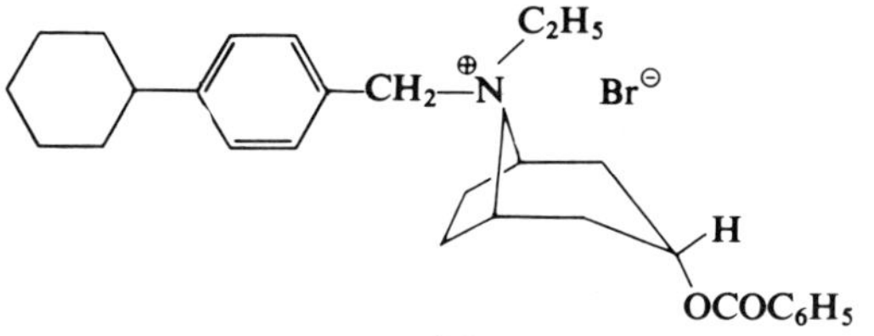

(V)

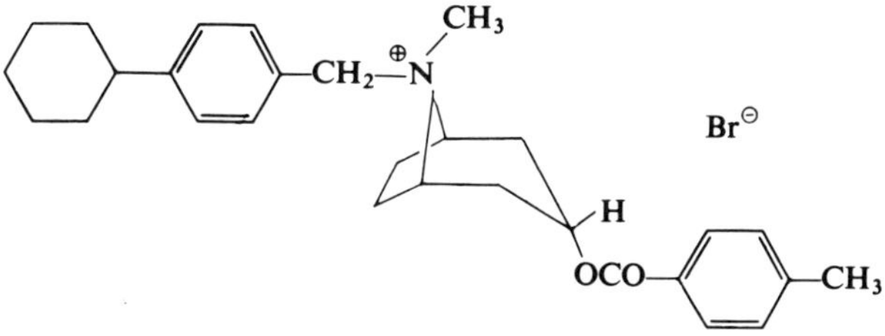

(VI)

B. Amidoximes and Amidines

1. *Structure and Nomenclature*

The amidoximes may be considered either as amidines in which the hydrogen atom of the imino group has been replaced by the hydroxy radical or as an amide, wherein the hydroxyimino group occurs in place of the oxygen atom of the carbonyl group. Tiemann (137) first assigned a structural formula to this functional group and named it "amidoxime". The possibility of two tautomeric forms (VII) and (VIII) was also considered by him and this has been the subject of recent structural studies by Bell *et al.* (10); most authors, however, accept the "imino oxime" form (VII) of the molecule.

$$R{-}C\begin{cases}{=}NOH\\ {-}NH_2\end{cases} \qquad\qquad R{-}C\begin{cases}{-}NHOH\\ {=}NH\end{cases}$$

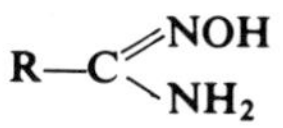

(VII) (VIII)

The amidoximes are amphoteric substances and are most commonly prepared by treatment of a nitrile with hydroxylamine:

$$R{-}CN + NH_2OH \longrightarrow R{-}C\begin{cases}{=}NOH\\ {-}NH_2\end{cases}$$

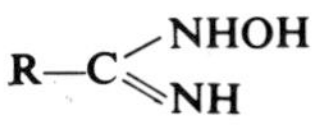

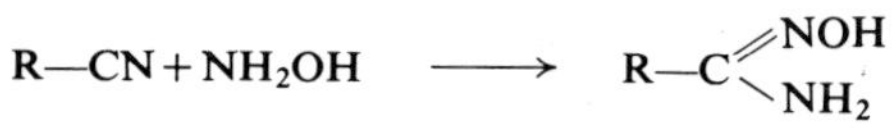

Numerous other methods are available for the synthesis of these compounds and a recent review (47) affords a comprehensive survey of the chemistry of the amidoximes.

Although the conventional structural formula (IX) employed by *Chemical Abstracts* to depict the amidine group is used throughout this survey, it should be remembered that these compounds are strongly basic and that the amidinium cation is more appropriately represented in the resonance form (X) (143).

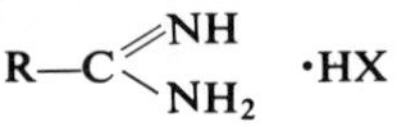

$$R-C\underset{NH_2}{\overset{NH}{<}} \cdot HX \qquad R-C\underset{NH_2}{\overset{NH_2}{<}} X^{\ominus}$$

(IX)    (X)

Acetamidine hydrochloride was first synthesized by Strecker (135) by passing hydrogen chloride through molten acetamide, but Pinner's (117) method of preparing amidines from nitriles via the imido esters is still one of the best methods described in the literature (132).

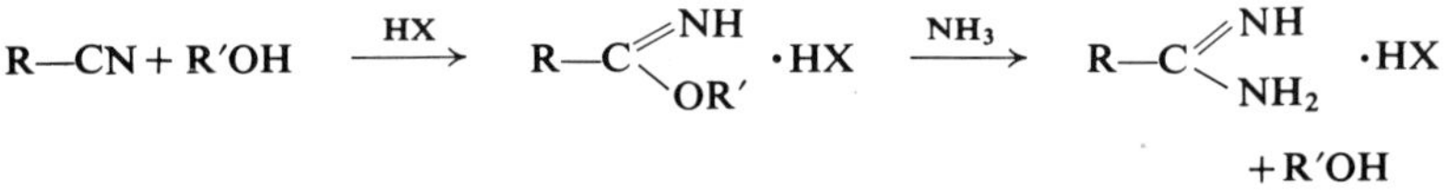

$$R-CN + R'OH \xrightarrow{HX} R-C\underset{OR'}{\overset{NH}{<}} \cdot HX \xrightarrow{NH_3} R-C\underset{NH_2}{\overset{NH}{<}} \cdot HX$$
$$+ R'OH$$

Amidoximes may also be converted to amidines by catalytic reduction at elevated temperatures (7) and recently a milder method, using rhodium on alumina, has been successfully employed (100).

An excellent study of the structure–activity relationships of amidine derivatives has been presented by Fastier (52).

2. Structure-Activity Relationships

Whereas the chemotherapy of the amidoximes has been the subject of numerous papers, a similar interest in the pharmacology of these compounds was not evident until the antihypertensive activity of 3-(hexahydro-1-azepinyl) propionamidoxime (XI) was noted (99).

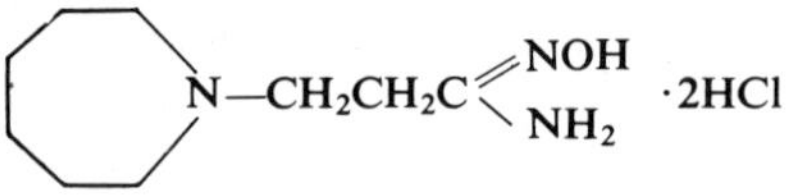

$$N-CH_2CH_2C\underset{NH_2}{\overset{NOH}{<}} \cdot 2HCl$$

(XI)

Su-4029*

This compound depressed the arterial pressure of unanesthetized neurogenic and renal hypertensive dogs, but did not markedly lower the pressure of the

* Designation used for compounds prepared in the CIBA-Summit laboratories.

unanesthetized or anesthetized normotensive animals. The antihypertensive effects were slow in onset and lasted for approximately 2–6 weeks following a single injection (30 mg per kilogram i.v.). Its mechanism of action has been studied by Maxwell *et al.* (86). The adrenergic neuronal blocking action of this compound is not marked. It is presumably dependent for its hypotensive action on the fact that it depletes stores of norepinephrine from the heart and blood vessels.

Chart I illustrates a few of the structural modifications of the original compound (XI) that were screened and studied for antihypertensive activity (88, 102).

Chart I

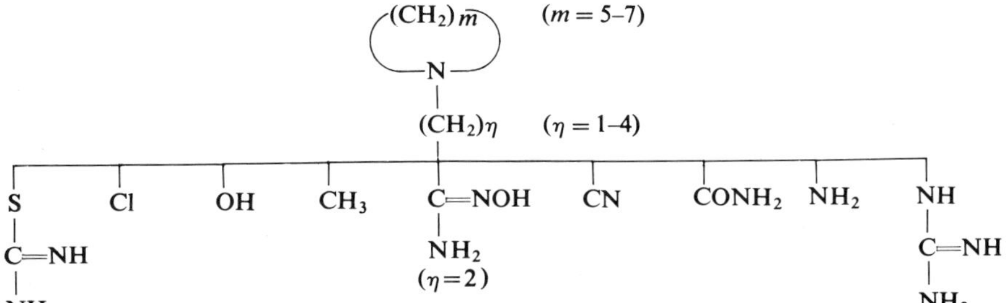

$$(CH_2)_m \quad (m = 5\text{--}7)$$
$$N$$
$$(CH_2)\eta \quad (\eta = 1\text{--}4)$$

S	Cl	OH	CH_3	C=NOH	CN	CONH_2	NH_2	NH
C=NH				NH_2				C=NH
NH_2				(η=2)				NH_2
				(XI)				

Maximum activity was noted with the hexahydroazepine ring compound and this activity diminished as the ring size was altered. Variation of the propionamidoxime side chain likewise resulted in a lessening of activity. The results of these structure-activity studies are similar to those observed with the large heterocyclic compounds containing the guanidino side chain and will be discussed in detail in Section III, C.

The clinical evaluation of (XI), however, proved disappointing since its hypotensive effect in the human was associated with a concomitant elevation of body temperature (110).

Other amidoximes (XII–XV) have since been reported to show hypotensive activity but details regarding their pharmacology and clinical efficacy are meager.

Catalytic reduction of the amidoxime (XI) gave the amidine (XVI) which when tested in the dog manifested antihypertensive activity similar to the original amidoxime (100). Additional related amidoximes were reduced and here too the resulting amidines were found to possess corresponding pharmacological properties. The correlation between structural variations and antihypertensive activity was the same as that found with the amidoximes.

Another amidine (XVII) with adrenergic neuronal blocking properties has

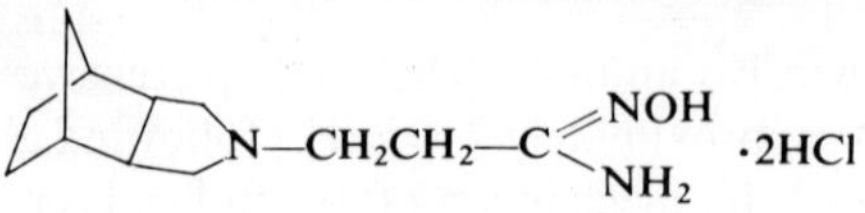

$$N-CH_2CH_2-C{\overset{NOH}{\underset{NH_2}{}}} \cdot 2HCl$$

(XII)

(12)

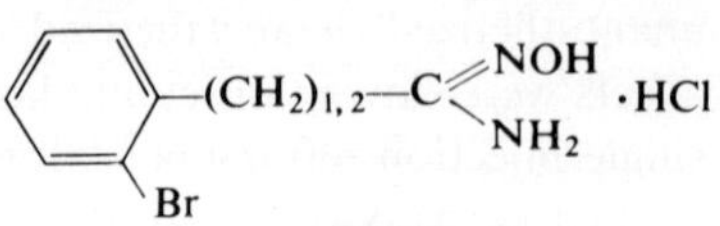

$${\overset{}{\underset{Br}{}}}-(CH_2)_{1,2}-C{\overset{NOH}{\underset{NH_2}{}}} \cdot HCl$$

(XIII)

(39)

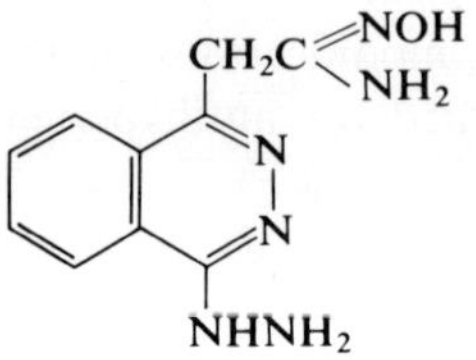

$$CH_2C{\overset{NOH}{\underset{NH_2}{}}}$$
N
N
NHNH_2

(XIV)

(145)

$$R-O(CH_2)_{1,2,3}-C{\overset{NOH}{\underset{NH_2}{}}} \cdot HCl$$

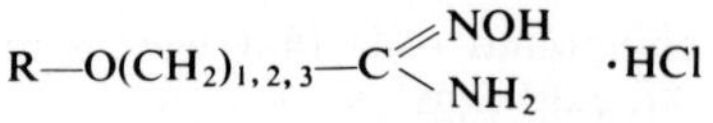

R = Ph or substituted Ph

(XV)

(28)

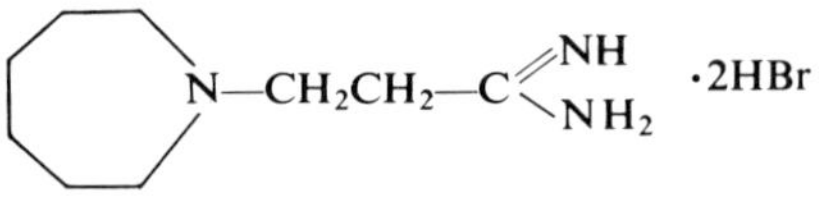

$$N-CH_2CH_2-C{\overset{NH}{\underset{NH_2}{}}} \cdot 2HBr$$

(XVI)

been synthesized by treatment of 2-(hexahydro-1-azepinyl)ethylamine with the hydrochlorides of ethyl acetimidate or acetamidine (16).

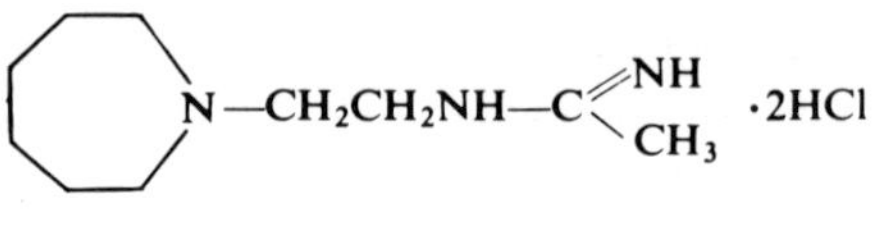

$$N-CH_2CH_2NH-C{\overset{NH}{\underset{CH_3}{}}} \cdot 2HCl$$

(XVII)

The method was employed to prepare other members in the series, but maximum activity was associated with this seven-membered ring compound; alteration of the length of the side chain gave compounds with weak activity.

A review of the structure-activity relationships of the amidoximes, amidines, and guanidines has been written by Schlittler et al. (124).

C. GUANETHIDINE

1. Structure and Nomenclature

As with the amidines, the more common structural representation of the guanidine salts (XVIII) will be utilized, although this does not adequately portray the resonance that occurs in the strongly basic guanidinium ion (XIX) (143).

$$R-NH-C{\overset{NH}{\underset{NH_2}{\diagup\diagdown}}} \cdot HX \qquad\qquad R-NH=\!\!=C{\overset{NH_2}{\underset{NH_2}{\diagup\diagdown}}}^{\oplus}\; X^{\ominus}$$

(XVIII)   (XIX)

It is this nucleophilic property which affords a possible explanation of structure-activity variations by compound receptor interaction requiring activation of the receptor by electron transfer (112, 113).

Guanidine itself occurs in small amounts in the juice of the sugar beet and other natural products and was first prepared by Strecker (136). His synthesis required a potassium chlorate oxidation of guanine in the presence of hydrogen chloride. Numerous methods have since been devised for the synthesis of guanidine and its derivatives (41), but the most frequently employed method for the compounds described in this section is that of Rathke (118, 119) using an amine and a salt of 2-methylthiopseudourea.

$$R-NH_2+NH=\!\!=C{\overset{SCH_3}{\underset{NH_2}{\diagup\diagdown}}}\cdot HX \longrightarrow R-NH-C{\overset{NH}{\underset{NH_2}{\diagup\diagdown}}}\cdot HX+CH_3SH$$

The cyanamide method of Erlenmeyer (48) and the use of 1-guanyl-3,5-dimethylpyrazole nitrate as a guanylation agent (126) have also been used. Recently, several alternative preparative methods have been reported (24, 29).

The preparation of different guanidine salts has been simplified by the ease with which the appropriate 2-methylthiopseudourea salt can be obtained when utilizing the method of Phillips and Baltzly (116) for the transformation of organic nitrogen base iodide and bromide salts to chlorides (97a).

2. Structure-Activity Relationships

Although papers have frequently appeared describing the biological properties of guanidine and its derivatives, only a few pertain to their cardiovascular effect. Large doses of guanidine have been reported to elevate the blood pressure in the anesthetized dog and cat (107) while decamethylene-diguanidine dihydrochloride (Synthalin)®* lowers it (81).

Kuroda (71) has claimed that 3,4-dihydroxybenzylguanidine and phenoxy-ethylguanidine cause a fall in blood pressure in the rabbit by a peripheral action. These instances of hypotensive action in the animal, however, were not followed by any immediate application to human hypertension. The first such clinically active agent, guanethidine (XX) was introduced in 1960.

Following the synthesis of 3-(hexahydro-1-azepinyl) propionamidoxime (XI), an effort was made to modify the molecule in such a manner that the untoward clinical side effects of fever, which occurred concomitantly with the

* This compound does not have a generic name.

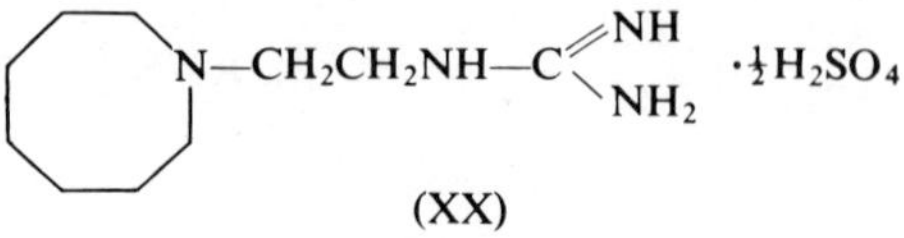

$$N-CH_2CH_2NH-C\begin{smallmatrix}NH\\ \\NH_2\end{smallmatrix} \cdot\tfrac{1}{2}H_2SO_4$$

(XX)

Guanethidine

fall of blood pressure, could be circumvented. Chemical consideration of the molecule prompted Maxwell et al. (85) and Mull et al. (98, 100, 101) to undertake terminal side chain and ring size variations. The importance of an $-C(=N-)-N=$ terminal group for activity leads logically to the study of the amidines and guanidines and the preparation of guanethidine. Guanethidine, in contrast to the amidoxime (XI), exhibited clearly discernible evidence of adrenergic neuronal blockade.

An extensive review of the literature on this drug is beyond the scope of this presentation; to date over 1500 scientific papers have dealt with guanethidine, so that only a summary of its chemistry and pharmacology will be given. Detailed reviews are given by Schlittler et al. (124), Green (61), and Sah et al. (122a).

The synthesis of guanethidine was originally accomplished according to Chart II.

Chart II

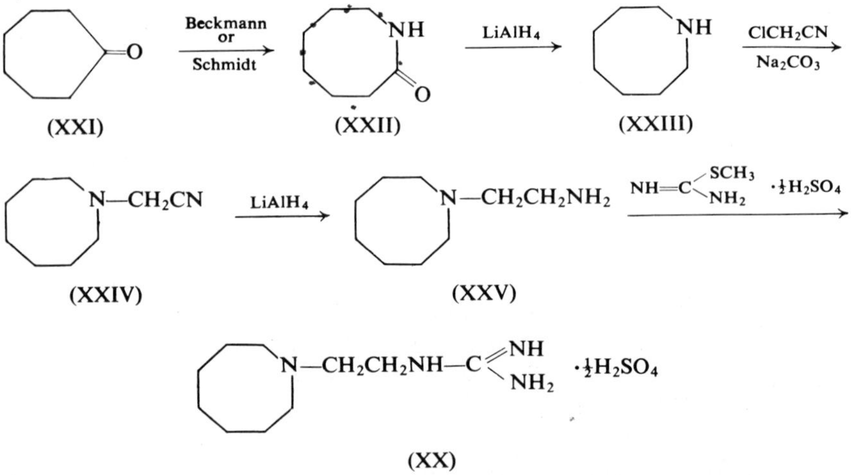

(XXI)   (XXII)   (XXIII)

(XXIV)   (XXV)

(XX)

Several modifications of this synthesis are feasible. Chen et al. (33), for example, have reported the preparation of guanethidine in which cycloheptanone (XXI) was synthesized via 1-nitromethylcyclohexanol by reduction using iron filings and hydrochloric acid. This method compares favorably with the results obtained by catalytic or electrolytic reduction. After ring expansion, the lactam (XXII) may then be converted to the thiolactam (69) and reduced electrolytically to the octahydroazocine (XXIII). Margerison and Shabica (82) give an alternative method of introducing the side chain by using ethyleneimine to give (XXV) and thus eliminate the second lithium aluminum hydride reduction. Other variations for preparing some of the intermediates have been described by Genas and Kern (58) and by Fel'dman and Lerner (53).

Mull *et al.* (98) found that replacement of the ring system in guanethidine by smaller rings such as pyrrolidine or piperidine fail to give compounds that exhibit marked activity, but an appreciable increase of activity occurs with the seven-membered ring and is optimum with the eight. Larger rings show decreased activity and in the case of the eleven-membered ring system there is a noticeable increase of toxic side effects. Quaternization of guanethidine gave an inactive compound.

Maximum activity was associated with the ethyl guanidine side chain and shorter or longer chain lengths produced either less active compounds or those with more pronounced side effects. Branching of the side chain or substitution of other groups in the chain produced compounds without pharmacological interest.

In addition to the guanidine end group, a large number of other terminal changes were studied for activity (see Chart I); only the amidoximes, amidines, guanidines, and amino guanidines are of sufficient pharmacological interest for inclusion in this review.

As a result of favorable clinical trials (57, 110, 120), guanethidine is widely used in treating moderate to severe hypertension. From both the chemical and biological viewpoint, however, it would seem that other guanidines might shortly be found which would further help to alleviate hypertension in the human. The large number of related compounds that are being studied by many investigators helps to corroborate this opinion. Some of the more important current investigations are being carried on with the compounds described in the following sections.

D. OTHER HETEROCYCLIC GUANIDINE DERIVATIVES

1. *Large Ring Compounds*

$$\text{N--CH}_2\text{CH}_2\text{NHNH--C}\underset{\text{NH}_2}{\overset{\text{NH}}{<}} \quad \cdot\tfrac{1}{2}\text{H}_2\text{SO}_4$$

(XXVI)

$$\text{N--CH}_2\text{CH}_2\text{NH--C}\underset{\text{NHNH}_2}{\overset{\text{NH}}{<}} \quad \cdot\tfrac{1}{2}\text{H}_2\text{SO}_4$$

(XXVII)

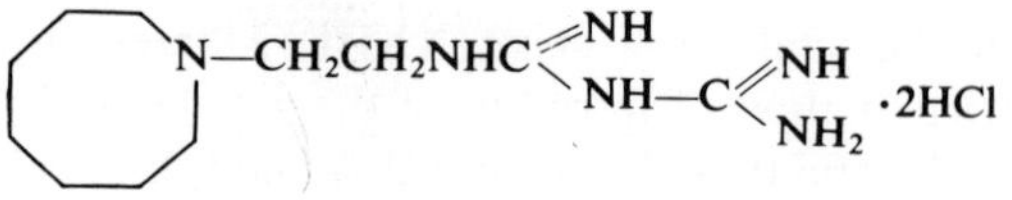

(XXVIII)

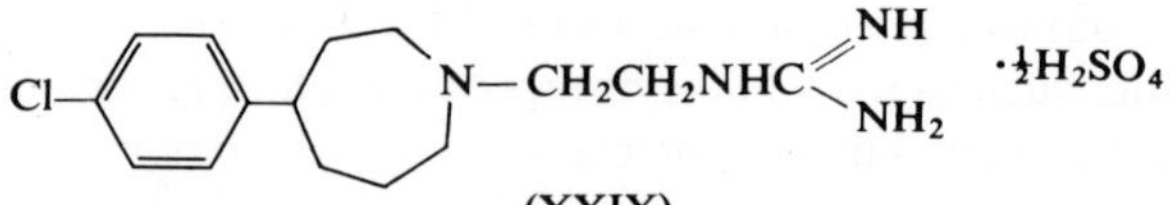

(XXIX)

Botton *et al.* (13) has reported that (XXVI), which may be prepared from the corresponding hydrazine compound and 2-methylthiopseudourea sulfate, produced marked hypotensive effects in the anesthetized rat, cat, and dog. Studies in dog cross circulation preparations indicated that the hypotensive activity was exclusively peripheral. The data suggest a dual mechanism of action: (a) an immediate but somewhat transient direct vasodilating action and (b) a prolonged interference of sympathetic transmission. Clinical results are, thus far, not available. It may be recalled that the aminoguanidine (XXVII) has guanethidinelike activity with a quick onset of action (94, 97, 103) and that the biguanide (XXVIII) is also claimed to be hypotensive (121). The introduction of substituents in the seven-membered ring compounds (e.g. XXIX) resulted in a decrease of hypotensive activity and an increase of toxicity (109).

2. Small Ring Compounds

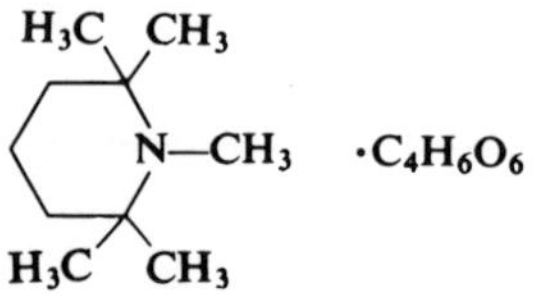

(XXX)

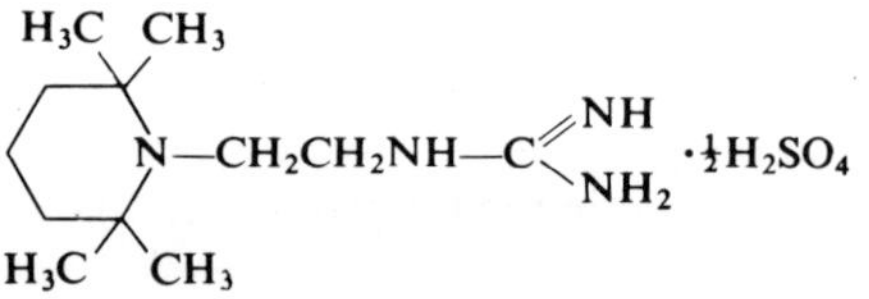

(XXXI)

The ganglionic blocking agent pempidine (XXX) (76, 134) has served as a useful model for the preparation of several compounds (XXXI, XXXII) with hypotensive properties. 2,2,6,6-Tetramethylpiperidine was prepared by Wolff-Kishner reduction of triacetone amine according to the procedure of Leonard and Nommensen (77) and the guanidine and aminoguanidino side chains introduced by routine methods described by Robertson *et al.* (122). The most potent member of this class (XXXII) is slightly more active in dogs and rats than pempidine and potentiates epinephrine and Hypertensin-CIBA pressor responses; its mode of action, however, is by ganglionic blockade (26).

Coda *et al.* (34) have prepared the monomethylpiperidine (XXXIII) by

H_3C CH_3 ring N—$CH_2CH_2N(NH_2)$—$C(=NH)NH_2$ · ½H_2SO_4 (XXXII)

CH_3 CH_3 ring N—CH_2CH_2NH—$C(=NH)NH_2$ · ½H_2SO_4 (XXXIV)

H_3C CH_3 pyrrolidine ring N—CH_2CH_2NH—$C(=NH)NH_2$ · ½H_2SO_4 (XXXVI)

CH_3—N piperazine N—CH_2CH_2NH—$C(=NH)NH_2$ · ½H_2SO_4 (XXXVIII)

CH_3—N ring N—CH_2CH_2NH—$C(=NH)NH_2$ · ½H_2SO_4 (XL)

CH_3 piperidine ring N—CH_2CH_2NH—$C(=NH)NH_2$ · H_2SO_4 (XXXIII)

H_3C tetrahydropyridine ring N—CH_2CH_2NH—$C(=NH)NH_2$ · ½H_2SO_4 (XXXV)

S thiophene ring CH_2NH—$C(=NCH_3)NHCH_3$ · HI (XXXVII)

CH_3—N piperazine N—CH_2CH_2NH—$C(=NH)NHNH_2$ · $2HI$ (XXXIX)

CH_3—N ring N—CH_2CH_2NH—$C(=NH)NH_2$ · ½H_2SO_4 (XLI) reduction of the N-(2-phthalimidoethyl)-2-methyl-pyridinium bromide, followed by hydrazinolysis and guanylation; it is reported to have hypotensive activity but no other details are given regarding its pharmacological properties. The *cis*-dimethyl compound (XXXIV) was also found to be hypotensive (64). The Δ^3-piperidinoethylguanidine (XXXV) (51) is a long-lasting blood pressure depressant with lower toxicity than the corresponding piperidino derivatives.

Various N-(2-guanidinoethyl)pyrrolidine derivatives have given evidence of lowering blood pressure, among these are the 3,3,4,4,-tetramethylpyrrolidine (XXXVI) and the 3,3-dimethyl-, the 3,4-dimethyl-, the 3,3,4-trimethyl, and the 3-methyl analogs. A published pharmacological appraisal of these substances is, thus far, unavailable (144).

A number of N,N'-dialkyl-N''-(2-thenyl)guanidines have been prepared from 2-aminomethylthiophene and the appropriately substituted 2-methylthiopseudoureas. These compounds are selective depressants for the sympathetic nervous system. The most active member of the group is (XXXVII) with structure-activity relationships similar to the benzylguanidine series (q.v.); this duration of action is short (141).

A large number of diazacyclic compounds have been prepared, primarily piperazine and homopiperazine derivatives. Mull *et al.* (101) found 2-(4-methylpiperazine)ethylguanidine (XXXVIII) to have interesting cardiovascular properties. This compound suppresses sympathetic nerve impulses, presumably at the efferent nerve terminals; it interferes with powerful vasoconstrictor reflexes to the limb while apparently reducing or eliminating their neurogenic tone. Since it has only mild hypotensive activity in normotensive animals and produces a minimum of early sympatheticlike actions following intravenous administration, it seemed a potential drug against those peripheral vascular diseases where sympathetic hyperactivity is suspected to play a part. Clinical results, however, were not encouraging and the drug was withdrawn from clinical trial.

The aminoguanidine (XXXIX) was found to be a quick-acting antihypertensive compound of the guanethidine type with a duration of activity of approximately 4–5 hours and which antagonizes the action of norepinephrine (94, 97).

The larger ring systems (XL, XLI) did not exhibit pharmacological activity greater than the corresponding piperazine compounds. This is in contrast to the remarkable increase in activity obtained with the previously described hexahydro-1-azepine and octahydro-1-azocine series (101, 131).

3. *Azaspiroalkanes*

Structure-activity studies of the N-(2-guanidinoethyl)azaspiroalkanes indicated that (XLII) inhibits the hypertensive action of *d,l*-amphetamine in the rat for 13 days; guanethidine inhibits it for 6–7 days. This difference is

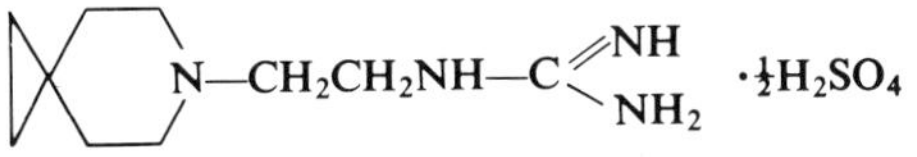

(XLII)

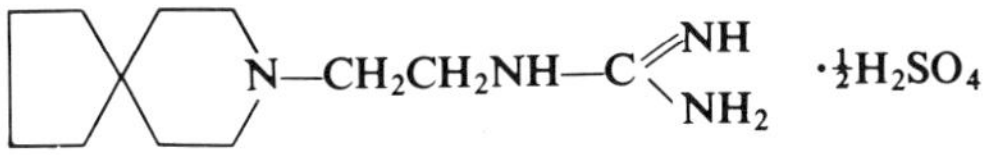

(XLIII)

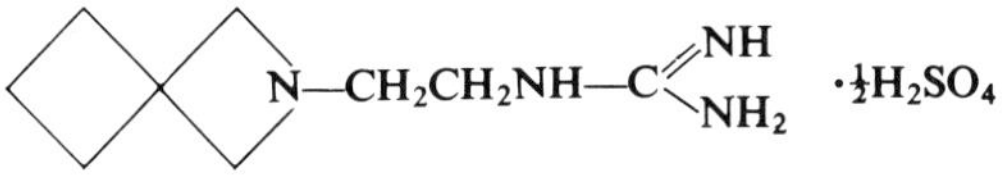

(XLIV)

attributed to the production of more intense depletion of catecholamines and more prolonged inhibition of cardiovascular sensitivity to *l*-norepinephrine by the spiro compound (60). Najer *et al.* (105) have found (XLIII) to be twice as active as guanethidine in the cat and dog and noted that reduction of ring size (XLIV) gave a compound that was much less active than guanethidine (106).

4. Bicyclic Compounds

a. One Ring with One Hetero Atom

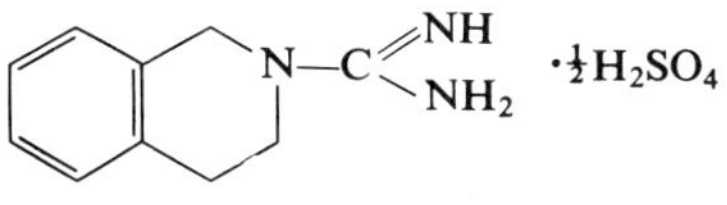

(XLV)

Debrisoquin
(Isocaramidine)

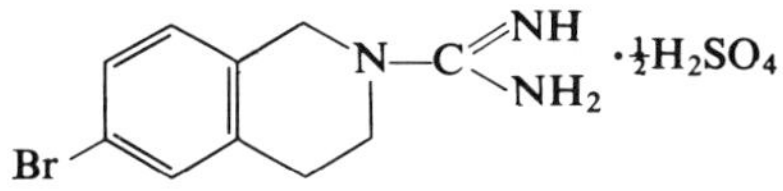

(XLVI)

Guanisoquin

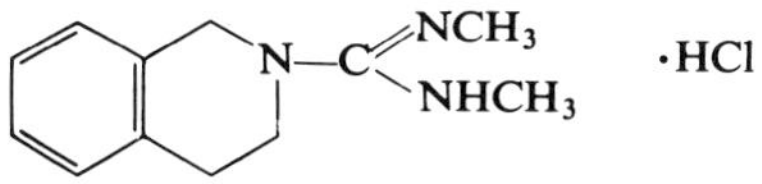

(XLVII)

Debrisoquin (XLV) has been found to be one of the more active members of a series of tetrahydroisoquinoline derivatives investigated for hypotensive properties. Wenner (142) has prepared these compounds from the appropriate 1,2,3,4-tetrahydroisoquinoline and 2-methylthiopseudourea sulfate or other standard guanylation procedures. The hypotensive activity is probably due to postganglionic blockage of the efferent sympathetic nervous system. Prelimi-

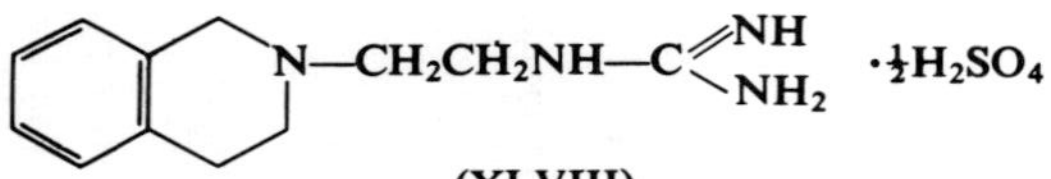

$$N{-}CH_2CH_2CH_2NH{-}C{\Big\langle}^{NH}_{NH_2} \quad \cdot\tfrac{1}{2}H_2SO_4$$

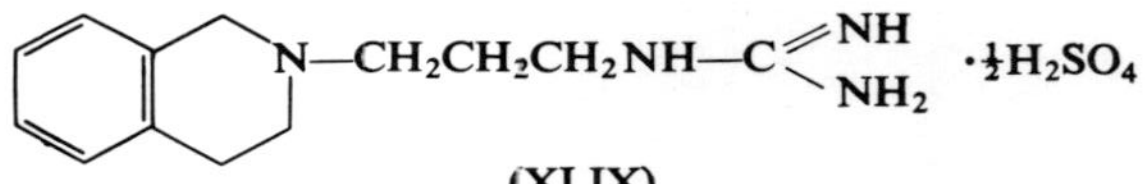

(XLIX)

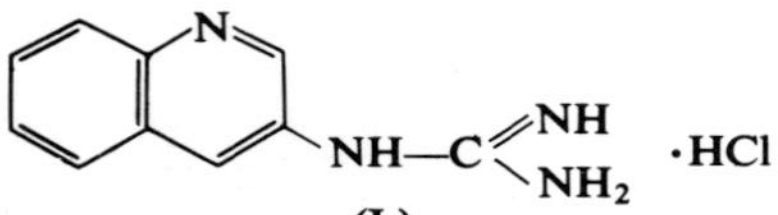

$$N{-}CH_2CH_2NH{-}C{\Big\langle}^{NH}_{NH_2} \quad \cdot\tfrac{1}{2}H_2SO_4$$

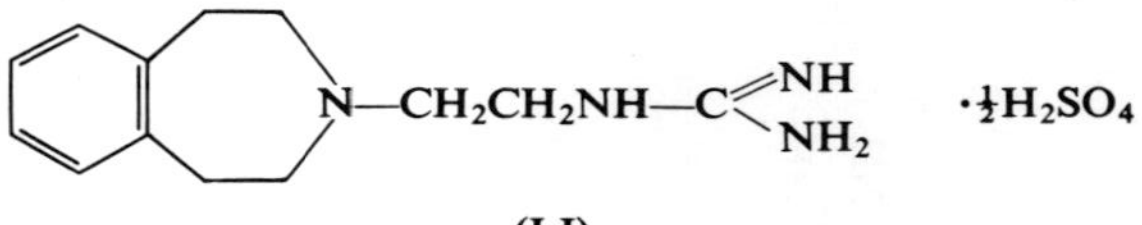

(LI)

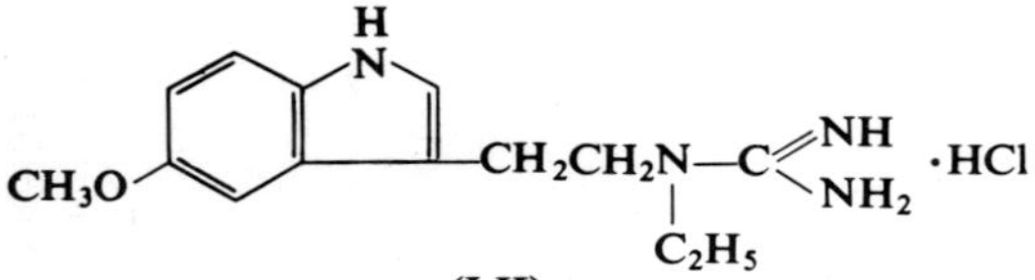

$$NH{-}C{\Big\langle}^{NH}_{NH_2} \quad \cdot HNO_3$$

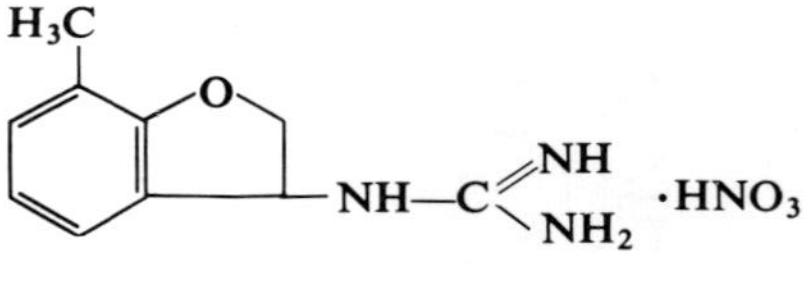

(LIII)

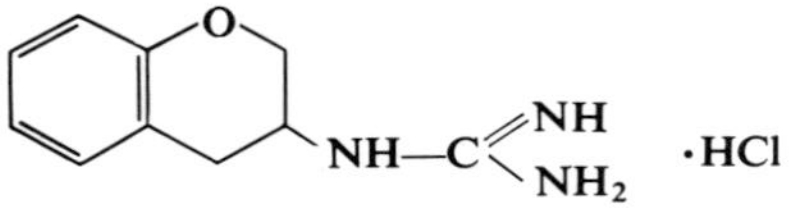

$$N{-}CH_2CH_2NH{-}C{\Big\langle}^{NH}_{NH_2} \quad \cdot\tfrac{1}{2}H_2SO_4$$

(XLVIII)

$$NH{-}C{\Big\langle}^{NH}_{NH_2} \quad \cdot HCl$$

(L)

$$CH_2CH_2N{=}C{\Big\langle}^{NH}_{NH_2} \quad \cdot HCl$$

(LII)

$$NH{-}C{\Big\langle}^{NH}_{NH_2} \quad \cdot HCl$$

(LIV)

136

nary clinical trials have shown this compound to produce hypotension of approximately 24 hours' duration (1, 67, 90) with a quicker onset of action (56). Following the withdrawal of debrisoquin, a prolonged (up to 1 year) augmentation of reserpine-chlorthalidone antihypertensive effect was noted in half of 32 ambulatory hypertensive subjects (25).

Scriabine *et al.* (128) have described the pharmacology of the corresponding 7-bromo compound (XLVI, guanisoquin) and found it to be similar to guanethidine. Peripheral vasodilation may also be partially responsible for lowering blood pressure. In man, at doses of 100–400 mg, arterial pressure was lowered. At the higher doses it lowered supine blood pressure mainly by reduction in cardiac index; the reduction in standing blood pressure was associated with a decrease in total systemic resistance and reduced reflex vasoconstriction. Nausea, diarrhea, and somnolence were common at 300 mg per day.

The N,N'-dimethyl derivative (XLVII) of debrisoquin has also been prepared and found to be hypertensive in acute experiments and slightly hypotensive during chronic administration (dog p.o.); it shows considerably less catecholamine-depleting activity than guanisoquin (XLVI) (127). Those compounds with longer side chains (XLVIII and XLIX) proved to be less active (2, 96) and the unreduced 3-guanidinoquinoline (L), although active in the animal, was less interesting in clinical trials (139).

The larger-membered ring compound, N-(2-guanidinoethyl)hexahydrobenzo[d]azocine sulfate (LI), lacks the initial sympathomimetic action of guanethidine, has little effect on the blood pressure of normotensive rats, but does lower that of renal hypertensive animals (62).

The reaction of N-ethyl-5-methoxytryptamine and cyanamide yields an indolyalkylguanidine (LII) which possesses hypotensive properties with few side effects in the animal; the effect in humans is not reported (115). A number of analogs have been prepared.

The action of some coumaran derivatives on the peripheral autonomic nervous system has been described by Fielden *et al.* (55). It is apparent that the structure (LIII) is related to that of xylocholine (I) if one envisions a ring closure involving the side chain of the latter compound. The cyclization of 2-tolyloxyacetyl chloride with aluminum chloride in dichloromethane at $-10°$ to $-15°C$, for example, gives 7-methyl-coumaran-3-one, the oxime of which can be reduced to the 3-aminocoumaran with sodium amalgam. Guanylation then occurs by treatment of the primary amine hydrochloride with cyanamide in boiling water. Isolation through the relatively insoluble bicarbonate and conversion to the nitrate is readily accomplished. It should be noted that these compounds have an asymmetric carbon atom and thus are capable of resolution; all, however, have been studied as racemic mixtures. The precise mode of action of this compound has yet to be determined but it does readily block for long periods the effects of stimulating adrenergic but not cholinergic nerves and does not generally antagonize the responses to epinephrine. In contrast to guanethidine, the norepinephrine content of rat hearts is not appreciably lowered 24 hours after a single dose.

Ferrini (54) has prepared 3-aminochromane from the oxime of 3-chromone by Raney nickel reduction. Guanylation gave (LIV) which was found to have antihypertensive activity in animals.

b. One Ring with Two Hetero Atoms

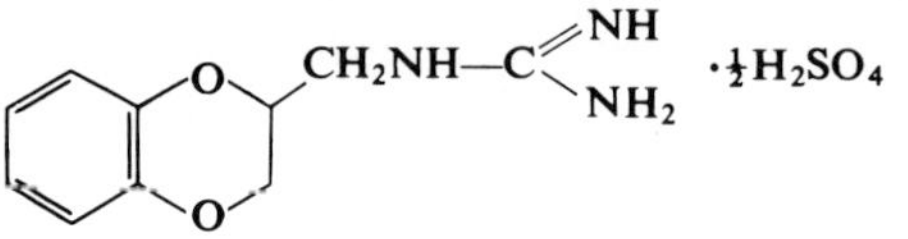

(LV)

Guanoxan

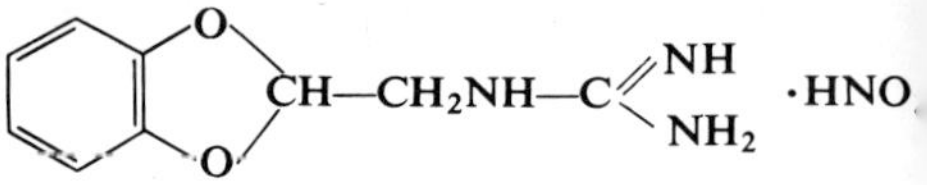

(LVI)

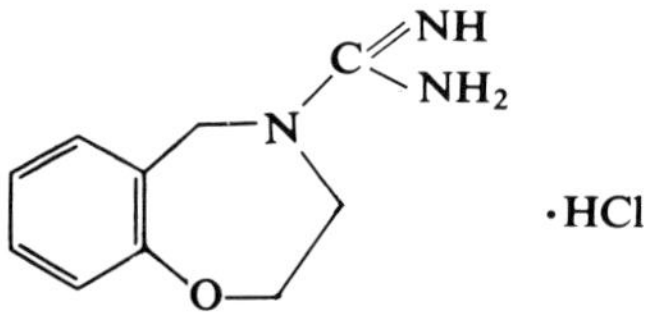

(LVII)

A large number of 1,4-benzodioxans and 1,3-benzodioxoles have been investigated for possible adrenergic neuronal blocking properties. The 2-substituted-1,4-benzodioxans were prepared either by treatment of catechol with a vicinal dibromide or an epihalohydrin in the presence of a base (Chart III) (5, 6).

Esterification of the alcohol (LVIII), followed by ammonolysis and lithium

Chart III

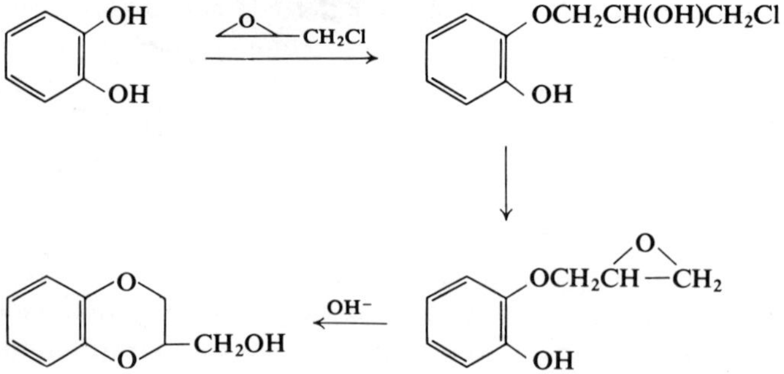

(LVIII)

aluminum hydride reduction gave the amine which then could be converted to the desired guanidine. When reductive procedures had to be avoided, the 2-hydroxy methyl derivative could be used to form the tosylate, and nucleophilic displacement with guanidine afforded an alternative method for the guanylation (91).

2-Guanidinomethyl-1,4-benzodioxan (LV; guanoxan) has proved to be a most interesting member of the series. It is reported to have greater antihypertensive effect than guanethidine in neurogenic or renal hypertensive dogs and was more active in antagonizing the pressor effects of tyramine in the cat and dog (3). Guanoxan lies close to guanethidine with respect to its ability to cause adrenergic neuronal blockade but depletes hypothalmic and adrenal catecholamine stores, which guanethidine does not (40). Clinically guanoxan has been reported to be useful in cases of hypertension which are severe or resistant to other compounds. The chief side effects are gastrointestinal, which can in most cases be tolerated or overcome (93, 114). The 1,3-benzodioxole analog (LVI) of guanoxan was found to be less active and the 4-guanyl-2,3,4,5-tetrahydro-1,4-benzoxazepine (LVII) has one-third the activity of guanethidine in the dog (123).

c. Azabicyclononanes

$$\left(R = (CH_2)_\eta - NH - C \begin{matrix} \nearrow NH \\ \searrow NH_2 \end{matrix} \right)$$

(LIX)   (LX)   (LXI)
(73, 74)   (70)   (95)

(LXII)   (LXIII)
(68, 72)   (73, 74)

d. Azabicyclooctanes

(LXIV)   (LXV)   (LXVI)
               (104)

Numerous azabicyclononanes and octanes have been prepared and evaluated for hypotensive activity; compounds (LIX) to (LXVI) are some of the more active ones. Pharmacological details pertaining to their mechanism are sparse although, in the main, they seem to manifest the guanethidinelike mode of action. Structure-activity relationships, too, are unclear although exchange of the guanidino in (LXI) for the amidoxime terminal group gave a less active compound. Another interesting observation revealed that the hydrogenated methanoisoindoles (LXVII) and (LXIX) were more active in their exo than in the endo forms (89).

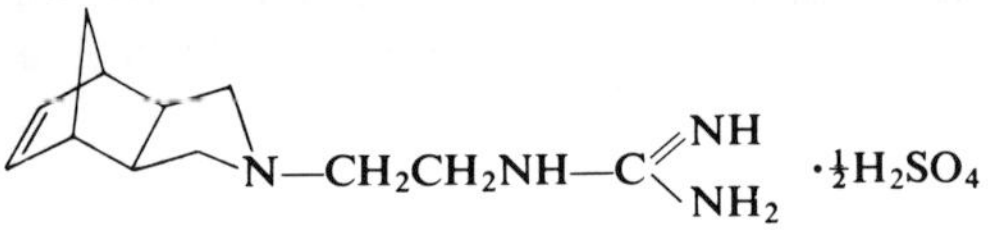

(LXVII) exo

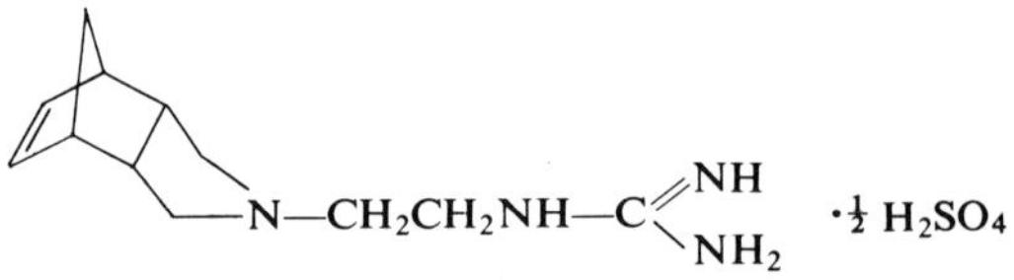

(LXVIII) endo

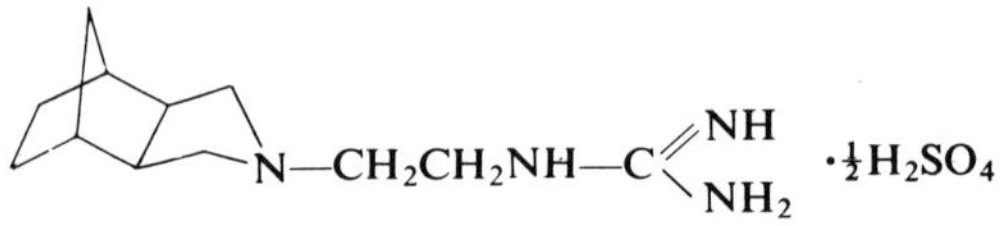

(LXIX) exo

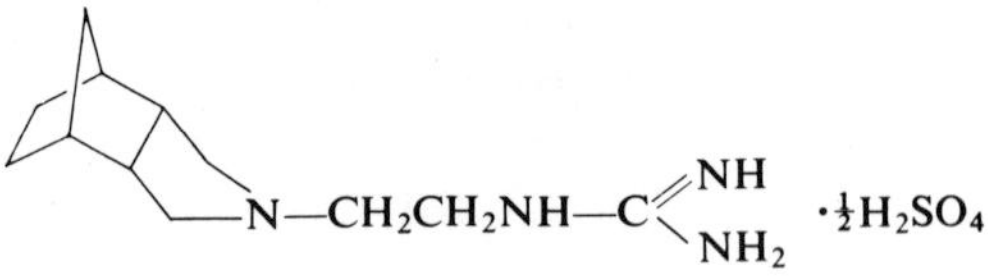

(LXX) endo

E. Aromatic Guanidine Derivatives

1. Benzyl Guanidines

As a result of the work with bretylium and guanethidine, Boura et al. (17) prepared a large number of aromatic guanidines; the benzyl guanidine series

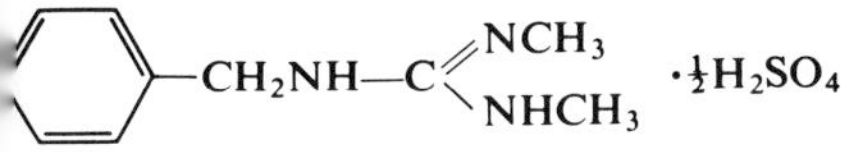

(LXXI) Bethanidine

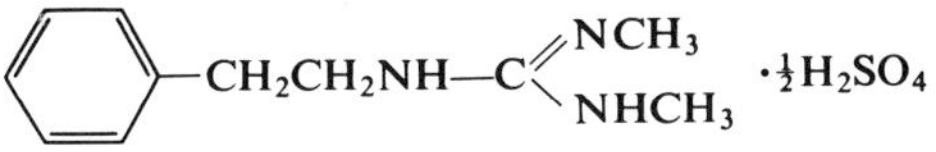

(LXXII)

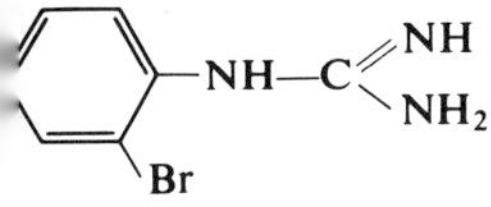

(LXXIII)

(LXXIV)

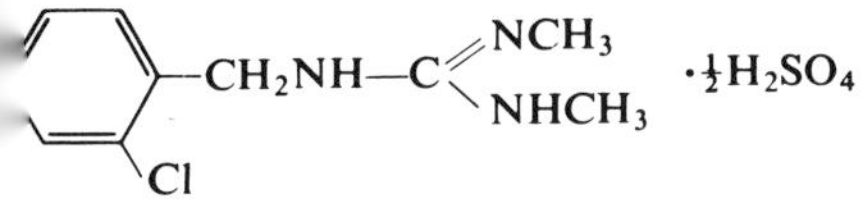

(LXXV)

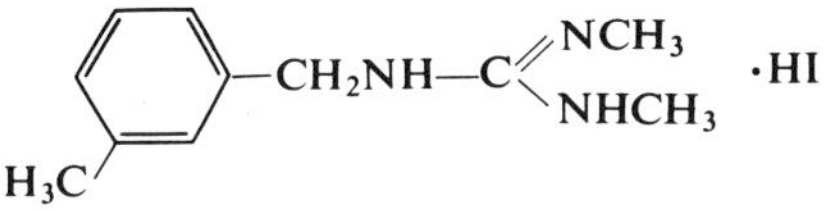

(LXXVI)

was particularly interesting. Preparation of these compounds from the appropriately substituted benzylamine and 2-methylthiopseudourea salts affords a convenient method (140). Structure-activity studies have demonstrated that ring substitution, chain length, and modification of the guanidine group are all important. The activity of the unsubstituted ring compounds (e.g. LXXI; bethanidine) was appreciably reduced when the chain length was increased (LXXII), whereas (LXXIII) was found to be inactive in the cat at 20 mg per kilogram, s.c. It is worth noting that the guanidine derivative (LXXIV) of tyramine has been reported to be a hypertensive agent (138). Terminal guanidine substitution was found to be optimum in the case of the dimethyl compound although other substituents (e.g., ethyl, propyl) were found to have some activity. Halogen in the 2-position of the ring was particularly beneficial (LXXV) but appreciable activity was not limited to substitution in this position; the 3-methylbenzyl compound (LXXVI), for example, was also active.

It has been demonstrated by Boura and Green (21) that bethanidine and (LXXV) are potent adrenergic neuronal blocking agents. The ^{14}C-labeled bethanidine has been studied in cats and found to have a selective affinity for adrenergic neurons (19). Clinically, bethanidine was found to exert blood pressure control in a manner similar to guanethidine. It is reported to be more rapid in onset (within 4–5 hours) and of shorter duration (12 hours). Side effects include postural hypotension, headache, and impotence (92, 133).

2. Cinnamyl Guanidines

Recent studies (8) with the cinnamyl guanidines have revealed an interesting structure-activity relationship. The cis and trans isomers were found to possess hypotensive activity in animals, the cis form (LXXVII) being more active than the trans (LXXVIII).

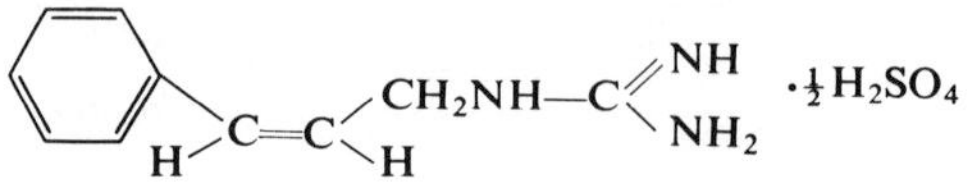

(LXXVII)

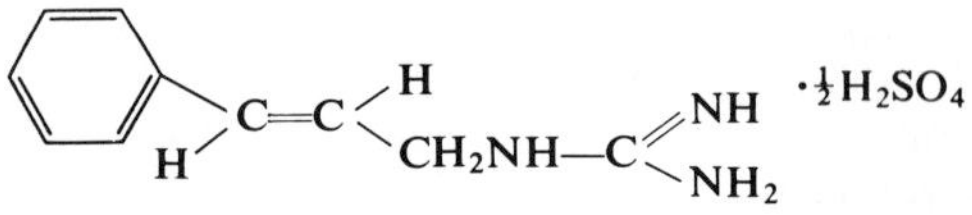

(LXXVIII)

The *trans*-cinnamylamine was prepared by Gabriel synthesis from the commercially available *trans*-cinnamylchloride; guanylation gave the desired compound. The cis compound was obtained by catalytic hydrogenation of (LXXIX), employing the Lindlar palladium-lead catalyst and subsequent hydrazinolysis of the phthalamide (LXXX) to give the *cis*-cinnamylamine which was converted to the *cis*-cinnamyl guanidine (LXXVII).

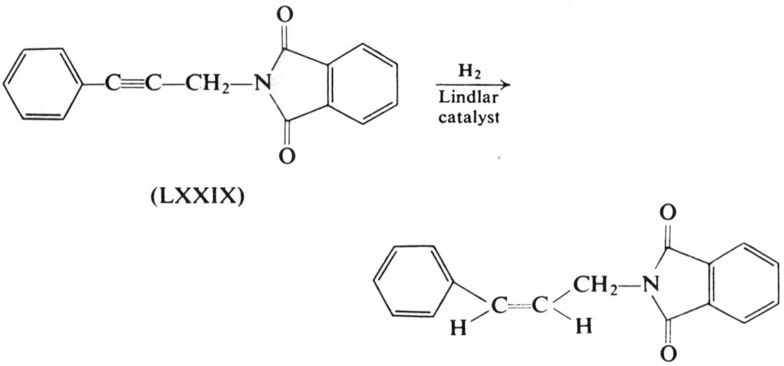

(LXXIX)

(LXXX)

cis-Cinnamyl guanidine differs from guanethidine in that it is more potent, manifests a more rapid onset and shorter duration of action, and produces less cumulation. The compound was orally active with a rapid onset of action in normotensive anesthetized and unanesthetized dogs and in unanesthetized renal hypertensive dogs. The pressor responses produced by injected *l*-epinephrine and *l*-norepinephrine were augmented while the pressor responses produced by injected amphetamine were inhibited or greatly decreased. The drug appeared to be more effective in the renal hypertensive dog than in the normotensive dog. The available pharmacological evidence indicates that the compound produces its hypotensive effect by some degree of blockade of the postganglionic sympathetic fiber. Clinical results are, thus far, unavailable.

3. *Phenoxy Guanidines*

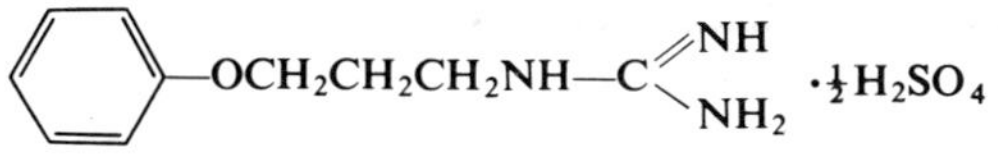

(LXXXI)

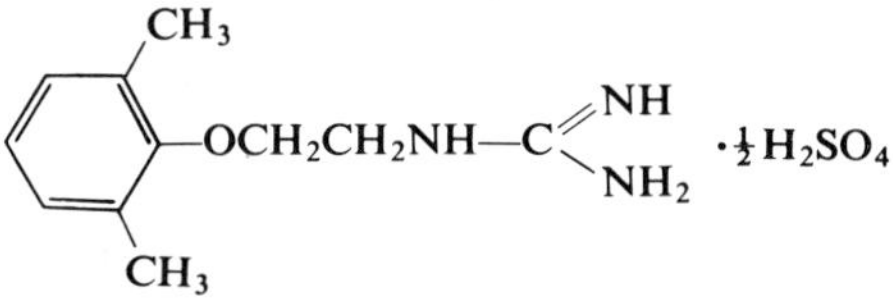

(LXXXII)

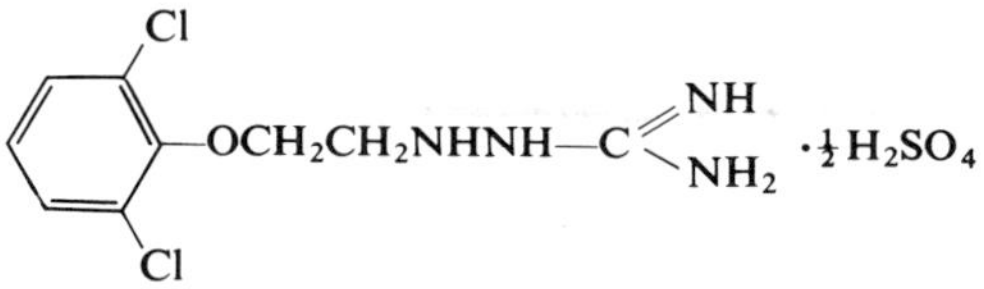

(LXXXIII)
Guanoclor

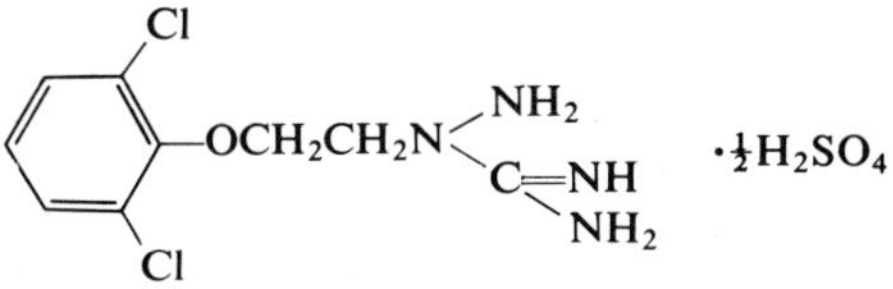

(LXXXIV)

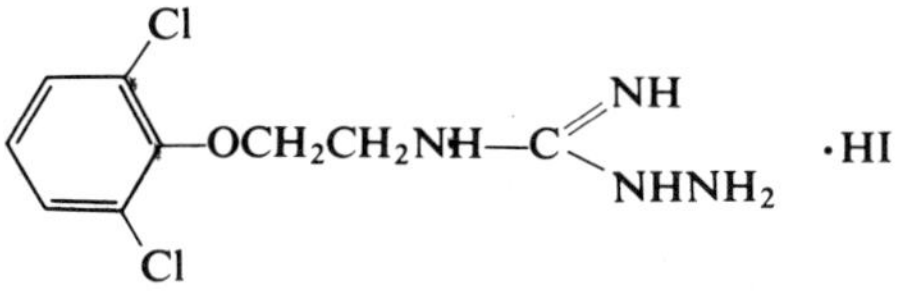

(LXXXV)

Another group of hypotensive compounds, the phenoxyguanidines, can be prepared by guanylation of the appropriate phenoxyalkylamines. These amines are synthesized from a substituted phenol by treatment with a chloronitrile and lithium aluminum hydride reduction of the resulting compound. The unsubstituted compound (LXXXI) has been shown to release peripheral catecholamine stores without significant effects on brain norepinephrine. The blood pressure of perinephritic renal hypertensive and neurogenic hypertensive dogs is thereby lowered (32); the 2,6-dichloro derivative is also hypotensive (27). The 2,6-dimethylphenoxyethylguanidine (LXXXII) has been reported to have antihypertensive activity in man similar to guanethidine (9).

Structure-activity studies with numerous analogs have shown the necessity of the two flanking methyl groups for maximum activity. Replacement of oxygen by sulfur in (LXXXII) gave a compound of comparative activity, relaxation of the nictitating membrane being observed at 10 mg per kilogram in the cat.

Another interesting structure-activity observation has been noted for the aminoguanidine (LXXXIII; guanoclor). Of the three aminoguanidine isomers, guanoclor is most active, (LXXXIV) shows little adrenergic neuronal blockade, and (LXXXV) is inactive (4).

Guanoclor was prepared by guanylation of 2-(2,6-dichloro-phenoxy)ethyl-hydrazine. Treatment of the appropriate cyanohydrazine, obtained by treatment of the hydrazine with cyanogen bromide, with ammonium sulfate and ammonia gave (LXXXIV). Compound (LXXXV) was synthesized from 2-(2,6-dichlorophenoxy)ethylamine and 3-methylthiosemicarbazide hydroiodide.

Guanoclor has both enzyme inhibitory and adrenergic neuronal blocking properties. It blocks dopamine-β-oxidase and a decreased norepinephrine excretion was noted (not with guanethidine) (3). The drug has been clinically effective, especially in combination with a thiazide diuretic. Side effects are not infrequent but have not as yet proved unduly troublesome (75).

4. Aralkoxy Guanidines

$$R-\langle\text{benzene ring}\rangle-CH_2ONH-C\underset{NH_2}{\overset{NH}{<}} \cdot HNO_3$$

(LXXXVI)
R = Cl, CH$_3$, etc.

A number of aralkoxyguanidines (e.g., LXXXVI) have been studied for pharmacological activity (83) but thus far no claims for significant hypotensive activity have been advanced, although anorexigenic properties were noted. The 1-(2-tertiary aminoethoxy)guanidines however, are reported to show hypotensive activity (111).

F. ALIPHATIC GUANIDINES

A few aliphatic guanidines have been found to possess antihypertensive activity, notably the dialkylaminoalkylguanidines (LXXXVII) and the tertiary octylguanidines (LXXXVIII). The former were prepared by reacting the amine hydrochloride and cyanamide or by heating an excess of the amine nitrate with calcium cyanamide in an autoclave (11). No detailed pharmacological data has been published (38).

tert-Octylguanidine (LXXXVIII) (80) is most conveniently prepared from

$$(CH_3)_2CH \diagdown$$
$$N—CH_2CH_2NH—C \diagup NH \diagdown NH_2 \quad \cdot HCl$$
$$(CH_3)_2CH \diagup$$

(LXXXVII)

$$H_3C—\overset{\overset{\displaystyle CH_3}{|}}{\underset{\underset{\displaystyle CH_3}{|}}{C}}—CH_2—\overset{\overset{\displaystyle CH_3}{|}}{\underset{\underset{\displaystyle CH_3}{|}}{C}}—NH—\overset{\overset{\displaystyle NH}{||}}{C}—NH_2 \quad \cdot HCl$$

(LXXXVIII)

the *tert*-octylcyanamide and ammonium chloride. The pharmacology of this compound indicates that its probable mode of action is by postganglionic sympathetic inhibition and reduction of endogenous norepinephrine stores (125). Clinically it has been reported to be an effective, but short-acting hypotensive agent (4–6 hours) with a mechanism of action different than guanethidine; its major disadvantage is this short period of action (37).

References

1. Abrams, W. B., Moe, R. A., Bates, H., Pocelinko, R., Whitman, E. N., and Stark, I., *Am. J. Cardiol.* **13**, 94 (1964).
2. Aroyan, A. A., Azaryan, A. S., and Iradyan, M. A., *Izv. Akad. Nauk Arm. SSR, Khim. Nauki* **18**, 76 (1965); *Chem. Abstr.* **63**, 6970 (1965).
3. Augstein, J., and Green, S. M., *Nature* **201**, 628 (1964).
4. Augstein, J., Green, S. M., Katritzky, A. R., and Monro, A. M.,*J. Med. Chem.* **8**, 395 (1965).
5. Augstein, J., Green, S. M., Monro, A. M., Potter, G. W. H., Worthing, C. R., and Wrigley, T. I.,*J. Med. Chem.* **8**, 446 (1965).
6. Baines, M. W., Cobb, D. B., Eden, R. J., Fielden, R., Gardner, J. N., Roe, A. M., Tertiuk, W., and Willey, G. L.,*J. Med. Chem.* **8**, 81 (1965).
7. Barber, H. J. and Self, A. D., U.S. Patent 2,375,611 (1945).
8. Barrett, W. E., Mull, R. P., and Plummer, A. J., *Experientia* **21**, 506 (1965).
9. Barron, D. I., Bavin, P. M. G., Durant, G. J., Natoff, I. L., Spickett, R. G. W., and Vallance, D. K., *J. Med. Chem.* **6**, 705 (1963).
10. Bell, C. L., Nambury, C. N. V., and Bauer, L., *J. Org. Chem.* **29**, 2873 (1964).
11. Bianchi, M., and Barzaghi, F., *Boll. Chim. Farm.* **103**, 490 (1964).
12. Bolger, J. W., U.S. Patent 3,118,904 (1964).
13. Botton, I., Kinnard, W. J., and Buckley, J. P., *Pharmacologist* **7**, 145 (1965).
14. Boura, A. L. A., Copp, F. C., Duncombe, W. G., Green, A. F., and McCoubrey, A., *Brit. J. Pharmacol.* **15**, 265 (1960).
15. Boura, A. L. A., Copp, F. C., and Green, A. F., *Nature* **184**, 70 (1959).
16. Boura, A. L. A., Copp, F. C., and Green, A. F., *Nature* **195**, 1213 (1962).
17. Boura, A. L. A., Copp, F. C., Green, A. F., Hodson, H. F., Ruffell, G. K., Sim, M. F., Walton, E., and Grivsky, E. M., *Nature* **191**, 1312 (1961).
18. Boura, A. L. A., Duncombe, W. G., and McCoubrey, A., *Brit. J. Pharmacol.* **17**, 92 (1961).

19. Boura, A. L. A., Duncombe, W. G., Robson, R. D., and McCoubrey, A., *J. Pharm. Pharmacol.* **14**, 722 (1962).
20. Boura, A. L. A., and Green, A. F., *Brit. J. Pharmacol.* **14**, 536 (1959).
21. Boura, A. L. A., and Green, A. F., *Brit. J. Pharmacol.* **20**, 36 (1963).
22. Boura, A. L. A., and Green, A. F., *Ann. Rev. Pharmacol.* **5**, 183 (1965).
23. Boura, A. L. A., Green, A. F., McCoubrey, A., Laurence, D. R., Moulton, R., and Rosenheim, M. L., *Lancet* **II**, 17 (1959).
24. Brown, J. P., U.S. Patent 3,177,218 (1965).
25. Bryant, J. M., Schvartz, N., Fertig, H., Fletcher, L., Jr., and Quan, R. B. F., *J. New Drugs* **4**, 221 (1964).
26. Buckley, J. P., Shanor, S., Gloss, J., and Kinnard, W. J., *J. Pharm. Sci.* **53**, 24 (1964).
27. Campbell, A., French Patent 1788 M (1963).
28. Campbell, A., U.S. Patent 3,139,455 (1964).
29. Carbon, J. A., U.S. Patent 3,080,374 (1963).
30. Carlsson, A., and Waldeck, B., *Acta Pharmacol. Toxicol.* **22**, 293 (1965).
31. Cass, R., Kuntzman, R., and Brodie, B. B., *Proc. Soc. Exptl. Biol. Med.* **103**, 871. (1960).
32. Chen, G., Ensor, C. R., McCarthy, D. A., McLean, J. R., and Campbell, A., *J. Pharmacol. Exptl. Therap.* **143**, 374 (1964).
33. Chen, H. Y., Yu, I. C., Wang, C. C., Cheng, Y. H., Chang, C. S., and Jen, H. C., *Yao Hsueh Hsueh Pao* **11**, 281 (1964).
34. Coda, S., Colo, V. A., Glaesser, A., and Pasini, C., French Patent 1,352,161 (1964).
35. Copp, F. C., British Patent 881,265 (1961).
36. Copp, F. C., and Coker, G. G., British Patent 924, 146 (1959).
37. Corcoran, A. C., Loyke, H., and Hirakawa, A., *J. Lab. Clin. Med.* **58**, 810 (1961).
38. Crowther, A. F., and Young, E. H. P., British Patent 969,851 (1964).
39. D'Alo, G., British Patent 876,079 (1961).
40. Davey, M. J., and Reinert, H., *Brit. J. Pharmacol.* **24**, 29 (1965).
41. Degering, E. F., *in* "An Outline of Organic Nitrogen Compounds" p. 464. University Lithoprinters,Ypsilante, Michigan, 1945.
42. Dengler, H. J., Spiegel, H. E., and Titus, E. O., *Nature* **191**, 816 (1961).
43. Dóda, M., Fehér, O., György, L., and Nádor, K., *Brit. J. Pharmacol.* **21**, 10 (1963).
44. Dóda, M., György, L., and Nádor, K., *Nature* **195**, 1108 (1962).
45. Dollery, C. T., Emslie-Smith, D., and McMichael, J., *Lancet* **II**, 261 (1960).
46. Dollery, C. T., Emslie-Smith, D., and Milne, M. D., *Lancet* **II**, 381 (1960).
47. Eloy, F., and Lenaers, R., *Chem. Rev.* **62**, 155 (1962).
48. Erlenmeyer, E., *Ann. Chem.* **146**, 258 (1868).
49. Exley, K. A., *Ciba Found. Symp. Adrenergic Mechanisms* p. 158 (1960).
50. Exley, K. A., *Brit. J. Pharmacol.* **12**, 297 (1957).
51. Farbenfabriken Bayer, A. G., British Patent 985,354 (1965).
52. Fastier, F. N., *Pharmacol. Rev.* **14**, 37 (1962).
53. Fel'dman, I. K., and Lerner, O. M., *Med. Prom. SSSR* **16**, 16 (1962).
54. Ferrini, P. G., unpublished results from the CIBA Laboratories, Basle, Switzerland.
55. Fielden, R., Roe, A. M., and Willey, G. L., *Brit. J. Pharmacol.* **23**, 486 (1964).
56. Finnerty, F. A., Jr., *Med. Clin. N. Am.* **48**, 329 (1964).
57. Frohlich, E. D., and Freis, E. D., *Med. Ann. District Columbia* **28**, 419 (1959).
58. Genas, M., and Kern, R., French Patent 1,371,942 (1964).
59. Gifford, R. W., Jr., *J. Am. Med. Assoc.* **193**, 961 (1965).
60. Giudicelli, R., Najer, H., and Lefevre, F., *Compt. Rend.* **260**, 726 (1965).
61. Green, A. F., *Advan. Pharmacol.* **1**, 161 (1962).

62. Hermansen, K., *Acta Pharmacol. Toxicol.* **20**, 201 (1963).
63. Hertting, G., Axelrod, J., and Whitby, L. G., *J. Pharmacol. Exptl. Therap.* **134**, 146 (1961).
64. Hoffmann-LaRoche and Co., Netherland Patent Appl. 6,409,619 (1965); *Chem. Abstr.* **63**, 2960 (1965).
65. Hurley, R. E., Page, I. H., and Dustan, H. P., *J. Am. Med. Assoc.* **172**, 2081 (1960).
66. Iversen, L. L., *J. Pharm. Pharmacol.* **17**, 62 (1965).
67. Kakaviatos, N., Finnerty, F. A., Jr., Chupkovich, V., and Tuckman, J., *Circulation* **28**, 746 (1963).
68. Klepping, J., Nouvel, G., Escousse, A., Franc, B., and Didier, J. T., *Therapie* **20**, 205 (1965).
69. Koštiř, J. V., and Pádr, Z., *Chem. Listy* **40**, 280 (1946).
70. Krieger, H., *Suomen Kemistilehti* **B35**, 218 (1962).
71. Kuroda, A., *Folia Pharmacol. Japon.* **18**, 106 (1934).
72. Lab. Lumière, French Patent 1701 M (1963).
73. Lab. Lumière, British Patent 972,088 (1964).
74. Lab. Lumière, British Patent 973,533 (1964).
75. Lawrie, T. D. V., Lorimer, A. R., McAlpine, S. G., and Reinert, H., *Brit. Med. J.* **I**, 402 (1964).
76. Lee, G. E., Wragg, W. R., Corne, S. J., Edge, N. D., and Reading, H. W., *Nature* **181**, 1717 (1958).
77. Leonard, N. J., and Nommensen, E. W., *J. Am. Chem. Soc.* **71**, 2808 (1949).
78. Levy, B., and Ahlquist, R. P., *in* "Pharmacology in Medicine" (J. R. DiPalma, ed.), 3rd ed., p. 463. McGraw-Hill, New York, 1965.
79. Lindmar, R., and Muscholl, E., *Arch. Exptl. Pathol. Pharmakol.* **247**, 469 (1964).
80. Luskin, L. S., and Short, J. H., U.S. Patent 3,140,231 (1964).
81. MacIntosh, F. C., and Paton, W. D. M., *J. Physiol. (London)* **109**, 190 (1949).
82. Margerison, R. B., and Shabica, A. C., French Patent 1,336,403 (1963).
83. Martin, D. G., Schumann, E. L., Veldkamp, W., and Keasling, H. H., *J. Med. Chem.* **8**, 456 (1965).
84. Maxwell, R. A., *in* "Pharmacology in Medicine" (J. R. DiPalma, ed.), 3rd. ed., p. 502. McGraw-Hill, New York, 1965.
85. Maxwell, R. A., Mull, R. P., and Plummer, A. J., *Experientia* **15**, 267 (1959).
86. Maxwell, R. A., Plummer, A. J., Daniel, A. I., Schneider, F., and Povalski, H., *J. Pharmacol. Exptl. Therap.* **124**, 127 (1958).
87. Maxwell, R. A., Plummer, A. J., Schneider, F., Povalski, H., and Daniel, A. I., *J. Pharmacol. Exptl. Therap.* **128**, 22 (1960).
88. Maxwell, R. A., Ross, S. D., and Plummer, A. J., *J. Pharmacol. Exptl. Therap.* **123**, 128 (1958).
89. Mizzoni, R. H., and Mull, R. P., unpublished results from the CIBA Laboratories, Summit, New Jersey.
90. Moe, R. A., Bates, H. M., Palkoski, Z. M., and Banziger, R., *Current Therap. Res. Clin. Exptl.* **6**, 299 (1964).
91. Monro, A. M., *Chem. & Ind. (London)* p. 1806 (1964).
92. Montuschi, E., and Pickens, P. T., *Lancet* **II**, 897 (1962).
93. Montuschi, E., and Lovel, T. W. I., *Lancet* **II**, 1339 (1964).
94. Mull, R. P., Belgian Patent 611,653 (1961).
95. Mull, R. P., U.S. Patent 3,078,272 (1963).
96. Mull, R. P., U.S. Patent 3,093,632 (1963).
97. Mull, R. P., U.S. Patent 3,189,599 (1965).

97a. Mull, R. P., unpublished results.
  98. Mull, R. P., Egbert, M. E., and Dapero, M. R., *J. Org. Chem.* **25**, 1953 (1960).
  99. Mull, R. P., Maxwell, R. A., and Plummer, A. J., *Nature* **180**, 1200 (1957).
 100. Mull, R. P., Mizzoni, R. H., Dapero, M. R., and Egbert, M. E., *J. Med. Pharm. Chem.* **5**, 651 (1962).
 101. Mull, R. P., Mizzoni, R. H., Dapero, M. R., and Egbert, M. E., *J. Med. Pharm. Chem.* **5**, 944 (1962).
 102. Mull, R. P., Schmidt, P., Dapero, M. R., Higgins, J., and Weisbach, M. J., *J. Am. Chem. Soc.* **80**, 3769 (1958).
 103. Najer, H., Giudicelli, R., and Sette, J., *Bull. Soc. Chim. France* p. 559 (1962).
 104. Najer, H., Giudicelli, R., and Sette, J., *Bull. Soc. Chim. France* p. 1593 (1962).
 105. Najer, H., Giudicelli, R., and Sette, J., *Bull. Soc. Chim. France* p. 2572 (1964).
 106. Najer, H., Giudicelli, R., Sette, J., and Menin, J., *Bull. Soc. Chim. France* p. 204 (1965)
 107. Nakazawa, F., and Abe, S. I., *Tohoku J. Exptl. Med.* **11**, 308 (1928).
 108. Nickerson, M., *in* "The Pharmacological Basis of Therapeutics" (L. S. Goodman and A. Gilman, eds.), 3rd ed., p. 546. Macmillan, New York, 1965.
 109. Ozawa, II., Gomi, Y., and Ohtsuki, I., *J. Pharm. Soc. Japan* **85**, 112 (1965).
 110. Page, I. H., and Dustan, H. P., *J. Am. Med. Assoc.* **170**, 1265 (1959).
 111. Paquette, L. A., U.S. Patent 3,200,111 (1965).
 112. Paton, W. D. M., *Brit. J. Anaesthesia* **28**, 470 (1956).
 113. Paton, W. D. M., *Proc. Roy. Soc.* **B154**, 21 (1961).
 114. Peart, W. S., and MacMahon, M. T., *Brit. Med. J.* **I**, 398 (1964).
 115. Philips, N. V., French Patent 1,388, 973 (1965).
 116. Phillips, A. P., and Baltzly, R., *J. Am. Chem. Soc.* **74**, 5231 (1952).
 117. Pinner, A., *in* "Die Imidoäther and ihre Derivate," p. 86. Berlin, Germany, 1892.
 118. Rathke, B., *Chem. Ber.* **14**, 1774 (1881).
 119. Rathke, B., *Chem. Ber.* **17**, 297 (1884).
 120. Richardson, D. W., and Wyso, E. M., *Virginia Med. Monthly* **86**, 377 (1959).
 121. Robertson, J. E., French Patent 1,320,255 (1963).
 122. Robertson, J. E., Biel, J. H., and DiPierro, F., *J. Med. Chem.* **6**, 381 (1963).
122a. Sah, H. J., Sah, P. P. T., and Peoples, S. A., *Arzneimittel-Forsch.* **16**, 33 and 199 (1966).
 123. Schenker, K., unpublished results from the CIBA Laboratories, Basle, Switzerland.
 124. Schlittler, E., Druey, J., and Marxer, A., *Progr. Drug Res.* **4**, 341–348 (1962).
 125. Schoepke, H. G., Brondyk, H. D., Wiemeler, L. H., and Schmidt, J. L., *Arch. Intern. Pharmacodyn.* **153**, 185 (1965).
 126. Scott, F. L., O'Donovan, D. G., and Reilly, J., *J. Am. Chem. Soc.* **75**, 4053 (1953).
 127. Scriabine, A., Booher, K. D., Pereira, J. N., Koch, R. C., *Federation Proc.* **23**, 331 (1964).
 128. Scriabine, A., Booher, K. D., Pereira, J. N., McShane, W. K., Constantine, J. W., Koch, R. C., and Miknius, S., *J. Pharmacol. Exptl. Therap.* **147**, 277 (1965).
 129. Shanker, L. S., and Morrison, A. S., *Intern. J. Neuropharmacol.* **4**, 27 (1965).
 130. Sheppard, H., and Zimmerman, J., *Pharmacologist* **1**, 69 (1959).
 131. Short, J. H., Biermacher, U., Dunnigan, D. A., and Leth, T. D., *J. Med. Pharm. Chem.* **6**, 275 (1963).
 132. Shriner, R. L., and Neumann, F. W., *Chem. Rev.* **35**, 351 (1944).
 133. Smirk, H., *Lancet* **I**, 743 (1963).
 134. Spinks, A., and Young, E. H. P., *Nature* **181**, 1397 (1958).
 135. Strecker, A., *Ann. Chem.* **103**, 321 (1857).
 136. Strecker, A., *Ann. Chem.* **118**, 155 (1861).

137. Tiemann, F., *Chem. Ber.* **17**, 126 (1884).
138. Truchot, R., Klepping, J., Michel, R., Escousse, A., and Tron-Loisel, H., *Compt. Rend. Soc. Biol.* **158**, 1249 (1964).
139. Urech, E., U.S. Patent 3,056,789 (1962).
140. Walton, E., and Ruffell, G. K., British Patent Appl. 44,071 (1960).
141. Wellcome Foundation Ltd., Belgian Patent 616,543 (1962).
142. Wenner, W., *J. Med. Chem.* **8**, 125 (1965).
143. Wheland, G. W., *in* "Resonance in Organic Chemistry," pp. 357 and 358. Wiley, New York, 1955.
144. Wollweber, H., Hiltmann, R., Wilms, H., Kroneberg, H. G., and Stopel, K., Belgian Patent 611,886 (1962).
145. Zugravescu, I., Petrovanu, M., and Rucinschi, E., *Rev. Chim. Acad. Rep. Populaire Roumaine* **7**, 1405 (1962).

CHAPTER IV

α-Methyldopa and Other Decarboxylase Inhibitors

T. L. Sourkes

H. R. Rodriguez

I. Introduction, 151
   A. The Search for Antihypertensive Antidecarboxylases, 151
   B. Clinical Significance of Antidecarboxylases, 153
   C. Biosynthesis of Catecholamines, 154
   D. Dihydroxyphenylalanine Decarboxylase, 156

II. Synthetic Decarboxylase Inhibitors, 157
   A. β-Phenylpropionic Acids, 158
   B. Chalcones and Flavones, 164
   C. Hydroxylamine and Hydrazine Derivatives, 164

III. Enzymology and Biochemical Pharmacology, 168
   A. Phenylpropionic Acid and Derivatives, 168
   B. Cinnamic Acid Derivatives and Chalcones, 169
   C. Flavones and Related Compounds, 172
   D. Derivatives of Hydroxylamine and Hydrazine, 172
   E. Decarboxylase Inhibition in Vivo, 179

IV. Methyldopa, 182
   A. Pharmacology, 182
   B. Clinical Applications of Methyldopa in Diseases Other than Hypertension, 185
   C. Metabolism, 186

   References, 186

I. Introduction

A. THE SEARCH FOR ANTIHYPERTENSIVE ANTIDECARBOXYLASES

This review is concerned with a retrospective examination of decarboxylase inhibition (15, 31), specifically with certain aspects of the inhibition of 3,4-dihydroxyphenylalanine (dopa) decarboxylase. This enzyme was discovered by Holtz et al. in 1938 (42) and has since been shown to decarboxylate 5-hydroxytryptophan and some other aromatic amino acids (reviewed in Sourkes, 97).

Indeed, there has even been a proposal to rename it "aromatic amino acid decarboxylase." This has been opposed because of the implication that the spectrum of substrates is indiscriminate, a claim not actually borne out by the work of some investigators.

For many years after the discovery of dopa decarboxylase, interest in its inhibition stemmed from such questions as product inhibition (4, 74, 85) and the relation of the enzyme to amine oxidase (74) in physiological regulation. With the development of the antimetabolite hypothesis of drug action, new suggestions were brought forward, among them those of G. J. Martin and his colleagues and of M. Goldenberg. Their interest in the subject was directed toward the search for compounds that would inhibit dopa decarboxylase, on the hypothesis that such inhibitors may be effective *in vivo*. At the present time, with our extensive knowledge of catecholamines, particularly norepinephrine, the effector substance released at the endings of sympathetic post-ganglionic nerves, it is intriguing to reflect that the hypothesis in 1947–50 had to be extended to include the probable, but not yet demonstrated, role of the decarboxylase in the biosynthesis of this substance. Martin at first investigated folic acid analogs and antagonists, some of which inhibit dopa decarboxylase weakly (51). This was confirmed by Schales and Schales (84) who found, for example, that 7-methylfolic acid and 2-amino-4-hydroxypteridine aldehyde inhibit 43 and 32%, respectively, when present at 0.0025 molar concentration. In 1950 Martin turned to structural analogs of dopa, observing inhibition with *p*-hydroxyphenylpyruvic acid *in vitro* and *in vivo* (52). Among the inhibitory compounds was 5-(3,4-dihydroxycinnamoyl)-salicylic acid (No. 62*). W. G. Clark's group then took up the problem and studied well over two hundred compounds in the search for suitable inhibitors. The work of this group is described in a series of important papers (15, 16, 41). The most active of their compounds was 5-(3-hydroxycinnamoyl)-salicylic acid (No. 55).

Goldenberg had a similar aim in mind: the synthesis of a specific anti-metabolite of dopa that would prevent its conversion to catecholamines. His suggestion, made toward the end of 1949, came at a time when norepinephrine had only recently been identified in mammalian tissues and established as the sympathetic neuroeffector substance (113). However, dopa and dopamine (3,4-dihydroxyphenylalanine and 3,4-dihydroxyphenethylamine) had not yet been recognized as normal bodily constituents. The Merck chemists to whom he proposed this working hypothesis had not long before prepared some α-methyl amino acids for a program in cancer research, and now the effort was extended to the aromatic amino acids and their derivatives. The initial biological results of the Merck intramural program on inhibitors were published in 1954 (95), and the chemical synthesis of the compounds in 1955

---

* The expression "No. X" in parentheses identifies the compounds mentioned in the tables.

(103). These articles included data on α-methyldopa [α-methyl-β-(3,4-di-hydroxyphenyl)-alanine] (No. 7).

In 1957–58 Dengler and Reichel described the interference by α-methyldopa with the pressor effect of intravenously administered L-dopa in various species (23). At about the same time, Westerman, Balzer and Knell reported success in antagonizing the effects of 5-hydroxytryptophan *in vivo* by employing α-methyldopa (117). They showed that α-methyldopa successfully prevents the formation of 5-hydroxytryptamine (serotonin) from its precursor. These findings were given currency in the autumn of 1958 on the occasion of the (first) Symposium on Catecholamines, held in October 1958 in Bethesda, Maryland, when H. Blaschko, P. Holtz, and W. G. Clark each referred to the biological research on α-methyldopa. As a result of this, S. Udenfriend and A. Sjoerdsma undertook some experiments with the compound in humans to determine if it exerts significant antidecarboxylase activity in man and if it can reduce blood pressure. Striking results were obtained on both counts in a patient with phaeochromocytoma and in others with essential hypertension. Further work indicated that α-methyldopa is a useful antihypertensive agent (64). L-α-Methyldopa (generic name, methyldopa) is the only compound with known and significant inhibitory properties toward dopa decarboxylase that has proved efficacious in essential hypertension. However, its principal mode of action as an antihypertensive agent does not stem from its antidecarboxylase properties but, in the first place, from its ability to act as a substrate for dopa decarboxylase, thereby leading to the formation of new amines (Section IV, B). It is one of the very few compounds that have advanced from design in the chemical laboratory to clinical practice in a minimal number of stages.

In this chapter no mention will be made of the many compounds that on test have proved to be devoid of antidecarboxylase activity. Compounds with substantial inhibitory action will be described, along with less active compounds where comparison is needed to adduce structure-activity relationships.

B. Clinical Significance of Antidecarboxylases

Theoretically, any process leading to the formation of amines or one of their further metabolic products should be subject to inhibition by a drug that acts on amino acid decarboxylases. Excessive norepinephrine was thought to be released in hypertension at the sympathetic nerve endings innervating arteriolar smooth muscle, and this was the theoretical basis for the research program that led to α-methyldopa. However, there is little evidence from urinary studies of excessive production of norepinephrine or its chief terminal product, 4-hydroxy-3-methoxymandelic acid (vanillylmandelic acid, VMA) in essential hypertension. This paradoxical situation arises from the phenomenon of re-uptake of neurally released norepinephrine by the heart, spleen, and other organs rich in postganglionic sympathetic nerve terminals. In this process the amine, which has escaped oxidation (by monoamine oxidase) or methylation (by catechol O-methyl transferase), or both, is returned to the storage vesicles in a state of binding that is indistinguishable from that of the endogenous amine already there.

The antidecarboxylases have greatly extended the possibilities of pharmacological control over the body's enzymic and physiological mechanisms in much the same way as have the monoamine oxidase inhibitors. Furthermore, these compounds have aided greatly in stimulating and extending research on biogenic amines and their precursors.

Excessive formation and excretion of catecholamines and their metabolic products are found in phaeochromocytoma, neuroblastoma, and ganglioneuroma; in malignant carcinoid much serotonin is produced. In addition, one can conceive of a use of antihistidine decarboxylases in the treatment of allergic and related phenomena.

Finally, the mild sedative action of α-methyldopa has recommended it for trial in certain psychiatric and neurological conditions, a subject that will be dealt with later in this article.

C. Biosynthesis of Catecholamines

The main pathway for the formation of epinephrine in mammalian tissues begins with the amino acid tyrosine. This compound occurs in all natural diets and additional amounts of it are available from the oxidation of phenylalanine through the action of the enzyme phenylalanine hydroxylase. Tyrosine undergoes oxidation to dopa, the immediate precursor of the catecholamines and melanin pigments. The enzyme that is involved, tyrosine hydroxylase, requires a tetrahydropteridine as well as ferrous ions for its action; it catalyzes a relatively slow step in catecholamine biogenesis. Decarboxylation of dopa is accomplished by an enzyme found in the soluble portion of many organs; the liver and kidney cortex are especially rich in it. This enzyme employs pyridoxal phosphate as its coenzyme. Thus, dopamine is the first of the catecholamines formed. Its natural occurrence in mammals was discovered only after epinephrine and norepinephrine were already well known.

Dopamine is oxidized to norepinephrine by a β-hydroxylase which, notably, contains cupric and cuprous ions in its structure, and whose activity can be appreciably diminished by application of disulfiram *in vivo* or *in vitro* (36), or by simple dietary deficiency of copper (57). Norepinephrine undergoes N-methylation, predominantly in the adrenal medulla, through the agency of S-adenosyl-L-methionine, as methyl donor, and a transferase. Epinephrine is formed.

BIOSYNTHESIS OF EPINEPHRINE

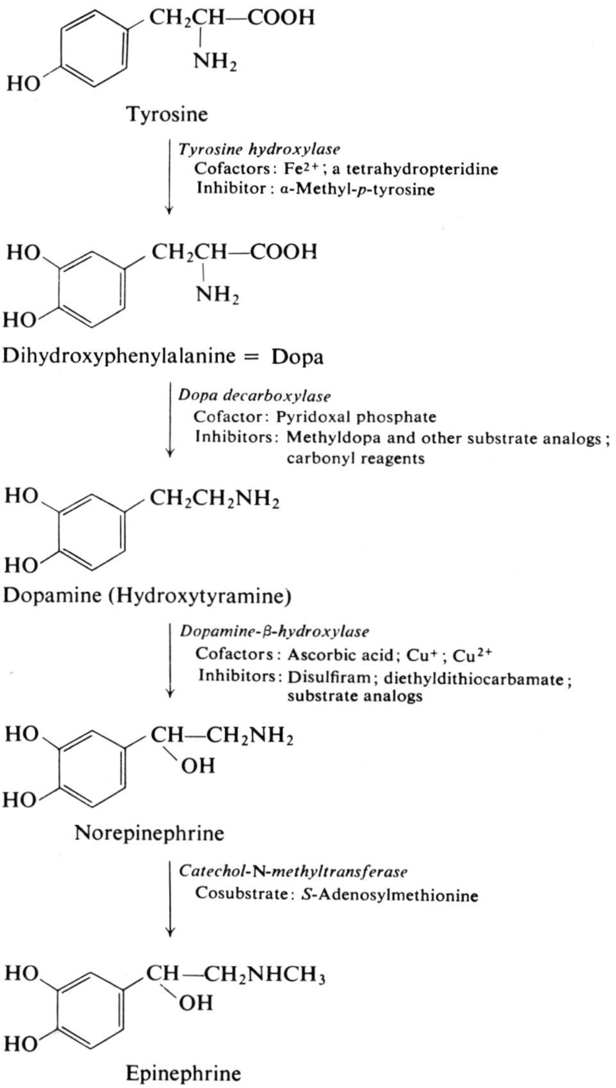

CH_2CH—$COOH$
|
NH_2

HO

Tyrosine

> *Tyrosine hydroxylase*
> Cofactors: Fe^{2+}; a tetrahydropteridine
> Inhibitor: a-Methyl-p-tyrosine

HO
CH_2CH—$COOH$
|
NH_2
HO

Dihydroxyphenylalanine = Dopa

> *Dopa decarboxylase*
> Cofactor: Pyridoxal phosphate
> Inhibitors: Methyldopa and other substrate analogs;
> carbonyl reagents

HO
$CH_2CH_2NH_2$
HO

Dopamine (Hydroxytyramine)

> *Dopamine-β-hydroxylase*
> Cofactors: Ascorbic acid; Cu^+; Cu^{2+}
> Inhibitors: Disulfiram; diethyldithiocarbamate;
> substrate analogs

HO
CH—CH_2NH_2
\
OH
HO

Norepinephrine

> *Catechol-N-methyltransferase*
> Cosubstrate: S-Adenosylmethionine

HO
CH—CH_2NHCH_3
\
OH
HO

Epinephrine

From the point of view of attempting to interfere with the formation of norepinephrine in order to diminish the efficacy of sympathetic nervous system function, three enzymes are worth considering. These are tyrosine hydroxylase, dopa decarboxylase, and dopamine-β-hydroxylase. Inhibition of the first would have the advantage of striking at the rate-limiting reaction in the biosynthesis of catecholamines, but might have the undesirable consequence of interfering with pigment formation, for which dopa is needed, as well as with the formation of dopamine and epinephrine, both of which have important roles to play independently of norepinephrine. Needless to say, medicinal chemistry is employing the direct approach of seeking inhibitors of the enzyme, the immediate and further consequences of inhibition to be assessed through extensive biological work. α-Methyl-p-tyrosine, an important inhibitor of this enzyme (112), is, however, without significant antihypertensive action. Antagonism of the pteridine cofactor or the interaction of this cofactor with catechols (109) may provide a useful approach to inhibition of this enzyme.

The third enzyme mentioned offers the most logical approach for enzyme inhibition because interference with its action would prevent the formation of norepinephrine, the desired target. The biosynthesis of epinephrine would also be suppressed, with the physiological consequences that ensue from loss of this adaptational hormone. However, epinephrine is a dispensable hormone, and bilaterally adrenalectomized humans function well as long as they receive adequate replacement therapy to make up for the conjoint loss of the adrenal cortex. Many substrate analogs and chelating agents have now been tested as inhibitors of dopamine-β-oxidase (36).

D. Dihydroxyphenylalanine Decarboxylase

Dopa decarboxylase (97) is a member of the family of L-amino acid decarboxylases, all requiring pyridoxal phosphate for their action. Some pyridoxal phosphate is tightly bound to the dopa apodecarboxylase as a Schiff's base, whereas another portion is dialyzable. Activity of freshly prepared organ extracts can often be increased substantially by adding small amounts of purified coenzyme to reaction mixtures.

The substrate specificity of dopa decarboxylase has been studied by many investigators in recent years. The enzyme acts not only on 3,4-dopa and its positional isomers, but also on 5-hydroxytryptophan, m-tyrosine, o-tyrosine, and *erythro*-3,4-dihydroxyphenylserine. It is likely that the body contains a limited number of enzymes which decarboxylate aromatic amino acids, but purification studies are required in order to clarify the precise number of aromatic amino acid decarboxylases in the mammalian organism (97). In testing for antidecarboxylase activity, any of these substrates can, theoretically, be used. Choice depends upon obtaining with a given substrate a relatively high rate of decarboxylation (especially for tests *in vitro* which usually measure the rate of evolution of CO_2) and ease of measurement of the amine product (particularly for tests performed *in vivo*). In practice, L-dopa and DL-5-hydroxytryptophan are commonly employed.

Antidecarboxylases should reduce the level of many amines in the tissues and urine. A few tests have been devised making use of this principle. These tests then measure an effect of the test compound on an endogenous metabolite, rather than the metabolism of some proffered substance. Reduction of norepinephrine levels in brain and heart have been used in this way (Table VI, tests B and C). As the amounts of endogenous amines are ordinarily very small and some of the amino acid precursors (e.g. dopa, 5-hydroxytryptophan) are normally undetectable, many tests make use of an exogenous source of the precursor, given by injection, and followed by determination of a specific amine. This is the case with the "mouse kidney, brain, and heart serotonin tests" (Table VI, tests D, G, and H), and the "dopa-load test" in the rat (Table VII). Carboxyl-labeled amino acids have been used (Table VI, tests E and I), so that the end point is the rate of conversion of the carboxyl group to respiratory $^{14}CO_2$; diminution of this rate by the administration of a test compound gives some measure of the antidecarboxylase activity of that compound. L-α-Methyldopa-$^{14}COOH$, a substrate with a less versatile metabolism than L-dopa, has also been used effectively (Table VIII). These tests of decarboxylase activity *in vivo* are physiologically indistinct: probably much of the decarboxylation occurs in the kidney, but the test gives no information as to (a) the quantitative contribution of the different organs, (b) the effect of the precursor and the amine on the blood supply which may secondarily affect the distribution of the precursor, and (c) further metabolism of the amine, the products of which are not being measured.

Finally, the direct test of antidecarboxylase activity *in vivo* has been used. In this case the activity of the enzyme in various organs is measured after administration of the test compound. An example is given in Table VI (test F).

An interesting test procedure in the tradition of classical bioassay is the use of the pressor response of the spinal cat given L-dopa intravenously to provoke the rise. The amino acid is converted to dopamine, which has the pressor action. The hypertension may be diminished or abolished completely by pretreatment of the animal with an effective inhibitor of dopa decarboxylase (Table VI, test A).

II. Synthetic decarboxylase inhibitors

The many substances that have proved effective as decarboxylase inhibitors *in vivo* and/or *in vitro* comprise several diverse classes of organic compounds. The large majority of compounds may be placed in the broad category of β-phenylpropionic acids. Depending upon the substitution pattern of the particular compound in this category, it may be included in one of the following subdivisions: "simple" β-phenylpropionic acids, cinnamic acids (dehydro-β-phenylpropionic acids), phenylpyruvic acids, phenylthiopyruvic acids, phenyllactic acids, and α-amino-β-phenylpropionic acids. In addition, chalcones, flavones, benzyloxyamines, and asymmetrically substituted hydrazines are represented.

A. β-PHENYLPROPIONIC ACIDS

The synthesis of "simple" β-phenylpropionic acids has been known for some time, the simplest method consisting of hydrogenation of the corresponding cinnamic acids (41) which are in turn prepared by a Perkin condensation of the appropriate arylaldehyde and an anhydride (66):

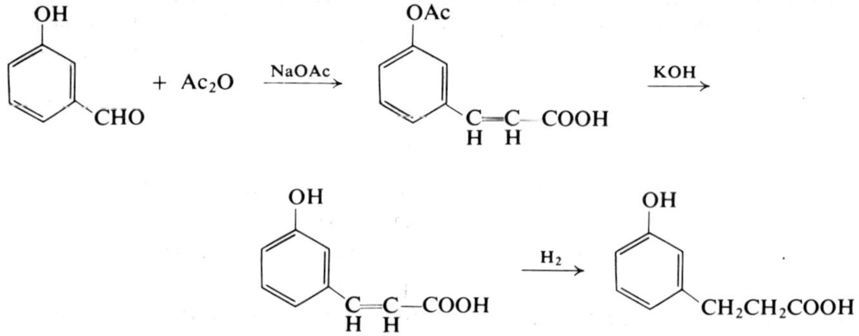

Substitution in the α-position of the cinnamic acids may be introduced in several ways. Alkyl substitution may be made by the proper choice of the base utilized (116):

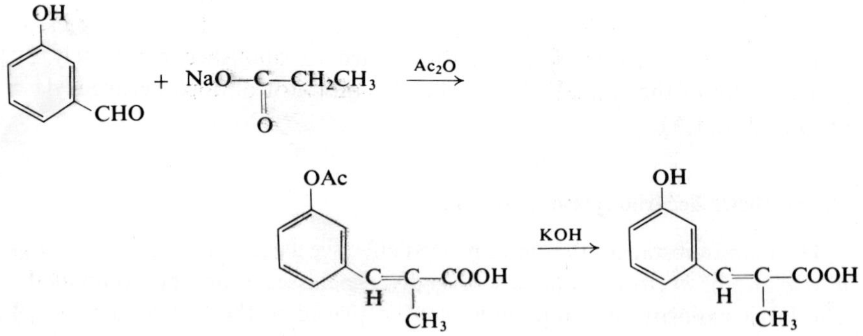

On the other hand, introduction of an α-acylamino group is accomplished by the condensation of an aryl aldehyde with N-acylglycine, rather than an anhydride, followed by mild basic hydrolysis (53):

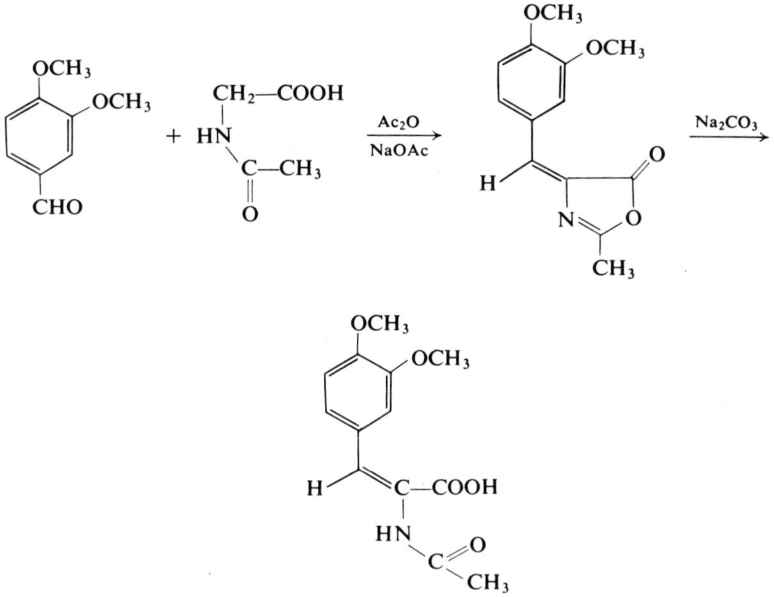

If an azlactone of type (I) or the corresponding α-acylamino cinnamic acid (II), synthesized according to the aforementioned sequence, is subjected to strong basic hydrolysis, a phenylpyruvic acid is produced (38):

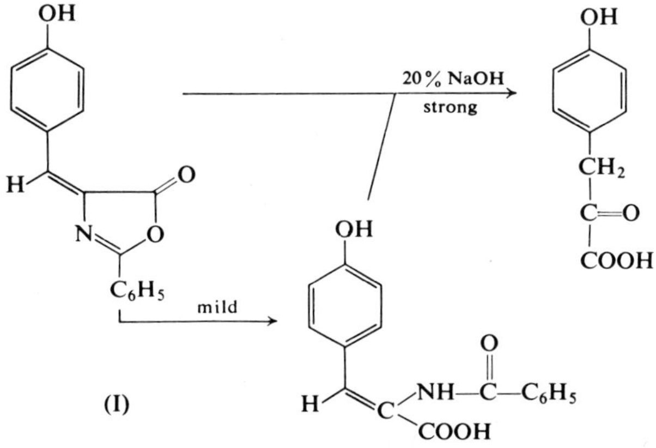

Thiophenylpyruvic acids are prepared in a similar manner, i.e., condensation of an aromatic aldehyde with rhodanine and subsequent basic hydrolysis (32):

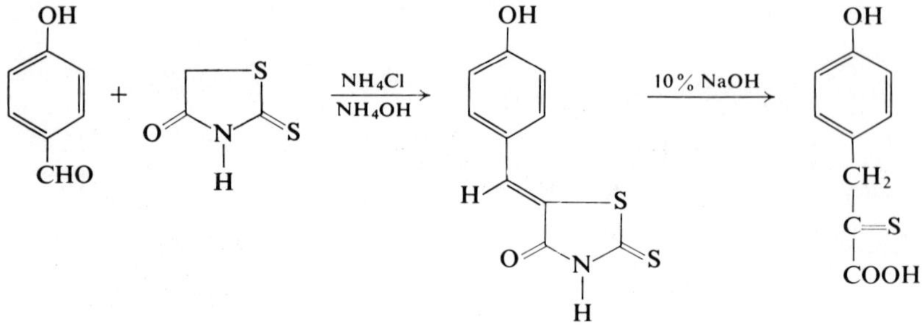

β-Phenyllactic acids, on the other hand, are available through several routes. Diazotization of the corresponding α-amino-β-phenylpropionic acids is a convenient route when the material is available (28):

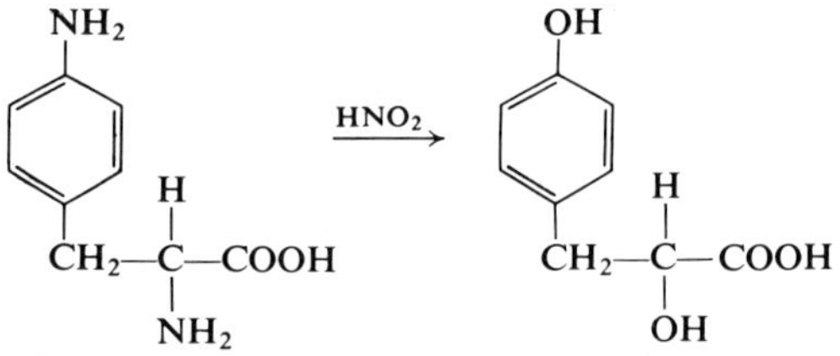

A more general method involves transformation of the readily available β-phenylpropionic acids (*vide supra*) to α-bromo-β-phenylpropionic acids via the Hell-Volhard-Zelinsky reaction and subsequent hydrolysis (30):

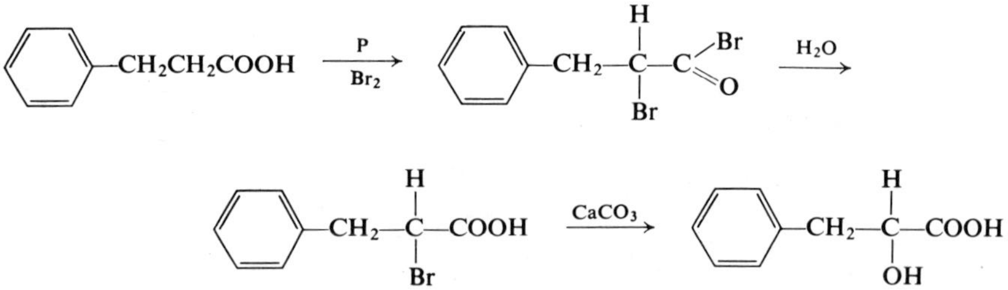

Finally, an alternate method consists in cyanohydrin formation and hydrolysis of the proper β-phenylacetaldehyde (27):

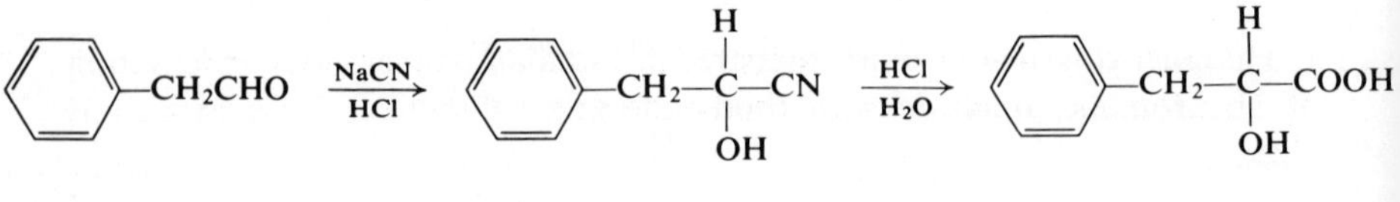

If alkyl substitution is desired in the α-position, a modification of the latter method is utilized (92):

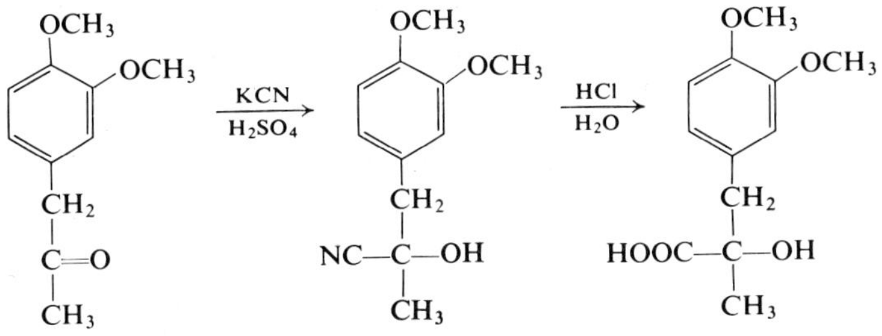

The α-amino-β-phenylpropionic acids comprising α-methyldopa and related compounds have generally been synthesized by the application of either a Bucherer hydantoin or Strecker synthesis on suitably substituted α-arylketones. In the case of α-methyldopa itself, Stein and associates (103) prepared the requisite 3,4-dimethoxyphenylacetone by the condensation of 3,4-dimethoxy-phenylacetonitrile with ethyl acetate, followed by acid hydrolysis. Subsequent formation of the corresponding hydantoin, basic hydrolysis, and acid cleavage of the aromatic methoxyls yielded α-methyldopa:

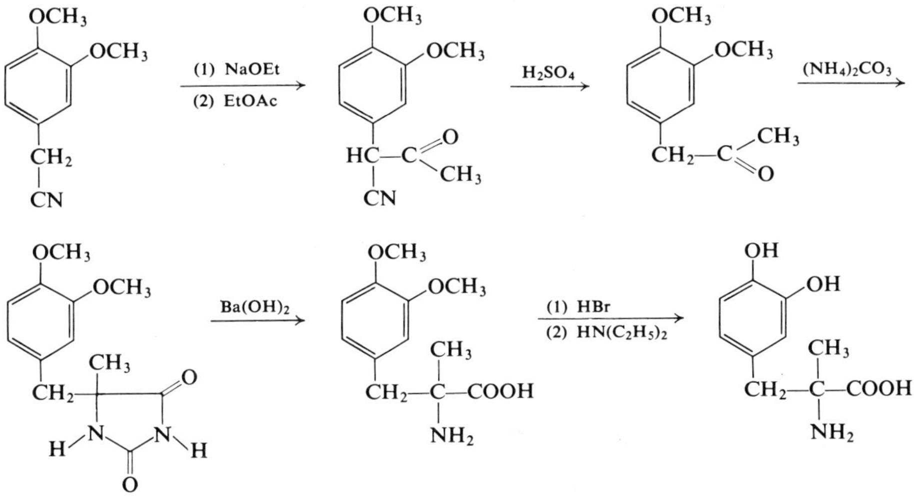

The synthesis as described is nonstereospecific and resolution is necessary to obtain the hypotensively active (−) isomer. Originally, the separation was achieved by fractional crystallization of the 1-phenylethylamine salts of racemic N-acetyl-3-(3,4-dimethoxyphenyl)-2-methylalanine, followed by acid hydrolysis (56). In another publication Stein et al. (103) described a method utilizing N-acetyl-3-(3,4-diacetoxyphenyl)-2-methylalanine. In the latter case, the quinine salts were employed for fractional crystallization. A still more recent and efficient method reported by Jones and associates (44) consisted in "direct" fractional crystallization of ($\pm$) α-methyldopa in the following manner. Addition of pure ($-$) isomer to a warm saturated solution of racemate yielded, upon cooling, approximately half of the total ($-$) isomer content of the solution in a pure crystalline form. Subsequent saturation at 35° of the filtrate from the above procedure with respect to racemate and addition of pure ($+$) isomer deposited, upon cooling, approximately 100% of the excess ($+$) isomer, leaving in solution substantially pure racemate. Racemization of the inactive ($+$) isomer and resolution of the racemate provides an efficient method for converting all the synthetic product to the hypotensively active isomer.

In a paper published by Tristram and co-workers (108), empirical evidence including optical rotatory dispersion measurements of α-methyldopa and its copper salt, as well as optical rotation measurements of α-methyldopa at various pH's and of its hydantoin derivative, indicate that the active ($-$) isomer has the L- or s-configuration (III):

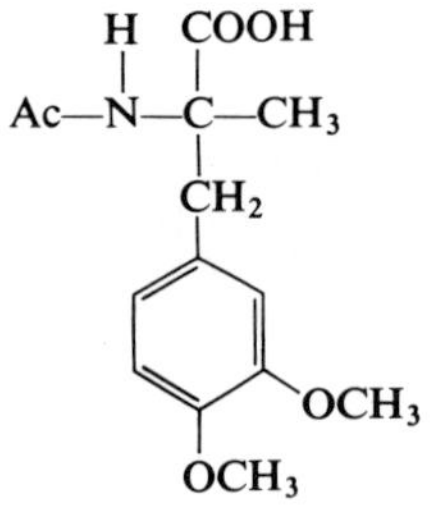

(III) 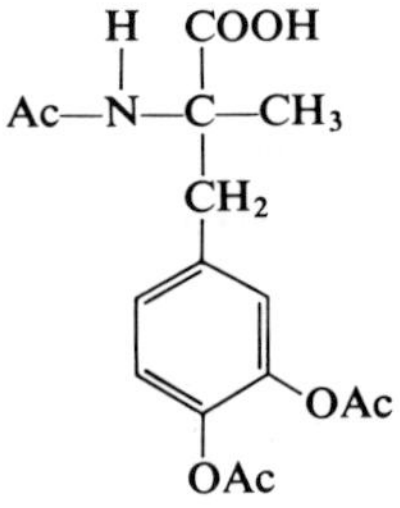　　　　　　(IV) 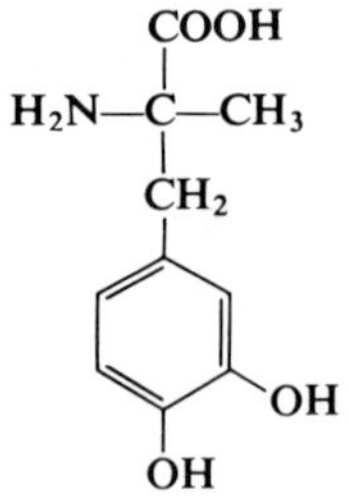　　　　　　L ($-$) α-Methyldopa
　　　　　　　　　　　　　　　　　　(V)

Formulas III and IV are merely convenient graphic representations of the racemic forms whereas formula V is a true configurational representation of L($-$) α-methyldopa.

Many structural modifications of α-methyldopa have been synthesized. They can be represented in the following manner:

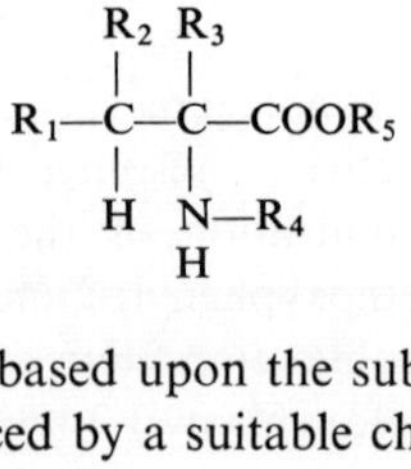

Variation in R_1 generally is based upon the substitution pattern of the aromatic system and is introduced by a suitable choice of starting material (7).

R_2, R_3, and R_5 may be H, CH_3, Et, Pr, and Bu, whereas R_4 is usually H, NH_2, or —COOR.

The introduction of alteration in R_3 has generally been accomplished by the performance of a Knoevenagel condensation of an arylaldehyde and an appropriate nitroalkane, followed by reductive hydrolysis of the resulting nitrostyrene (6):

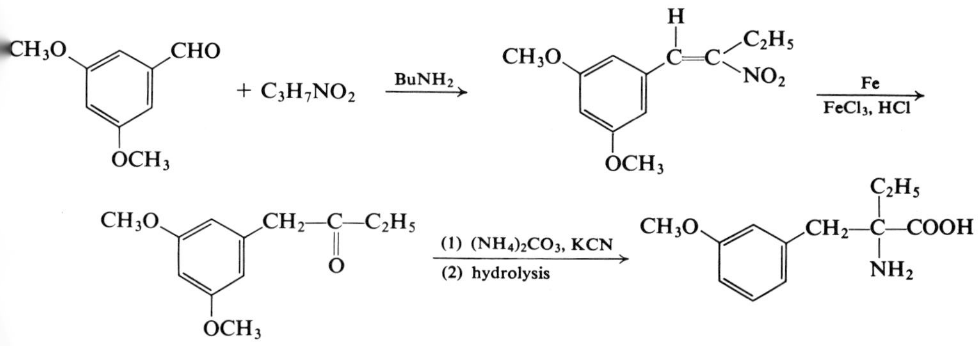

Variation of R_2 may be brought about by means of base-catalyzed alkylation of the intermediate α-arylketone (6):

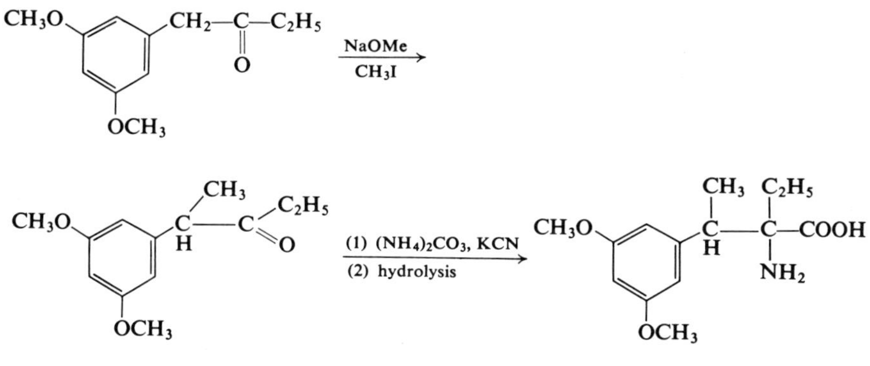

Modification of R_5 involves simple esterification of the amino acid. Similarly, introduction of an amide moiety (R_4=—COR) can be accomplished by acylation of the amino acid in basic media. In the case where R_4 is an amino group, alteration of the basic synthetic approach becomes necessary. This modification is then obtained by the application of a Strecker reaction to the β-arylketone rather than the usual Bucherer synthesis. The product is an α-hydrazino acid (92):

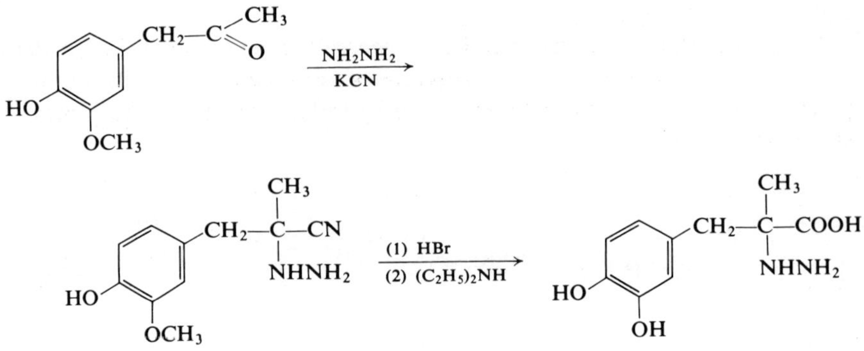

B. CHALCONES AND FLAVONES

Chalcones, another class of compounds known for some time, are generally prepared by base-catalyzed aldol condensation of an arylaldehyde and an aralkylketone (26):

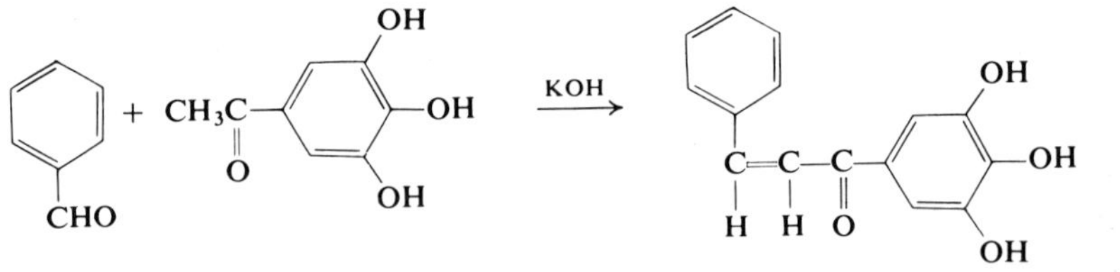

Many of the flavones tested for antidecarboxylase activity are naturally occurring substances. However, the synthesis of the parent compound, flavone, illustrates the methods available for the preparation of this class of compound (118):

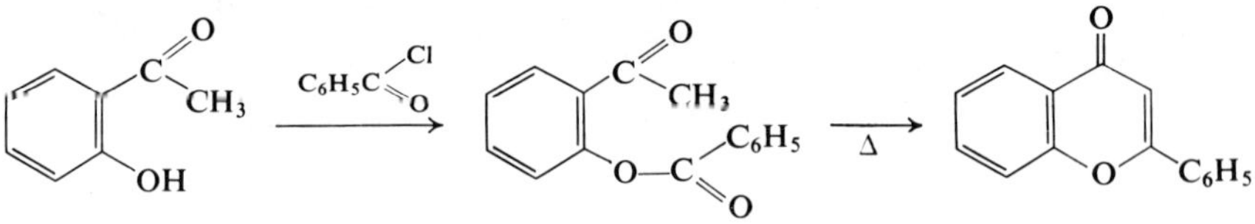

C. HYDROXYLAMINE AND HYDRAZINE DERIVATIVES

Benzyloxyamines may be prepared by a base catalyzed condensation of an appropriate benzyl halide and N-hydroxyphthalimide. The resulting phthalimide yields the desired hydroxylamine derivative on hydrazinolysis (94):

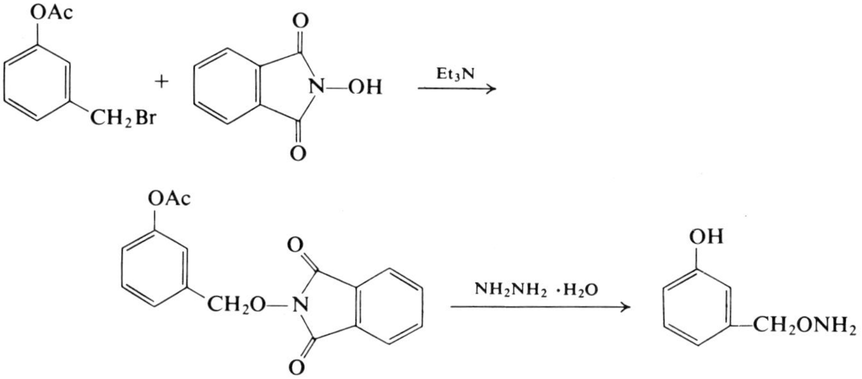

Several procedures are available for the production of substituted hydrazines, depending upon the degree, placement, and type of substitution on the hydrazine moiety. Simple monosubstituted aralkylhydrazines may be obtained by condensation of an aralkylhalide with a large excess of hydrazine (3):

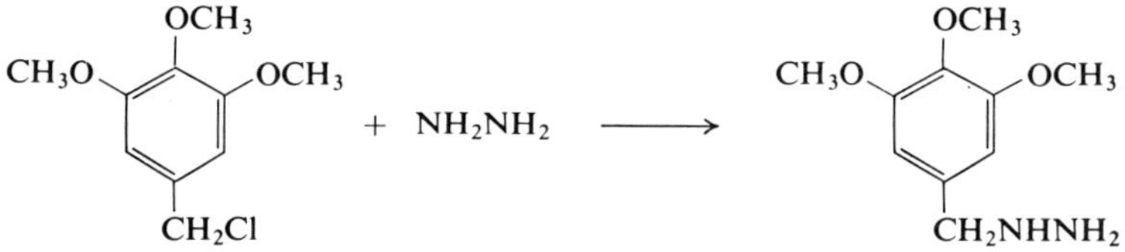

Although several approaches are possible for the synthesis of asymmetrically disubstituted hydrazines, the best method consists in nitrosation of the corresponding secondary amine, followed by reduction with $LiAlH_4$ (3):

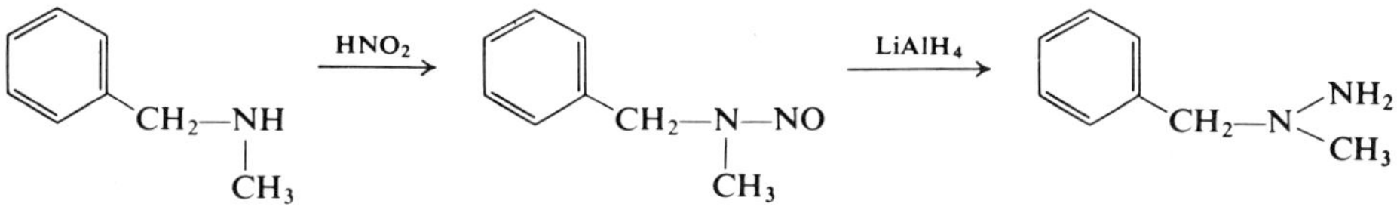

It is known that the reaction of asymmetrically substituted hydrazines with esters tends to give low yields of the corresponding hydrazides and, therefore, the best synthetic approach is perhaps formation of the unsubstituted hydrazide first, condensation with the appropriate carbonyl moiety, and reduction (3):

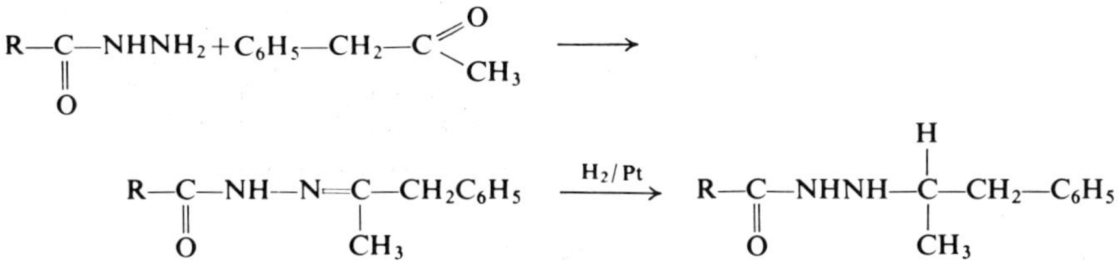

Table I

Decarboxylase Inhibition *in Vitro* by β-Phenylpropionic Acids

Number	Compound	3	4	α	α	RM[a]	% Inhibition[b]	Reference
1	Phenylpropionic acid	H	H	H	H	1.0	0	(41)
2	3-Hydroxyphenylpropionic acid	OH	H	H	H	1.0	0	(41)
3	4-Hydroxyphenylpropionic acid	H	OH	H	H	1.0	9	(41)
4	3,4-Dihydroxyphenylpropionic acid	OH	OH	H	H	0.22	63	(41)
5	Phenyllactic acid	H	H	OH	H	1.0	0[c]	(41)
6	p-Hydroxyphenyllactic acid	H	OH	OH	H	1.0	24	(41)
7	α-Methyldopa	OH	OH	NH$_2$	CH$_3$	0.1	71[a]	(95)
8	Phenylpyruvic acid	H	H	–O–		1.0	60[c]	(41)
9	3-Hydroxyphenylpyruvic acid	OH	H	–O–		0.5	72	(41)
10	4-Hydroxyphenylpyruvic acid	H	OH	–O–		1.0	60	(41)
11	3,4-Dihydroxyphenylpyruvic acid	OH	OH	–O–		0.1	60	(41)

No.	Compound				–S–	RM[a]	Inhibition (%)[b]	Ref.
12	Thiophenylpyruvic acid	H	H		H	1.0	67	(41)
13	Phenylalanine	H	H	NH$_2$	CH$_3$	5.0	–[c]	(29)
14	α-Methylphenylalanine	H	H	NH$_2$	CH$_3$	1.0	6	(95)
21	α-Methyltyrosine	H	OH	NH$_2$	CH$_3$	1.25	16	(95)
22	α-Methyl-m-tyrosine	OH	H	NH$_2$	CH$_3$	0.125	74	(95)
23	α-O-Dimethyl-m-tyrosine	CH$_3$O	H	NH$_2$	CH$_3$	1.25	18	(95)
24	α,O,O-Trimethyldopa	CH$_3$O	CH$_3$O	NH$_2$	CH$_3$	1.0	27	(95)
25	N-Methyldopa	OH	OH	NHCH$_3$	H	1.7	30	(95)
26	N-Cyanoethyldopa	OH	OH	NHCH$_2$CH$_2$CN	H	1.0	18	(95)
27	3,4-Dimethyldopa[e]	CH$_3$O	CH$_3$O	NH$_2$	H	1.25	25	(95)
28	3-O-Methyldopa	CH$_3$O	OH	NH$_2$	H	1.25	18	(95)
29	N,O-Dimethyldopa	CH$_3$O	OH	NHCH$_3$	H	1.6	0	(95)

[a] Relative molarity: ratio of molar concentration of inhibitor to initial molar concentration of L-substrate.

[b] Inhibitory activity in vitro was measured by the Warburg technique, using L-dopa as substrate, pig kidney cortex as the source of enzyme, and phosphate buffer, pH 6.8. A supplement of the coenzyme pyridoxal phosphate was added. Incubation under nitrogen was at 37°C for 7–10 minutes; inhibitors were added at the same time as the substrate (41); in other cases, the inhibitors were incubated for 10–15 minutes with the enzyme preparation before substrate was added.

[c] Using adrenal medullary decarboxylase, the percentage inhibition was 50% for No. 5, 77% for No. 8, and 0% for No. 13. See Fellman (29).

[d] See Sourkes (95).

[e] 2,4-Dimethoxyphenylalanine (or "2,4-dimethyldopa") gave 22% inhibition at the same RM (see Sourkes 95). 3,5-Diiodotyrosine was weakly inhibitory (15% at RM = 1.15).

III. Enzymology and biochemical pharmacology

A. PHENYLPROPIONIC ACID AND DERIVATIVES

A variety of compounds related structurally to phenylpropionic acid are shown in Table I. Of the immediate derivatives the only one with significant inhibitory potency is 3,4-dihydroxyphenylpropionic acid. The corresponding α-hydroxy, α-thio, and α-oxo compounds are weakly inhibitory, except for 3,4-dihydroxyphenylpyruvic acid.

In the α-amino-α-methyl series, β-methylphenylalanine and α-methyl-tyrosine are essentially inactive, but α-methyl-*m*-tyrosine and α-methyldopa have relatively strong inhibitory action. In the initial report on these compounds (95) it was stated that α-methyl-3-hydroxy-4-methoxyphenylalanine is a strong inhibitor. It has since been found that the compound is only weakly active. All inhibitory activity of the α-methyl amino acids resides in the L-isomer (77).

N-Alkylated derivatives of dopa have been tested as inhibitors. They have long been known not to undergo enzymic decarboxylation: the amino group is essential for binding of the coenzyme pyridoxal phosphate (5, 96, 99), and the alkyl group interferes, thus preventing oriented access of the carboxyl group to the decarboxylatic site on the apoenzyme. Three such analogs have been tested as inhibitors, *N*-methyl- and *N*-cyanoethyldopa (Nos. 25 and 26), and *N*-methyl-4-hydroxy-3-methoxyphenylalanine (No. 29), but they are very weak in this respect.

The importance of the *m*-hydroxyl group on the ring for biological activity has been emphasized before (95). Thus, α-methyl-*m*-tyrosine (No. 22) is much more potent an inhibitor than α-methyl-*p*-tyrosine (No. 21). Furthermore, it is important to have the ring hydroxyl free for maximal activity: the *m*-*O*-methyl-substituted hydrazino analog of α-methyldopa is far less active than the parent dihydroxy compound (*cf.* Nos. 19 and 20). This conclusion stems also from the comparison of the pairs formed by Nos. 22 and 23, and 7 and 24.

Hartman *et al.* (41) have shown through extensive tests that aromatic compounds with a 1- or 2-carbon side chain have little or no activity as decarboxylase inhibitors. The series they studied embraces the phenylacetic acids, 2-phenylglycines, mandelic acids, acetophenones, and benzoic acids. The only compounds with any activity worth noting were 3,4-dihydroxyphenylacetic acid (88% inhibition at a relative molarity of 1.0), 2-mercaptobenzoic acid (and its dithio oxidation product), and certain naphthoic acid derivatives. Phenols were, in general, inactive.

Mechanism of Action

Inhibition of dopa decarboxylase by α-methyldopa *in vitro* presents the characteristics of a slowly reversible inhibitor affecting the apoenzyme (95). This has been confirmed by Lovenberg *et al.* (47). They state that the competitive inhibitory kinetics are apparent when the inhibitor and substrate are added to the enzyme simultaneously or when the inhibitor is preincubated with the holoenzyme. However, if the inhibitor is preincubated with the enzyme without addition of exogenous pyridoxal phosphate (often added in order to saturate the enzyme with coenzyme), then the inhibition is noncompetitive. Certain amino acids and amines, including the catechol derivatives, can combine nonenzymically with pyridoxal (89) or pyridoxal phosphate (95, 96) to form isoquinolines, which are then devoid of coenzymic activity. However, this reaction does not seem to be involved in the action of α-methyldopa, for the rate of combination of this amino acid with pyridoxal phosphate is insufficiently rapid (except at very high concentrations) to sequester significant amounts of the coenzyme from the decarboxylase. Furthermore, the inhibition is not reversed by high concentrations of pyridoxal phosphate. Finally, if this reaction were an important mechanism of inhibition, one would expect the bacterial tyrosine decarboxylase to be inhibited to a greater degree than it is by α-methyldopa (95).

The product formed by reacting pyridoxal phosphate and DL-dopa has virtually no inhibitory activity (95).

α-Methyl-5-hydroxytryptophan inhibits dopa decarboxylase in the same manner as α-methyldopa does (47).

4-Hydroxyphenylpyruvic acid (No. 10) is reported to be a noncompetitive inhibitor of dopa decarboxylase (41).

B. CINNAMIC ACID DERIVATIVES AND CHALCONES

A large number of cinnamic acid derivatives have been tested, chiefly by Hartman and his colleagues (41). Again, the importance of the m-hydroxyl on the ring for good inhibitory activity is seen in this series. This is exemplified in Table II by Nos. 32 and 35 (the latter is caffeic acid). But in addition to this, the o-hydroxyl also plays an important role. Thus, cinnamic acid itself (No. 30) is not inhibitory; 2-hydroxycinnamic acid (No. 31) is effective, and 2,6-dihydroxycinnamic acid (No. 36) much more so.

3,4-Diacetoxycinnamic acid (No. 42) is as active an inhibitor as 3,4-dihydroxycinnamic acid (No. 35), but substitution of alkoxy groups in these positions, as in Nos. 39, 40, and 41 (Table II), abolishes most of the inhibitory action. Esterification of the carboxyl group also yields effective inhibitors (cf. Nos. 47 and 48). The enzyme preparation used in these studies contained an esterase, and presumably this enzyme could hydrolyze the ester groups from compounds such as Nos. 42, 47, and 48.

2- or 3-Hydroxybenzalacetone is more effective than 3-hydroxycinnamic acid (cf. Nos. 37 and 38 with No. 32). 3-Mercaptocinnamic acid is even more active (No. 43).

Table II

DECARBOXYLASE INHIBITION *in Vitro* BY CINNAMIC ACIDS

Compound number	2	3	4	6	α	R	RM[a]	% Inhibition[b]	Reference
30	H	H	H	H	H	OH	1.0	0	(41)
31	OH	H	H	H	H	OH	1.0	52	(41)
32	H	OH	H	H	H	OH	0.2	37	(41)
33	H	H	OH	H	H	OH	0.2	7	(41)
34	OH	H	OH	H	H	OH	1.0	9	(41)
35	H	OH	OH	H	H	OH	0.2	74	(41)
36	OH	H	H	OH	H	OH	0.1	84	(41)
37	OH	H	H	H	H	CH_3	0.1	31	(41)

170

No.							Rel. molarity[a]	Activity[b]	Ref.
38	H	OH	H	H	H	CH_3	0.1	31	(41)
39	H	C_2H_5O	H	C_2H_5O	H	OH	1.0	5	(41)
40	H	OH	H	CH_3O	H	OH	1.0	19	(41)
41	H	CH_3O	H	OH	H	OH	1.0	5	(41)
42	H	CH_3COO	H	CH_3COO	H	OH	0.2	60	(41)
43	H	SH	H	H	H	OH	0.05	78	(41)
44	H	NH_2	H	H	H	OH	1.0	10	(41)
45	H	NO_2	H	H	H	OH	1.0	15	(41)
46	H	H	H	H	CH_3	OH	0.2	37	(41)
47	H	OH	H	H	H	OCH_3	0.2	60	(41)
48	H	OH	H	OH	H	OC_2H_5	0.15	90	(41)
49	H	OH	H	H	H	NH_2	0.2	19	(41)
50	H	CH_3O	H	CH_3O	$NHCOCH_3$	OH	2.0	20	(95)
51	H	CH_3O	H	CH_3O	$NHCOC_6H_5$	OH	1.0	51	(95)

[a] Relative molarity: ratio of molar concentration of inhibitor to initial molar concentration of L-substrate.

[b] Inhibitory activity *in vitro* was measured by the Warburg technique, using L-dopa as substrate, pig kidney cortex as the source of enzyme, and phosphate buffer, pH 6.8. A supplement of the coenzyme pyridoxal phosphate was added. Incubation under nitrogen was at 37°C for 7–10 minutes; inhibitors were added at the same time as the substrate (41); in other cases, the inhibitors were incubated for 10–15 minutes with the enzyme preparation before substrate was added.

3-Hydroxy-ω-nitrostyrene is moderately active compared with its isostere 3-hydroxycinnamic acid. Other derivatives in this series are described in the article by Hartman *et al.* (41).

A somewhat related group of compounds is to be found among the chalcones, as shown in Table III. Here the most potent substances were 5-(3,4 dihydroxy-cinnamoyl)-salicylic acid (No. 62), its triacetyl derivative (No. 63), 5-(3-hydroxycinnamoyl)-salicylic acid (No. 55), and its diacetyl derivative (No. 53). Other effective inhibitors are 3-hydroxychalcone (No. 54) and polyhydroxy-lated chalcones (Nos. 59 and 60).

Mechanism of Action

Caffeic and 3-hydroxycinnamic acids are competitive inhibitors of dopa decarboxylase. The same mechanism applies to the 5-(hydroxycinnamoyl)-salicylic acids (Nos. 55 and 62).

C. FLAVONES AND RELATED COMPOUNDS

The data of Table IV indicate that some degree of hydroxylation of at least one of the flavone rings is necessary for dopa decarboxylase inhibition. Gossypin and rutin, both glycosides, have quite different inhibitory potencies. As their glycosidic linkages are in different positions, it would appear that substitution on the 3-position (as in rutin) sterically hinders attachment of the inhibitor to the enzyme.

D. DERIVATIVES OF HYDROXYLAMINE AND HYDRAZINE

Hydroxylamine and hydrazine, as carbonyl reagents, can bind the coenzyme of amino acid decarboxylases, pyridoxal phosphate. Some derivatives of these compounds can also bind the coenzyme. By combining this property in the molecule with a moiety offering the possibility of substrate competition, powerful inhibitors can be anticipated. The data of Table V illustrate this point. Thus, 3-hydroxybenzyloxyamine (No. 70), N-(3-hydroxybenzyl)-N-methylhydrazine (No. 71), an unsymmetrically substituted hydrazine derivative, and N-(2,3,4-trihydroxybenzyl)-hydrazine (No. 75) are much more potent than α-methyldopa. N-Seryl-N'-(2,3,4-trihydroxybenzyl)-hydrazine (No. 74), each nitrogen of which bears a substituent, is also very effective, although in the test used the compound was preincubated with the enzyme preparation for 1 hour before the substrate was added. The enhanced potency of the molecule bearing the —$NHNH_2$ group is illustrated further by the series of hydrazine analogs of amino acids shown in Table V. For example, α-hydra-zino-α-methylphenylpropionic acid (No. 15) has significant action whereas at

Table III

DECARBOXYLASE INHIBITION *in Vitro* BY CHALCONES[a]

Compound number	3	4	2'	3'	4'	RM[b]	% Inhibition[c]
52	H	H	OH	OH	OH	1.0	24
53	CH₃COO	H	H	COOH	CH₃COO	0.01	50
54	OH	H	H	H	H	0.1	100
55[a]	OH	H	H	COOH	OH	0.01	85
56	H	OH	H	H	OH	0.2	16
57	CH₃O	OH	OH	H	OH	1.0	15
58	OH	H	H	H	H	0.05	85
59	OH	OH	OH	H	H	0.1	90
60	OH	OH	OH	H	OH	0.05	85
61	OH	OH	OH	H	CH₃COO	0.1	75
62[a]	OH	OH	H	COOH	OH	0.001	87
63	CH₃COO	CH₃COO	H	COOH	CH₃COO	0.001	64

[a] See Hartman *et al.* (41).

[b] Relative molarity: ratio of molar concentration of inhibitor to initial molar concentration of L-substrate.

[c] Inhibitory activity *in vitro* was measured by the Warburg technique, using L-dopa as substrate, pig kidney cortex as the source of enzyme and phosphate buffer, pH 6.8. A supplement of the coenzyme pyridoxal phosphate was added. Incubation under nitrogen was at 37°C for 7–10 minutes; inhibitors were added at the same time as the substrate (41); in other cases, the inhibitors were incubated for 10–15 minutes with the enzyme preparation before substrate was added.

[d] See Yuwiler *et al.* (120), in which this compound was tested at pH 6.8 and at 8.0, with 5-hydroxytryptophan as substrate, and found to be a competitive inhibitor.

Table IV

Decarboxylase Inhibition *in Vitro* by Flavones and Derivatives[a]

Number	Compound	3	5	7	8	3'	4'	RM[b]	% Inhibition[c]
64	—	H	H	H	H	H	H	0.2	0
65	—	H	H	H	H	OH	OH	0.01	59
66	Gossypin	OH	OH	OH	OH[a]	OH	OH	0.1	77
67	Rutin	OH[e]	OH	OH	H	OH	OH	0.1	5
68	A flavanone	H[f]	OH	OH	H	OH	OH	0.1	86
69	d-Catechin[g]	OH[f]	OH	OH	H	OH	OH	0.1	50[h]

[a] See Hartman *et al.* (41).

[b] Relative molarity: ratio of molar concentration of inhibitor to initial molar concentration of L-substrate.

[c] Inhibitory activity *in vitro* was measured by the Warburg technique, using L-dopa as substrate, pig kidney cortex as the source of enzyme, and phosphate buffer, pH 6.8. A supplement of the coenzyme pyridoxal phosphate was added. Incubation under nitrogen was at 37°C for 7–10 minutes; inhibitors were added at the same time as the substrate (41); in other cases, the inhibitors were incubated for 10–15 minutes with the enzyme preparation before substrate was added.

[d] Glucoside linkage.

[e] Rutinoside linkage.

[f] The ring is reduced in the 2,3-position.

[g] The carbonyl oxygen at the 4-position is reduced completely.

[h] When catechin was preincubated with the enzyme for 15 minutes before addition of substrate, the inhibition was 66%. See Sourkes (95).

Table V

<small>DECARBOXYLASE INHIBITION *in Vitro* BY DERIVATIVES OF HYDROXYLAMINE AND HYDRAZINE</small>

Number	Compound	RM[a]	Inhibition[b] %	Inhibition[b] RMP[c]	Reference
7	DL-α-Methyldopa	2.5×10^{-1}	50	—	(79)[d]
70	3-Hydroxybenzyloxyamine[e]	6.7×10^{-4}	50	—	
71	N-(3-Hydroxybenzyl)-N-methylhydrazine[f]	2.0×10^{-3}	50	—	
7	DL-α-Methyldopa	2.0×10^{-1}	64	1	(78, 92)
15	HA[g] of α-Methylphenylalanine (No. 14)[h]	2.0×10^{-2}	77	16	
16	HA of 4-Methoxyphenylalanine[i]	2.0×10^{-2}	55	4.5	
17	HA of m-Tyrosine[j]	2.0×10^{-4}	50	450	
18	HA of Dopa[k]	2.0×10^{-4}	72	1500	
19	HA of α-Methyldopa[l]	2.0×10^{-4}	85	1500	
20	3-O-Methyl derivative of No. 19	2.0×10^{-2}	83	20	
74	Seryl-trihydroxybenzylhydrazine[m]	7.5×10^{-5}	70	—	(12)[n]
75	Trihydroxybenzylhydrazine[o]	2.5×10^{-4}	89	—	
75	Trihydroxybenzylhydrazine	5.0×10^{-3}	44	—	(12)[p]

[a] Relative molarity: ratio of concentration of inhibitor to initial concentration of L-substrate.

[b] Inhibitory activity *in vitro* was measured by the Warburg technique, using L-dopa as substrate, pig kidney cortex as the source of enzyme, and phosphate buffer, pH 6.8. A supplement of the co-enzyme pyridoxal phosphate was added. Incubation under nitrogen was at 37°C for 7–10 minutes; inhibitors were added at the same time as the substrate (41); in other cases, the inhibitors were incubated for 10–15 minutes with the enzyme preparation before substrate was added.

[c] Relative molar potency: the ratio of molar concentrations causing 50% inhibition *in vitro*, taking α-methyldopa as the standard (RMP = 1.0).

[d] Dopa decarboxylase of pig kidney was used; the substrate was L-dopa.

[e] NSD 1024.

[f] NSD 1034.

[g] HA = hydrazino analog of DL-amino acids. The α-carbon bears —NHNH$_2$ instead of the amino group.

[h] α-Hydrazino-α-methylphenylpropionic acid.

[i] α-Hydrazino-β-(4-methoxyphenyl)propionic acid.

[j] α-Hydrazino-β-(3-hydroxyphenyl)propionic acid.

[k] α-Hydrazino-β-(3,4-dihydroxyphenyl)propionic acid.

[l] α-Hydrazino-α-methyl-β-(3,4-dihydroxyphenyl)propionic acid; MK 485.

[m] N^1-(DL-Seryl)-N^2-(2,3,4-trihydroxybenzyl)hydrazine; Ro 4-4602.

[n] Rat kidney decarboxylase was used; the substrate was DL-5-hydroxytryptophan. The inhibitor was incubated with the enzyme for 1 hour before assay.

[o] N-(2,3,4-trihydroxybenzyl)hydrazine; Ro 4-5127.

[p] Same conditions as in footnote (n), except that the inhibitor and enzyme were preincubated for only 10 minutes. In comparable conditions, the percentage inhibition with dopa as substrate was 37%; with m-tyrosine it was 40%.

Table VI

INHIBITION OF DECARBOXYLASE *in Vivo*

Number	Compound	Test used	ED$_{50}$[a] mg/kg	ED$_{50}$[a] μM/kg	Reference
55	5-(3-Hydroxycinnamoyl)-salicylic acid	A[b]	6.6	23.2	(15)
62	5-(3,4-Dihydroxycinnamoyl)-salicylic acid		15.7	523	
81	Chlorogenic acid		31.4	88.7	
35	Caffeic acid		50.8	283	
32	3-Hydroxycinnamic acid		23.5	143	
69	d-Catechin		55.0	190	
66	Gossypin		18.9	39.5	
2	3-Hydroxyphenylpropionic acid		33.0	199	
7	DL-α-Methyldopa	B[c]	64.9	308	(77)
7	D-α-Methyldopa		>200	>950	
22	DL-α-Methyl-m-tyrosine		24.4	125	
77	DL-α-Methyl-2,3-dopa		>200	>950	
78	DL-α-Methyldopamine		>200	>1200	
79	DL-α-Methyl-m-tyramine		65.9	440	
80	Reserpine		0.47	0.77	
7	DL-α-Methyldopa	C[d]	55.3	262	(77)
7	L-α-Methyldopa		20.7	98	
7	D-α-Methyldopa		>200	>950	
22	DL-α-Methyl-m-tyrosine		2.2	11.3	
77	DL-α-Methyl-2,3-dopa		>200	>950	
78	DL-α-Methyldopamine		9.5	57.2	
79	DL-α-Methyl-m-tyramine		1.4	9.3	
80	Reserpine		0.05	0.08	

7	L-α-Methyldopa	D^e	2.63	12.48	(77)
7	D-α-Methyldopa		>100	>475	
22	DL-α-Methyl-m-tyrosine		23.50	121	
77	DL-α-Methyl-2,3-dopa		2.70	12.8	
7	DL-α-Methyldopa	D^e	4.7	22.27 (1)^f	(78)
18	HA^g of dopa		0.06	0.29 (77)	
19	HA of α-Methyldopa		0.09^h	0.40 (57)	
17	HA of m-Tyrosine		0.19	0.90 (23)	
15	HA of α-Methylphenylalanine		2.0	10.30 (2)	
20	HA of 3-O-Methyl-α-methyldopa		3.0	12.50 (2)	
16	HA of 4-Methoxyphenylalanine		22.0	113 (0.2)	
7	L-α-Methyldopa	E^i	82	388	(39)
22	DL-α-Methyl-m-tyrosine		176	903	
19	HA of α-methyldopa		1.8	8.5	
71	N-(3-Hydroxybenzyl)-N-methylhydrazine (NSD-1034)		2.2	8.8	
7	α-Methyldopa (i.p.)	F^j	120	569	(25)
70	3-Hydroxybenzyloxyamine (NSD 1024) (i.p.)		3	17.1	
70	3-Hydroxybenzyloxyamine (p.o.)		30	171	
71	N-(3-Hydroxybenzyl)-N-methylhydrazine (p.o.)		1	4.0	
74	Seryl-trihydroxybenzylhydrazine	G^k	20	77.8	(72)
74	Seryl-trihydroxybenzylhydrazine	H^l	0.5	1.94	
74	Seryl-trihydroxybenzylhydrazine	F^j	2.86	15	(71)
7	DL-α-Methyldopa	F^j	211	1000	
19	HA of α-Methyldopa	I^m	0.3	1.32	(40)
71	N-(3-Hydroxybenzyl)-N-methylhydrazine		0.3	1.20	
76	NSD 1045		0.5	1.52	
74	Seryl-trihydroxybenzylhydrazine		0.9	3.07	

NOTE—See footnotes, p. 178.

FOOTNOTES TO TABLE VI

[a] Dose that is effective in the respective tests described for 50% of the animals used; or the dose that causes a response that is 50% of the control effect.

[b] Inhibition of the pressor response to the intravenous administration of L-dopa in the spinal cat. The test compound is given intravenously also.

[c] Reduction in the cerebral norepinephrine in mice; drug given intraperitoneally.

[d] Reduction of cardiac norepinephrine in mice; drug given intraperitoneally.

[e] Prevention of accumulation of serotonin in the kidneys of mice injected with DL-5-hydroxytryptophan and pretreated (16 hours before the test) with phenylisopropylhydrazine, an inhibitor of monoamine oxidase (77, 78). This is the "mouse kidney serotonin test."

[f] Figures in parentheses are the molar potencies of the test compounds relative to DL-α-methyldopa, which is assigned the value 1.0.

[g] HA = Hydrazino analog.

[h] The figure for the oral route of administration is 0.56 mg per kilogram (2.48 μM per kilogram.)

[i] Inhibition of the conversion *in vivo* of carboxyl-labeled DL-dopa to respiratory $^{14}CO_2$. The dopa is injected into mice by the intravenous route, the inhibitor by the intraperitoneal route (39).

[j] Inhibition *in vivo* of 5-hydroxytryptophan decarboxylase of brain (25).

[k] Prevention of accumulation of serotonin in the brain after administration of DL-5-hydroxytryptophan (72).

[l] Prevention of accumulation of serotonin in the heart after administration of DL-5-hydroxytryptophan (72).

[m] Inhibition of the conversion *in vivo* of $^{14}COOH$-DL-5-hydroxytryptophan to respiratory $^{14}CO_2$. The substrate is injected intravenously.

178

a 5-fold greater concentration α-amino-α-methylphenylpropionic acid (α-methylphenylalanine, No. 14) has none. Again, the potency of the hydrazino analog of α-methyldopa is some 1500 times greater than that of the α-methyldopa itself. It is interesting that the hydrazino analog of dopa is also very active; it thus becomes clear that the α-methyl group is not essential when there is a hydrazino function on the molecule.

Other compounds of this type are mentioned in the discussion of results obtained *in vivo* (Section III, E).

Mechanism of Action

Burkard *et al.* (12) have carefully studied the kinetics of inhibition by trihydroxybenzylhydrazine (No. 75). They find that the inhibition is competitive, but of the pseudoirreversible type. Addition of pyridoxal phosphate to the inhibited reaction mixture increases the enzymic activity, but the percentage inhibition remains constant. This feature holds also for the inhibition caused by the seryl derivative of trihydroxybenzylhydrazine (No. 74). Dialysis does not reverse the inhibition by either compound.

The mechanism of decarboxylase inhibition by hydrazino compounds has been considered also by Porter and his colleagues (78). They regard the three most potent inhibitors of dopa decarboxylase, Nos. 17–19 (Table V), as being closely related structurally to substrates of the enzyme and, hence, capable of acting as competitive inhibitors. For the less inhibitory hydrazino derivatives that they studied, a greater role for trapping of pyridoxal phosphate is envisaged. They recognize that the hydrazino analog of α-methyldopa, for example, may also bind the coenzyme but consider that this probably does not by itself account satisfactorily for the great activity of the inhibitor.

E. Decarboxylase Inhibition *in Vivo*

The work of five laboratories active in the antidecarboxylase field is summarized in Tables VI–VIII. The data are based on the use of many different biological tests, though some are more pertinent to the problem of antihypertensive action than others (*cf.* Section I, D).

A list of drugs that have been tested, along with their ED_{50}, is provided in Table VI. 5-(3-Hydroxycinnamoyl)-salicylic acid (No. 55), perhaps the most active inhibitor *in vitro* (except for the derivatives of hydroxylamine and hydrazine), was the most effective of a group of compounds tested on the spinal cat's blood pressure (test A). It is similarly active in blocking the blood pressure rise that follows after the injection of *m*-tyrosine and in reducing the amount of *m*-tyramine subsequently excreted (73).

In a test designed to prevent the formation of serotonin (and its accumulation

Table VII

INHIBITION OF DECARBOXYLATION OF DOPA *in Vivo*[a]

| | | Dose used | | % |
Number	Compound	mg/kg	$\mu M/kg$[b]	Inhibition
14	α-Methylphenylalanine	100	557	8
81	α-Methyl-*o*-tyrosine	100	470	19
22	α-Methyl-*m*-tyrosine	100	470	57
82	α-Methyl-β-(4-hydroxy-3-methoxyphenyl)-			
	alanine	100	443	8
24	α-Methyl-3,4-dimethoxyphenylalanine	100	395	2
83	α-Methyl-2,5-dopa	100	474	60
84	α-Methyltryptophan	100	458	9
72	α-Methyl-5-hydroxytryptophan	50	213	69
72	α-Methyl-5-hydroxytryptophan	100	426	90
73	α-Methylmethionine	100	613	9

[a] See Murphy and Sourkes (61). Rats weighing 213–245 g were injected with the compounds 0.5 hour before L-dopa (10 mg per kilogram) was given. All injections were by the intraperitoneal route. The column headed "% Inhibition", refers to the inhibition of conversion of injected L-dopa to urinary dopamine in the course of 24 hours.

[b] The calculation takes into account water of crystallization in some of the test compounds.

Table VIII

INHIBITION OF THE DECARBOXYLATION OF CARBOXYL-LABELED
L-α-METHYLDOPA *in Vivo*[a]

| | | Dose used | | % |
Number	Compound	mg/kg	$\mu M/kg$	Inhibition
19	Hydrazino analog of α-methyldopa	100	450	85
		122	540	98
22	L-α-Methyl-*m*-tyrosine	106	543	57
		200	1025	82
55	5-(3-Hydroxycinnamoyl)-salicylic acid	142	500	34
		284	1000	91
72	DL-α-Methyl-5-hydroxytryptophan	126	538	58
		200	850	92

[a] See Moran and Sourkes (58). Rats were injected with the test compound just prior to receiving ¹⁴COOH-L-α-methyldopa (1.7 mg, 1.89 mc per millimole).

in the kidneys) when its precursor is injected (Table VI, test D), α-methyldopa (No. 7) and its 2,3-isomer (No. 77) showed approximately equal efficacy, and α-methyl-m-tyrosine somewhat less. In the dopa-load test (Table VII) α-methyldopa itself could not be used because of chemical interference of its metabolic products with the determination of urinary dopamine. α-Methyl-m-tyrosine (No. 22) and α-methyl-2,5-dopa showed strong inhibition in this test, but α-methyl-5-hydroxytryptophan (No. 72) was even more powerful. The methylation of phenolic groups (Nos. 24 and 82) abolished antidecarboxylase activity under these conditions.

When the hydrazino analogs of amino acids were studied in the mouse kidney serotonin test (Table VI, test D), three of them—the analogs of dopa, α-methyldopa, and m-tyrosine—proved to be very active. Even the analogs of α-methylphenylalanine and α-methyl-4-hydroxy-3-methoxyphenylalanine (No. 20), which are very weak inhibitors relative to other hydrazines tested, were of the same order of activity as α-methyldopa. Porter and his colleagues (78, 92) have estimated the relative molar potencies of some of these compounds in both the test *in vitro* and the kidney serotonin test. A comparison of the results in Tables V and VI shows that the hydrazino analogs of the amino acids all show far greater activity than α-methyldopa *in vitro* than *in vivo*. This result may stem from factors such as poor access of the hydrazine derivatives *in vivo* to the substrate, rapid conversion of the inhibitor to inactive or less active substances, or rapid excretion of the inhibitor.

Comparable tests using radioactive-labeled substrate *in vivo* are shown in Table VI (tests E and I). Again, α-methyldopa and α-methyl-m-tyrosine show equivalent activity (counting only the L-isomer). The hydrazine derivatives (Nos. 19, 71, 74, and 76) were all far more active. A comparison of the results with two of them using carboxyl-labeled dopa (test E) and 5-hydroxytryptophan (test I) indicates that the latter is the more sensitive test: the ED_{50} is considerably smaller when it is used.

The effect of some antidecarboxylases on endogenous constituents has also been examined. In test F (Table VI), inhibition of the brain decarboxylase was attained with high levels of α-methyldopa and, as expected, much smaller doses of the Smith and Nephew compounds (Nos. 70 and 71), and of the Hoffmann–LaRoche compound (No. 74). Such an inhibition would be expected to cause a lowering of tissue amines by interfering with their biosynthesis. This is actually observed for brain (Table VI, test B) and heart (test C), although the mechanism of the fall in tissue amines as a result of administering α-methyldopa or α-methyl-m-tyrosine is complex and not to be explained simply by decarboxylase inhibition (91). Reserpine has been included in the table only for comparative purposes. It lowers the concentration of tissue amines by releasing them from their stores and preventing their binding; it is not an antidecarboxylase. Seryl-trihydroxybenzylhydrazine given in repeated dosage to mice and guinea pigs lowers the concentration of catecholamines in brain, heart, and adrenals and of serotonin in brain and duodenum (11).

Many of the studies with radioactive-labeled amino acids have used racemic mixtures. In the case of dopa, the two isomers exhibit sufficient differences in metabolism (98) to warrant caution in drawing conclusions about the action of antidecarboxylases *in vivo* when $^{14}COOH$-DL-dopa is used. In fact, an examination of this problem (58) using tyrosine-, dopa- and α-methyldopa-^{14}C showed that α-methyldopa and some other members of the α-methyl series inhibit enzymes *in vivo* besides the decarboxylase. Hence, there is lack of specificity. $^{14}COOH$-L-Dopa proved to be a useful substrate, but $^{14}COOH$-L-α-methyldopa even better, perhaps because of its readier concentration in the kidney as against the more disperse metabolism of L-dopa. Results using the labeled α-methyldopa as substrate are shown in Table VIII.

In the study by Moran and Sourkes (58) it was found that α-methyldopa and some related compounds with antidecarboxylase action were very effective in preventing the formation of $^{14}CO_2$ from ^{14}C-labeled tyrosine, whether the amino acid bore the label in the carboxyl group or methylene carbon of the side chain. In any case, there is a very limited loss even of the carboxyl carbon of tyrosine by direct decarboxylation in the course of its intermediary metabolism. This illustrates what has just been said about the action of α-methyldopa *in vivo* on other enzymes than the decarboxylase. It is noteworthy that in such experiments α-methyl-5-hydroxytryptophan and 5-(3-hydroxycinnamoyl)-salicylic acid did not inhibit the formation of respiratory $^{14}CO_2$ from carboxyl-labeled tyrosine. Because of this greater specificity, or predilection, for the decarboxylase (Table VIII), these two compounds are recommended as standards for tests designed to measure antidecarboxylase action *in vivo*.

IV. Methyldopa

A. Pharmacology

1. *Cardiovascular Effects*

Methyldopa causes a marked drop in the blood pressure of renal-hypertensive rats, but not if it is administered after the animals have been injected with a potent antidecarboxylase (18). This suggests that the antihypertensive action requires preliminary decarboxylation of the methyldopa, a view for which there is now considerable support (45, 111). Clinically, the reduction of blood pressure of hypertensive patients is thoroughly documented, and only a few references (2, 8, 13, 24, 33, 34, 43, 64, 81, 86) can be cited. The drug lowers blood pressure in essential hypertensives in both the standing and supine positions. It has proved useful even in some cases of malignant hypertension (13). It does not lower the blood pressure in normotensive persons.

Bradycardia at rest is occasionally seen with chronic use of methyldopa, but it is much more common upon exercising (24, 82). However, exercise does not then cause a severe hypotension (24). There is disagreement about the effect of the drug on the cardiac output. Sannerstedt and his colleagues recognize no change in this parameter (82), but Onesti *et al.* observed a decrease in some of their patients (65). In either case the blood pressure-lowering effect of methyldopa certainly involves a reduced resistance of the peripheral vessels, including those of the kidney (33, 82).

A side effect of treatment of some patients with methyldopa is postural hypotension. This, together with bradycardia and a reduction in the Valsalva overshoot suggests that some form of sympathetic blockade is occurring (24), although methyldopa is neither an adrenergic nor ganglionic blocking agent (35, 105).

2. *Metabolic Effects*

A few reports state that there is a decreased urinary output of VMA during treatment with methyldopa, but these contradict the weight of evidence that no significant change occurs. The excretion of methyldopa and metabolic products interferes in the determination of catecholamines, but separation of the various catechols shows that there is no change in the excretion of norepinephrine either. Young and Edwards (119) find that methyldopa, dopa, and the amines corresponding to them cause the excessive excretion of certain amino acids. They attribute this to tubular competition between these substances for the neutral transport system.

3. *Side Effects*

The most commonly reported side effect is sedation or drowsiness in the initial period of therapy. It usually passes off thereafter. It may occur even in patients who do not respond with a fall in blood pressure. The sedative action was originally described by Smith (93) in experimental animals, and he compared it to the effect of reserpine. Orthostatism has already been mentioned. Psychiatric effects including depression, neurotic behavior, and hallucinations have been reported. The sleep rhythm may be disturbed. Other effects noted are vertigo, nausea, palpitations, headache, skin rashes, and fluid retention. All are readily reversed on withdrawing the drug or, in some cases, upon reducing its dosage. Tolerance to methyldopa occurs in some cases.

4. *Interaction with Biogenic Amines*

Two interesting effects of methyldopa, observed when certain amines are tested in conjunction with it, have been described. It has already been mentioned that pretreatment of experimental animals with methyldopa abolishes the acute effects of amine precursors. For example, the pressor effect of L-dopa is diminished (23); bronchoconstriction in guinea pigs resulting from the injection of 5-hydroxytryptophan and central excitation in mice from this compound are both prevented (117). Clinically, it has been found that the intravenous administration of dopa in amounts that do not cause a pressor effect in control subjects will cause a rise in blood pressure in patients who have received methyldopa chronically (83).

The other effect has to do with tyramine. The administration of tyramine causes a pressor response which is enhanced in patients taking methyldopa chronically (54, 68). Paradoxically, there was no alteration in the response to norepinephrine in these subjects (54), but this is consistent with the present view that tyramine (and other pressor amines like it) acts through the release of norepinephrine. Experimentally, methyldopa does not affect the cardio-vascular actions of norepinephrine (107).

A well-documented action of methyldopa is the depletion of tissue amines (69, 90, 92, 101, 110, 111). It causes a short-lasting fall in brain dopamine and serotonin, but a long-lasting depletion of norepinephrine. The latter effect does not seem now to come about through the antidecarboxylase action of methyldopa because the depletion of norepinephrine lasts long after decar-boxylase inhibition has worn off. In fact, many of the actions of methyldopa have now been distinctly separated from its decarboxylase-inhibiting effect (9, 17, 46). The view is that methyldopa gives rise to the active agent in the course of its metabolism, an agent which competes successfully with the sympathetic transmitter for storage sites. The first evidence for this was the demonstration of the decarboxylation of methyldopa *in vivo* in the rabbit, with the formation of "α-methyldopamine," and the further oxidation of this substance to α-methylnorepinephrine. This work of Carlsson and Lindqvist (14) was followed by evidence (111) that α-methyl-m-tyrosine must be decarboxylated in order to bring about the release of norepinephrine from the heart. The products derived from α-methyl-m-tyrosine, i.e. α-methyl-m-tyramine and metaraminol, are both potent releasers of norepinephrine (77, 111). Day and Rand then advanced the theory of stoichiometric displacement of norepinephrine from sympathetic nerve endings by a surrogate transmitter derived metabolically from methyldopa or from a related compound (20, 21). Muscholl and Maître (63) obtained physiological evidence for this hypothesis by showing that both α-methylnorepinephrine and norepinephrine are released when sympathetic nerves to the heart of methyldopa-treated animals are stimulated. They furthermore estimated the ratio of the two compounds in the perfusate to be the same as in the heart itself. These results are supported by evidence of Porter *et al.* (76) using methyldopa-2-^{14}C that the heart acquires a labeled substance, probably α-methylnorepinephrine, which is much more resistant to the amine-releasing action of reserpine than norepinephrine is. Brain extracts also contained this compound as well as another one that was chromatographically like α-methyldopamine.

The false, or surrogate, transmitter hypothesis is now generally accepted for the action of methyldopa. This hypothesis accounts satisfactorily for many facts obtained in experiments on the interaction of methyldopa and reserpine in the pharmacology of amines (91). In terms of the antihypertensive action of methyldopa, the hypothesis argues that α-methylnorepinephrine is formed from the amino acid and may then act in at least two ways: (1) by replacing norepinephrine at the sympathetic postganglionic nerve endings stoichiometrically (19), at least in the initial depletion of the amine (110); in this action the α-methylnorepinephrine serves as an amine-releaser (77, 111) in the same sense as reserpine. (2) Philippu and Schümann (70) have adduced evidence that an important process in the depletion of the cardiac store of catecholamines after giving methyldopa is competition between α-methyldopamine and endogenous dopamine for the enzyme that oxidizes these structures on the β-carbon atom.

The reviews by Muscholl (62) and Stone and Porter (106) contain many details of the pharmacology and mode of action of methyldopa.

B. CLINICAL APPLICATIONS OF METHYLDOPA IN DISEASES OTHER THAN HYPERTENSION

Methyldopa has been tested in the carcinoid syndrome, as a means of preventing the formation of excess serotonin in the tumor tissue. Little, if any, success has attended this treatment. Some investigators have found a reduction in the flushing caused by serotonin when it is released, but no amelioration of the diarrhea.

The drug has not proved useful in the treatment of psychoses (59, 100), although in one study it brought about a reduction in total symptoms in schizophrenia, along with an increase in the depressive content (80).

Because of the beneficial effect of reserpine in Huntington's chorea and because of the amine-depleting action of methyldopa, this drug has undergone trial in that disorder. The results showed that minor (102) or no improvement (49) results from its use. In Parkinson's disease, quite discrepant results have been reported: a decrease in tremor without any effect on the muscular rigidity (50); an increase in tremor (1); and no effect at all (49). Schnieden observed no effect of methyldopa in experimental tremor (88), but Stern and Przic found a protective action in mice given the tremorigenic agent N,N-diethylcysteamine (104). It is interesting to mention that some clinicians have observed Parkinsonism as a side effect of methyldopa therapy (37, 55, 67).

Methyldopa inhibits the nonspecific histidine decarboxylase of guinea pig kidney (79, 87, 115), but not the specific enzyme (79). The latter fact probably is sufficient explanation for the failure of methyldopa to affect mastocytosis (22).

C. Metabolism

The substitution of the α-hydrogen atom of an amino acid by a methyl group renders the compound unavailable for transamination but this does not affect it qualitatively as a substrate for decarboxylation. Postulated by Westheimer on theoretical grounds, the noninvolvement of the α-hydrogen bond in the decarboxylation process was demonstrated by Mandeles *et al.* (48) for bacterial decarboxylases and by Weissbach *et al.* (114) for mammalian dopa decarboxylase. Thus, methyldopa (i.e., the L-isomer of α-methyldopa) undergoes decarboxylation, but at a considerably slower rate than is observed with the corresponding natural amino acid. The reaction also occurs *in vivo* (10, 14, 100, 119).

The major product of metabolism of methyldopa in man is the mono-*O*-sulfate (10). In the rat it is methyldopa itself (119). Small amounts of α-methyldopamine appear in the urine (10, 100, 119). Some of the methyldopa is methylated in the 3-hydroxy position of the ring (10, 119), and a small amount is converted into a neutral product of unknown structure (10) which may be a deaminated derivative of α-methyldopamine (75). α-Methyldopamine is oxidized in part, as already mentioned, to α-methylnorepinephrine.

When methyldopa is administered intravenously, it is cleared rapidly from the plasma; it does not enter the erythrocytes appreciably (100). After oral administration, much of it (but not all) is absorbed from the gastrointestinal tract (10). D-α-Methyldopa is not as readily absorbed (119).

For fluorimetric determination of methyldopa and α-methyldopamine, the method of Sourkes and Murphy is available (60, 100). For the detailed isolation of methyldopa and its metabolites from urine, the article of Buhs and his colleagues (10) should be consulted.

References

1. Barbeau, A., Murphy, G. F., and Sourkes, T. L., *in* "Monoamines et système nerveux central" (J. de Ajuriaguerra, ed.), pp. 247–262. Georg, Geneva, Switzerland, and Masson, Paris, 1962.
2. Bayliss, R. I. S., and Harvey-Smith, E. A., *Lancet* I, 763 (1962).
3. Biel, J. H., Drukker, A. E., Mitchell, T. F., Sprengler, E. P., Nuhfer, P. A., Conway, A. C., and Horita, A., *J. Am. Chem. Soc.* **81**, 2805 (1959).
4. Blaschko, H., *J. Physiol. (London)* **101**, 337 (1942).
5. Blaschko, H., *Biochim. Biophys. Acta* **4**, 130 (1950).
6. Bollinger, F. W., and Sletzinger, M., Merck and Co., Inc., Belgian Patent 612,406 (1962).
7. Bollinger, F. W., and Sletzinger, M., Merck and Co., Inc., Belgian Patent 614,410 (1962).

8. Brest, A. N., and Moyer, J. H., *Am. J. Cardiol.* **9**, 116 (1962).
9. Brodie, B. B., Kuntzman, R., Hirsch, C. W., and Costa, E., *Life Sci.* **1**, 81 (1962).
10. Buhs, R. P., Beck, J. L., Speth, O. C., Smith, J. L., Trenner, N. R., Cannon, P. J., and Laragh, J. H., *J. Pharmacol. Exptl. Therap.* **143**, 205 (1964).
11. Burkard, W. P., Gey, K. F., and Pletscher, A., *Experientia* **18**, 411 (1962).
12. Burkard, W. P., Gey, K. F., and Pletscher, A., *Arch. Biochem. Biophys.* **107**, 187 (1964).
13. Cannon, P. J., Whitlock, R. T., Morris, R. C., Angers, M., and Laragh, J. H., *J. Am. Med. Assoc.* **179**, 673 (1962).
14. Carlsson, A., and Lindqvist, M., *Acta Physiol. Scand.* **54**, 87 (1962).
15. Clark, W. G., *Pharmacol. Rev.* **11**, 330 (1959).
16. Clark, W. G., and Pogrund, R. S., *Circulation Res.* **9**, 721 (1961).
17. Creveling, C. R., Van der Schoot, J. B., and Udenfriend, S., *Biochem. Biophys. Res. Commun.* **8**, 215 (1962).
18. Davis, R. A., Drain, D. J., Horlington, M., Lazare, R., and Urbanska, A., *Life Sci.* **3**, 193 (1963).
19. Day, M. D., and Rand, M. J., *J. Pharm. Pharmacol.* **15**, 631 (1963).
20. Day, M. D., and Rand, M. J., *Brit. J. Pharmacol.* **22**, 72 (1964).
21. Day, M. D., and Rand, M. J., *Intern. J. Neuropharmacol.* **3**, 173 (1964).
22. Demis, D. J., and Zimmer, J. G., *Arch. Internal Med.* **111**, 309 (1963).
23. Dengler, H., and Reichel, G., *Arch. Exptl. Pathol. Pharmakol.* **234**, 275 (1958).
24. Dollery, C. T., and Harington, M., *Lancet* **I**, 759 (1962).
25. Drain, D. J., Horlington, M., Lazare, R., and Poulter, G. A., *Life Sci.* **1**, 93 (1962).
26. Ellison, T. E., *J. Chem. Soc.* p. 1720 (1927).
27. Erlenmeyer, E., *Chem. Ber.* **13**, 303 (1880).
28. Erlenmeyer, E., *Ann. Chem.* **219**, 226 (1883).
29. Fellman, J. H., *Proc. Soc. Exptl. Biol. Med.* **93**, 413 (1956).
30. Fischer, E., and Zempler, G., *Chem. Ber.* **42**, 4878 (1909).
31. Folkers, K., *Chem. Eng. News* **40**, 106 (1962).
32. Gaudry, R., and McIvor, R. A. *Can. J. Chem.* **29**, 427 (1951).
33. Gelfman, N. A., Landau, S. J., Mulrow, P. J., Friedewald, W. T., and Dalessio, D. J., *J. Chronic Diseases* **16**, 217 (1963).
34. Gillespie, L., Oates, J. A., Crout, J. R., and Sjoerdsma, A., *Circulation* **25**, 281 (1962).
35. Goldberg, L. I., De Costa, F. M., and Ozaki, M., *Nature* **188**, 503 (1960).
36. Goldstein, M., *Pharmacol. Rev.* **18**, 77 (1966).
37. Groden, B. M., *Brit. Med. J.* **I**, 1001 (1963).
38. Hahn, G., Bärwald, L., Sehales, O., and Werner, H., *Ann. Chem.* **520**, 107 (1935).
39. Hansson, E., and Clark, W. G., *Proc. Soc. Exptl. Biol. Med.* **111**, 793 (1962).
40. Hansson, E., Fleming, R. M., and Clark, W. G., *Intern. J. Neuropharmacol.* **3**, 177 (1964).
41. Hartman, W. J., Akawie, R. I., and Clark, W. G., *J. Biol. Chem.* **216**, 507 (1955).
42. Holtz, P., Heise, R., and Lüdtke, K., *Arch. Exptl. Pathol. Pharmakol.* **191**, 87 (1938).
43. Irvine, R. O. H., O'Brien, K. P., and North, J. D. K., *Lancet* **I**, 300 (1962).
44. Jones, R. T., Krieger, K. H., and Lago, J., Merck and Co., Inc., Belgian Patent 620,113 (1963).
45. Kroneberg, G., and Stoepel, K., *Arch. Exptl. Pathol. Pharmakol.* **246**, 11 (1963).
46. Levine, R. J., and Sjoerdsma, A., *J. Pharmacol. Exptl. Therap.* **146**, 42 (1964).
47. Lovenberg, W., Barchas, J., Weissbach, H., and Udenfriend, S., *Arch. Biochem. Biophys.* **103**, 9 (1963).
48. Mandeles, S., Koppelman, R., and Hanke, M. E., *J. Biol. Chem.* **209**, 327 (1954).
49. Markham, C. H., Clark, W. G., and Winters, W. D., *Life Sci.* **2**, 697 (1963).

50. Marsh, D. O., Schnieden, H., and Marshall, J., *J. Neurol., Neurosurg., Psychiat.* [N.S.] **26**, 505 (1963).
51. Martin, G. J., and Beiler, J. M., *Arch. Biochem.* **15**, 201 (1947).
52. Martin, G. J., Brendel, R., and Beiler, J. M., *Exptl. Med. Surg.* **8**, 5 (1950).
53. Martinez, M. P., *Anales Real Acad. Farm.* **23**, 387 (1957).
54. McCurdy, R. L., Prance, A. J., Jr., Lipton, M. A., and Cochrane, C. M., *Proc. Soc. Exptl. Biol. Med.* **116**, 1159 (1964).
55. Menon, G. N., *Indian Med. J.* **59**, 21 (1965).
56. Merck and Co., Inc., South African Patent 61,950 (1962).
57. Missala, K., Lloyd, K., Gregoriadis, G., and Sourkes, T. L., *European J. Pharm.* **1**, 6 (1967).
58. Moran, J. F., and Sourkes, T. L., *J. Pharmacol. Exptl. Therap.* **148**, 252 (1965).
59. Mosher, L. R., Klerman, G. L., and Greaney, J. F., *Am. J. Psychiat.* **122**, 1185 (1966).
60. Murphy, G. F., and Sourkes, T. L., *Rev. Can. Biol.* **18**, 379 (1959).
61. Murphy, G. F., and Sourkes, T. L., *Arch. Biochem. Biophys.* **93**, 338 (1961).
62. Muscholl, E., *Ann. Rev. Pharmacol.* **6**, 107 (1966).
63. Muscholl, E., and Maître, L., *Experientia* **19**, 658 (1963).
64. Oates, J. A., Gillespie, L., Udenfriend, S., and Sjoerdsma, A., *Science* **131**, 1890 (1960).
65. Onesti, G., Brest, A. N., Novack, P., and Moyer, J. H., *Am. J. Cardiol.* **9**, 863 (1962).
66. Pandya, K. C., and Vakidy, T. A., *Proc. Indian Acad. Sci.* **A4**, 140 (1936).
67. Peaston, M. J. T., *Brit. Med. J.* **II**, 168 (1964).
68. Pettinger, W. A., Horwitz, D., Spector, S., and Sjoerdsma, A., *Nature* **200**, 1107 (1963).
69. Pfeifer, A. K., and Galambos, E., *Biochem. Pharmacol.* **14**, 37 (1965).
70. Philippu, A., and Schümann, H. J., *Life Sci.* **4**, 2039 (1965).
71. Pletscher, A., Burkard, W. P., and Gey, K. F., *Biochem. Pharmacol.* **13**, 385 (1964).
72. Pletscher, A., and Gey, K. F., *Biochem. Pharmacol.* **12**, 223 (1963).
73. Pogrund, R. S., Drell, W., and Clark, W. G., *J. Pharmacol. Exptl. Therap.* **131**, 294 (1961).
74. Polonovski, M., Schapira, G., and Gonnard, P., *Bull. Soc. Chim. Biol.* **28**, 735 (1946).
75. Porter, C. C., and Titus, D. C., *J. Pharmacol. Exptl. Therap.* **139**, 77 (1963).
76. Porter, C. C., Totaro, J. A., and Burcin, A., *J. Pharmacol. Exptl. Therap.* **150**, 17 (1965).
77. Porter, C. C., Totaro, J. A., and Leiby, C. M., *J. Pharmacol. Exptl. Therap.* **134**, 139 (1961).
78. Porter, C. C., Watson, L. S., Titus, D. C., Totaro, J. A., and Byer, S. S., *Biochem. Pharmacol.* **11**, 1067 (1962).
79. Reid, J. D., and Shepherd, D. M., *Life Sci.* **1**, 5 (1963).
80. Saint Jean, A., Donald, M. W., and Ban, T. A., *Union Méd. Canada* **92**, 1420 (1963).
81. Sannerstedt, R., Bojs, G., Varnauskas, E., and Werkö, L., *Acta Med. Scand.* **174**, 53 (1963).
82. Sannerstedt, R., Varnauskas, E., and Werkö, L., *Acta Med. Scand.* **171**, 75 (1962).
83. Schaer, H., and Ziegler, W. H., *Klin. Wochschr.* **40**, 959 (1962).
84. Schales, O., and Schales, S. S., *Arch. Biochem.* **24**, 83 (1949).
85. Schapira, G., *Compt. Rend. Soc. Biol.* **140**, 173 (1946).
86. Schaub, F., Nager, F., Schaer, H., Ziegler, W., and Lichtlen, P., *Schweiz. Med. Wochschr.* **92**, 620 (1962).
87. Schayer, R. W., and Sestokas, E., *Biochim. Biophys. Acta* **111**, 557 (1965).
88. Schnieden, H., *J. Neurol., Neurosurg., Psychiat.* [N.S.] **26**, 500 (1963).
89. Schott, H. F., and Clark, W. G., *J. Biol. Chem.* **196**, 449 (1952).
90. Sharman, D. F., and Smith, S. E., *J. Neurochem.* **9**, 403 (1962).
91. Sourkes, T. L., *Brit. Med. Bull.* **21**, 66 (1965).

92. Sletzinger, M., Chemerda, H. M., and Bollinger, F. W., *J. Med. Pharm. Chem.* **6**, 101 (1963).
93. Smith, S. E., *Brit. J. Pharmacol.* **15**, 319 (1960).
94. T. J. Smith, and Nephew, Ltd., Belgian Patent 609,907 (1962).
95. Sourkes, T. L., *Arch. Biochem. Biophys.* **51**, 444 (1954).
96. Sourkes, T. L., *Rev. Can. Biol.* **14**, 49 (1955).
97. Sourkes, T. L., *Pharmacol. Rev.* **18**, 53 (1966).
98. Sourkes, T. L., Distler, M. H. W., Moran, J. F., Murphy, G. F., and Saint Cyr, S., *Biochem. J.* **93**, 469 (1964).
99. Sourkes, T. L., Heneage, P., and Trano, Y., *Arch. Biochem. Biophys.* **40**, 185 (1952).
100. Sourkes, T. L., Murphy, G. F., and Chavez-Lara, B., *J. Med. Pharm. Chem.* **5**, 204 (1962).
101. Sourkes, T. L., Murphy, G. F., Chavez, B., and Zielinska, M., *J. Neurochem.* **8**, 109 (1961).
102. Sourkes, T. L., Pivnicki, D., Brown, W. T., Distler, M. H. W., Murphy, G. F., Sankoff, I., and Saint Cyr, S., *Psychiat. Neurol.* **149**, 7 (1965).
103. Stein, G. A., Bronner, H. A., and Pfister, K., III, *J. Am. Chem. Soc.* **77**, 700 (1955).
104. Stern, P., and Przic, R., *Life Sci.* **2**, 213 (1962).
105. Stone, C. A., and Beyer, K. H., *Am. J. Cardiol.* **9**, 830 (1962).
106. Stone, C. A., and Porter, C. C., *Pharmacol. Rev.* **18**, 570 (1966).
107. Stone, C. A., Ross, C. A., Wenger, H. C., Ludden, C. T., Blessing, J. A., Totaro, J. A., and Porter, C. C., *J. Pharmacol. Exptl. Therap.* **136**, 80 (1962).
108. Tristram, E. W., tenBroeke, J., Reinhold, D. F., Sletzinger, M., and Williams, D. E., *J. Org. Chem.* **29**, 2053 (1964).
109. Udenfriend, S., *Pharmacol. Rev.* **18**, 43 (1966).
110. Udenfriend, S., Connamacher, R., and Hess, S. M., *Biochem. Pharmacol.* **8**, 419 (1961).
111. Udenfriend, S., and Zaltzman-Nirenberg, P., *J. Pharmacol. Exptl. Therap.* **138**, 194 (1962).
112. Udenfriend, S., Zaltzman-Nirenberg, P., and Nagatsu, T., *Biochem. Pharmacol.* **14**, 837 (1965).
113. von Euler, U. S., *Pharmacol. Rev.* **18**, 29 (1966).
114. Weissbach, H., Lovenberg, W., and Udenfriend, S., *Biochem. Biophys. Res. Commun.* **3**, 225 (1960).
115. Werle, E., *Naturwissenschaften* **48**, 54 (1961).
116. Werner, G., *Chem. Ber.* **28**, 1997 (1895).
117. Westermann, E., Balzer, H., and Knell, J., *Arch. Exptl. Pathol. Pharmakol.* **234**, 194 (1958).
118. Wheeler, T. S., *Org. Syn.* **6**, 478 (1963).
119. Young, J. A., and Edwards, K. D. G., *J. Pharmacol. Exptl. Therap.* **145**, 102 (1964).
120. Yuwiler, A., Geller, E., and Eiduson, S., *Arch. Biochem. Biophys.* **89**, 143 (1960).

CHAPTER V

Rauwolfia Alkaloids

E. Schlittler

H. J. Bein

PART ONE—Hypotensive Drugs from *Rauwolfia* spp., 191

I. Introduction, 191
II. Chemical Classification of *Rauwolfia* Alkaloids, 193
III. Chemistry of Reserpine-type Alkaloids, 193
IV. Alkaloids Related to Reserpine, 194
V. Semisynthetic Reserpine Derivatives, 196
    A. Esterification in Positions 16 and 18, 196
    B. Etherification of the Hydroxyl Group in Position 18, 197
VI. Total Synthesis of Reserpine and Reserpine Analogs, 197
VII. Synthesis of Model Compounds, 198

PART TWO—Pharmacology of Reserpine, 205

VIII. Effect of Reserpine on the Central Nervous System, 206
IX. Effect of Reserpine on the Sympathetic Nervous System, 207
X. Effect of Reserpine on the Circulatory System, 210
XI. Effect of Reserpine on Various Endocrine Functions, 212
XII. Interference with the Action of Reserpine, 214
    References, 215

Part One

Hypotensive Drugs from *Rauwolfia* spp.

I. Introduction

The chemistry of *Rauwolfia* alkaloids and specifically of the reserpine alkaloids has been reviewed very recently (156). The same author [together with A. J. Plummer (157)] has also reported on the tranquilizing drugs from *Rauwolfia* in the present series of monographs. For this reason the chemical part of this chapter is kept to a minimum with the principal emphasis being given to structure–activity relationships.

Contrary to the easily observable tranquilizing activity of *Rauwolfia* extracts and of certain *Rauwolfia* alkaloids, their hypotensive activity is more difficult to observe. Most *Rauwolfia* species contain alkaloids which have a short hypotensive effect dissimilar to the typical reserpine effect (serpentine, ajmaline etc.). Because of this short hypotensive activity, such alkaloids cannot be used for therapeutic purposes. It is difficult, therefore, to state exactly who has first observed the typical reserpine activity, i.e., a blood-pressure depression extending over many hours, because in most cases it has been a "mixed effect." Kirtikar and Basu (84) have been mentioned in this respect (36) but it would probably be difficult to substantiate such claims.

Although *Rauwolfia* was investigated in the nineteenth century and the presence of alkaloids indicated (60), a systematic investigation of *Rauwolfia* was only started by Siddiqui and Siddiqui (170, 171) in 1931. Five alkaloids were isolated at this time and in spite of the fact that one alkaloid (serpentine) had a blood-pressure reducing effect, none of the five showed the characteristics which were later called "reserpinelike." About the same time, a Dutch group (192) investigated the same plant and isolated three alkaloids. However, only one of these compounds was properly described. Twenty years later Steenhauer (173) claimed that one of the two ill-defined compounds had indeed been identical with reserpine.

Whereas this early chemical work was not too meaningful, pharmacological and clinical work indicated that in addition to serpentine (see above) another hypotensive agent was likely to be present in extracts of *Rauwolfia serpentina*. Indian investigators (19, 163) had claimed hypotension with simultaneous tranquilizing activity and there is no doubt that such extracts therefore must have contained reserpine. This observation has also been confirmed by Chopra *et al.* (38) and other Indian investigators. For years it was thought that *Rauwolfia* contained two different media, namely, a tranquilizing neutral compound and an antihypertensive alkaloid (61). It is obvious that this problem could only be solved after pure components from *Rauwolfia* extracts were made available to the pharmacologists. In the meantime, the *Rauwolfia* problem got a big stimulus from an Indian paper dealing with the antihypertensive activity of *Rauwolfia* extracts in man, published in a Western scientific periodical (191), and it is probably correct to state that this was the point from which modern *Rauwolfia* research started. Reserpine, the most important *Rauwolfia* alkaloid, was isolated in 1952 (117). Shortly afterward, it was demonstrated by Bein (11) that reserpine was at the same time tranquilizing and hypotensive; this finding ended the confusion which had prevailed for such a long time.

II. Chemical classification of *Rauwolfia* alkaloids

The arbitrary (1956) classification of *Rauwolfia* alkaloids (158, 205) has been simplified. All alkaloids have a yohimbinoid skeleton and are conveniently subdivided as follows: (1) yohimbines (all yohimbine isomers); (2) 18-hydroxy yohimbines (reserpine-type alkaloids); (3) ring E heterocycles and their anhydronium analogs (ajmalicine, serpentine); (4) ajmaline-type alkaloids.

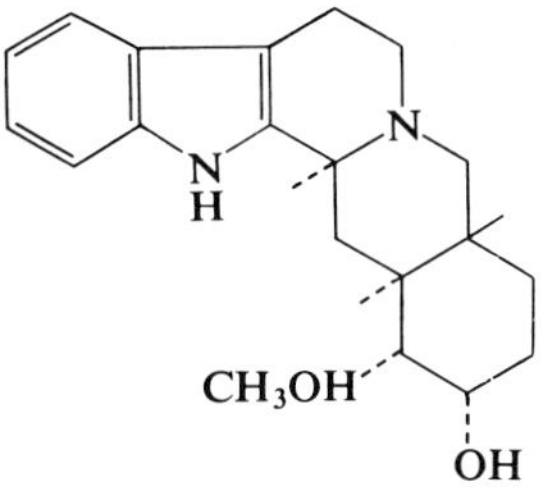

Yohimbine

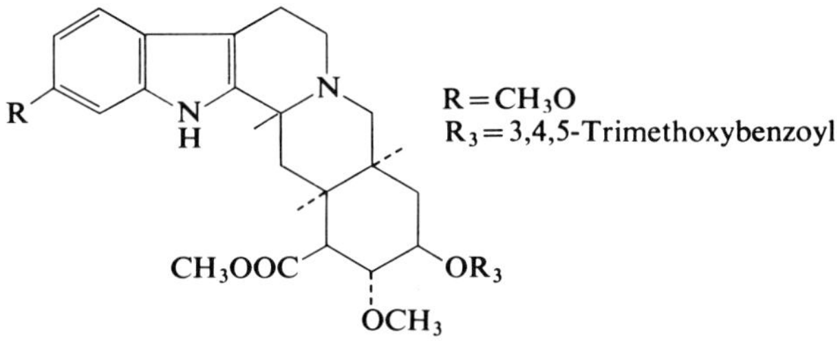

Reserpine

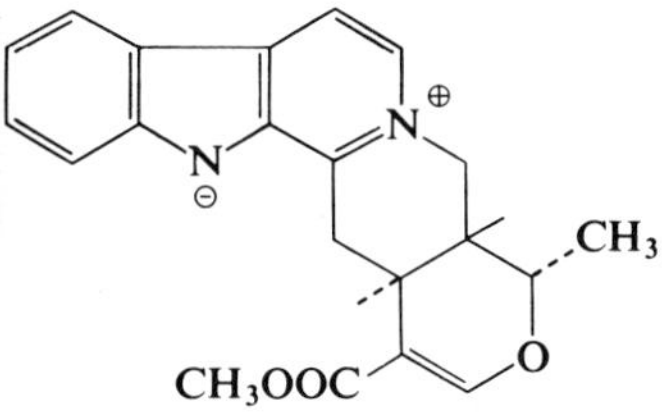

R = CH_3O
R_3 = 3,4,5-Trimethoxybenzoyl

Serpentine

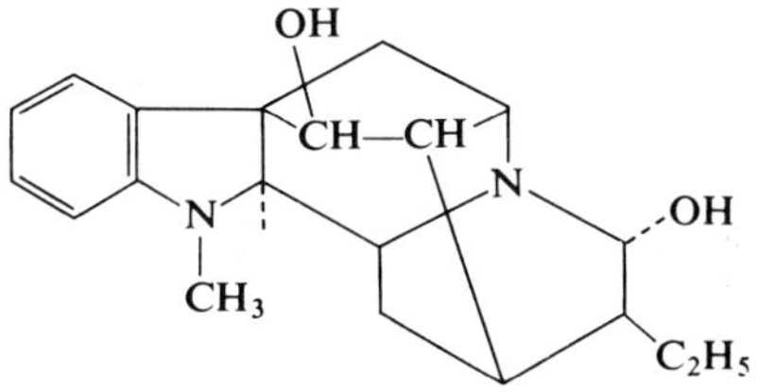

Ajmaline

Only the esterified 18-hydroxy yohimbines (reserpine-type alkaloids) possess typical, therapeutically useful qualities and will therefore be treated in detail. The serpentine alkaloids and ajmaline show atypical, therapeutically uninteresting hypotensive properties and most of the yohimbines act as sympathicolytics.

III. Chemistry of reserpine-type alkaloids

Intensive structural work, X-ray crystallographic studies on a deserpidine derivative (129), and an elegant synthesis (206, 207) of reserpine have yielded independent proofs of the constitution of *l*-reserpine or 11,17α-dimethoxy-16β-carbomethoxy-18β-(3′,4′,5′-trimethoxybenzoyloxy)-3β,20α-yohimbane (I), one of the 64 possible isomers. All stereoisomers of reserpine in the following tabulation have been prepared by chemical manipulations. They all retain the cis-C-15, C-20 ring structure. So far no diastereoisomer with *trans* fused D/E ring system has been prepared.

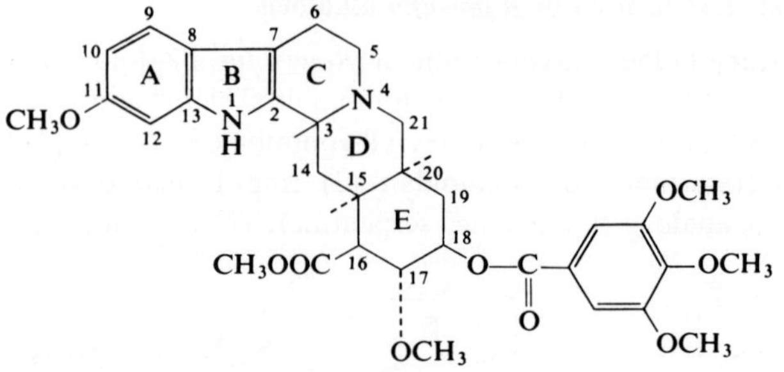

(I)

Only 16,17,18-epireserpine has retained some hypotensive but no sedative activity of reserpine. All other stereoisomers are of no pharmacological interest, not even 3-isoreserpine which differs from reserpine in the stereochemistry of only one carbon atom.

Table I

STEREOISOMERS OF RESERPINE

Stereoisomers	3H	16-COOCH$_3$	17-OCH$_3$	18-O-TMB[a]	Reference
Reserpine	β	β	α	β	
3-Isoreserpine	α	β	α	β	(101)
16-Epireserpine	β	α	α	β	(189)
16-Epi-17-epireserpine (neo-Reserpine)	β	α	β	β	(151)
18-Epireserpine	β	β	α	α	} (148)
18-Epi-3-isoreserpine	α	β	α	α	
16,17,18-epireserpine	β	α	β	α	(190)

[a] TMB = 3,4,5-trimethoxybenzoyl.

IV. Alkaloids related to reserpine

The occurrence of reserpine has been reported for all *Rauwolfia* species except about six, where it probably occurs in minute amounts. Renoxidine, the *N*-oxide of reserpine, with somewhat reduced activity, has been found only in *Rauwolfia serpentina*, *R. canescens*, *R. vomitoria* (188), and in *Rauwolfia ligustrina* (118). Deserpidine, which produces the same degree of central depression as reserpine, and rescinnamine, which is weaker, have been isolated from about ten species. The other reserpinelike alkaloids either have a greatly

Table II

ADDITIONAL NATURALLY OCCURRING RESERPINE-TYPE ALKALOIDS

Alkaloid		Reference
Deserpidine	$R_1 = H$ $R_2 = CH_3$ $R_3 = TMB^a$	(159)
Raunescine	$R_1 = H$ $R_2 = H$ $R_3 = TMB$	(73)
Isoraunescine	$R_1 = H$ $R_2 = TMB$ $R_3 = H$	(73)
Pseudoreserpine	$R_1 = CH_3O$ $R_2 = H$ $R_3 = TMB$	(85, 86)
Raugustine	$R_1 = CH_3O$ $R_2 = TMB$ $R_3 = H$	(118)
Rescinnamine	$R_1 = CH_3O$ $R_2 = CH_3$ $R_3 = TMC^b$	(62)
Rescidine	$R_1 = CH_3O$ $R_2 = H$ $R_3 = TMC$	(136)

[a] TMB = 3,4,5-trimethoxybenzoyl.
[b] TMC = 3,4,5-trimethoxycinnamoyl.

reduced antihypertensive activity or are completely inactive. In Table II the three alkaloids without a methoxyl group in position 11 of ring A (deserpidine, raunescine, isoraunescine) and the four alkaloids which contain this methoxyl substituent (pseudoreserpine, raugustine, rescinnamine, and rescidine) are grouped together. In the first group no trimethoxycinnamate ester analogous to rescinnamine has been isolated.

Since reserpine and deserpidine show the same degree of hypotensive activity, it is obvious that the methoxy group in position 11 of reserpine is not essential for activity. Alkaloids with a trimethoxycinnamate group in position 18 are, in general, less active than the corresponding trimethoxy-benzoates. Reserpic acid, methyl reserpate, and reserpic acid 18-o-trimethoxy-benzoate (position 16 = —COOH, position 18 = 3,4,5-trimethoxybenzoyl,) (99) are completely inactive. A hydroxy group in position 17 (instead of methoxyl) reduces activity (raunescine, pseudoreserpine). Acylation of the hydroxyl in position 17 with trimethoxybenzoic acid leaving a hydroxyl in position 18 gives an inactive compound (isoraunescine, raugustine). The structure of rescidine, originally uncertain as to the position of the trimethoxycinnamate moiety (136), has now been established (138). It was recently found (164, 165) that raujemidine (187) and deserpideine (172) are the $\Delta^{19, 20}$ derivatives of reserpine and deserpidine respectively. Both raujemidine (Su-3885*, personal information from Dr. A. Plummer (132)) and deserpideine retain about 60% of the antihypertensive activity of reserpine in the anesthetized dog.

V. Semisynthetic reserpine derivatives

A. Esterification in Positions 16 and 18

Soon after the discovery of reserpine, work was initiated to prepare deriva-tives with possibly higher and modified activities or with fewer side reactions. These investigations were primarily aimed at alterations of the antihypertensive activity rather than the tranquilizing activity. The easiest approach to the

(II)

problem of qualitative and quantitative changes was the variation of the ester groupings in positions 16 and especially 18 (46, 98, 99). Among a large number of diesters, none proved to be quantitatively more active than reserpine and deserpidine. In some compounds the sedative activity was more reduced than

* All compounds with a Su- number as well as many others referred to here have been prepared in the chemical laboratories of CIBA Pharmaceutical Company, Summit, New Jersey.

the antihypertensive activity, although at the expense of total strength. With high doses, the tranquilizing activity became noticeable again. Among the many diesters prepared from reserpic acid or methyl reserpate by partial synthesis, syrosingopine (II) is hypotensive at an average daily dose of 3 mg (reserpine 0.3 mg) with only minimal sedation (166) [see also Ernest and Protiva (47, 49)]. 1-[2-(Diethylamino)ethyl]-reserpine (III) is presently in

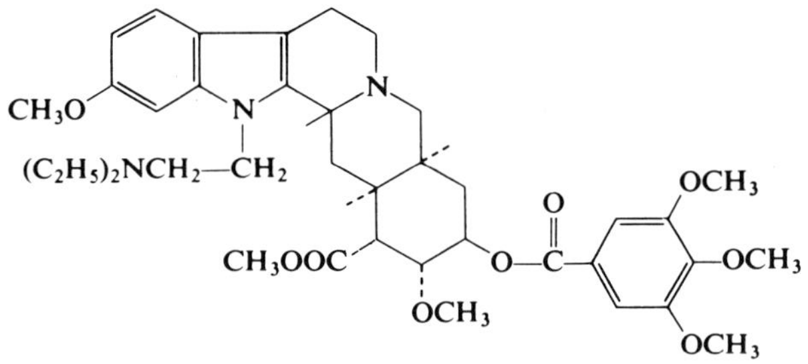

CH$_3$O

(C$_2$H$_5$)$_2$NCH$_2$—CH$_2$

CH$_3$OOC

OCH$_3$

O

OCH$_3$

O—C

OCH$_3$

OCH$_3$

(III)

clinical trial as a reserpine derivative with exclusively antihypertensive activity at daily oral doses of 20–40 mg (18). None of the side effects of reserpine were noted.

B. ETHERIFICATION OF THE HYDROXYL GROUP IN POSITION 18

The etherification of the hydroxyl group in position 18 has been extensively investigated (137, 148–150). Etherification has predominantly yielded tranquilizing derivatives and therefore will not be considered in this discussion (156).

VI. Total synthesis of reserpine and reserpine analogs

This problem has been dealt with in an earlier review (156, 157). By modification of Woodward's reserpine synthesis, changes were made in rings A, C, and E of the reserpine molecule and qualitative differences in hypotensive and sedative activities were claimed. 10-Methoxydeserpidine (199) is stated to act only antihypertensively and it is claimed to be superior to reserpine in chronic rat experiments (198). Carbethoxysyringoylester of 10-methoxydeserpidate has been prepared by several investigators (48, 119) but no pharmacologic data are available on this compound. 12-Methylmercaptodeserpidine (49) was found to possess considerable antihypertensive activity and was therefore recommended for clinical investigation. The same claims have been made for 17α-methyl- and for 17α-ethyl 17-demethoxyreserpines (45) and for 12-methoxydeserpidine (197, 198).

VII. Synthesis of model compounds

The synthetic approach to simplified model compounds with antihypertensive activity was handicapped for several reasons. First and most important, there was not much of an incentive for preparing such compounds because a number of synthetic substances belonging to chemically different classes have been developed within the past 15 years and have become very successful drugs, especially in the treatment of severe hypertension. Secondly, only minor changes (like inversions at one C-atom or simple substitution, e.g., at N_1) destroy both antihypertensive and sedative activity of reserpine completely and it could therefore not be expected that model compounds would be active. Certainly the famous cocaine-procaine precedent would not be valid; i.e., where a model compound structurally quite different from the natural alkaloid showed high anesthetic activity.

Cocaine   Procaine

It was therefore somewhat surprising when it was reported by Miller and Weinberg (114) that a trimethoxybenzoate of a simple amino alcohol had a "reserpinelike" activity of about one-third that of reserpine.

Su-12,449

This compound has been resynthesized several times and its activity has been reported as being from nonexistent to only weakly and noncharacteristically active (126, 132, 195). However, the Miller and Weinberg publication has induced many investigators to synthesize reserpine model compounds and today there exists a vast literature concerning this subject.

As mentioned previously, the expectation to find a "simplified reserpine" has not been fulfilled and so far no such compound could substitute for reserpine in therapy. In numerous publications on reserpine model compounds, a "reserpinelike" pharmacologic activity is claimed (mostly in nebulous terms) but no mention is made of whether this applies to hypotension or sedation. Many papers contain statements as to later publications of pharmacologic details, which however, are only rarely followed up.

These model compounds can be classified into three different categories and it may be worth while to give a few examples, although evaluation as to their activities is mostly impossible.

1. *Synthetic Yohimbanes with Aromatic Ring E*

Such compounds were already synthesized in the 1930's (65). For compound IV (96) a pronounced hypotension in the anesthetized dog or rabbit has been observed (even after 2 hours) whereas compound V possessed only very weak activity at the same dose of 10 mg per kilogram (97). Nogradi (122) did not find activity for IV. Similar pentacyclic derivatives were synthesized by

(IV) R=H   (V) R=OCH₃

Short *et al.* (169), Plieninger and Kiefer (131), Ribbens and Nauta (147), Buzas *et al.* (29), and others. In most cases these papers do not contain pharmacological results.

2. *Synthetic Models Containing at least an Indole Nucleus*

a. Tetrahydroharmine Derivatives. Compounds (vi)–(x) may be mentioned, but here again, accurate evaluation is difficult.

b. Some Indole Derivatives. Compounds (xi)–(xv) may also be mentioned.

c. Linear Derivatives. Compounds are *inter alia* similar to the Miller and Weinberg compounds (xvi)–(xxviii).

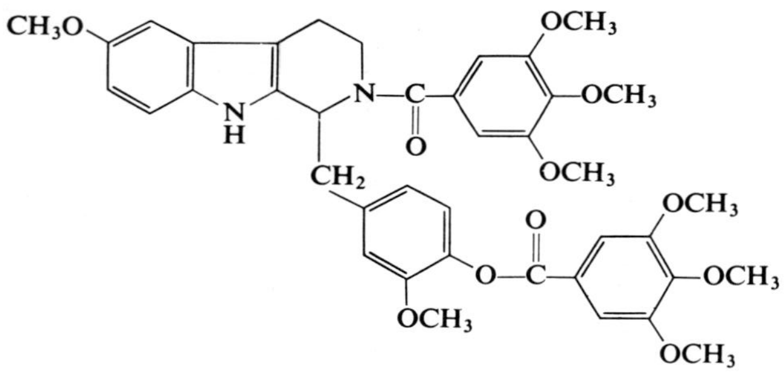

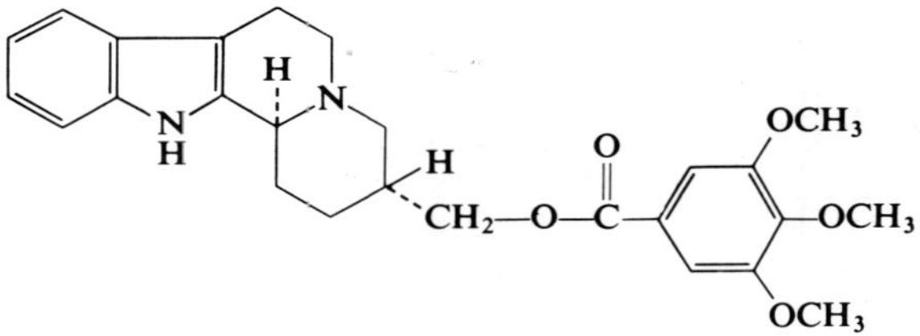

(VII)

deGroot and Strating (40)

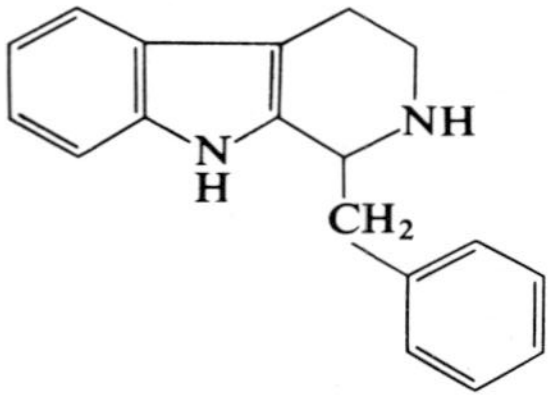

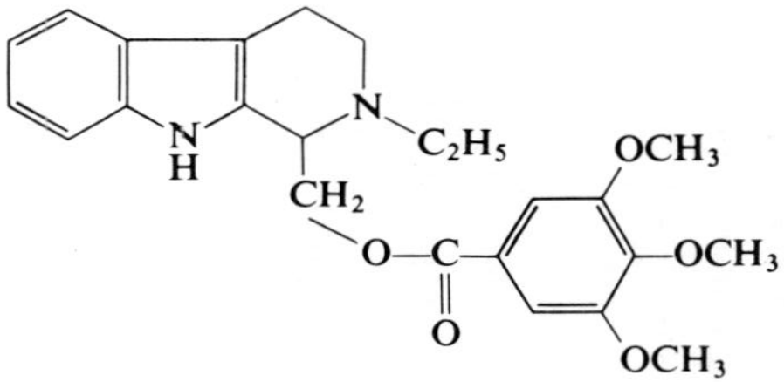

(X)

Vejdelek *et al.* (196)

(VI)

Logemann *et al.* (96)

(IX)

Protiva *et al.* (140)

(VIII)

Protiva *et al.* (139)

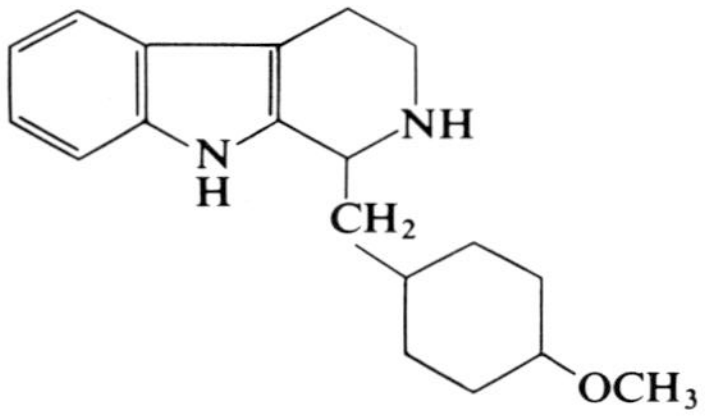

200

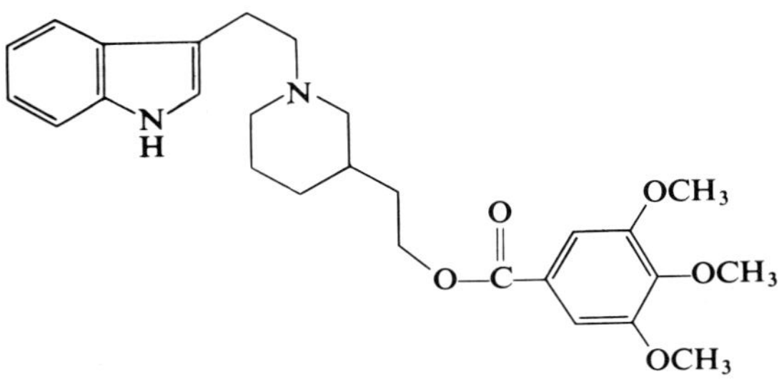

(XII)

Nogradi (122)

(XI)

Najer et al. (121)

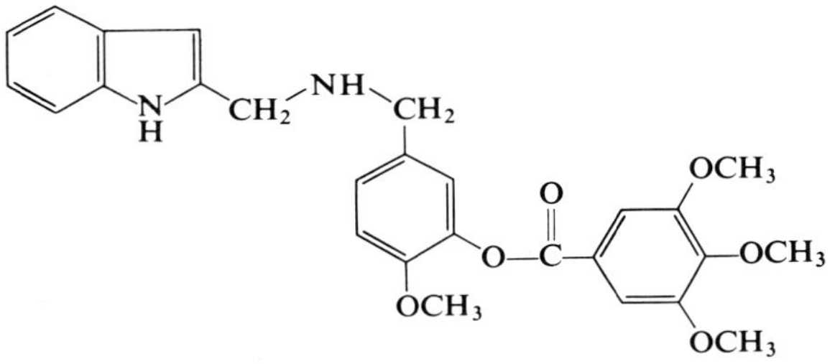

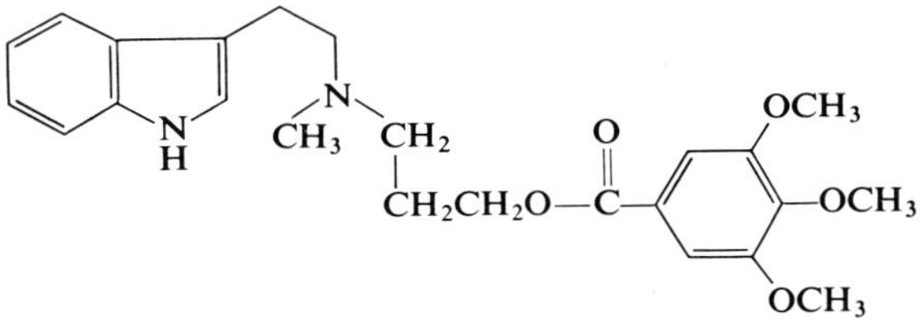

(XV)

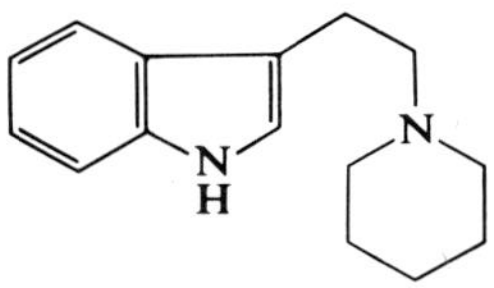

Protiva et al. (141)
Onda et al. (124)

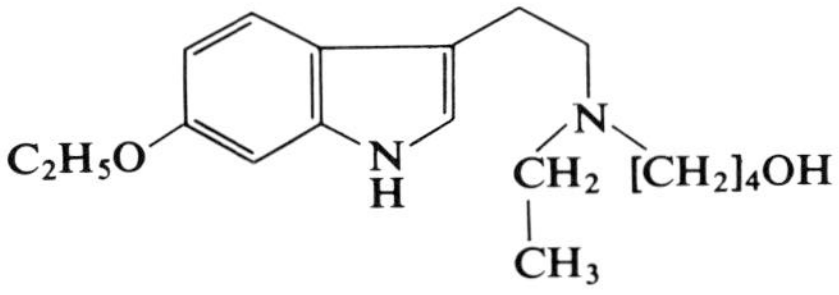

(XIV)

Kralt et al. (89)

(XIII)

Nogradi (123)

201

(XVI)

$$R-COO[CH_2]_4N{<}^{R_1}_{R_1}$$

Vazakas-Doluisio (194)
Lunsford et al. (100)
Sastry and Lasslo (154)
Majumdar and Paul (106)

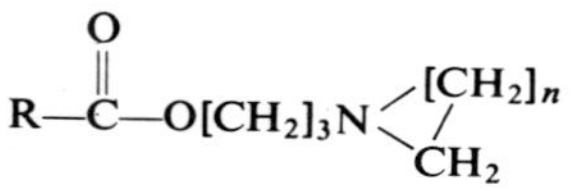

(XVII)

$$R-\overset{O}{\overset{\|}{C}}-O[CH_2]_3N{<}^{[CH_2]_n}_{CH_2}$$

diPaco and Tauro (42)

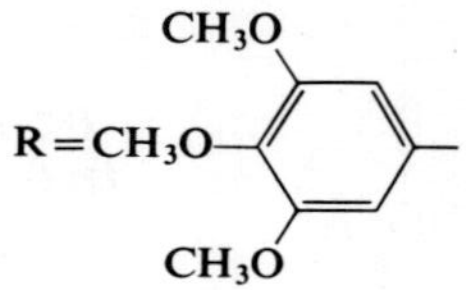

$$R = CH_3O-\text{(trimethoxyphenyl)}$$

CH$_3$O, CH$_3$O, CH$_3$O

$R_1 =$ alkyl

(XVIII)

$$R-\overset{O}{\overset{\|}{C}}-X[CH_2]_4N{<}^{R_1}_{R_1}$$

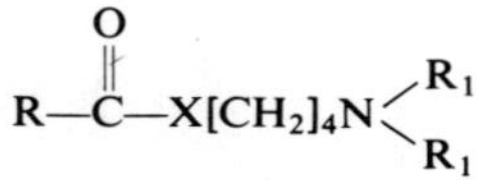

X = O or N

Tauro and diPaco (178)

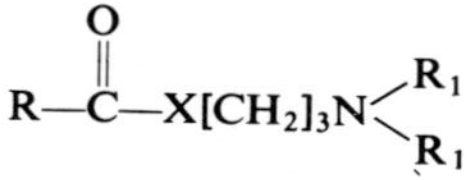

(XIX)

$$R-\overset{O}{\overset{\|}{C}}-X[CH_2]_3N{<}^{R_1}_{R_1}$$

X = O or N

Tauro and diPaco (177)

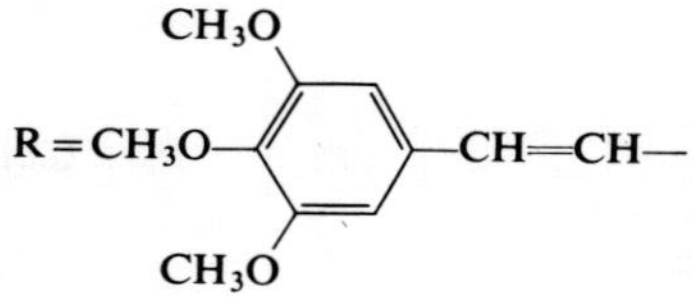

$$R = CH_3O-\text{, } CH=CH-$$

CH$_3$O, CH$_3$O

$R_1 =$ alkyl or alkylene imine

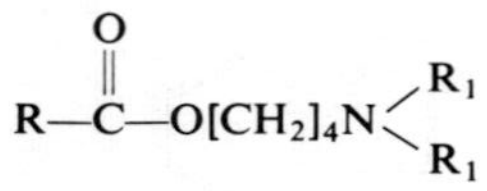

(XX)

$$R-\overset{O}{\overset{\|}{C}}-O[CH_2]_4N{<}^{R_1}_{R_1}$$

Bramanti et al. (24)

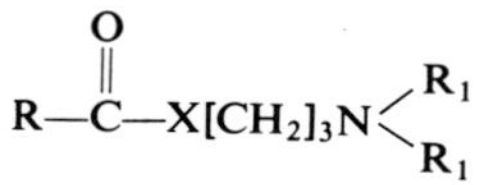

(XXI)

$$R-\overset{O}{\overset{\|}{C}}-X[CH_2]_3N{<}^{R_1}_{R_1}$$

Tauro et al. (179)

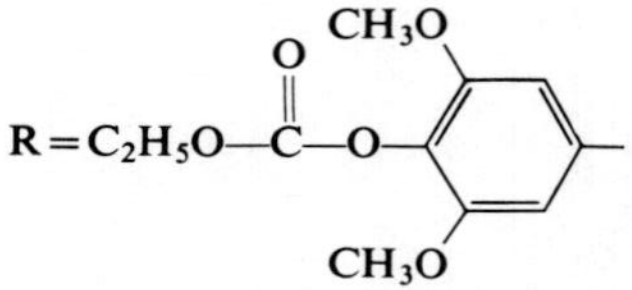

$$R = C_2H_5O-\overset{O}{\overset{\|}{C}}-O-$$

CH$_3$O, CH$_3$O

$R_1 =$ alkyl or alkylene imine

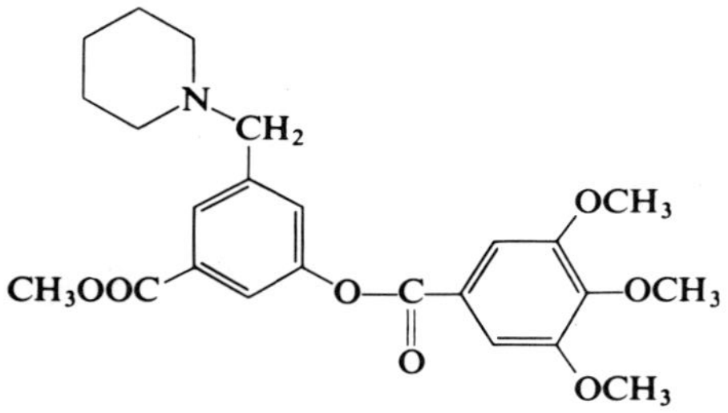

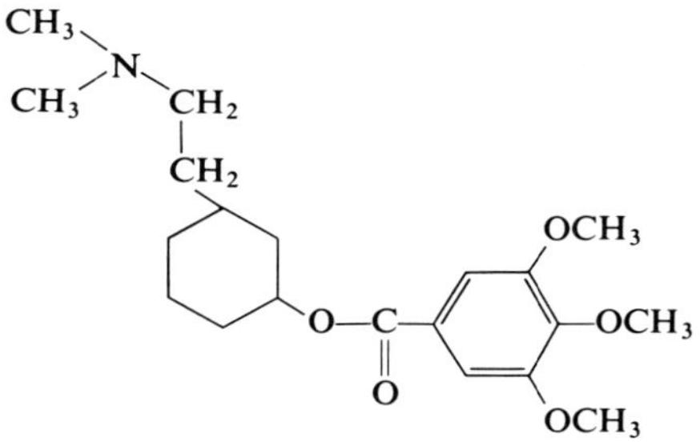

(XXIV)
Protiva et al. (140)

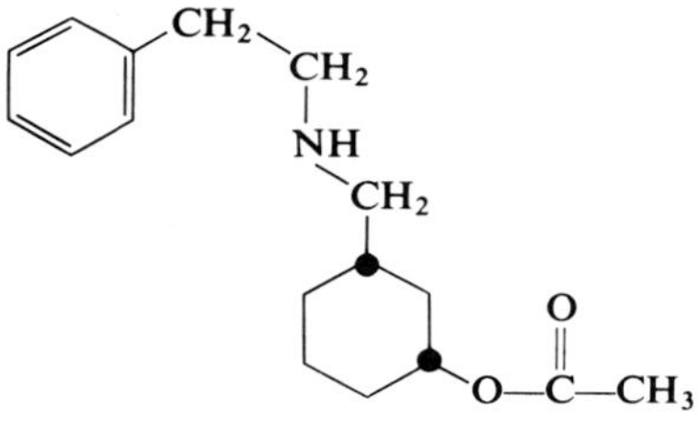

(XXIII)
LeVine and Gearien (94)

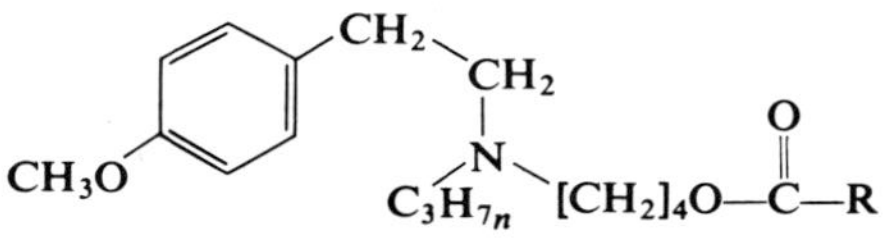

(XXVI)
Kralt et al. (90)

(XXII)
Turner and Gearien (186)

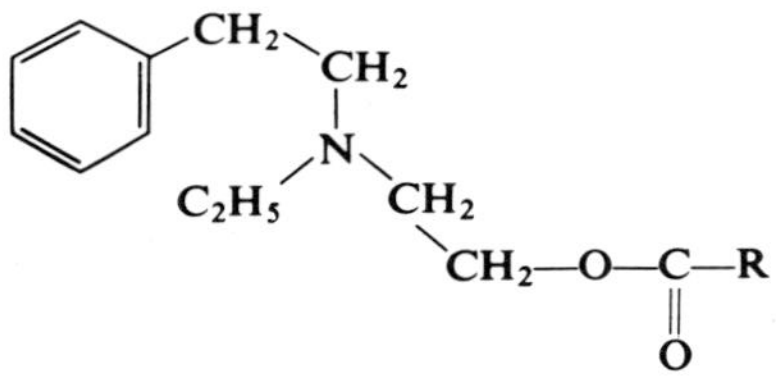

(XXV)
Kralt et al. (89)

203

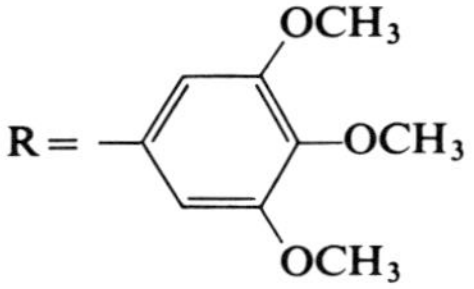

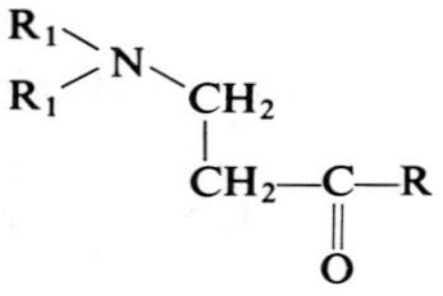

or

R$_1$ = alkyl

R =

n = 3-5

R =

R$_1$\
$\quad$N—CH$_2$\
R$_1$$\qquad$CH$_2$—C—R\
$\qquad\qquad$‖\
$\qquad\qquad$O

(XXVII)

Bruening and Nobles (27)

R$_1$\
$\quad$N—CH$_2$—CH\
R$_1$$\qquad$[CH$_2$]$_n$—CH—O—C—R\
$\qquad\qquad\qquad\qquad$‖\
$\qquad\qquad\qquad\qquad$O

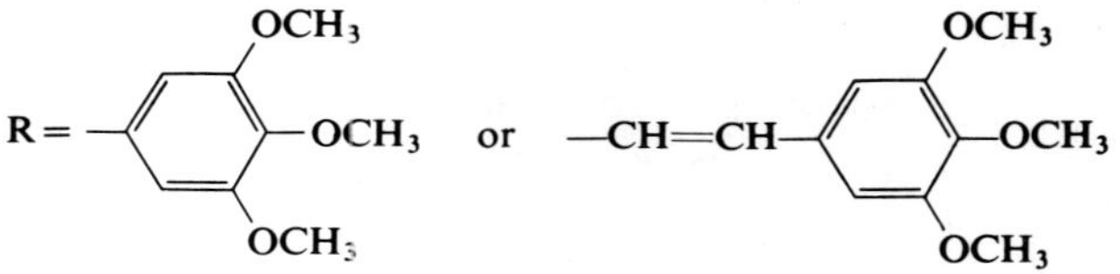

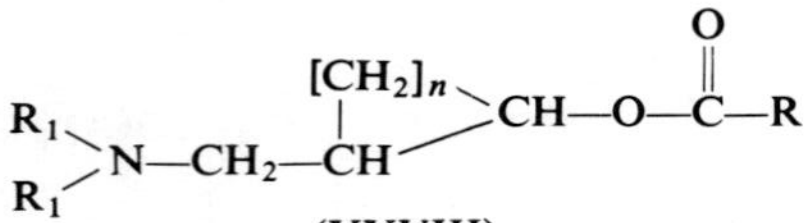

(XXVIII)

Ratouis and Combes (144)

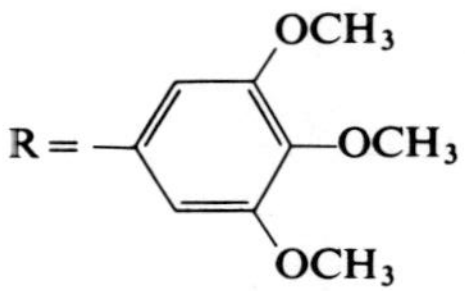

204

Part Two

Pharmacology of Reserpine

A wealth of information on the pharmacology of reserpine has been accumulated since its isolation, but its extremely complex pharmacological picture has not yet been fully elucidated. In terms of weight, reserpine is an extremely potent agent, possessing both central and peripheral points of attack. Some of its pharmacological effects can be explained by a depletion, others by a liberation of endogenous substances; but there are also certain other aspects of its activity in respect of which the establishment of a causal relationship with endogenous substances is still a matter of speculation.

Some of the above-mentioned *Rauwolfia* compounds have been tested for a possible influence on the concentration of amines in the tissues. These studies, however, were undertaken at a time when decisive details on the mode of action of reserpine were not yet available and when it was still the practice merely to determine the total catecholamine concentrations. Another problem which makes it difficult to evaluate the results obtained is the fact that usually no dose-effect ratios were established; instead, only single, fixed doses were employed. Finally, not enough attention was paid to differences in the duration of action of the various derivatives in relation to any one particular pharmacological effect. The duration of action of syrosingopine, for example, is considerably shorter than that of reserpine.

Compared with reserpine itself, a number of reserpine derivatives were found to exert a stronger influence on the amine concentrations in the periphery than in the brain. These findings do not necessarily apply to man, however, because very marked species differences exist in this connection: in the rabbit, for instance, 10-methoxydeserpidine as well as syrosingopine lower the catecholamine concentration in the periphery, but not in the brain, whereas in the cat the catecholamine concentration is reduced in the brain in the same way as in the periphery (200). Relevant pharmacological comparisons are therefore only possible to a very limited extent; in the present review, we therefore propose to concentrate on reserpine.

In 1955, Pletscher *et al.* (130) showed that reserpine causes a loss of 5-hydroxytryptamine (5-HT) from brain tissue; in 1956, Holzbauer and Vogt (70) and, independently, Carlsson and Hillarp (32) found that it also affects the concentration of norepinephrine in various tissues. These observations marked the beginning of a new era in our understanding of the physiology and pharmacology of the autonomic nervous system, and reserpine thus became an important tool for the pharmacologist; today, in fact, it is rare to find a pharmacological journal in which there is not at least one paper featuring the use of reserpine in some experimental procedure. The terms "reserpinization" and "reserpinized animal" have likewise found ready and widespread acceptance.

An exhaustive account of the pharmacology of reserpine would be beyond the scope of this review; it would be impossible to enumerate the many experimental findings or to discuss all the results which vary from one author to the other. The present paper neither deals with the influence of reserpine on the cellular and subcellular structures of nervous and nonneural structures [in this connection see, for example, the review of Burnstock and Merrillees (28)], nor does it pretend to treat clinical aspects in extenso. However, in view of the sometimes indiscriminate manner in which reserpine is employed experimentally—especially in experiments designed to determine the mode of action of other compounds—it should be borne in mind that the full picture of the activity of reserpine can by no means be traced back to a simple pharmacological component.

The very prolonged pharmacological action of reserpine, and the fact that its onset of effect is sometimes preceded by a pronounced latency period, led first to the assumption that it might possibly not act per se (11). The data available today on the metabolism, fate, and excretion of reserpine (135, 167, 168) no longer support the view that reserpine necessarily acts by a secondary mechanism. In the brain of mice, for example, reserpine can be traced even after its gross pharmacological action has subsided (103).

The two main features of the action of reserpine on which its widespread use in hypertension is based are a lowering of arterial blood pressure associated with bradycardia—which in animals, however, is species dependent (13)—and a peculiar sedative effect, which at the time of its first pharmacological characterization led to the coining of the term "tranquillizer" by F. F. Yonkman in 1953.

Clinical hypertension can be brought about by differing mechanisms. The hypertension of phaeochromocytoma and that associated with adrenal dysfunction indicate involvement of the endocrine system; on the other hand, hypertensive disease may be often connected with neural components. (See also Chapter 1.)

In the following sections an outline will be given of the action exerted by reserpine on central and peripheral portions of the autonomic nervous system and its effect on the endocrine system.

VIII. Effect of reserpine on the central nervous system

It has, unfortunately, been customary not to consider possible differences concerning the intimate mode of action of reserpine on the various central systems and on the central portions of the autonomic nervous system. It is not known which specific central mechanism or mechanisms, if any, may be responsible for lowering blood pressure in normotensive and more especially, in hypertensive subjects.

There is an abundance of pharmacological results showing decisive differences between reserpine and general central nervous depressants [for details, see Bein (13)]. It is also agreed that reserpine differs from the barbiturates, for example, and that it acts on selective central systems; on the other hand, its intimate mode of action in the brain is still strongly disputed.

When it was first shown that reserpine releases stored 5-HT, Brodie and Shore (26) advanced the hypothesis that the central actions of the alkaloid are mediated through the free indole derivative. The discovery that reserpine also releases norepinephrine led to the assumption that it is a depletion of norepinephrine in the brain which accounts for the central actions of reserpine, and that it is a lack rather than an excess of endogenous amines in the brain which should be regarded as being responsible for the effects exerted by this alkaloid (34). From the published evidence it now emerges that there is no correlation between behavior and a change in the total amine content of the brain [for discussion, see Bein (15) and Häggendal and Lindqvist (63)]. On the other hand, new methodologies for the precise location of amines in connection with specific neuropharmacological effects may be expected to open up fresh vistas.

At all events, the sedative effect of reserpine does not depend on the presence of 5-HT (23, 52, 105). In view of the complex pharmacological picture presented by reserpine, the possibility that more than one basic effect is involved has to be considered. In fact, a multitude of biochemical changes have been found in the brain after administration of reserpine. Each of the various biochemical alterations observed might well have a significant bearing on only one very restricted pharmacological component. Whereas some of these alterations are claimed to be correlated with certain pharmacological actions [e.g., dopamine (161, 162)], there are other biochemical changes whose precise significance has not yet been established [e.g., increase in the concentration of glycogen (2, 9), decrease in the concentration of γ-aminobutyric acid (8)]. Recently it has been found that another amine—histamine, whose function in the nervous system has also still to be elucidated—is influenced by reserpine. Reserpine reduces the concentration of histamine in the hypothalamus and medial thalamus, but not in the pituitary (1). It does not release histamine from mast cells, but it does release 5-HT from them, as from other tissues (20). Reserpine obviously also displays a certain kind of selectivity of action with regard to histamine as well.

IX. Effect of reserpine on the sympathetic nervous system

Though no causal relationship between the various biochemical changes in the brain and the changes in behavior in response to reserpine has been firmly established, there is no doubt that reserpine induces a depletion of the stores of neurohumoral transmitter substances in peripheral adrenergic nerves with consequent impairment of function (34, 120). In the case of the peripheral portion of the autonomic nervous system, in particular, it can be seen that changes in the concentration of an endogenous substance, e.g., norepinephrine, are not necessarily bound to cause a change in function: although reserpine diminishes the norepinephrine content in the sympathetic ganglia, it does not impair ganglionic transmission (11, 14, 145).

There is as yet no generally accepted view concerning the exact mechanism by which reserpine depletes catecholamine stores [for details see, for example, Brodie and Beaven (25), Iversen *et al.* (76), and Stjärne (174)].*
Catecholamine stores in peripheral sympathetic nerves and in the brain are probably composed of various compartments having different functions (59, 181). Reserpine causes depletion of these stores by acting upon one particular compartment, referred to by Glowinski and Axelrod (59) as the "reserpine-releasable pool." According to these authors, only physiologically inactive metabolites of norepinephrine are released by reserpine in the brain. The norepinephrine released by reserpine from peripheral sympathetic nerves is also inactivated by intraneuronal monoamine oxidase (MAO) before it leaves the nerve (88). Carlsson (31) regards inhibition of the uptake of the amines as the important component in the action of reserpine. Reserpine exerts its depleting effect by specifically inhibiting the adenosine triphosphate-Mg^{2+}-dependent incorporation of norepinephrine and related compounds into specific intracellular particles (33, 82). An agent selectively inhibiting the uptake of amines into the intracellular stores without at the same time affecting spontaneous outflow would cause a rapid depletion owing to the high turnover of the amines (174). It is therefore not necessary to presuppose a direct releasing action in order to explain the depletion caused by reserpine. There are other amine-concentrating mechanisms located in the cell membrane which are insensitive to reserpine (33). Consequently, exogenous norepinephrine is transported into reserpine-pretreated tissues at a normal rate, but is not invulnerable to enzymic destruction inside the cells, probably because it cannot be protected by binding in the storage granules. Refilling the depleted stores in reserpinized tissue by administration of norepinephrine is impossible (76).

The protracted effect of reserpine is not a function of the rate of biosynthesis of the amines—independent of the presence of reserpine—since, in the guinea pig brain, the rate of biosynthesis should be sufficient to replenish severely depleted stores of norepinephrine within 4 hours (127). The prolonged effect

---

* After completion of this manuscript, an excellent and very comprehensive review of "Drugs which Block the Storage of 5-Hydroxytryptamine and Related Amines" appeared. However, it has not been possible to refer to it here. (A. Carlsson in *Handbook of Experimental Pharmacology*, New Series, Vol. XIX; Springer-Verlag, 1965.)

can be explained, however, in terms of a blockade of the uptake mechanism in the storage granules (33)—possibly by reserpine itself.

⌐ Such a blocking action of reserpine on the uptake of an amine is not confined to norepinephrine or epinephrine, but has also been shown to occur, for example, in the case of dopamine (83) and 5-HT, whose rate of metabolism is increased by reserpine because the unbound amine is susceptible to enzymic transformation (5).

Since recent investigations (see above) indicate that reserpine does not release norepinephrine in an active form, one would not expect the alkaloid to produce pharmacological effects due to the release of catecholamines. Despite this, there are certain pharmacological effects of reserpine which might possibly be ascribed to a liberation of norepinephrine. These include: an increase in blood pressure occasionally seen in spinal cats and spinal dogs (especially after pretreatment with ganglionic blockers) (108); increased bladder tension observed in the dog (109); and tachycardia in the dog heart-lung preparation, first noted by Plummer *et al.* (134) and Krayer, and intensively studied by the latter (91, 92, 125). The hyperglycemia occurring in rats in response to reserpine has also been connected with the liberation of amines (175), as well as piloerection in mice (50). It is possible, however, that ganglionic blocking agents may modify the pharmacological activity of reserpine, since they interfere with its action on the tissue amine concentration (68).

In view of the fact that it produces widespread depletion of the peripheral sympathetic transmitter, there is a strong belief that the action of reserpine in the sympathetic system is exclusively confined to the postganglionic portion. During the first to third hour after intravenous injection of low and medium doses of reserpine, Bein (11, 11a, 14) found no impairment of function in the peripheral sympathetic pathways, even though relaxation of the nictitating membrane, a decrease in arterial pressure, bradycardia, and inhibition of centrally mediated pressor reflexes were fully apparent. Significant impairment of peripheral sympathetic transmission is usually found after a much longer latency period. Bianchi and Fargier (21), for example, state that a loss of adrenal catecholamine in the dog and a lack of responsiveness to nervous stimulation could not be demonstrated until 8–24 hours after administration of reserpine.

There are conflicting reports as to whether or not preganglionic sympathetic activity is reduced by reserpine. Bein (11a) observed a decrease in the electrical activity of preganglionic sympathetic cardioaccelerator nerves in the cat together with bradycardia, whereas Iggo and Vogt (75) found no change in the electrical activity of cervical sympathetic nerve fibers; nor, for that matter, did they observe any bradycardia in response to reserpine. In this connection, it is interesting to note that, where isolated hearts from untreated cats are compared with those from animals pretreated with reserpine, there is no difference in the heart rate (176). A slow, progressive, and marked diminution in efferent splanchnic nerve activity was observed in cats and dogs by McCubbin and Page (102) and a moderate depression of efferent splanchnic nerve activity by Dontas (43). Plummer (133) points out that, when cats are pretreated with reserpine, the nictitating membrane displays a greater hypersensitivity to epinephrine than to norepinephrine, the condition thus resembling preganglionic rather than postganglionic denervation. In cross-circulation experiments in dogs, Wang *et al.* (202) noted no change in the excitability of the vasopressor area of the medulla in response to electrical stimulation. In cats, however, the influence of reserpine on medullary vasomotor centers was reported to be far less than on rostrally situated structures (11a).

Though there are many hypotheses concerning the influence which changes in the concentration of brain amines exert on behavior, the possible influence of such changes on central autonomic substrates has received little attention. In a penetrating analysis of Carlsson's (31), it is postulated that different sympathetic centers may act selectively on different parts of the sympathetic system. Drugs may conceivably influence these various sympathetic centers in a selective manner. Since orthostatic reactions after reserpine are extremely rare, it might be inferred from this that the drug acts partly centrally (31).

The capacity of reserpine to deplete the amine stores in the peripheral portion of the sympathetic nervous system shows certain peculiar features. In some animals and organs the full depleting effect of reserpine is more readily obtained in the presence of an intact sympathetic innervation [for details, see Stjärne (174)]. The norepinephrine which, following denervation, has not been depleted by reserpine, proves resistant to further reserpine injections, but can be released by electrical nerve stimulation (160); reserpine-resistant stores of norepinephrine in denervated nerves can also be released by the action of other drugs, e.g. tyramine (51). Hertting *et al.* (68) have assumed that the sympathetic nerves play a permissive role in the mechanism governing reserpine-induced depletion of the amine stores; the releasing action of reserpine would thus be partially dependent on nerve impulses. Here it must be borne in mind that the compartments accessible to reserpine are probably not always identical with those accessible to nerve impulses (182). Though the observation of Trendelenburg (182) is species dependent, it might be inferred that reserpine influences only certain sympathetic functions.

X. Effect of reserpine on the circulatory system

Generally speaking, depletion of neurohumoral transmitter substances in the adrenergic system results in a failure of adrenergic neurotransmission. On this basis, one would expect a fall in blood pressure and a reduction in peripheral vascular resistance, and this is in fact what happens both in animals and in man [for review, see Bein (13)]; in nonanesthetized dogs, reserpine causes an increase in renal plasma flow and in glomerular filtration rate (201), [see Wagle and Plummer (201) also for references to clinical effects].

In the human, the dilatation of peripheral vessels is mainly confined to vessels of the skin (22, 203). This selectivity of action of reserpine on peripheral vessels in man is difficult to explain.

That reserpine diminishes the concentration of norepinephrine in the tissues has also been demonstrated in man by direct estimation of norepinephrine in the atrial appendages of five patients (37).

Since species differences have been observed with regard to reserpine-releasable pools (see above), findings obtained in man therefore call for particularly careful interpretation. In man, Whelan and Skinner (203) found that reserpine exerted a prolonged dilator action on peripheral blood vessels, but that it did not interfere with sympathetic reflex activity or with the vasoconstrictor response to ephedrine and amphetamine; in chronically sympathectomized limbs, reserpine elicited its normal response, whereas the constrictor response of the limb vessels to ephedrine and amphetamine has been shown to be dependent on the integrity of the sympathetic nerves. If reserpine were in fact to act by depleting the tissues of norepinephrine, these tissue norepinephrine stores would not play a part in reflex activity but would be involved in mediating tonic influences on the vessels (203). Other authors have reported that, after reserpine has been given over a very prolonged period, the reflex venoconstriction (and reflex arteriolar constriction) in the forearm of normal subjects elicited by leg exercise and by cold stimulation is inhibited (107).

The hypothesis that reserpine exerts a specific action on different catecholamine stores could also account for the surprisingly low incidence of orthostatic reactions in response to reserpine. While the explanation advanced by Whelan and Skinner (203) seems a likely one, there are other possible mechanisms which should also be considered.

Tripod and Meier (183, 184) showed that in acute experiments reserpine acts as a strong antagonist toward various agents—including especially $BaCl_2$—which contract smooth muscle; a recent report confirms its antagonistic action toward $BaCl_2$ in the pial artery in mice (152). Kirpekar and Lewis (80) showed that in strips of horse carotid artery, reserpine counteracts the vasoconstrictor effect of a variety of stimulants and that it is also able to produce direct relaxation of smooth muscle; it has consequently been postulated that reserpine interferes with metabolic processes within the smooth muscle (55–57, 81).

After prolonged treatment with reserpine, its pattern of activity against various vasoconstrictors changes (185). Results obtained in acute experiments do not therefore necessarily apply to the more complex pharmacological situation arising after chronic treatment.

Reserpine lowers the arterial pressure in hypertensive patients as well as in animals rendered hypertensive by various methods [for references see Bein (13) and Bein and Brunner (16)]. The antihypertensive effect of reserpine, or of guanethidine, methyldopa, or hydralazine, can be effectively inhibited by beta blocking agents (16, 67). It remains to be seen whether such findings indicate that the antihypertensive component of these various compounds with differing pharmacological actions may be governed by an as-yet-unknown mechanism.

Some of the circulatory effects of reserpine in the cat have been ascribed by Zaimis (208) to a damaging action and to histological alterations in the myocardium described as widespread degenerative changes; but careful studies undertaken by other workers (69, 176) have failed to reveal such degenerative changes after reserpine. The conclusions drawn by Zaimis are, moreover, very difficult to reconcile with the finding that reserpine does not change the contractile force of the cat heart (176), that it affects neither contractility in excised papillary muscles of the cat (30), or in isolated rabbit atria (95), nor the interval-strength relationship of the isolated kitten heart (87), and that it exercises a beneficial influence on the recovery of isolated myocardium from anoxia (128). The oxygen consumption of rabbit atria has been found to undergo no change after reserpine (95). In dogs, the cardiovascular response to ether or to cyclopropane anesthesia, including especially the ventricular contractile force, showed no alteration following reserpine (6, 7).

The vascular reactivity of reserpine-pretreated animals toward autonomic nervous agents, which Withrington and Zaimis (204) reported to be greatly reduced, was studied by various other authors, e.g., Tripod et al. (185) and Baum (10), and found to be unchanged.

XI. Effect of reserpine on various endocrine functions

Since reserpine has proved of clinical value in the treatment of tachycardia associated with hyperthyroidism, the possibility that reserpine might exert an influence on the thyroid received attention quite early [e.g. Vanotti (193)]. The relief which it affords from tachycardia, however, can be traced to the bradycrotic action of reserpine, which is independent of thyroid function. As in many other organs, a prolonged decrease in the 5-HT concentration also occurs in the thyroid gland after reserpine (104). Though the endocrine glands are influenced by reserpine in a variety of ways [for details see, for example, Gaunt et al. (53a, 54)], few data are available with regard to changes in the concentrations of endogenous amines due to reserpine in connection with the endocrinological reactions produced by the drug.

On the other hand, there is definite evidence that reserpine is able to alter the hormone concentrations and thus to elicit endocrinological responses. Many of these effects are confined to the experimental animal and have little, if any, importance in man. Here again there are marked species differences, e.g., birds are particularly sensitive to the pituitary-depressant effects of reserpine (53a, 54).

As the influence of reserpine on the endocrine system also displays certain central features affecting peripheral organs, a few examples will be discussed by way of illustration.

Reserpine can induce crop sac secretion in the pigeon (4) and mammary secretion in various species of animals [estrogen-primed rat (112), or rabbit (155), or rabbit pretreated with chorionic gonadotropin (110)]. Besides strain differences (180), seasonal influences have also been observed to operate (79). According to Meites (111), reserpine, even in single doses, increases the prolactin content in the mature female rabbit, but development of the mammary glands and lactation occur only in the presence of estrogen. In ovariectomized estrogen-primed rabbits, a single dose of reserpine lowers the pituitary prolactin content and induces lactation (77). Reserpine acts similarly when minute amounts of it are implanted into the posterior median eminence, whereas reserpine implantation into the pituitary has no effect (78). The action exerted by reserpine on the pituitary seems to be independent of neural connections: in hypophysectomized rats reserpine no longer has a lactogenic effect, although a pituitary transplant in the renal capsule restores a certain amount of activity (41). Ratner and Meites (143) suggest that reserpine depresses the "prolactin-inhibiting factor" of the hypothalamus, thus removing hypothalamic inhibition to pituitary prolactin release. Besides reserpine, there are a great variety of stimuli that are capable of inducing lactation in the estrogen-primed animal (53a). These stimuli, however, are not governed by any common mechanism of action; in rats, for example, iproniazid inhibits lactation elicited by electrical stimulation of the uterine cervix, but not lactation induced by reserpine (115).

Gaunt et al. (53a) have drawn attention to the fact that, in general, the same stimuli which cause pseudopregnancy or lactation also give rise to adrenocorticotropic hormone (ACTH) release, and that adrenal steroids are necessary for the full action of lactogenic hormone. Reserpine induces increased adrenocortical activity, which manifests itself in the form of adrenal hypertrophy, lymphatic involution, reduction of adrenal ascorbic acid, and secretion of adrenal steroids. The effect of reserpine on the adrenal system does not appear to be mediated by any direct action on the part of the adrenal glands, since no activation is found either in hypophysectomized animals (3, 39, 116) or after pretreatment with cortisol (3). The steroidogenic activity of ACTH is not influenced by reserpine (58, 66).

The assumption that the action of reserpine on the endocrine system, including especially its effect on the pituitary gland, is a nonspecific stressful action (153) is probably too simple an explanation. The ACTH-releasing effect of reserpine was blocked by iproniazid under certain experimental conditions, but was only partially blocked following exposure to cold; Gaunt *et al.* (53) conclude that the action of reserpine on the pituitary is different from that of exposure to cold.

That some degree of specificity is involved has likewise been demonstrated by studies with various derivatives of methyl reserpate (53). Chemical modification of the reserpine molecule (see Section V, ff.) can change its pharmacological pattern in such a way as to accentuate some of its actions on the endocrine system.

Single doses of reserpine may have an extraordinarily long duration of action when tested by reference to certain endocrine parameters: the lactogenic effect of 1 mg per kilogram i.v. lasted more than 1 month in the rabbit (110); the heat response in ovariectomized rats primed with estrogen could be activated for several weeks after a single dose of 2 mg per kilogram (113), and in female rats one single prepuberal treatment lowered the pituitary lactogenic hormone concentration for 60 days (35). These effects thus last much longer than the amine-depleting action of reserpine, the only finding to the contrary being an observation by Hagen and Barrnett (64), who noted that in chickens depletion of the catecholamines in the adrenal persisted for up to 90 days after administration of reserpine.

XII. Interference with the action of reserpine

The selectivity of reserpine and the peculiar mechanisms underlying its activity determine its behavior with regard to other pharmacologically active substances. This is a field of research in which such a vast number of observations have been published during recent years that only a few conclusions emerging from them can be outlined here. The way in which reserpine and other drugs interfere with one another's activity is sometimes extraordinarily complex; for instance, compounds which lower the blood pressure like reserpine and can also be classified as sympathetic inhibitors, e.g., methyldopa, partially antagonize reserpine (17); alternatively, such compounds may radically alter the effect normally exerted by reserpine on a third substance, such as tyramine or amphetamine (93, 142). Species differences become particularly apparent when the possible interactions between reserpine and monoamine oxidase inhibitors are studied; here, the chemical nature of the MAO inhibitor employed and the respective dosage ratios also have a decisive influence [see, for example, Hull and Horita (74), Resnick *et al.* (146), and Vogt (200)].

In man, too, much depends upon which MAO inhibitor is used. In normal subjects, for example, isocarboxazid potentiates the sedative and hypotensive action of reserpine, whereas niamide inhibits the effects of reserpine (146).

In view of the complex character of hypertensive disease, it is tempting to speculate that a drug displaying such a wide variety of pharmacological features as reserpine might prove particularly suitable for the treatment of a disease like hypertension. However, although speculations of this kind are frequently met with in the literature on the clinical use of reserpine, precise evidence to substantiate them is still lacking. Modern antihypertensive therapy has at all events achieved a decrease in mortality and, though it is hardly possible to give an exact estimate of the degree to which reserpine has contributed to this therapeutic success, there can be no doubt that the drug has played its part here, since reserpine was one of the earliest additions to the antihypertensive armamentarium and, as such, was also one of the constituent elements of the antihypertensive regimens on which statistical analyses of a number of studies on the clinical course of hypertension in drug-treated, as compared with untreated hypertensives, have been based [e.g. Dustan *et al.* (44), Hoobler and Lauwers (71), and Hood *et al.* (72)]. The sedative properties of reserpine could be of advantage as regards the drug's clinical use; it is certain that, in the treatment of hypertension, its ability to reduce the blood pressure is of major importance. Its effect in lowering the blood pressure is brought about, in the first place, by depletion of the neurohumoral transmitter substance in the peripheral portion of the sympathetic nervous system; but, in addition, it must be assumed that reserpine also exerts an influence on the central substrates which serve to regulate the circulation; finally, there is some evidence to suggest that it has a direct peripheral site of attack as well. It is probably an inadmissible simplification to equate its antihypertensive activity solely with inhibition of the postganglionic portion of the sympathetic nervous system.

References

1. Adam, H. M., and Hye, H. K. A., *J. Physiol.* (*London*) **171**, 37P (1964).
2. Albrecht, W., *Klin. Wochschr.* **35**, 588 (1957).
3. Ashford, A., and Shapero, M., *Brit. J. Pharmacol.* **19**, 458 (1962).
4. Assenmacher, I., and Baylé, J. D., *Compt. Rend. Soc. Biol.* **158**, 255 (1964).
5. Axelrod, J., and Inscoe, J. K., *J. Pharmacol. Exptl. Therap.* **141**, 161 (1963).
6. Bagwell, E. E., Woods, E. F., and Durst, G. G., *Anesthesiology* **25**, 149 (1964).
7. Bagwell, E. E., Woods, E. F., and Linker, R. P., *Anesthesiology* **25**, 15 (1964).
8. Balzer, H., Holtz, P., and Palm, D., *Experientia* **17**, 38 (1961).
9. Balzer, H., and Palm, D., *Arch. Exptl. Pathol. Pharmakol.* **243**, 65 (1962).
10. Baum, T., *J. Pharmacol. Exptl. Therap.* **141**, 30 (1963).
11. Bein, H. J., *Experientia* **9**, 107 (1953).
11a. Bein, H. J., *Ann. N.Y. Acad. Sci.* **61**, 4 (1955).
12. Bein, H. J., *Abstr. Rev. 20th Intern. Physiol. Congr. Brussels*, 1956, pp. 455–465. St. Catherine Press Ltd., Bruges (1956).
13. Bein, H. J., *Pharmacol. Rev.* **8**, 435 (1956).
14. Bein, H. J., *in* "Psychotropic Drugs" (S. Garattini and V. Ghetti, eds.), p. 325. Elsevier, Amsterdam, 1957.

15. Bein, H. J. *Proc. 2nd Intern. Pharmacol. Meeting, Prague, 1963* Vol. 7, p. 87. Pergamon Press, Oxford, 1965.
16. Bein, H. J., and Brunner, H., *in* "Antihypertensive Therapy, Principles and Practice" (F. Gross, ed.), p. 15. Springer, Berlin, 1966.
17. Benfey, B. G., and Varma, D. R., *Brit. J. Pharmacol.* **22**, 366 (1964).
18. Berthaux, P., and Newman, M., *Arzneimittel-Forsch.* **14**, 1040 (1964).
19. Bhatia, B. B., *J. Indian Med. Assoc.* **11**, 262 (1942).
20. Bhattacharya, B. K., and Lewis, G. P., *Brit. J. Pharmacol.* **11**, 411 (1956).
21. Bianchi, M., and Fargier, M. C., *Compt. Rend. Soc. Biol.* **156**, 1797 (1962).
22. Bock, K. D., and Müller, H., *Klin. Wochschr.* **34**, 318 (1956).
23. Boullin, D. J., *Psychopharmacologia* **5**, 28 (1963/64).
24. Bramanti, G., diPaco, G., and Tauro, C. S., *Boll. Chim. Farm.* **99**, 448 (1960).
25. Brodie, B., and Beaven, M. A., *Med. Exptl.* **8**, 320 (1963).
26. Brodie, B., and Shore, P. A., *Ann. N. Y. Acad. Sci.* **66**, 631 (1957).
27. Bruening, C. H., and Nobles, W. L., *J. Pharm. Sci.* **54**, 925 (1965).
28. Burnstock, G., and Merrillees, N. C. R., *Proc. 2nd Intern. Pharmacol. Meeting, Prague, 1963* Vol. 6, p. 1. Pergamon Press, Oxford, 1964.
29. Buzas, A., Hoffmann, C., and Regnier, G., *Bull. Soc. Chim. France* p. 645 (1960).
30. Cairoli, V. J., Reilly, J. F., and Roberts, J., *Brit. J. Pharmacol.* **18**, 588 (1962).
31. Carlsson, A., *in* "Antihypertensive Therapy, Principles and Practice" (F. Gross, ed.), p. 5. Springer, Berlin, 1966.
32. Carlsson, A., and Hillarp, N.-A., *Kgl. Fysiograf. Sallskap. Lund, Forh.* **26**, 1 (1956).
33. Carlsson, A., Hillarp, N.-A., and Waldeck, B., *Med. Exptl.* **6**, 47 (1962).
34. Carlsson, A., Rosengren, E., Bertler, A., and Nillson, J., *in* "Psychotropic Drugs" (S. Garattini and V. Ghetti, eds.), p. 363. Elsevier, Amsterdam, 1957.
35. Carraro, A., Corbin, A., Fraschini, F., and Martini, L., *J. Endocrinol.* **32**, 387 (1965).
36. Chatterjee, A., *Fortschr. Chem. Org. Naturstoffe* **10**, 390 (1953).
37. Chidsey, C. A., Braunwald, E., Morrow, A. G., and Mason, D. T., *New Engl. J. Med.* **269**, 653 (1963).
38. Chopra, R. N., Gupta, J. C., Bose, B. C., and Chopra, I. C., *Indian J. Med. Res.* **31**, 71 (1943).
39. Cushman, P., and Hilton, J. G., *J. Endocrinol.* **31**, 181 (1965).
40. deGroot, S., and Strating, J., *Rec. Trav. Chim.* **80**, 121 (1961).
41. Desclin, L., *Compt. Rend. Soc. Biol.* **151**, 1774 (1957).
42. diPaco, G., and Tauro, C. S., *Pharmaco, Sci. Ed.* **13**, 64 (1958).
43. Dontas, A. S., *J. Pharmacol, Exptl. Therap.* **116**, 17 (1956).
44. Dustan, H. P., Meaney, T. F., and Page, I. H., *in* "Antihypertensive Therapy, Principles and Practice" (F. Gross, ed.), p. 544. Springer, Berlin, 1966.
45. Ernest, I., *Collection Czech. Chem. Commun.* **24**, 266 (1964); U.S. Patent 3,167,558 (1965).
46. Ernest, I., Jilek, J. O., Vedjelek. Z. J., and Protiva, M., *Collection Czech. Chem. Commun.* **28**, 1022 (1963).
47. Ernest, I., and Protiva, M., *Naturwissenschaften* **47**, 156 (1960).
48. Ernest, I., and Protiva, M., *Collection Czech. Chem. Commun.* **26**, 1137 (1961).
49. Ernest, I., and Protiva, M., *Collection Czech. Chem. Commun.* **28**, 3106 (1963).
50. Everett, G. M., Thoman, J. E. P., and Smith, A. H., *Federation Proc.* **16**, 296 (1957).
51. Fischer, J. E., Kopin, I. J., and Axelrod. J., *J. Pharmacol. Exptl. Therap.* **147**, 181 (1965).
52. Gal, E. M., Drewes, P. A., and Barraclough. C. A., *Biochem. Pharmacol.* **8**, 32 (1961).
53. Gaunt, R., Renzi, A. A., and Chart, J. J., *Endocrinology* **71**, 527 (1962).
53a. Gaunt, R., Chart, J. J., and Renzi, A. A., *Ann. Rev. Pharmacol.* **3**, 109 (1963).

54. Gaunt, R., Chart, J. J., and Renzi, A. A., "Reviews of Physiology, Biochemistry and Experimental Pharmacology," Vol. 56, pp. 115–172. Springer, Berlin, 1965.
55. Gillis, C. N., *J. Pharmacol. Exptl. Therap.* **127**, 265 (1959).
56. Gillis, C. N., and Lewis, J. J., *Nature* **178**, 859 (1956).
57. Gillis, C. N., and Lewis, J. J., *Nature* **179**, 820 (1957).
58. Girod, C., and Slimane-Taleb, S., *Compt. Rend. Soc. Biol.* **151**, 1158 (1957).
59. Glowinski, J., and Axelrod, J., *J. Pharmacol. Exptl. Therap.* **149**, 43 (1965).
60. Greshoff, M., *Chem. Ber.* **23**, 3537 (1890).
61. Gupta, J. C., Ghosh, S., Dutta, A. T., and Kahali, B. S., *J. Am. Pharm. Assoc.* **36**, 416 (1947).
62. Haack, E., Popelak, A., Spingler, H., and Kaiser, F., *Naturwissenschaften* **41**, 214 (1954); see also Klohs, M. W., Draper, M. D., and Keller, F., *J. Am. Chem. Soc.* **76**, 2843 (1954).
63. Häggendal, J., and Lindqvist, M., *Intern. J. Neuropharmacol.* **3**, 59 (1964).
64. Hagen, P., and Barrnett, R. J., *Ciba Found. Symp.*, *Adrenergic Mechanisms* p. 83 (1960).
65. Hahn, G., and Haensel, A., *Chem. Ber.* **71**, 2195 (1938).
66. Halkerston, I. D. K., Feinstein, M., and Hechter, O., *Proc. Soc. Exptl. Biol. Med.* **115**, 292 (1964).
67. Hedwall, P. R., Brunner, H., and Meier, M., *Arch. Exptl. Pathol. Pharmakol.* **251**, 132 (1965).
68. Hertting, G., Potter, L. T., and Axelrod, J., *J. Pharmacol. Exptl. Therap.* **136**, 289 (1962).
69. Hess, R., *Proc. European Soc. Study of Drug Toxicity*, *Advances in Toxicological Methodology*, 1965, Vol. V, 130, Excerpta Medica Foundation, Amsterdam (1965).
70. Holzbauer, M., and Vogt, M., *J. Neurochem.* **1**, 8 (1956).
71. Hoobler, S. W., and Lauwers, P., *in* "Essentielle Hypertonie" (K.D. Bock and P. Cottier, eds.), p. 292. Springer, Berlin, 1960.
72. Hood, B., Aurell, M., Falkheden, T., and Björk, S., *in* "Antihypertensive Therapy, Principles and Practice" (F. Gross, ed.), p. 370. Springer, Berlin, 1966.
73. Hosansky, N., and Smith, E., *J. Am. Pharm. Assoc. Sci. Ed.* **44**, 639 (1955).
74. Hull, L. D., and Horita, A., *Nature* **202**, 604 (1964).
75. Iggo, A., and Vogt, M., *J. Physiol. (London)* **150**, 114 (1960).
76. Iversen, L. L., Glowinski, J., and Axelrod, J., *J. Pharmacol. Exptl. Therap.* **150**, 173 (1965).
77. Kanematsu, S., Hilliard, J., and Sawyer, C. H., *Acta Endocrinol.* **44**, 467 (1963).
78. Kanematsu, S., and Sawyer, C. H., *Proc. Soc. Exptl. Biol. Med.* **113**, 967 (1963).
79. Kehl, R., Czyba, J. C., and Becache, A., *Compt. Rend. Soc. Biol.* **155**, 807 (1961).
80. Kirpekar, S. M., and Lewis, J. J., *J. Pharm. Pharmacol.* **10**, 255 (1958).
81. Kirpekar, S. M., and Lewis, J. J., *Brit. J. Pharmacol.* **14**, 40 (1959).
82. Kirshner, N., *Science* **135**, 107 (1962).
83. Kirshner, N., Rorie, M., and Kamin, D. L., *J. Pharmacol. Exptl. Therap.* **141**, 282 (1963).
84. Kirtikar, R. K., and Basu, B. D., *in* "Indian Medicinal Plants," Vol. II, p. 777. Bahadurganj-Allahabad, India, 1918.
85. Klohs, M. W., Keller, F., Williams, R. E., and Kusserow, G. W., *Chem & Ind. (London)* p. 187 (1956).
86. Klohs, M. W., Keller, F., Williams, R. E., and Kusserow, G. W., *J. Am. Chem. Soc.* **79**, 3763 (1957).
87. Koch-Weser, J., *J. Pharmacol. Exptl. Therap.* **150**, 184 (1965).

88. Kopin, I. J., and Gordon, E. K., *J. Pharmacol. Exptl. Therap.* **140**, 207 (1963).
89. Kralt, T., Asma, W. J., Hoech, H. H., and Moed, H. D., *Rec. Trav. Chim.* **80**, 313 (1961).
90. Kralt, T., Asma, W. J., and Moed, H. D., *Rec. Trav. Chim.* **80**, 431 (1961).
91. Krayer, O., and Fuentes, J., *Federation Proc.* **15**, 449 (1956).
92. Krayer, O., and Fuentes, J., *J. Pharmacol. Exptl. Therap.* **123**, 145 (1958).
93. Kroneberg, G., and Stoepel, K., *Experientia* **19**, 252 (1963).
94. LeVine, P. B., and Gearien, J. E., *J. Org. Chem.* **26**, 4060 (1961).
95. Levy, J. V., and Richards, V., *J. Pharmacol. Exptl. Therap.* **147**, 205 (1965).
96. Logemann, W., Almirante, L., Caprio, L., and Meli, A., *Chem. Ber.* **88**, 1952 (1955).
97. Logemann, W., Caprio, L., Almirante, L., and Meli, A., *Chem. Ber.* **89**, 1043 (1956).
98. Lucas, R. A., Kuehne, M. E., Ceglowski, M. J., Dziemian, R. L., and MacPhillamy, H. B., *J. Am. Chem. Soc.* **81**, 1928 (1959).
99. Lucas, R. A., Kiesel, R. J., and Ceglowski, M. J., *J. Am. Chem. Soc.* **82**, 493 (1960).
100. Lunsford, C. D., Murphey, R. S., and Rose, E. K., *J. Org. Chem.* **22**, 1225 (1957).
101. MacPhillamy, H. B., Huebner, C. F., Schlittler, E., St. Andre, A. F., and Ulshafer, P. R., *J. Am. Chem. Soc.* **77**, 4335 (1955).
102. McCubbin, J. W., and Page, I. H., *Circulation Res.* **6**, 816 (1958).
103. Maggiolo, C., and Haley, T. J., *Proc. Soc. Exptl. Biol. Med.* **115**, 149 (1964).
104. Magus, R. D., Krause, F. W., and Riedel, B. E., *Biochem. Pharmacol.* **13**, 115 (1964).
105. Magus, R. D., Krause, F. W., and Riedel, B. E., *Biochem. Pharmacol.* **13**, 943 (1964).
106. Majumdar, D. N., and Paul, B., *J. Proc. Inst. Chemists (India)* **33**, 22 (1961).
107. Mason, D. T., and Braunwald, E., *J. Clin. Invest.* **43**, 1449 (1964).
108. Maxwell, R. A., Plummer, A. J., Osborne, M. W., and Ross, S., *J. Pharmacol. Exptl. Therap.* **116**, 42 (1956).
109. Maxwell, R. A., Plummer, A. J., Ross, S. D., and Osborne, M. W., *Proc. Soc. Exptl. Biol. Med.* **92**, 227 (1956).
110. Meites, J., *Proc. Soc. Exptl. Biol. Med.* **96**, 728 (1957).
111. Meites, J., *Proc. Soc. Exptl. Biol. Med.* **97**, 742 (1958).
112. Meites, J., Nicoll, C. S., and Talwalker, P. K., *Proc. Soc. Exptl. Biol. Med.* **101**, 563 (1959).
113. Meyerson, B. J., *Psychopharmacologia* **6**, 210 (1964).
114. Miller, F. M., and Weinberg, M. S., *Chem. Eng. News* **34**, 4760 (1956); *Abstr. Papers 130th Meeting, Am. Chem. Soc., Atlantic City*, p. 11N, 1956.
115. Mizuno, H., Talwalker, P. K., and Meites, J., *Proc. Soc. Exptl. Biol. Med.* **115**, 604 (1964).
116. Montanari, R., and Stockham, M. A., *Brit. J. Pharmacol.* **18**, 337 (1962).
117. Mueller, J. M., Schlittler, E., and Bein, H. J., *Experientia* **8**, 338 (1952).
118. Mueller, J. M., *Experientia* **13**, 479 (1957).
119. Muller, G., and Allais, A., *Naturwissenschaften* **47**, 82 (1960).
120. Muscholl, E., and Vogt, M., *J. Physiol. (London)* **141**, 132 (1958).
121. Najer, H., Giudicelli, R., Loiseau, J., and Menin, J., *Bull. Soc. Chim. France* p. 2831 (1963).
122. Nogradi, T., *Monatsh. Chem.* **88**, 1087 (1957a).
123. Nogradi, T., *Monatsh. Chem.* **88**, 768 (1957b).
124. Onda, M., Kawanishi, M., and Sasamoto, M., Japanese Patent 1483 (1958); *Chem. Abstr.* **53**, 1386 (1959).
125. Paasonen, M. K., and Krayer, O., *J. Pharmacol. Exptl. Therap.* **123**, 153 (1958).
126. Palazzo, G., Bizzi, L., and Pozzati, C., *Ann. Chim. (Rome)* **49**, 853 (1959).
127. Paulsen, E. C., and Hess, S. M., *J. Neurochem.* **10**, 453 (1963).

128. Penn, R. G., *Brit. J. Pharmacol.* **24**, 253 (1965).
129. Pepinski, R., Turley, J. W., Okaya, Y., Doyne, T., Vand, V., Shimada, A., Lowell, F. M., and Sogo, Y., *Acta Cryst.* **10**, 811 (1957).
130. Pletscher, A., Shore, P. A., and Brodie, B. B., *Science* **122**, 374 (1955).
131. Plieninger, H., and Kiefer, B., *Chem. Ber.* **90**, 617 (1957).
132. Plummer, A. J., private communication (1962).
133. Plummer, A. J., *in* "Hypertension: Second Hahnemann Symposium on Hypertensive Disease" (A. N. Brest and J. H. Moyer, eds.), Lea & Febiger, Philadelphia, Pennsylvania, 1961.
134. Plummer, A. J., Earl, A. E., Schneider, J. A., Trapold, J., and Barrett, W., *Ann. N.Y. Acad. Sci.* **59**, 8 (1954).
135. Plummer, A. J., Sheppard, H., and Schulert, A. R., *in* "Psychotropic Drugs" (S. Garattini and V. Ghetti, eds.), p. 350. Elsevier, Amsterdam, 1957.
136. Popelak, A., Haack, E., Lettenbauer, G., and Spingler, H., *Naturwissenschaften* **48**, 73 (1961).
137. Popelak, A., and Lettenbauer, G., *Arch. Pharm.* **295**, 427 (1962).
138. Popelak, A., and Lettenbauer, G., *Arch. Pharm.* **296**, 261 (1963).
139. Protiva, M., Jilek, J. O., Hachova, E., Novak, L., Vejdelek, Z. J., and Adlerova, E., *Collection Czech. Chem. Commun.* **24**, 74 (1957a).
140. Protiva, M., Jilek, J. O., Hach, V., Adlerova, E., and Michajlyszyn, V., *Collection Czech. Chem. Commun.* **24**, 83 (1957b).
141. Protiva, M., Vejdelek, Z. J., Jilek, J. O., and Macek, K., *Collection Czech. Chem. Commun.* **24**, 3978 (1959).
142. Quinton, R. M., and Halliwell, G., *Nature* **200**, 178 (1963).
143. Ratner, A., and Meites, J., *Federation Proc.* **23**, 110 (1964).
144. Ratouis, R., and Combes, G., *Bull. Soc. Chim. France* p. 576 (1959).
145. Reinert, H., *J. Physiol.* (*London*) **167**, 18 (1963).
146. Resnick, O., Krus, D., Raskin, M., and Freeman, H., *Arch. Gen. Psychiat.* **8**, 481 (1963).
147. Ribbens, C., and Nauta, W. T., *Rec. Trav. Chim.* **79**, 854 (1960).
148. Robison, M. M., Lucas, R. A., MacPhillamy, H. B., Dziemian, R. L., Hsu, I., Kiesel, R. J., and Morris, M. J., *Abstr. Papers, 139th Meeting, Am. Chem. Soc. St. Louis, Missouri, 1961*, p. 3N.
149. Robison, M. M., Lucas, R. A., MacPhillamy, H. B., Barrett, W., and Plummer, A. J., *Experientia* **17**, 14 (1961b).
150. Robison, M. M., Lucas, R. A., MacPhillamy, H. B., Dziemian, R. L., Hsu, I., and Kiesel, R. J., *J. Am. Chem. Soc.* **83**, 2694 (1961).
151. Rosen, W. E., and O'Connor, J. M., *J. Org. Chem.* **26**, 3051 (1961).
152. Rosenblum, W., and Zweifach, B., *J. Pharmacol. Exptl. Therap.* **145**, 58 (1964).
153. Saffran, M., and Vogt, M., *Brit. J. Pharmacol.* **15**, 165 (1960).
154. Sastry, B. V. R., and Lasslo, A., *J. Org. Chem.* **23**, 1577 (1958).
155. Sawyer, C. H., *Anat. Record* **127**, 362 (1957).
156. Schlittler, E., *Alkaloids* **8**, p. 287 (1965).
157. Schlittler, E., and Plummer, A. J., *in* "Psychopharmacological Agents" (M. Gordon, ed.), Vol. 1, p. 9. Academic Press, New York, 1964.
158. Schlittler, E., Schneider, J. A., and Plummer, A. J., *Angew. Chem.* **66**, 386 (1954).
159. Schlittler, E., Ulshafer, P. R., Pandow, M. L., Hunt, R., and Dorfman, L., *Experientia* **11**, 64 (1955).
160. Sedvall, G., and Thorson, J., *Biochem. Pharmacol.* **12**, Suppl., abstr. No. 222, 65 (1963).
161. Seiden, L. S., and Carlsson, A., *Psychopharmacologia* **5**, 178 (1964).

162. Seiden, L. S., and Hanson, L. C. F., *Psychopharmacologia* **6**, 239 (1964).
163. Sen, G., and Bose, K. C., *Indian Med. World* **2**, 194 (1931).
164. Shamma, M., and Walker, E. F., *Chem. & Ind.* (*London*) p. 1866 (1962).
165. Shamma, M., and Shine, R. J., *Tetrahedron Letters* **33**, 2277 (1964).
166. Sheppard, H., Lucas, R. A., and Tsien, W. H., *Arch. Intern. Pharmacodyn.* **103**, 256 (1955).
167. Sheppard, H., Tsien, W. H., Plummer, A. J., Peets, E. A., Giletti, B. J., and Schulert, A. R., *Proc. Soc. Exptl. Biol. Med.* **97**, 717 (1958).
168. Sheppard, H., Tsien, W. H., Sigg, E. B., Lucas, R. A., and Plummer, A. J., *Arch. Intern. Pharmacodyn.* **113**, 160 (1957).
169. Short, J. H., Freifelder, M., and Stone, G. R., *J. Org. Chem.* **26**, 2560 (1961).
170. Siddiqui, S., and Siddiqui, R. H., *J. Indian Chem. Soc.* **8**, 667 (1931); **9**, 539 (1932); **12**, 37 (1935).
171. Siddiqui, S., *J. Indian Chem. Soc.* **16**, 421 (1939).
172. Smith, E., Jaret, R. S., Shamma, M., and Shine, R. J., *J. Am. Chem. Soc.* **86**, 2083 (1964).
173. Steenhauer, A. J., *Pharm. Weekblad* **89**, 161, 617 (1954).
174. Stjärne, L., *Acta Physiol. Scand.* **62**, Suppl. 228, 97S (1964).
175. Taketomo, Y., Shore, P. A., Tomich, E. G., Kuntzman, R., and Brodie, B., *J. Pharmacol. Exptl. Therap.* **119**, 188 (1957).
176. Tanz, R. D., and Marcus, St. M., *J. Pharmacol. Exptl. Therap.* **151**, 38 (1966).
177. Tauro, C. S., and diPaco, G. F., *Boll. Chim. Farm.* **98**, 646 (1959).
178. Tauro, C. S., and diPaco, G. F., *Boll. Chim. Farm.* **98**, 707 (1959).
179. Tauro, C. S., Bramanti, G., and diPaco, G., *Pharmaco., Sci. Ed.* **14**, 801 (1959).
180. Tindal, J. S., *J. Endocrinol.* **20**, 78 (1960).
181. Trendelenburg, U., *Pharmacol. Rev.* **15**, 225 (1963).
182. Trendelenburg, U., *J. Pharmacol. Exptl. Therap.* **147**, 313 (1965).
183. Tripod, J., and Meier, R., *Arch. Intern. Pharmacodyn.* **97**, 251 (1954).
184. Tripod, J., and Meier, R., *Arch. Intern. Pharmacodyn.* **99**, 104 (1954).
185. Tripod, J., Studer, A., Wirz, E., and Meier, R., *Arch. Intern. Pharmacodyn.* **126**, 126 (1960).
186. Turner, F. A., and Gearien, J. E., *J. Org. Chem.* **24**, 1952 (1959).
187. Ulshafer, P. R., Pandow, M. L., and Nugent, R. H., *J. Org. Chem.* **21**, 923 (1956).
188. Ulshafer, P. R., Taylor, W. I., and Nugent, R. H., *Compt. Rend.* **244**, 2988 (1957).
189. Ulshafer, P. R., personal communication (1965).
190. Ulshafer, P. R., and Taylor, W. I., to be published (1967).
191. Vakil, R. J., *Brit. Heart J.* **11**, 350 (1949).
192. van Itallie, L., and Steenhauer, A. J., *Arch. Pharm.* **270**, 313 (1932).
193. Vanotti, A., *Schweiz. Med. Wochschr.* **87**, No. 14, Suppl., 412 (1957).
194. Vazakas, A. J., and Doluisio, J. T., *J. Pharm. Sci.* **53**, 165 (1964).
195. Vejdelek, Z. J., and Trcka, V., *Collection Czech. Chem. Commun.* **24**, 1860 (1959).
196. Vejdelek, Z. J., Trcka, V., and Protiva, M., *J. Med. Pharm. Chem.* **3**, 427 (1961).
197. Velluz, L., Muller, G., and Allais, A., French Patent 1,180,514 (1958).
198. Velluz, L., Peterfalvi, M., and Jequier, R., *Compt. Rend.* **247**, 1905 (1958).
199. Velluz, L., *Ann. Pharm. Fran.* **17**, 15 (1959).
200. Vogt, M., *in* "Comparative Neurochemistry" (D. Richter, ed.), p. 395. Pergamon Press, Oxford, 1964.
201. Wagle, G. L., and Plummer, A. J., *Arch. Intern. Pharmacodyn.* **151**, 1 (1964).
202. Wang, H.-H., Kanai, T., Markee, S., and Wang, S. C., *J. Pharmacol. Exptl. Therap.* **144**, 186 (1964).

203. Whelan, R. F., and Skinner, S. L., *Brit. Med. Bull.* **19**, 121 (1963).
204. Withrington, P., and Zaimis, E., *Brit. J. Pharmacol.* **17**, 380 (1961).
205. Woodson, R. E., Youngken, K. W., Schlittler, E., and Schneider, J. A., "Rauwolfia: Botany, Pharmacognosy, Chemistry and Pharmacology." Little, Brown, Boston, Massachusetts 1957.
206. Woodward, R. B., Bader, F. E., Bickel, H., Frey, A. J., and Kierstad, R. W., *J. Am. Chem. Soc.* **78**, 2023 and 2657 (1956).
207. Woodward, R. B., Bader, F. E., Bickel, H., Frey, A. J., and Kierstad, R. W., *Tetrahedron* **2**, 1 (1958).
208. Zaimis, E., *Nature* **192**, 521 (1961).

CHAPTER VI

Hydralazines

J. Druey

J. Tripod

I. Introduction, 223

II. Chemistry of Hydrazinophthalazines and Related Compounds, 224
    A. Syntheses of Hydrazinophthalazines, 224
    B. Structural Analogs of Hydralazine—Relationship between Chemical Structure and Hypotensive Properties, 225

III. Biochemistry, 234
    A. Analytical Methods, 234
    B. Biochemical Behavior, 236
    C. Metabolic Fate, 238

IV. Pharmacodynamics and Therapeutic Use in Man, 239
    A. Cardiovascular Activity, 239
    B. Other Pharmacodynamic Properties, 252
    C. Therapeutic Use in Man, 254

V. Summary and Conclusions, 256

    References, 257

I. Introduction

The hypotensive and antihypertensive properties of hydralazine (1-hydra-zinophthalazine) in animal tests were first reported by Gross *et al.* (82). Their findings were confirmed and broadened soon after by Craver and Yonkman (47). The first clinical observations came from Reubi (153, 154), Schroeder (169, 170), Grimson *et al.* (77), Freis and Finnerty (64), and Page (135). The drug was introduced on the market in 1953. In the same year, dihydralazine (1,4-dihydrazinophthalazine) was launched in European countries. At that time, the ganglionic blockers were the only antihypertensive agents available. They had the undeniable merit of being the first compounds of real value for the drug treatment of high blood pressure. But they have been more or less abandoned since, whereas hydralazine and dihydralazine are still widely used, particularly in combinations. Eight years after their introduction and despite the advent of many other drugs such as the hydrochlorothiazides and guan-ethidine, Moyer and Brest (129, 130) started their paper on "Hydralazine in the Treatment of Hypertension" with the words: "Hydralazine is among the most interesting and most useful antihypertensive agents currently available."

In some series of drugs a large spectrum of chemically different types is available, compounds either produced by nature or synthetically by the chemist. Analgesics or tranquilizing drugs might be mentioned as examples. Others are somewhat less diversified, such as the series of antihistaminics or diuretics. It is quite remarkable in this respect that the hydralazine type of antihypertensive agent has remained unique. 1-Hydrazinophthalazine (hydralazine) and 1,4-dihydrazinophthalazine (dihydralazine) have not found any successor in spite of the fact that chemists have played around with the

Hydralazine　　　　　　　　　Dihydralazine

molecule, as in other cases, in order to find improved properties. It will be worthwhile, therefore, to examine the structure–activity relationship in detail.

II. Chemistry of hydrazinophthalazines and related compounds

A. SYNTHESES OF HYDRAZINOPHTHALAZINES

The usual method of introducing a hydrazino group into a heterocyclic ring is by reaction of a corresponding halogen (mainly chlorine), mercapto, alkylmercapto, alkoxy, substituted, or unsubstituted amino group with hydrazine.

Hydralazine has been prepared by reacting 1-chlorophthalazine with hydrazine (43, 55). The original method is still the most practical one for large-scale production. 1-Hydroxyphthalazine or phthalazone, which is used as a starting product, can be obtained mainly by two methods: (1) Reduction of phthalic anhydride to phthalide, chlorination or bromination to α-halo-genophthalide, hydrolysis, and ring closure of the intermediate o-phthal-aldehydic acid to phthalazone. (2) Oxidation of naphthalene to phthalonic acid, which is converted to phthalazone–carboxylic acid with hydrazine; decarboxylation yields phthalazone.

Hydralazine has encountered considerable interest as an antihypertensive drug behind the Iron Curtain, where it is known by the name Apressin. For industrial production using procedure (2), see, for example, Sycheva *et al.* (184, 185). Phthalazone is available as a commercial product in Western countries.

Dihydralazine may be obtained from 1,4-dichlorophthalazine by the general method. The reaction is advantageously carried out in the presence of, for example, methanol, or by using 1-chloro-4-methoxy-phthalazine as starting material (18, 42, 180). Another method, which is particularly interesting for industrial production, yields dihydralazine in one step from commercially available phthalodinitrile (37). Other methods for the synthesis of

hydralazine derivatives will be referred to in the discussion of some particular analogs in the following section.

B. STRUCTURAL ANALOGS OF HYDRALAZINE—RELATIONSHIP BETWEEN CHEMICAL STRUCTURE AND HYPOTENSIVE PROPERTIES

A great effort has been made to elucidate structure–activity relationships in the hydralazine series, mainly by the chemists and biologists of the firm whence the drug originated (54, 165).

In dealing with structure–activity problems, as simple criteria as possible have to be used for the evaluation of activity. In the following tables the terms good, fair, low, and none will be used under the heading "activity." Good activity means a long-lasting hypotensive effect in the anesthetized animal (mainly rabbits), as is typical of hydralazine (see Section IV). Hypotensive effects of short duration, even if they are very pronounced, will not be reported as good activity.

Tables IA to V give a selection of representative compounds which have been examined, but not an exhaustive compilation. The data given for activity are mostly based on unpublished results of the authors of this review.

Substituents in the heterocyclic part of the phthalazine ring are listed in Tables IA and IB. Substituents in the aromatic part of hydrazinophthalazines are to be found in Table II.

Tables IA, IB, and II refer to compounds which are still very closely related to hydralazine itself. They all belong to the phthalazine series and the free hydrazino group is maintained in all of them. It is not surprising that fair-to-good activity is observed in most of them. No improvement could be achieved, however, over hydralazine and dihydralazine.

J. Druey and J. Tripod

Table IA

4-SUBSTITUTED HYDRAZINOPHTHALAZINES

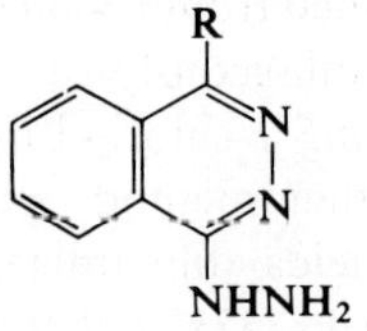

R	Activity	References
H (hydralazine)	Good	(82)
CH_3	Good	(82)
C_2H_5	Good	(55)
C_3H_7 (n)	Fair	(55)
C_4H_9 (i)	Fair	(55)
C_6H_5	Fair to low	(55)
$CH_2C_6H_5$	Fair to low	(55)
Cl	Fair	(55)
$NHNH_2$ (dihydralazine)	Good	(82)
$CH_2CONHNH_2$	Fair	(54)
$CH_2C_5H_5N$ (α-picolyl)	Good	(44, 54)
$CH_2C_5H_5N$ (γ-picolyl)	Good	(44, 54)
$CH_2C(=NOH)NH_2$	Fair	(210)

Table IB

HYDRAZINOPHTHALAZONES

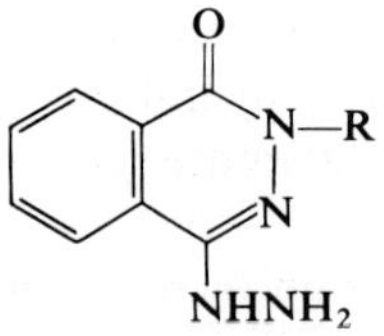

R	Activity	References
H	Low	(54)
		(99)
CH_3	Fair to low	(54)
C_3H_5	Fair to low	(54)
C_6H_4Cl (p)	None	(54)
$CH_2CH_2N(C_2H_5)_2$	None	(54)

Table II

SUBSTITUENTS IN THE AROMATIC PART OF HYDRAZINOPHTHALAZINES

Substituents	Activity	References
5-Cl, 4-H	Not published	(19)
6-Cl, 4-H	Good	(20, 54)
7-Cl, 4-H	Good	(20, 54)
7-OH, 4-H	Fair	(55)
7-OCH$_3$, 4-H	Good	(55)
8-Cl, 4-H	Not published	(19)
6,7-di-Cl, 4-NHNH$_2$	Good	(67, 99)

The last compound of Table IA is an example of combining two structural functions known from other products like guanethidine to carry hypotensive properties, i.e., the amidoxime group (131a, b) added to the hydralazine part. The expected additive effect is hardly ever attained when this procedure is applied in the search for new or better drugs.

1. *Substituents on the Hydrazino Group of Hydrazinophthalazines*

The hydrazino group is highly reactive and plays very probably an important role in the biological activity of hydralazine. It is likely to combine with some of the ubiquitous carbonyl derivatives in the body fluids, among which enzymes would be of particular importance, e.g., pyridoxal as coenzyme of decarboxylase (109). The chemical blocking of the hydrazine function, e.g., by preparing hydrazone or by alkylating it, offered a way of verifying the assumption that the hydrazino group is of primary importance in the mechanism of action of hydralazine.

For further hydrazones with substituted benzaldehydes and acetophenones see Biniecki *et al.* (17, 94), and Sycheva and Shchukina (185). Menziani (121, 122) has prepared many other sugar derivatives, without indicating the biological activity. When sodium hydrogen sulfite is added to the formaldehyde derivative of hydralazine (first compound of Table IIIA) the correspondingly substituted hydrazine —NHNHCH$_2$SO$_3$Na is obtained (159).

Table IIIA

HYDRAZONES OF HYDRALAZINE

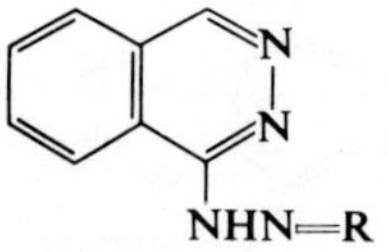

NHN=R

R	Activity	References
CH_2	Good	(55)
$CHCH_3$	Good	(54)
$C(CH_3)_2$	Good	(55)
$C(CH_3)COOH$	Fair	(55, 109)
CHC_6H_5	Fair	(55, 109)
$C(CH_3)C_6H_5$	Good	(17, 55)
(Glucose)	Fair	(54, 121)
(Galactose)	—	(54, 121)

Mention must be made here of a particular compound which combines the hydralazine molecule with a hydrochlorothiazide derivative:

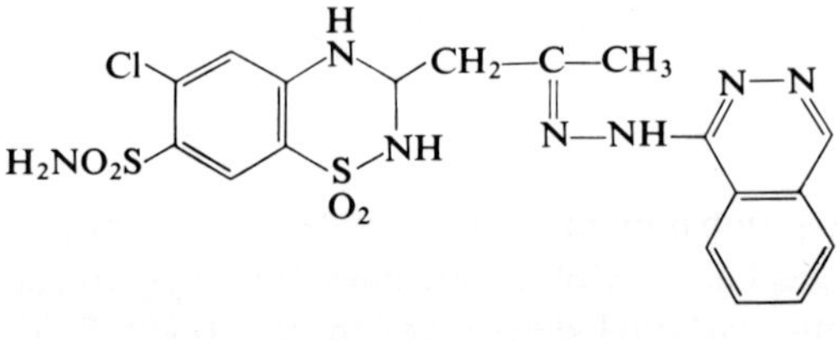

A long-lasting mild hypotensive effect has been reported (57). For toxicological data, see Yeary *et al.* (208).

The data in Tables IIIA and IIIB and particularly the lack of activity of the last two compounds in Table IIIB suggest that a free NH_2 group in the hydrazine function is essential for a typical long-lasting hypotensive effect. The hydrazones (Table IIIA) are chemically rather unstable and it is safe to conclude that their good activity is due to cleavage to hydralazine in the organism. The chemically more stable *N,N*-alkyl substituted derivatives of Table IIIB are not devoid of hypotensive properties, but the type of activity is completely different.

Table IIIB

N-ALKYLHYDRAZINOPHTHALAZINES

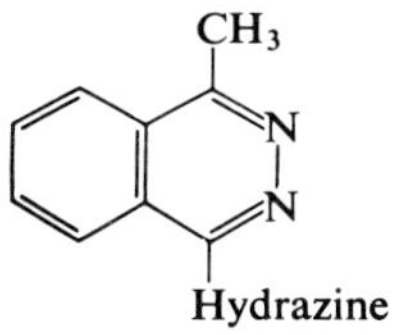

Hydrazine

Hydrazine	Activity	References
$N(CH_3)NH_2$	Fair	(54, 55)
$N(CH_3)NHCH_3$	None	(54, 55)
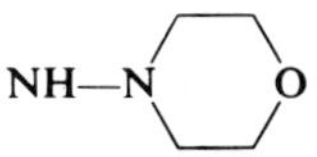 NH—N$\bigcirc$O	None	(54, 55)

2. s-Triazolo[3,4-a]phthalazines

This type of phthalazine compound, the formula of which is shown below,

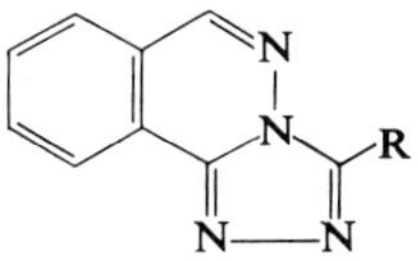

Triazolophthalazines

merits some attention in view of possible metabolites of hydralazine (cf. Section III, C). It has been shown by Druey and Ringier (55) that acylating agents do not give the expected N-acyl derivatives with hydrazine. Ring closure occurred, and in every case a new type of ring compound, the triazolo-phthalazines, was obtained. Biniecki et al. (17), on the other hand, claim to have obtained N-carbethoxy derivatives from hydralazine and dihydralazine with ethylchloroformate, whereas nicotinoyl and isonicotinoyl chloride yielded the correspondingly substituted triazolophthalazines. Douglass and Hogan (53) and McIsaac and Kanda (109) report the isolation of an N-acetyl-hydrazinophthalazine as a metabolite from hydralazine, a compound which could be obtained by chemical synthesis too. The melting point of their product (178°C) is very close to the one given by Druey and Ringier for the product obtained from hydralazine and acetic anhydride, and which is un-doubtedly 3-methyl-s-triazolo-3,4-a-phthalazine (m.p. 171°–172°C). Reynolds et al. (157) have shown that in the reaction of dihydralazine and formic acid, ring closure occurs with one hydrazino group only, whereas the other is formylated.

Compounds of the following type have been examined biologically: $R = H$, CH_3, C_4H_9, C_6H_5, Cl, OH, SH, NH_2, $NHNH_2$. None of them has shown hypotensive activity, not even the last-mentioned hydrazino derivative.

3. *Hydrazinopyridazines*

In the first paper on the pharmacological properties of hydralazine by Gross *et al.* (82), reference is made to a compound 6084 which almost equals hydralazine in its hypotensive activity. Owing to an error, compound 6084 is reported as belonging to the phthalazine series, whereas it is in fact a pyridazine derivative ($R_3 = C_6H_5$ in Table IV). Several hydrazinopyridazines have been found to have both hypotensive and antihypertensive properties. One of them (1325 TH, last compound in Table IV) has been studied in detail (6, 168). It has never been marketed.

Table IV

HYDRAZINOPYRIDAZINES

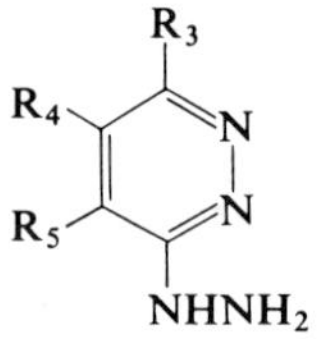

R_3	R_4	R_5	Activity	References
CH_3	H	H	Fair	(54)
H	CH_3	CH_3	Fair	(54)
C_6H_5	H	H	Good	(54, 101)
α- and β-Naphthyl	H	H	Fair	(54)
C_6H_5	C_6H_5	H	Good	(44a, 54)
$NHNH_2$	H	H	Good	(54, 177)
$NHNH_2$	CH_3	CH_3	Good	(54)
$CONH_2$	H	H	Good	(41, 101)

The main types of hydrazinopyridazine that have been examined are summarized in Table IV. In contrast to the generally good hypotensive activity encountered in this series, a derivative with the hydrazino group in 4-position has been found to lack any similar effect (54, 177).

$$NH_2NH-\text{(pyridazine ring)}$$

The 3,4-diphenyl derivative of the above series has been tried in human beings, where it has been found to be active but without any advantage over hydralazine. A new method of synthesizing pyridazines of this type has been described (166).

4. Hydrazine Compounds Other than Phthalazines and Pyridazines

When hydralazine was found to be a hypotensive drug, no other hydrazine derivative was in use for therapeutic purposes. The question arose, therefore, of whether its biological effects were merely connected with the hydrazine grouping and whether other structures bearing it, particularly other heterocyclic rings, would have similar properties. This possibility has been investigated rather thoroughly. Very few types of compounds have been found to display a hydralazinelike activity. These are:

(I) (II) (III)

All three compounds are very closely related to hydralazine or dihydralazine in their chemical structure. Hydrazinoisoquinoline (I) (43a) underwent clinical trials, as did probably compound II (38). The triazine derivative III (54) is somewhat less active. Therapeutic value has also been claimed for a compound isomeric to II, 1,4-dihydrazino-6-azaphthalazine (148).

Dihydrazinopyrimidines of the type

$$NH_2NH-\text{(pyrimidine ring)}-NHNH_2$$
$$R \quad (NH_2)$$

have been claimed to possess long-lasting hypotensive effects (39, 101).

Dihydrazinotriazines are reported to be good hypotensives, the compounds where R is ethyl or propyl, being the most active ones of the series (100).

$$NH_2NH-\text{(triazine ring)}-R$$
$$NHNH_2$$

Hydrazino derivatives of the following heterocyclic structures have been found to be without interest as antihypertensives (according to tests conducted by the authors of the present review; published work by others is also listed).

Pyridine	Quinoxaline (99, 101)
Quinoline	Phenanthroline
Phenanthridine	Triazole
Cinnoline	sym-Triazine
Quinazoline (99, 101)	

Hydrazino compounds of the aliphatic, aromatic, and araliphatic series have, of course, also been screened for hypotensive properties. No characteristic hydralazine effect could be detected, although a fall in blood pressure was observed in many cases. Some hydrazines (and hydrazides) of this type, e.g. hydrazinophenylpropane

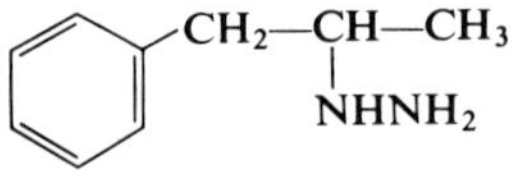

$$CH_2—CH—CH_3$$
$$|$$
$$NHNH_2$$

became known as monoamine oxidase (MAO) inhibitors, a class of drugs which will not be discussed here.

It has been said above (p. 227) that when two structural elements as carriers of certain biological properties are combined in the same molecule, additive effects are hardly ever attained. The following example of a type of compound containing stigmata of both the hydralazine and hydrochlorothiazide molecules (IV) might be considered as an exception to this rule. A hypotensive

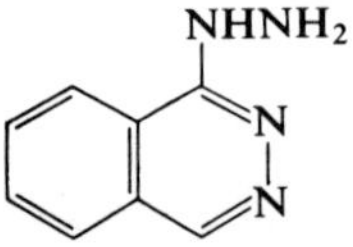

Hydralazine	(IV)	Hydrochlorothiazide ring system

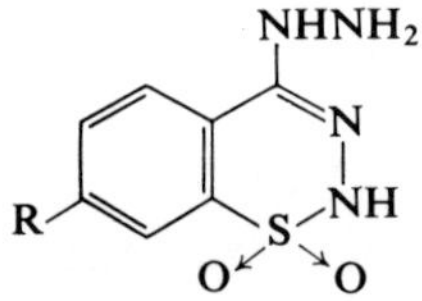

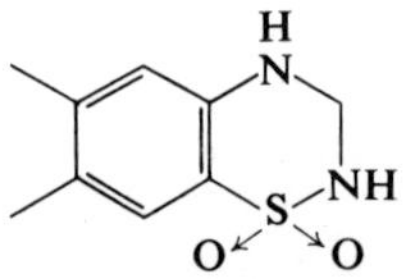

effect similar to that of hydralazine and remarkable diuretic properties have been found in compound IV in which R is ethoxy (167). A hypotensive effect has also been described for (IV) R = H (57).

5. Replacement of the Hydrazino Group of Hydralazine by Other Radicals

From what has been said in the preceding section, it can be concluded that the hydrazino group is not mainly or not solely responsible for the characteristic activity of hydralazine. Its replacement by other radicals, the phthalazine ring being maintained, was therefore also examined in the course of studies on structure–activity relationships, although the chances of obtaining a good activity were low in view of the conclusions of Table IIIB. Table V summarizes some typical examples of compounds. Where no reference is given in Table V, the compounds and their activity are taken from unpublished work by the authors.

Table V

VARIOUS 1-SUBSTITUTED PHTHALAZINES

Compound number	R	Activity	References
1	H	None	
2	NH_2	None	(177)
3	$N(CH_3)_2$	None	
4		None	
5		Hypotensive	
6	$NH(CH_2)_2N(C_2H_5)_2$	Hypotensive	
7		Not given	(99)
8	OH	None	
9	$OCH_2CH_2N(CH_3)_2$	Not given	(66)
10	SH	Low	(54, 66)
11	SCN	Not given	(16)
12	$SCH_2CH_2N(CH_3)_2$	Not given	(66)

One could expect that in replacing the hydrazino group by a basically substituted amino group (as in compounds 5 and 6 in Table V), the hypotensive activity would at least be partly retained. This is, in fact, the case, but the type of activity—of short duration though pronounced in terms of millimeters of mercury—is quite different from that of hydralazine.

Mercaptophthalazine (compound 10 of Table V) surprisingly showed antihypertensive properties of a hydralazine type, but only in high doses. These findings were nevertheless considered worth studying further, particularly in view of some accompanying sedative effects. A related derivative of the pyridazine series (V)

$$\text{(V)}$$

went to clinical trials. No useful effect could be shown.

6. *Open Ring Structures*

From the extensive experimental facts on structure–activity relationships, one must assume that a free hydrazino group is an essential constituent of therapeutic compounds of the hydralazine type. The hydrazine group being highly reactive, the hypothesis of an interference with enzymes in the organism, particularly those with an aldehydic function, is a reasonable biochemical concept to explain the mechanism of action.

According to Schuler (173), aminoguanidine

is one of the most potent inhibitors of diamino-oxidase. Hydralazine also inhibits this enzyme (84) as do many other hydrazine derivatives of varying chemical structure. There is no evidence of any parallelism between hypotensive action and blocking effect on diamino-oxidase. Several compounds structurally related to hydralazine as well as to aminoguanidine, i.e., particularly those of the hydrazidine type

have been included in these trials.

In concluding this review on structural analogs of hydralazine one can say that hypotensive effects are rather frequently obtained but that the characteristic type of a slowly beginning and long-lasting blood-pressure lowering action is reserved to a narrow, specific, molecular structure.

III. Biochemistry

A. ANALYTICAL METHODS

1-Hydrazinophthalazine and 1,4-dihydrazinophthalazine as free bases are rather unstable compounds, sensitive to oxidizing agents at a pH over 5–6.

For stability as a function of pH, see McIsaac and Kanda (109) and Schulert (177). In the form of their salts with strong acids they are stable.

Hydralazine is the hydrochloride, $C_8H_8N_4 \cdot HCl$, a white or slightly yellowish crystalline powder melting between 270°–280° C with decomposition. It is soluble in water at a pH of 3.0–4.0 (2% solution), sparingly soluble in methanol and ethanol. Ultraviolet absorption of an aqueous solution:

$$\lambda_{min} \ 228 \ m\mu, \ \text{extinction} \ \epsilon = 10,200$$
$$\lambda_{max} \ 240 \ m\mu, \quad\quad\quad \epsilon = 11,100$$
$$\lambda_{min} \ 251 \ m\mu, \quad\quad\quad \epsilon = 10,000$$
$$\lambda_{max} \ 260 \ m\mu, \quad\quad\quad \epsilon = 10,650$$
$$\lambda_{max} \ 303 \ m\mu, \quad\quad\quad \epsilon = 5,150$$

With sodium nitrite in aqueous solution, a characteristic tetrazole derivative, m.p. 210° C, is formed.

Dihydralazine is the sulfate of 1,4-dihydrazinophthalazine, $C_8H_{10}N_6 \cdot H_2SO_4$, a slightly yellowish crystalline powder, melting at 242° to 246° C with decomposition. It is less soluble in water than hydralazine, and very sparingly soluble in organic solvents. Ultraviolet absorption in water:

$$\lambda_{min} \ 281 \ m\mu, \ \text{extinction} \ \epsilon = 4,240$$
$$\lambda_{max} \ 321 \ m\mu, \quad\quad\quad \epsilon = 5,910$$

A tetrazole derivative, m.p. 149°–152° C, is formed in aqueous solution with sodium nitrite.

For injection purposes, a water-soluble methane sulfonate of dihydrazinophthalazine is available, $C_8H_{10}N_6 \cdot CH_3HSO_3$, m.p. 224°–227° C, the 1% aqueous solution having a pH of 5.6–6.2.

Most of the analytical methods described in the literature deal with hydralazine. The British *Pharmacopeia* advocates titration with potassium iodate, using amaranth solution as an indicator. Other methods published are based on the following reagents:

Ninhydrin (137, 138)
Cinnamic aldehyde (103)
Naphthoquinone sulfonate (160)
p-Dimethylamino-benzaldehyde (201)
p-Hydroxybenzaldehyde (177)
Sodium nitrite (160)
Thallium oxide (gasometrically) (40)
Reduction with zinc (161)

Several oxidometric and potentiometric procedures using bromate, iodate, periodate, or permanganate have been described (89, 110, 160, 162). For paper chromatography see Ruggieri (160) and McIsaac and Kanda (109).

B. Biochemical Behavior

The ease with which it forms complexes or chelates with metal ions is one of the salient properties of hydralazine. This property is of particular importance in connection with the compound's behavior in the presence of enzymes and in the living organism. Much study has therefore been devoted to this problem right from the beginning of hydralazine therapy. Special mention must be made here of the pioneering work done by Schroeder and Perry. They have drawn attention to the fact that hydralazine combines with Fe^{2+}, Fe^{3+}, Cu^{2+}, Mn^{2+}, Sn^{2+}, Ag^+, Hg^{2+}, V^{3+} and V^{5+} (138, 143). The ability to complex copper into a chelate has been shown to be of particular interest in experiments on the isolated rabbit heart, in which the constrictive properties of copper sulfate on the coronary vessels are abolished by hydralazine (92). Reference may be made in this connection to a remark by Schroeder who said that the basic action of hydralazine might be chelation with a trace metal, possibly copper, in the smooth muscle cell of the arterial wall (171). Hydralazine, furthermore, plays an important role in the rate of oxidation of biogenic amines in the presence of metal ions as catalysts, particularly Cu^{2+} (116).

The behavior of hydralazine in the presence of Fe^{2+} and Fe^{3+} has been thoroughly studied by Fallab (59, 60, 61, 198, 199). Some striking differences from other closely related hydrazino derivatives demonstrate the exceptional position of hydralazine. It reacts with molecular oxygen in the presence of Fe^{2+} to give a dimeric oxidation product with a tetrazane structure, which forms a deep red coordination compound with Fe^{2+}. With Fe^{3+}, particularly when used in excess, hydralazine is rapidly oxidized to phthalazine and molecular N_2. It is remarkable that the rate of oxidation by Fe^{3+} is 500 times faster for hydralazine than for unsubstituted hydrazine.

A hydralazine-iron chelation complex has also been studied by Kirpekar and Lewis (96). Their results do not support the view that this drug acts as an antihypertensive by virtue of its ability to form metal chelates.

It was of particular interest to study the influence of hydralazine on enzymes which play an important physiological role in maintaining blood pressure at a normal level. The results obtained by different authors diverge to some extent.

There is complete agreement as to the inhibitory action of hydralazine on diamine oxidase (45, 84, 200). The inhibition is not specific. Hydralazine shares this effect with many other hydrazine derivatives (84, 173).

The published findings regarding hydralazine's action on monoamine oxidase are not unequivocal. Werle *et al.* (200) found variable but weak inhibition, as did Perry *et al.* (147) whereas Schroeder (171) reported a fairly strong enhancing effect, which is not shared by any other known organic substance. According to Cohn and Shore (45), hydralazine does not inhibit MAO, whereas other hydrazine derivatives such as iproniazid belong to the typical group of MAO inhibitors.

Dihydroxyphenylalanine (dopa) decarboxylase is partly inhibited by hydralazine, as well as by a number of other hydrazines (147). This has been confirmed by Werle (200); see also Schroeder (171). Bygdeman and Stjarne (35, 36) have examined the effect of dihydralazine on the epinephrine and norepinephrine content in different organs. A depletion of the organ stores of catecholamines has been found and it is tempting to consider the possibility that this effect is due to inhibition of synthesis, possibly via interference with dopa decarboxylase. Histidine decarboxylase is also inhibited by hydralazine (200).

Catalase activity is inhibited *in vitro* but not *in vivo* at high dose levels of hydralazine (95).

Hydrazinophthalazine has been found to inhibit the acetylation of sulfanilamide and glucosamine in liver extracts (52). According to a recent paper by Jenne and Orser (93) it also inhibits "isoniazid transacetylase" isolated from human liver.

A rapid fall in total serum cholesterol after the inception of hydralazine therapy was reported as far back as 1954; however, when treatment was maintained for 6 months or more, the level tended to return to its initial value (143). In further clinical observations, the average depression in 112 hypertensive patients was 29 mg per 100 ml of plasma following oral hydralazine therapy; however, among the 66 patients with high control levels, the fall was 48.2 mg in the first 6 months, and thereafter 43.5 mg per 100 ml of plasma (144). Some cases were followed for many years. A report by Perry and Mills (142) lists 160 patients who had received hydralazine treatment in daily doses ranging from 100 to 1600 mg and who had been kept under observation for periods of up to 10 years. The average depression of plasma cholesterol was 25 mg per 100 ml.

Schuler and Albrecht (174) have tested hydralazine for antiatherosclerotic activity in diet-induced atheromatosis in rabbits. Both the rise in aortic cholesterol following the diet and the development of macroscopically visible atheromatosis were sharply reduced. In their experiments, however, hydralazine did not exert any effect on hypercholesterolemia.

Hydralazine has been shown to exert a protective effect in mice exposed to a lethal dose of total-body X-ray irradiation. It shares this property with other antihypertensive agents such as reserpine or guanethidine (90). The mechanism of this effect has not yet been elucidated. From experiments designed for simulation of radiated aqueous systems it can be concluded, however, that the peculiar redox-kinetic behavior of hydralazine toward strong oxidizing agents is at least partly responsible, particularly in view of the role played by peroxides in irradiation damage (62).

Brief mention must be made of some other effects of interest in connection with the biochemical behavior of hydralazine. Ability to react with carbonyl compounds has been reported in this connection (143), many enzymes having a carbonyl group as reactive part in their molecular structure. The same authors in several papers insisted on the ability of hydralazine to combine with sulfhydryl compounds (138, 139, 143, 171). Kirpekar and Lewis (96, 97) have shown an inhibitory effect on the iron-catalyzed formation of cystine from cystein.

Hydralazine inactivates the pressor substances angiotensin and pherentasin (171, 172).

C. METABOLIC FATE

The first studies on the fate of hydralazine in hypertensive patients were conducted by Perry (137), who devised a colorimetric method for its determination depending on a ninhydrin complex. He showed that the total renal excretion of free or easily hydrolyzable compound approximated to only 5% of the dose administered. Within 30 minutes of oral administration, urine concentration began to rise gradually and some excretion continued for 24 hours following a therapeutic dose. The levels in protein-free blood filtrates approached the limit of the method. They were maximal 90–180 minutes after ingestion. In subsequent papers, more details on the laboratory technique and some further results in patients were given. Less than 2% of a dose of hydralazine was excreted unchanged, although 2–6% was present in the urine in the form of labile conjugates (138, 139). The fate of hydralazine was again thoroughly examined in a study on the combined hexamethonium and hydralazine ("Hyphex") treatment of hypertension (143, 146). Therapeutic plasma levels averaged 0.023 mg/100 ml (=0.23 μg per milliliter). Over 90% of the drug was found to be metabolized in some way. The mean recovery of free drug in the urine was 2.9% of a single oral dose; half of it appeared within 5 hours. A fraction of renally excreted hydralazine was apparently "bound" to sulfhydryl compounds. This fraction decreased as therapy progressed, as though the body stores of sulfhydryl compounds were depleted.

Douglass and Hogan (53) were the first to identify a metabolite of hydralazine, in the form of an acetyl derivative. The structure was confirmed by synthesis (*cf.* Section II, B, 2).

Schulert (177), using a colorimetric method for the determination of hydralazine, has found somewhat higher plasma levels than Perry: 1–3 μg per milliliter in patients who were receiving 125–150 mg of the drug orally four times a day, i.e., 500 to 600 mg per day altogether. Maximum plasma concentration in humans was found to occur 3–4 hours after oral administration. Urinary excretion amounted to 1–2% only of the administered dose, confirming the findings of Perry.

Preliminary evidence by Schulert suggested moderate localization of hydralazine in the kidney. The technique using a ^{14}C-labeled drug confirmed these findings (145). A high level of ^{14}C was detected in the aorta too, an observation which had been reported 2 years earlier by Moore-Jones and Perry (126). Their radioautographs revealed a remarkable affinity of the radiocarbon for blood vessels, particularly in the kidney, and for arteries and arterioles more than veins. The aortic level decreased slowly and the renal level rapidly (141). Nearly half of the injected ^{14}C appeared in the urine within 16 hours.

A comprehensive study on the metabolism of 1-hydrazinophthalazine using ^{14}C-labeled drug was published by McIsaac and Kanda in 1964. Hydralazine was shown to be rapidly absorbed and distributed, but the level of activity circulating in the blood 8 hours after intraperitoneal administration was still approximately 18% of the dose. The rate of excretion in the urine indicated that metabolism was fairly rapid, 75% of the dose having been excreted in 24 hours.

Using the isotope dilution technique, it was found that 9.7% of an i.p. administered dose of hydralazine was excreted unchanged. Even if this value is somewhat higher than the ones reported by Perry (139) and Schulert (177), it confirms the previous findings, i.e., that this drug is metabolized to a very high degree.

The following metabolites have been identified by McIsaac and Kanda (109): 1-hydrazinophthalazine-O-glucuronide, hydroxy-1-hydrazinophthalazine, N-acetyl-1-hydrazinophthalazine, and 1-hydrazinophthalazine pyruvic acid hydrazone.

Acetylation of hydralazine is an important pathway since 17.7% of a dose was found to be excreted in the form of the N-acetyl derivative. Hydroxylation in the aromatic ring has proved to be the major metabolic pathway. Only a small amount, however, is excreted as the free phenol, the glucuronide of it accounting for about 50% of the total urinary metabolites. Chromatographic comparison with a synthetic compound has shown that hydroxylation does not occur at the 7-position.

IV. Pharmacodynamics and therapeutic use in man

A. CARDIOVASCULAR ACTIVITY

The main pharmacodynamic properties of the hydrazinophthalazines are their hypotensive and antihypertensive effects. A hypotensive action is encountered in response to doses as low as 0.1–1 mg per kilogram intravenously in various species of animal and is marked by a fall in arterial blood pressure which greatly differs qualitatively from that observed with other drugs. It sets in gradually, lasts for a particularly long time, but does not exceed a certain degree even if the dose is increased. Furthermore, it is as a rule accompanied by an increase in respiration and heart rate; these two effects, however, sometimes disappear more rapidly than the effect on the blood pressure (10, 82).

In the spinal cat, in which the arterial blood pressure has been reduced to

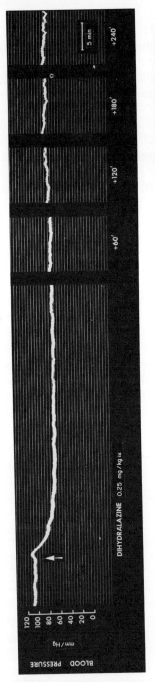

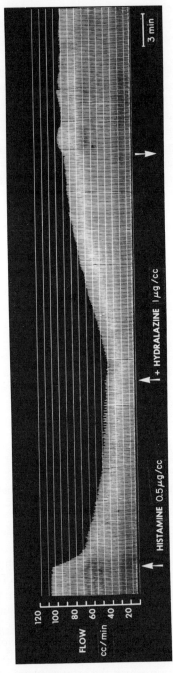

Fig. 1. (top) Dihydralazine, 0.25 mg per kilogram i.v., produces a long-lasting hypotensive effect in the rabbit.

Fig. 2. (bottom) The vasoconstriction produced by a perfusion of histamine, 0.5 μg per cubic centimeter, in the isolated vessels of the rabbit hind leg is inhibited by hydralazine, 1 μg per cubic centimeter.

240

50–60 mm Hg by exclusion of some nervous mechanisms responsible for regulating the circulation, hydrazinophthalazine produces little, if any, reduction in arterial blood pressure. On the other hand, if in this same spinal animal the arterial pressure is increased artificially—for example, by means of ephedrine or ergotamine—hydralazine again displays a hypotensive effect similar to that observed in the normal animal.

The fact that hydrazinophthalazine fails to bring about any appreciable fall in arterial blood pressure in the spinal animal cannot simply be explained by supposing that it acts only via the central nervous system. It can, however, be assumed that the drug also influences certain circulatory mechanisms, including in particular the marked hypotension which develops following section of the medulla oblongata.

In addition, it is safe to say that hydrazinophthalazine must exert an effect on the peripheral circulation, either by decreasing total peripheral resistance, or by reducing cardiac activity (10). We shall revert to this point in greater detail later, but it should be emphasized at this time that the acute hypotensive effect of hydralazine differs qualitatively from that of other hypotensive agents in the normotensive animal (114, 119).

A quantitative analysis of the characteristics of various acute hypotensions provides certain criteria, on the basis of which substances most likely to exert an antihypertensive action can then be tested in animals with artificially induced hypertension. If the substance in question is still found to be active in this second experimental stage and if the duration and intensity of its effect depend not only on dosage but also on the animal's pathological cardiovascular condition, the drug may well be of value in the control of hypertensive syndromes in man. At present, however, it is still not possible to predict that a drug will exert a reliable antihypertensive effect simply because it possesses an acute hypotensive action.

To revert to the question of changes in local peripheral resistance, numerous perfusion studies carried out, for example, by Tripod and Meier (190) have shown that hydralazine and dihydralazine markedly antagonize the peripheral vasoconstriction produced either by histamine or by $BaCl_2$ (as musculotropic agent), whereas the "sympathicolytic" properties of these hydralazines, as revealed by their antagonism toward epinephrine and norepinephrine, are less pronounced.

On the coronary blood vessels, the reactivity of which often differs from that of peripheral vessels in the rest of the organism, the hydralazines in a concentration as low as 0.1–1 μg per cubic centimeter produce considerable dilatation, accompanied by some negatively inotropic and negatively chronotropic effect, in contrast to the above-mentioned tachycardia observed in the intact animal (10). Hydralazines also markedly antagonize the vasoconstriction induced by either vasopressin or $BaCl_2$ in the coronary vessels.

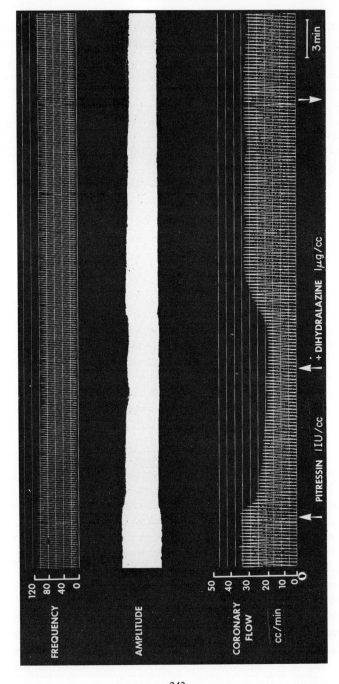

Fig. 3. Dihydralazine, 1 μg per cubic centimeter, antagonizes the constriction produced in the coronary vessels of the isolated rabbit heart by a perfusion of Pitressin (vasopressin), 1 IU per cubic centimeter.

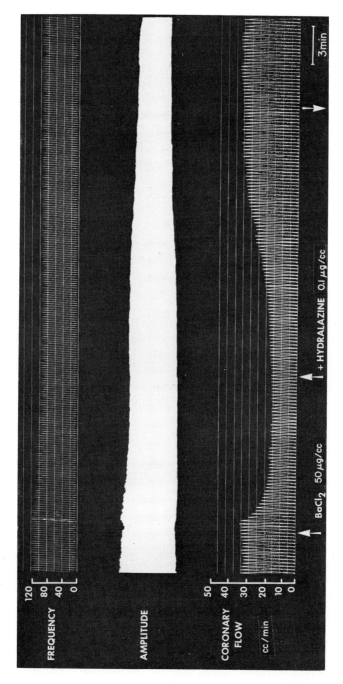

Fig. 4. Hydralazine, 0.1 μg per cubic centimeter, antagonizes the constriction produced in the coronary vessels of the isolated rabbit heart by a perfusion of BaCl₂, 50 μg per cubic centimeter.

All these observations show, therefore, that the hydralazines exert what appears to be a fairly complex series of primary effects and antagonistic actions on the peripheral circulation; furthermore, they do not influence, for example, isolated vessels and coronary vessels in exactly the same way.

From the qualitative point of view, this peripheral activity displays certain special features: the primary effects and the antagonistic actions set in slowly, develop gradually, persist for a long time, and are practically irreversible. Kinetically, therefore, the hydralazines differ fundamentally from drugs acting via the adrenergic, cholinergic, or histaminergic systems, and from other types of "spasmolytics."

In a further series of tests, Tripod *et al.* (192) studied the peripheral vascular response to hydralazines and other hypotensives not by direct perfusion, but rather by first treating animals, as a rule for 10 days, and then perfusing them with various vasoconstrictor agents. Following this pretreatment, the hydralazines give rise to a range of antagonistic effects which differ greatly from those observed in the direct perfusion experiments mentioned above. The findings showed that this pretreatment sets in motion a whole series of mechanisms—central, autonomic nervous, hormonal, etc.—which bring about certain functional changes and thus help to determine the final effect on the peripheral circulation. This method also takes account of the metabolism of the compounds employed, of the rate at which they are broken down, and of the extent to which they give rise to metabolites possessing an activity that might possibly be different from that of the parent compound injected. An additional factor to be borne in mind is the depletion of substances such as serotonin, epinephrine, norepinephrine, etc. The interaction of all these extremely complex elements produces various types of "final hypotension," which differ both qualitatively and quantitatively.

Hydralazine is not only a very active and diversely acting modifier of vascular sensitivity, as we have just seen, but also, as Tripod and Meier (191) have demonstrated in certain standard isolated test systems, it antagonizes $BaCl_2$ in the rabbit intestine, histamine in the guinea pig intestine, and epinephrine in the guinea pig seminal vesicle. However, it exerts absolutely no anticholinergic effects in the rabbit intestine.

To sum up, all these tests reveal ranges of activity which suggest that hydralazine is a multivalent "vascular spasmolytic" and that the quality and intensity of its effects display very subtle differences depending on the organ or species of animal concerned.

To revert to the changes in peripheral vascular reactivity, it should be pointed out that this reactivity also depends on the innervation of the vessel, the structure of the vascular wall (203), the tone of the vascular wall (12, 113), the internal environment or "milieu interne" (50, 186, 193, 194), and of course the species of animal (49, 68), and the anatomical and topographical distribution of the vascular receptors (34, 50, 98). To take account of these considerations, Studer and Tripod (182), for example, perfused segments of the abdominal aorta as well as the vessels of the hind leg in the rabbit. The abdominal aorta is a vascular element whose structure and function certainly differ from those of the peripheral vessels, perfusion of which involves arterial, precapillary, postcapillary, and venous factors—in other words, an entire vascular bed (182).

Under these experimental conditions, the sensitivity of the abdominal aorta is generally less marked than that of the peripheral vessels in the hind leg. In both cases, hydralazine exerts the same antagonistic effect on constriction caused by histamine or 5-hydroxytryptamine (serotonin). This is not the case with other hypotensive or antihypertensive agents such as acetylcholine or reserpine (11), for instance, which exhibit virtually no antagonism toward epinephrine, angiotensin, histamine, serotonin, or $BaCl_2$ in the aorta, whereas their activity in the vessels of the hind leg is well known. These observations show that the pattern of the receptors in the abdominal aorta, for example, differs from that in the vessels of the hind leg both qualitatively and quantitatively, with the result that vascular reactivity in the two preparations is not identical for each vasoconstrictor and its antagonists. In other words, it appears that the pharmacodynamic activity of a hypotensive agent is governed not simply by the pattern of its effects on certain receptors, but also by the pattern of these receptors themselves in different vascular beds. If account is also taken of modifications due to changes in the "milieu interne," as described by Meier and Tripod (117) and Tripod et al. (194), it is clear that, together, these three factors (pattern of effects, pattern of receptors, and pattern of the "milieu interne") can give rise to a virtually infinite number of possible pharmacological reactions which will ultimately influence circulatory processes. From the point of view of function alone, the interaction of these three factors is sufficient by itself to ensure that vascular reactivity adapts in a very subtle fashion to a wide variety of normal and pathological situations.

As regards the cardiac activity of the hydrazinophthalazines, it has been observed in the normotensive animal, especially the nonanesthetized dog, that hydralazine causes a qualitative change in the electrocardiogram, associated in particular with marked tachycardia (164). Other authors state that this tachycardia, produced, for example, by injecting hydralazine into a cerebral ventricle, is suppressed by vagotomy, but not by section of efferent sympathetic pathways. Thus, it would seem to be due to an inhibition of cardioinhibitory centers in the central—not, probably, the autonomous—nervous system (85).

Whereas hydralazine exerts, as we have already seen, a pronounced antagonistic effect on vasopressin-induced coronary vasoconstriction in various species of animal (13), it does not modify the constrictor reflex in the coronary vessels of the dog following an artificial embolism produced by injecting lycopodine and by the resultant prolonged vasoconstriction (202). In this test, however, no other compound—procaine, atropine, ganglionic blocking agents such as tetraethylammonium chloride or hexamethonium bromide, or even nitroglycerine—is effective either (202).

Nonetheless, the antihypertensive effect of the hydrazinophthalazines is one of their principal pharmacodynamic properties and has been subjected to detailed experimental study. Bein, Meier, Gross, etc. analyzed the possible mechanisms underlying hormonal or renal hypertension in the animal. They described the various methods used to produce different kinds of artificial hypertension in the animal (8, 78, 80, 83, 114). A review of these methods is also given by Plummer in the present volume (151). In principle, the effect of these methods is to modify certain humoral, and thus also, electrolytic balances and to alter the function of "cardiovascular segments" in such a way as to obtain a lasting rise in arterial blood pressure. Hypertension of various types—neurogenic, renal, endocrine, hemodynamic, dietetic, etc.—can be produced in this manner (8). These syndromes, however, are not necessarily comparable to the various types of hypertension met with in man, which may secondarily involve mechanisms analogous to those employed in the animal, but which are in many cases primary and spontaneous.

Despite this, renal and endocrine hypertension are the most widely used experimental methods and have yielded results which are of quite considerable interest. Hydralazines, for example, have been found to exert a very favorable effect in rats with experimental renal hypertension (8, 10). In this test, devised originally by Williams *et al.* (204) and calling for the application of precise criteria—the blood pressure should return to normal not only after a few doses but should also remain normal for a period of treatment lasting at least 12 days, so as to ensure that no tolerance develops—hydralazine is particularly active (7, 8, 10, 114). Similar results were obtained in our laboratories by Sulser who induced hypertension in animals by administering excessive doses of various steroids such as deoxycorticosterone, cortisone, hydrocortisone, etc., as well as by including an excess of NaCl in the diet. Sulser showed that hydralazine and dihydralazine exert a definite antihypertensive effect when employed either prophylactically or therapeutically; furthermore, a combination of hydralazine and reserpine, even used prophylactically, produces an even more marked effect (183), as do other chemically and pharmacologically unrelated compounds which potentiate their antihypertensive activity (76).

Although several different methods can be employed to induce hypertension, it is certainly true that some antihypertensive agents are more effective in one type of hypertension than in another. In this connection, hydralazine and reserpine display the broadest range of antihypertensive activity, although it has not yet been discovered exactly why this should be so (8).

It is impossible within the confines of the present review to evaluate in detail the relative importance of the various factors—nervous, renal, endocrine,

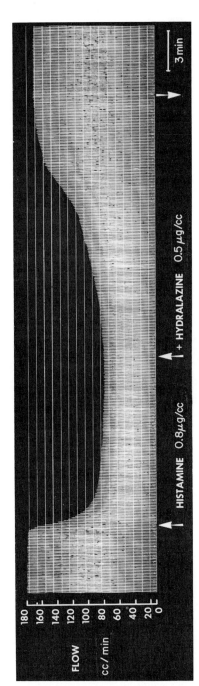

Fig. 5. The vasoconstriction of the rabbit aorta produced by a perfusion of histamine, 0.8 μg per cubic centimeter, is fully inhibited by hydralazine, 0.5 μg per cubic centimeter.

Fig. 6. The hypotensive effect of hydralazine in the rabbit (0.5 mg per kilogram i.v.) is entirely inhibited by previous incubation at room temperature for 24 hours in homologous serum.

247

dietary, genetic, etc.—which help to induce experimental hypertension in the rat and dog, the animals generally employed for the purpose, and in the rabbit and monkey, which are occasionally used (79, 80, 151). A complete evaluation of the renal and extrarenal factors would call for a detailed analysis of renin, of the substrate on which renin acts, and of the final substance which might play a part in local vasoconstriction.

Nor is it possible here to discuss the relative importance of the various steroids, especially corticosteroids, whose effect on vascular reactivity in general and renal vascular reactivity in particular constitutes an essential element in the pathophysiology of experimental hypertension (79, 81). Such a discussion would have to take account not only of most of the adrenal steroids but also of thyroid hormones, sex hormones, etc. (81).

In all these cases, however, it is clear that vascular lesions in animals with artificially induced hypertension can be influenced by antihypertensive agents. In hypertensive rats treated with hydralazine, in particular, Bein and Brunner (8), and also Masson et al. (106) have observed a certain correlation between arterial blood pressure levels and the nature of the vascular lesions. Moreover, the latter authors found that these vascular lesions tended to disappear when the arterial blood pressure returned to normal.

Nevertheless, it is extremely difficult to determine whether this reduction in elevated blood pressure is responsible for the disappearance of the lesions, or whether other pharmacological effects produced by the antihypertensive agents outside the circulatory system may also play an important role.

No generalizations can be made or final conclusions drawn, for Bein et al. (9) found in rats with renal hypertension that the severity of the lesions was not, in principle, related to the absolute increase in arterial blood pressure, to the duration of the hypertension, or to the rate at which the hypertension had developed. They concluded that constriction of the renal artery produces per se a vascular lesion which causes a disturbance in the renal circulation; this disturbance leads, in turn, to mesenchymal reactions which are not necessarily connected with the factors responsible for the hypertension. Since the factors modifying mesenchymal reactivity seem to be independent of those modifying arterial blood pressure, it is difficult to accept that renal hypertension in the rat is due merely to a renal factor. It is more probable that as a result of this factor all the blood vessels in the organism become more susceptible to atheromatous lesions, which undeniably play a part in the genesis of hypertension. In this connection, however, Loustalot et al. (102) have found that the experimental production of atheromatosis (referred to in Section III, B) depends largely on the method employed and, in particular, on the atherogenic content of the diet. Schuler and Albrecht (174) reported that hydralazine exerted a marked therapeutic effect when administered in daily doses of approximately 1 mg per kilogram to rabbits with experimental atheromatosis, whose aortic cholesterol levels were appreciably elevated and whose atheromatous lesions were clearly visible under the microscope. One striking feature, however, was that no modification—above all, no reduction— of the hypercholesterolemia was observed in those animals whose artificial atherosclerosis had responded to hydralazine (174).

Another technique, consisting in enucleating one adrenal in the rat, removing the contralateral kidney, and administering 1% sodium chloride in the diet, gives rise to a generalized hypertension which shows an extremely good response to hydralazine (70).

Also in the rat (71), the regular administration of epinephrine can likewise produce hypertension as a result of renal arteriolar necrosis. This necrosis can be prevented by giving the animals hydralazine simultaneously with the epinephrine. While on the subject of the kidney, it should be recalled that rats subjected to heminephrectomy and receiving a corticosteroid may exhibit experimental pyelonephritis, in addition to hypertension. These two symptoms respond favorably to hydralazine (207). Finally, according to other authors, only renal lesions produced by clamping the renal artery are affected by hydralazine, whereas those induced by the administration of excessive doses of steroids do not respond to this drug, even if the arterial blood pressure of the animals rendered hypertensive in this way is restored to normal (69).

Hence, vascular—particularly renal—lesions produced by experimental hypertension and their disappearance in response to hydralazine or other antihypertensive agents must be dissociated to some extent from the reduction in arterial blood pressure brought about by these agents in such animals. This is the conclusion reached by Tripod and Bein (188) in the light of their studies in rats with experimental renal hypertension; these authors examined the effects of a series of vasoconstrictor agents, using as their criteria peripheral vascular constriction and inhibition of edema formation. Under these experimental conditions, they obtained the following results: epinephrine and, especially, histamine and angiotensin were more active vasoconstrictors in hypertensive rats than in control animals, and their inhibitory effect on the formation of peripheral edema was also more marked in the hypertensive rats. On the other hand, the vasoconstrictor action of norepinephrine is less pronounced in hypertensive animals than in controls; as for vasopressin, its vasoconstrictor effect is more marked in nonhypertensive rats, but it strongly inhibits edema formation in both hypertensive and normotensive animals. Finally, the situation differs once again in the case of serotonin, which tends to produce less vasoconstriction in operated rats without hypertension, and less inhibition of edema formation in controls (188).

From the quantitative and, especially, qualitative point of view, therefore, peripheral vascular reactivity in rats with renal hypertension differs fundamentally from that encountered in controls or in "operated but nonhypertensive" animals. There is also a difference between the peripheral vasoconstrictor effect and the inhibition of edema. In other words, a renal intervention is capable by itself of modifying vascular reactivity throughout the organism, even in the absence of hypertension. This suggests the existence of very complex relationships between the various renal vascular factors involved in hypertension—factors which, indeed, simply reflect modifications in the vascular sensitivity of the entire organism. If, therefore, one were to confine oneself to studying the peripheral vasoconstrictor effect of a single vasoconstrictor or of a single antagonist, the conclusions one would draw might well be only partial and insufficient, because the vascular phenomena involved in hypertension cannot be separated from the overall reactivity of the circulatory system. It is very difficult to decide in these cases which is the cause and which the effect of the hypertension. The problem is already complex enough in the case of a single antihypertensive agent such as hydralazine, and it is not surprising that it should become even more complicated if other substances too are considered, such as guanethidine, reserpine, ganglionic blocking agents, or diuretics. In connection with the diuretics, account has to be taken of their effects on the retention of water and of certain electrolytes, including in particular Na^+ and K^+, and of the fact that, as a result of their influence on the "milieu interne" (117), they exert a direct effect on the antihypertensive action of compounds such as hydralazine.

In other types of relatively short-term, artificially induced hypertension, e.g., hypertension caused by eliciting the carotid sinus reflex in the cat, very low doses (0.01 mg per kilogram intravenously) of hydralazine are sufficient to decrease this reflex considerably (10). The same applies to another experimental procedure employed in the dog (197). In this species, stimulation of the central trunk of the vagus or of the sciatic nerve causes a brief increase in arterial blood pressure, a phenomenon which several authors, such as Binet and Burstein (15), Erspamer (58), Diaz et al. (51), and Page (135), believe to be connected with the release of certain substances in the central nervous system. One striking property of hydralazine in this experimental procedure is its ability to diminish this artificially induced acute pressor effect as well. In the intact animal, hydralazine has been reported to antagonize serotonin (135) or enteramine (51).

The fact that hydralazine exerts an antagonistic effect in types of hypertension induced by factors involving a nervous component shows that this compound, apart from its direct action on the peripheral vessels, would also seem to act on certain nervous substrates. This action, however, does not take the form of ganglionic blockade because hydralazine has no effect on transmission across autonomic nervous synapses even if, under certain experimental conditions, it is capable of potentiating the effect of classic ganglionic blocking agents such as azamethonium (10).

Further evidence that hydralazine might exert a central action is provided by the fact that it reduces the adenosine triphosphate level in the brain, while at the same time increasing the concentration of adenosine diphosphate. Kirpekar and Lewis (96) have concluded from this that hydralazine modifies certain normal processes of oxidation in the brain. In this connection, it may also be mentioned that hydralazine can potentiate the hypnotic effect produced by hexabarbital (132); this potentiation, however, is known today to be produced by so many drugs that it can no longer be regarded as specific.

Hydralazine has another extremely interesting property. Quite recently, the use of a β-adrenergic receptor blocking agent, pronethalol, has made it possible to study certain special features of hydralazine's action in the anesthetized or normal dog. Thus, Brunner et al. (31) found that the hypotension and tachycardia produced by hydralazine were antagonized by pronethalol in the normal animal, whereas in the anesthetized animal the tachycardia was not affected and the hypotension potentiated. The same authors (32) report that pronethalol also antagonizes the hypotensive effect of guanethidine, but not that of methyldopa. Finally, Meier et al. (111) consider that the combined effects of hydralazine and propranolol on the myocardium can be summed up as follows: reduction in arterial blood pressure, bradycardia, slight increase in cardiac output, and diminution in oxygen consumption. These various observations definitely show that the specific actions of hydralazine on certain elements of the circulatory system are connected with those of specific β-adrenergic blocking agents. Despite the observations already mentioned to the effect that hydralazine exerts virtually no antagonistic action on epinephrine or norepinephrine in some tests, these other series of experiments involving either the intact animal or certain parts of its circulatory system indicate that this compound does after all interfere with adrenergic regulation.

In addition, detailed studies have been conducted in normotensive animals on the role played by modifications of the "milieu interne" (98, 113, 117, 182), the composition of which in terms of Na^+, Mg^{2+}, Ca^{2+}, O_2, CO_2, and especially K^+ (195) can be altered at will so as to produce changes in the reactivity of an isolated organ—a procedure employed, for example, by Meier and Tripod (117) using isolated vessels of the rabbit hind leg or coronary vessels. These changes in the composition of the "milieu interne," allied to those involving lactic and malonic acid, adenosine triphosphate, adenosine phosphoric acid, or even steroids such as cortisone or hydrocortisone, also exert an extremely complex effect on the vascular response to various vasoconstrictors and their antagonists. The spectrum of activity of hydralazine is likewise considerably affected by these changes. O_2, for instance, can reinforce certain antagonistic effects produced by hydralazine, whereas an excess of K^+ or of Ca^{2+} weakens them (117).

B. Other Pharmacodynamic Properties

In addition to their numerous peripheral actions on the cardiovascular system, the hydrazinophthalazines also exert effects on other organs, functions, and cells.

Apart from its effect on the deposition of cholesterol, which has already been mentioned, and on mesenchymal reactions, hydralazine displays a marked action on the growth of foreign-body granuloma in the rat and on local inflammation produced by mustard oil (115), as well as on the amount of exudate occurring in rats with exudative pleurisy following an intrapleural injection of turpentine, as recently demonstrated by Jaques (91). This anti-inflammatory effect, however, is not necessarily connected with the hypotensive, antihypertensive, and/or monoamine oxidase inhibiting properties of hydralazine, for these various effects are dissociated in some derivatives of this chemical group. On the other hand, guanethidine, a powerful hypotensive drug, exhibits only a weak anti-inflammatory effect, whereas aminoguanidine counteracts inflammation only in doses which reduce arterial blood pressure (91). These observations, however, seem to depend on the species of animal involved, because in the guinea pig Meilman *et al.* (120) found that hydrazinophthalazine, for example, failed to exert any antiinflammatory effect on the granuloma produced by injecting a polygalactoside.

Hydralazine also potentiates the effect of hydrocortisone in endotoxin shock in the dog, a condition caused by innumerable cardiovascular factors (196). Other authors, in contrast, believe that all vasodepressor agents, including hydralazine in particular, aggravate endotoxin shock (127). This indicates how difficult it is to analyze the circulatory response in a condition as complex as experimental shock.

It is also very difficult to explain the protective effect exerted by hydralazine against lethal irradiation of the whole body, as described in detail by Jaques (90) in the mouse. This syndrome is due to so many factors of a functional and cellular nature that it is hard to establish the exact site of attack of hydralazine. All that can be said is that this reflects the drug's extremely wide range of activity.

Some authors are of the opinion that hydralazine produces an irreversible suppression of ganglionic transmission in the anesthetized cat; this conclusion is based on the drug's effect on contraction of the nictitating membrane following preganglionic and postganglionic stimulation of the cervical sympathetic nerve (72). Bucher (33) also believes that hydralazine antagonizes the increase in pulmonary elasticity produced by histamine or epinephrine in the rabbit.

Finally, it should be pointed out that hydralazine exerts a fungicidal effect *in vitro*, although in a series of hydrazinophthalazines no correlation could be found between hypotensive effect on the one hand and fungistatic activity on the other, which would have been very striking (209).

We have already seen in Section III that hydralazine exerts an influence on certain enzymes; it inhibits, for example, diamino-oxidase (84). We should like to recall this activity of hydralazine in order to stress that there is no parallelism between the drug's hypotensive action and its inhibition of diamino-oxidase or monoamino-oxidase (175, 176). The same applies to inhibition of dopa-decarboxylase and to the formation of complexes with metals such as Co, Ni, Cu, Se, and Mn (118); here, too, no absolute parallelism exists between these various phenomena and the drug's hypotensive effect. As a matter of fact, a whole series of hydrazinophthalazine derivatives studied by Schuler and Wyss (176) do not necessarily display at the same time the typical hypotensive properties mentioned at the beginning of this article. Albrecht (3), however, found that hydralazine differed from other hypotensive agents in that it failed to modify alkaline phosphatase activity in the rat aortic wall.

As regards the catalytic activity of various metal ions on the oxidation or auto-oxidation of epinephrine, norepinephrine, and serotonin, as well as the changes brought about in this activity by hydralazine, Meier and Schuler (116) showed that this phenomenon depends as much on the metal and the substrate as on the hydralazine derivative employed.

It should also be noted that, according to certain authors, hydralazine inhibits decarboxylase and thus, secondarily, the content of norepinephrine and dopamine in certain tissues (163). The fact that it diminishes the serotonin concentration in chromaffin cells of the intestine (105) demonstrates once again the diversity of its peripheral effects. It must also be recalled that Gillis and Lewis (74, 75) emphasized the effect of hydrazinophthalazines on carbohydrate metabolism in smooth muscle, and suggested that this antagonistic action was exerted via the tricarboxylic acid cycle. Finally, Moore et al. (125) observed that hydralazine, like reserpine, does not affect renal or myocardial tissue respiration in normotensive animals, but increases it in cases where it has been reduced in animals with cortexone-induced hypertension.

One very striking feature already mentioned in Section III and reported by Tripod and Meier (189) and Meier et al. (118) is that hydralazine and dihydralazine are capable of binding extremely firmly with homologous or heterologous sera, proteins, polypeptides, or even a protein hydrolyzate. Once bound in this way, hydralazine loses entirely its hypotensive effect, as well as various of its previously mentioned antagonistic actions in peripheral blood vessels. It would appear that the reaction with serum or blood constituents "detoxicates," as it were, the direct effect of hydralazine on the vascular wall.

Hence, the overall picture of the known actions of the hydrazinophthalazines, their more or less specific antagonistic effects on cardiovascular function and on cellular enzymic processes, their extremely varied and diverse sites of attack, and their mechanisms of action which are usually far different from the classic adrenergic mechanisms serve to indicate that the hydrazinophthalazines also possess accessory properties. These properties probably have no direct or indirect bearing on hypotensive action, but serve to illustrate above all the complexity of the pharmacodynamic effects and of the mechanisms underlying anatomico-pathological lesions in experimental hypertension and the syndromes encountered in clinical forms of the disease.

Some of these properties of hydralazine are definitely responsible for the hypotensive effect of these drugs in normotensive animals or in animals with experimental hypertension; some diminish specific reactions to various vasopressor agents; some modify tissue and cellular reactivity; and some are probably responsible for certain side effects which will be discussed in the following section.

C. Therapeutic Use in Man

A complete description and detailed analysis of the clinical use of hydralazine in various hypertensive syndromes is given by other authors in this volume.

A common tendency in the treatment of hypertension is to combine several antihypertensive agents with the aim of improving their therapeutic effects by making full use of their different points of attack. Thus, hydralazine is as a rule combined with other antihypertensives such as reserpine, ganglionic blocking agents, methyldopa, and, especially, saluretics. This type of treatment does not consist simply in using several of these agents in the form of fixed combinations but, depending on the severity and course of the disease, in proceeding successively from one drug to another.

During the past few years, extremely detailed reviews have appeared on this subject. In 1957 Smirk (179) for example, published a very full analysis of arterial hypertension, as well as of its pathophysiology, pharmacology, and, above all, treatment. In 1960 proceedings of a symposium on essential hypertension were brought out by Reubi et al. (156) and this publication constitutes an extraordinarily rich source of information for any one interested in the mechanisms and treatment of this disease. The same applies to the volume issued by Pickering et al. (149) and to the symposium proceedings edited by Brest and Moyer (23) who discuss theoretical and factual aspects of the etiology, pathology, pharmacology, and treatment of hypertension in man.

Brest and Moyer (24–29, 128, 129, 131), Page (135, 136), Freis (63) and Mohler and Freis (124) in the United States, and Bickel (14), Bock (21, 22), Cottier (46), Gessler (73), Moeschlin (123), Nager (133), and Staub (181) in Europe have analyzed in more specialized papers hypertensive syndromes of varying etiology and have reported the therapeutic results they obtained either with hydralazine derivatives alone or, more often, with combined treatment. These authors have emphasized the value of various combined treatments, of the saluretics, and of dietary measures.

In view of its many different sites of attack, particularly in the blood vessels, hydralazine and its derivatives have been successfully employed in some forms of hypertension whose etiology differs quite considerably from that of essential hypertension. Thus, pre-eclampsia or eclampsia has fairly rapidly become one of the major indications for hydralazine and its derivatives, both in Europe and in Anglo-Saxon countries (1, 4, 48, 95, 108, 134). The reason for this probably lies in hydralazine's affinity for the renal vessels, an affinity which has already been stressed on several occasions in both experimental and clinical studies, particularly in those published by Reubi (155, 156). The same affinity is probably also responsible for the successful results obtained with the help of hydralazine in nephrotic syndrome and nephritis. According to Rossi (158), nephrotic syndrome responds favorably to combined treatment with steroids and hydralazine, and according to Mach (104), patients with nephritis display a reduction in arterial hypertension following hydralazine, especially if the latter is combined with other drugs and with dietary measures.

Since hydralazine and its derivatives have so many different sites of attack in the organism and so many different modes and mechanisms of action, as well as being endowed with a particular affinity for various anatomico-functional elements of the circulatory system, it is inevitable that, particularly if given in high doses over a long period of time, they should also possess side effects. The first side effect to be reported, both by American (2, 30, 56, 88, 150, 178, 205) and European (86, 87, 140) authors, was a sort of "disseminated lupus erythematosus," accompanied in some instances by rheumatoid arthritis, a monarthritis in the majority of cases. This side effect is so well known today that it is referred to as the "hydralazine syndrome." Other drugs, however, such as penicillin, phenylbutazone, certain sulfonamides, hydantoin derivatives, etc. can give rise to the same secondary reaction (88, 205). Quite recently, it has even been suggested that a genetic factor may be involved (205). Fairly complete studies of the clinical picture, prognosis, and diagnostic criteria of this lupus-like syndrome, as well as data on the dosages of hydralazine which give rise to it, have been published in the past few years (2, 30, 56, 150). It has not, however, been possible to reproduce this syndrome in animals, even by administering massive doses over a long period of time, as McCoy and Leach (107) attempted to do, for example, in the pig. On the other hand, the formation of antibodies against hydralazine has been observed in cases of lupus erythematosus in which fairly high daily doses of the drug had been administered over a period of several years (65). Nonetheless, the hypothesis that hydralazine-induced lupus erythematosus may have an allergic etiology has not yet been confirmed.

Other side effects which have been reported in man following long-term treatment with high doses of hydralazine include, in particular, tachycardia (206), relative anemia accompanied by hyperglobulinemia (145), and peripheral neuropathy due to pyridoxine deficiency (152). On the other hand, hepatic steatosis with accumulation of periportal lipids but without cellular necrosis has been observed only in the rat under special conditions; neither adrenalectomy nor adrenergic blocking agents had any effect on this steatosis (5).

V. Summary and conclusions

In a subject as vast as that of the hydralazines, constant reviews are necessary, even if these reviews are simply confined to drawing more or less arbitrary comparisons between the hydralazines and other hypotensive and antihypertensive agents. Despite this, there will inevitably be numerous gaps in our knowledge. Nevertheless, the observations described above do not reveal any parallelism between all the pharmacodynamic properties of various hydralazines and their hypotensive or antihypertensive effects.

Similarly, no parallelism is to be found between various types of experimental hypertension in animals and clinical hypertension in man, although it would appear that these different forms of the disease do have some etiological mechanisms in common.

The above-mentioned reviews on the subject underline in particular the need to employ a whole series of experimental methods involving various mechanisms in order to arrive at a better understanding of the phenomena in question.

A study confined to measuring the fall in blood pressure produced by hydralazines in normotensive animals is incapable of providing a full picture of the potentialities of these drugs as antihypertensive agents. Moreover, considerable differences exist in the range of antagonistic effects produced by antihypertensive agents in the peripheral vascular system; these differences depend in part on whether the agents are given singly or in combination with one another, or whether they are associated with modifications in the "milieu interne." Some hypotensive drugs have a wider range of activity, and some have virtually no effect on specific peripheral receptors. On the other hand, studies of peripheral vascular reactivity in normotensive animals or in animals with various types of experimental hypertension have revealed functional interdependences which, if judiciously utilized, may give rise to therapeutic applications.

It is extremely difficult for experimental pharmacodynamic research to allocate antihypertensive or hypotensive agents definitely to a particular pharmacodynamic group on the basis of their site of attack, mode or mechanism of action, etc. This research should devote all its efforts to demonstrating that a given molecule may display a mosaic of more or less specific effects, some of which may be encountered in the intact animal and others in certain isolated organs. It should also demonstrate that the animal or human organism, in its turn, contains a mosaic of specific receptors to which the molecules can attach themselves more or less permanently and thus produce therapeutic effects and also, of course, depending on the case in question and the dose employed, certain side effects.

In the case of the hydralazines, we do not think that pharmacodynamic researchers, left to themselves, would have been able on the basis of animal experiments to make a final choice among the large number of synthetic derivatives, even if they had called upon all available knowledge in the fields of physiology and biochemistry. In other words, research in this area could never have succeeded in supplying clinicians with an ideal antihypertensive agent. This research was confined, in fact, to discovering a combination of pharmacodynamic properties corresponding to a pattern of therapeutic effects which were associated in animal experiments with a minimum of secondary reactions. But pharmacodynamic researchers did not—and still do not—possess the decisive experimental methods for producing types of hypertension equivalent to those encountered in man.

Consequently, it is still extremely difficult, if not impossible, today to predict the relative value of the experimental properties of a substance or of the factors which are finally responsible for its therapeutic effect.

Only by constantly comparing experimental observations with clinical results and by taking account of the largest possible number of physiological, pharmacodynamic, biochemical, and pathological factors can we hope on the basis of the very rapid developments that have taken place in the past few years to discover additional, new, and still more effective approaches to the treatment of the various hypertensive syndromes (187).

References

1. Adams, J. Q., and Cameron, W. B., *Am. J. Obstet. Gynecol.* **80**, 253 (1960).
2. Alarcon-Segovia, D., Worthington, J. W., Ward, L. E., and Wakim, K. G., *New Engl. J. Med.* **272**, 462 (1965).
3. Albrecht, W., *Helv. Physiol. Pharmacol. Acta* **18**, 376 (1960).
4. Alexander, J. A., Rogers, S. T., Jacobs, W. M., and Wills, S. H., *Am. J. Obstet. Gynecol.* **89**, 77 (1964).
5. Amenta, J. S., Dominguez, A. M., and Saunders, J. P., *Federation Proc.* **22**, 371 (1963).
6. Bargeton, D., and Roquet, J., *Arch. Intern. Pharmacodyn.* **137**, 428 (1962).
7. Barrett, W. E., Povalski, H., and Rutledge, R., *Federation Proc.* **24**, 712 (1965).
8. Bein, H. J., and Brunner, H., "Antihypertensive Therapy, Principles and Practice" (F. Gross, ed.), p. 15. Springer, Berlin, 1966.
9. Bein, H. J., Desaulles, P. A., and Loustalot, P., *Experientia* **13**, 130 (1957).
10. Bein, H. J., Gross, F., Tripod, J., and Meier, R., *Schweiz. Med. Wochschr.* **83**, 336 (1953).
11. Bein, H. J., Gross, F., Tripod, J., and Meier, R., *Schweiz. Med. Wochschr.* **83**, 1007 (1953).
12. Bein, H. J., and Meier, R., *Intern. Arch. Allergy Appl. Immunol.* **6**, 304 (1955).
13. Bein, H. J., Tripod, J., and Meier, R., *Experientia* **8**, 74 (1952).

14. Bickel, G., *Schweiz. Med. Wochschr.* **92**, 1047 (1962).
15. Binet, L., and Burstein, M., *Compt. Rend. Soc. Biol.* **143**, 1344 and 1347 (1949).
16. Biniecki, S., and Gutkowska, B., *Acta Polon. Pharm.* **11**, 27 (1955); *Chem. Abstr.* **50**, 12062h (1956).
17. Biniecki, S., Haase, A., Izdebski, J., Kesler, E., and Rylski, L., *Bull. Acad. Polon., Sci., Ser. Sci., Chim., Geol. Geograph.* **6**, 227 (1958); *Chem. Abstr.* **52**, 18424f (1958).
18. Biniecki, S., and Izdebski, J., *Acta Polon. Pharm.* **15**, 421 (1957); *Chem. Abstr.* **52**, 15540g (1958).
19. Biniecki, S., Moll, M., and Rylski, L., *Ann. Pharm. Franç.* **16**, 421 (1958); *Chem. Abstr.* **53**, 7187e (1959).
20. Biniecki, S., and Rylski, L., *Ann. Pharm. Franç.* **16**, 21 (1958); *Chem. Abstr.* **52**, 18446h (1958).
21. Bock, K. D., *Deut. Med. Wochschr.* **86**, 743 (1961).
22. Bock, K. D., *Münch. Med. Wochschr.* **104**, 1262 (1962).
23. Brest, A. N., and Moyer, J. H., eds., "Hypertension: Second Hahnemann Symposium on Hypertensive Disease." Lea & Febiger, Philadelphia, Pennsylvania, 1961.
24. Brest, A. N., and Moyer, J. H., *Progr. Cardiovascular Diseases* **3**, 350 (1961).
25. Brest, A. N., and Moyer, J. H., *Diseases Chest* **41**, 582 (1962).
26. Brest, A. N., and Moyer, J. H., *Praxis (Bern)* **51**, 738 (1962).
27. Brest, A. N., and Moyer, J. H., *Angiology* **14**, 64 (1963).
28. Brest, A. N., Onesti, G., and Moyer, J. H., *Geriatrics* **18**, 444 (1963).
29. Brest, A. N., and Moyer, J. H., *Diseases Chest* **45**, 345 (1964).
30. Braverman, I. M., *New Engl. J. Med.* **272**, 920 (1965).
31. Brunner, H., Hedwall, P. R., and Meier, M., *Experientia* **21**, 136 (1965).
32. Brunner, H., Hedwall, P. R., and Meier, M., *Experientia* **21**, 231 (1965).
33. Bucher, K., *Helv. Physiol. Pharmacol. Acta* **19**, 84 (1961).
34. Burn, J. H., *Physiol. Rev.* **18**, 137 (1938).
35. Bygdeman, M., and Stjarne, L., *Nature* **184**, 1646 (1959).
36. Bygdeman, M., and Stjarne, L., *Nature* **186**, 82 (1960).
37. Cassella Farbwerke Mainkur, West German Patent 845,200 (1952).
38. Cassella Farbwerke Mainkur, West German Patent 932,128 (1955).
39. Cassella Farbwerke Mainkur, West German Patent 962,165 (1957).
40. Chaigneau, M., and Hubert, M., *Compt. Rend.* **254**, 1432 (1962).
41. Chimie et Atomistique, British Patent 856,409 (1960).
42. CIBA Limited, U.S. Patent 2,484,785 (1949).
43. CIBA Limited, U.S. Patent 2,484,029 (1949).
43a. CIBA Limited, U.S. Patent 2,719,158 (1955).
44. CIBA Limited, U.S. Patent 2,960,504 (1960).
44a. CIBA Limited, British Patent 868,462 (1961)
45. Cohn, V. H., Jr., and Shore, P. A., *Federation Proc.* **19**, 283 (1960).
46. Cottier, P., *Therap. Umschau* **19**, 182 (1962).
47. Craver, B. N., and Yonkman, F. F., *Federation Proc.* **9**, 265 (1950).
48. Cretti, A., *Am. J. Obstet. Gynecol.* **90**, 1319 (1964).
49. Dale, H. H., and Richards, A. N., *J. Physiol. (London)* **52**, 110 (1918).
50. Daly, J. de B., Foggie, P., and Hebb, C., *Quart. J. Exptl. Physiol.* **30**, 21 (1940).
51. Diaz, J., de la Barreda, P., Molina, A. F., and Alcala, R., *Bull. Inst. Med. Res., Federation Malaya* **5**, 65 (1952).
52. Douglass, C. D., Dillaha, C. J., Dillaha, J., and Kountz, S. L., *J. Lab. Clin. Med.* **49**, 561 (1957).
53. Douglass, C. D., and Hogan, R., *Proc. Soc. Exptl. Biol. Med.* **100**, 446 (1959).

54. Druey, J., and Marxer, A., *J. Med. Pharm. Chem.* **1**, 1 (1959).
55. Druey, J., and Ringier, B. H., *Helv. Chim. Acta* **34**, 195 (1951).
56. Dubois, E. L., and Tuffanelli, D. L., *J. Am. Med. Assoc.* **190**, 104 (1964).
57. Edlin, A. I., Kinnard, W. J., Vogin, E. E., and Buckley, J. P., *J. Pharm. Sci.* **54**, 20 (1965).
58. Erspamer, V., *A.M.A. Arch. Internal Med.* **90**, 505 (1952).
59. Fallab, S., *Bull. Soc. Chim. France* p. 1486 (1961).
60. Fallab, S., *Helv. Chim. Acta* **45**, 1957 (1962).
61. Fallab, S., and Erlenmeyer, H., *Helv. Chim. Acta* **40**, 363 (1957).
62. Fallab, S., and Erlenmeyer, H., *Experientia* **19**, 374 (1963).
63. Freis, E. D., *Am. Heart J.* **67**, 133 (1964).
64. Freis, E. D., and Finnerty, F. A., Jr., *Proc. Soc. Exptl. Biol. Med.* **75**, 23 (1950).
65. Friedman, H., and Heine, W. I., *Experientia* **19**, 10 (1963).
66. Fujii, K., and Sato, S., G. Tanabe Co. Ltd., Ann. Rept. Vol. 1, p. 1 (1956); *Chem. Abstr.* **51**, 6650b (1957).
67. Fujisawa Pharmaceutical Company, Japanese Patent 10,027 (1960); *Chem. Abstr.* **55**, P8439e (1961).
68. Furchgott, R. F., *Pharmacol. Rev.* **7**, 183 (1955).
69. Gardner, D. L., *Brit. J. Exptl. Pathol.* **41**, 60 (1960).
70. Gardner, D. L., and Brooks, P. W., *Brit. J. Exptl. Pathol.* **43**, 276 (1962).
71. Gardner, D. L., and Brooks, P. W., *Brit. J. Exptl. Pathol.* **44**, 31 (1963).
72. Gertner, S. B., and Romano, A., *J. Pharmacol. Exptl. Therap.* **138**, 309 (1962).
73. Gessler, U., *Deut. Med. J.* **13**, 496 (1962).
74. Gillis, C. N., and Lewis, J. J., *Nature* **178**, 859 (1956).
75. Gillis, C. N., and Lewis, J. J., *Nature* **179**, 820 (1957).
76. Goldstein, S., and Rossi, G. V., *J. Pharmacol. Exptl. Therap.* **126**, 168 (1959).
77. Grimson, K. S., Chittum, J. R., and Metcalf, B. H., *Federation Proc.* **9**, 279 (1950).
78. Gross, F., *Arch. Exptl. Pathol. Pharmakol.* **232**, 161 (1957).
79. Gross, F., *Nauheimer Fortbildungs-Lehrgänge* **25**, 34 (1960).
80. Gross, F., *in* "Essential Hypertension" (K. D. Bock and P. Cottier, eds.), pp. 92–109. Springer, Berlin, 1960.
81. Gross, F., *Verhandl. Deut. Ges. Kreislaufforsch.* **28**, 11 (1962).
82. Gross, F., Druey, J., and Meier, R., *Experientia* **6**, 19 (1950).
83. Gross, F., Noelpp, B., Sulser, F., Doebelin, R., and Kündig, H., *Klin. Wochschr.* **33**, 372 (1955).
84. Gross, F., Schuler, W., Tripod, J., and Meier, R., *Experientia* **8**, 229 (1952).
85. Gupta, K. P., and Bhargava, K. P., *Arch. Intern. Pharmacodyn.* **155**, 84 (1965).
86. Hennemann, H. H., *Therap. Gegenwart* **102**, 1112 (1963).
87. Herzberg, J. J., *Internist* **4**, 475 (1963).
88. Holley, H. L., *Ann. Internal Med.* [N.S.] **55**, 1036 (1961).
89. Jančik, F., Budĕšínský, B., and Körbl, J., *Cesko. Farm.* **9**, 304 (1960); *Chem. Abstr.* **55**, 9790a (1961).
90. Jaques, R., and Meier, R., *Experientia* **16**, 75 (1960).
91. Jaques, R., *Helv. Physiol. Pharmacol. Acta* **23**, 54 (1965).
92. Jaques, R., Tripod, J., and Meier, R., *Arch. Exptl. Pathol. Pharmakol.* **230**, 26 (1957).
93. Jenne, J. W., and Orser, M., *J. Clin. Invest.* **44**, 1992 (1965).
94. Kesler, E., and Biniecki, S., *Acta Polon. Pharm.* **16**, 93 (1959); *Chem. Abstr.* **53**, 18046h (1959).
95. Kirchhoff, H., *Deut. Med. J.* **10**, 565 (1959).
96. Kirpekar, S. M., and Lewis, J. J., *Brit. J. Pharmacol.* **14**, 40 (1959).
97. Kirpekar, S. M., and Lewis, J. J., *J. Pharm. Pharmacol.* **11**, Suppl., 203T (1959).

98. Kordik, P., *Brit. J. Pharmacol.* **6**, 75 (1951).
99. Kumada, S., Watanabe, N., Yamamoto, K., and Zenno, H., *Yakugaku Kenkyo* **30**, 635 (1958); *Chem. Abstr.* **53**, 20554g (1959).
100. Libermann, D., and Jacquier, R., *Bull. Soc. Chim. France* p. 383 (1961).
101. Libermann, D., and Rouaix, A., *Bull. Soc. Chim. France* p. 1793 (1959).
102. Loustalot, P., Schuler, W., and Albrecht, W., *Proc. Symp. Drugs Affecting Lipid Metabo.*, *Milan*, 1960, p. 271. Elsevier, Amsterdam, 1961.
103. Luk'jančikova, G. I., *Med. Prom. SSSR* **16**, 46 (1962).
104. Mach, R. S., *Schweiz. Med. Wochschr.* **94**, 173 (1964).
105. Maškovskij, M. D., Jakovleva, A. J., and Sachnazazova, N. G., *Farmakol. i Toksikol.* **24**, 44 (1961).
106. Masson, G. M. C., McCormack, L. J., Dustan, H. P., and Corcoran, A. C., *Am. J. Pathol.* **34**, 817 (1958).
107. McCoy, F. W., and Leach, W. J., *Proc. Soc. Exptl. Biol. Med.* **101**, 183 (1959).
108. McFadyen, I. R., *Lancet* **II**, 1009 (1960).
109. McIsaac, W. M., and Kanda, M., *J. Pharmacol. Exptl. Therap.* **143**, 7 (1964).
110. McKennis, H., Jr., and Yard, A. S., U.S. Dept. Com., *Office Tech. Serv.* **143**, 914 (1957); *Chem. Abstr.* **55**, 17375i (1961).
111. Meier, M., Hedwall, P., and Brunner, H., *Helv. Physiol. Pharmacol. Acta* **23**, C36 (1965).
112. Meier, R., and Bein, H. J., *Biochim. Biophys. Acta* **4**, 144 (1950).
113. Meier, R., and Bein, H. J., *Helv. Physiol. Pharmacol. Acta* **8**, 436 (1950).
114. Meier, R., Bein, H. J., Gross, F., and Tripod, J., *Proc. 3rd Intern. Congr. Internal Med., Stockholm*, 1954, *Acta. med. Scand.* **154**, Suppl. 312, 1956, p. 165.
115. Meier, R., and Desaulles, P. A., *J. Physiol.* (*Paris*) **49**, 667 (1957).
116. Meier, R., and Schuler, W., *Helv. Physiol. Pharmacol. Acta* **15**, 284 (1957).
117. Meier, R., and Tripod, J., *Compt. Rend. 2nd Congr. Intern. Angeiol. Fribourg, 1955*, p. 46.
118. Meier, R., Tripod, J., and Brüni, C., *Arch. Exptl. Pathol. Pharmakol.* **223**, 338 (1954).
119. Meier, R., Tripod, J., and Brüni, C., *Arch. Intern. Pharmacodyn.* **101**, 158 (1955).
120. Meilman, E., Urivetzky, M., and Rapoport, C., *Arthritis Rheumat.* **8**, 69 (1965).
121. Menziani, E., *Boll. Sci. Fac. Chim. Ind. Bologna* **12**, 162 (1954); *Chem. Abstr.* **50**, 356b (1956).
122. Menziani, E., *Med. Sper.* **25**, 277 (1954); *Chem. Abstr.* **50**, 828h (1956).
123. Moeschlin, S., *Schweiz. Med. Wochschr.* **91**, 193 (1961).
124. Mohler, E. R., and Freis, E. D., *Am. Heart J.* **60**, 329 (1960).
125. Moore, K. E., Murray, J. R., and Huston, M. J., *Arch. Intern. Pharmacodyn.* **118**, 340 (1959).
126. Moore-Jones, D., and Perry, H. M., *Circulation* **26**, 763 (1960).
127. Morris, J. A., Smith, R. W., and Assali, N. S., *Am. J. Obstet. Gynecol.* **91**, 491 (1965).
128. Moyer, J. H., *J. Am. Med. Assoc.* **182**, 220 (1962).
129. Moyer, J. H., and Brest, A. N., *Med. Clin. N. Am.* **45**, 2 (1961).
130. Moyer, J. H., and Brest, A. N., *Med. Clin. N. Am.* **45**, 375 (1961).
131. Moyer, J. H., and Brest, A. N., *J. Michigan State Med. Soc.* **61**, 1377 (1962).
131a. Mull, R. P., Maxwell, R. A., and Plummer, A. J., *Nature* **180**, 1200 (1957).
131b. Mull, R. P., Schmidt, P., Dapero, M. R., Higgins, J., and Weisbach, M. J., *J. Am. Chem. Soc.* **80**, 3769 (1958).
132. Mullen, J. O., and Fouts, J. R., *Biochem. Pharmacol.* **14**, 305 (1965).
133. Nager, F., *Praxis* (*Bern*) **53**, 485 (1964).
134. Newton, M., *Am. J. Obstet. Gynecol.* **88**, 972 (1964).
135. Page, I. H., *J. Am. Med. Assoc.* **147**, 1311 (1951).

136. Page, I. H., *Ann. Internal Med.* [N.S.] **57**, 96 (1962).
137. Perry, H. M., *Federation Proc.* **11**, 121 (1952).
138. Perry, H. M., *J. Clin. Invest.* **32**, 595 (1953).
139. Perry, H. M., *J. Lab. Clin. Med.* **41**, 566 (1953).
140. Perry, H. M., *Ann. Internal Med.* [N.S.] **57**, 441 (1962).
141. Perry, H. M., Comens, P., and Yunice, A., *J. Lab. Clin. Med.* **59**, 456 (1962).
142. Perry, H. M., and Mills, E. J., *Am. J. Med. Sci.* **243**, 564 (1962).
143. Perry, H. M., and Schroeder, H. A., *Am. J. Med. Sci.* **228**, 396 (1954).
144. Perry, H. M., and Schroeder, H. A., *J. Chronic Diseases* **2**, 520 (1955).
145. Perry, H. M., Schroeder, H. A., and Comens, P., *Am. J. Med. Sci.* **244**, 44 (1962).
146. Perry, H. M., Schroeder, H. A., and Morrow, J. D., *Am. J. Med. Sci.* **228**, 405 (1954).
147. Perry, H. M., Teitlebaum, S., and Schwartz, P. L., *Federation Proc.* **14**, 113 (1955).
148. Persch, W., U.S. Patent 2,742,467 (1956); *Chem. Abstr.* **51**, P1305c (1957).
149. Pickering, G., Cranston, W. I., and Pears, M. A., "The Treatment of Hypertension." Thomas, Springfield, Illinois, 1961.
150. Pigeon, G., and Genest, J., *Can. Med. Assoc. J.* **83**, 743 (1960).
151. Plummer, A. J., this volume, p. 67.
152. Raskin, N. H., and Fishman, R. A., *New Engl. J. Med.* **273**, 1182 (1965).
153. Reubi, F., *Helv. Med. Acta* **16**, 297 (1949).
154. Reubi, F., *Proc. Soc. Exptl. Biol. Med.* **73**, 102 (1950).
155. Reubi, F., *3rd Intern. Congr. Clin. Pathol., Brussels, 1957* p. 376. Presses Acad. Europ., Brussels, 1958.
156. Reubi, F., *in* "Essential Hypertension" (K. D. Bock and P. Cottier, eds.), p. 317. Springer, Berlin, 1960.
157. Reynolds, G. A., VanAllan, J. A., and Tinker, J. F., *J. Org. Chem.* **24**, 1205 (1959).
158. Rossi, E., *Schweiz. Med. Wochschr.* **89**, 537 (1959).
159. Ruggieri, R., *Giorn. Med. Militare* **107**, 239 (1957); *Chem. Abstr.* **52**, 2021c (1958).
160. Ruggieri, R., *Farmaco (Pavia) Ed. Prat.* **11**, 571 (1956); *Chem. Abstr.* **53**, 14421a (1959).
161. Ruzhentseva, A. K., Tubina, I. S., and Bragina, L. N., *Med. Prom. SSSR* **14**, 34 (1960); *Chem. Abstr.* **55**, 9789g (1961).
162. Sandri, G. C., *Boll. Chim. Farm.* **96**, 431 (1957); *Chem. Abstr.* **52**, 4109g (1958).
163. Sano, I., Taniguchi, K., Gamo, T., Takesada, M., and Kakimoto, Y., *Klin. Wochschr.* **38**, 57 (1960).
164. Schaper, W. K. A., and Jageneau, A. H. M., *Arzneimittel-Forsch.* **11**, 1102 (1961).
165. Schlittler, E., Druey, J., and Marxer, A., *Progr. Drug Res.* **4**, 295 (1962).
166. Schmidt, P., and Druey, J., *Helv. Chim. Acta* **37**, 134 (1954).
167. Schmidt, P., Eichenberger, K., and Wilhelm, M., *Helv. Chim. Acta* **45**, 996 (1962).
168. Schmitt, H., and Schmitt, H., *J. Physiol.* (*Paris*) **52**, 525 (1960).
169. Schroeder, H. A., *Proc. Am. Heart Assoc., 24th Sci. Session, 1951*.
170. Schroeder, H. A., *J. Clin. Invest.* **30**, 672 (1951).
171. Schroeder, H. A., *in* "Hypertension: First Hahnemann Symposium on Hypertensive Disease" (J. H. Moyer, ed.), Saunders, Philadelphia, Pennsylvania, 1959.
172. Schroeder, H. A., Perry, H. M., Dennis, E. G., and Mahoney, L. E., *J. Exptl. Med.* **102**, 319 (1955).
173. Schuler, W., *Experientia* **8**, 230 (1952).
174. Schuler, W., and Albrecht, W., *Schweiz. Med. Wochschr.* **92**, 1007 (1962).
175. Schuler, W., and Meier, R., *Helv. Physiol. Pharmacol. Acta* **13**, 106 (1955).
176. Schuler, W., and Wyss, E., *Arch. Intern. Pharmacodyn.* **128**, 431 (1960).
177. Schulert, A. R., *Arch. Intern. Pharmacodyn.* **132**, 1 (1961).
178. Shulman, L. E., *Arthritis Rheumat.* **6**, 558 (1963).

179. Smirk, F. H., "High Arterial Pressure." Blackwell, Oxford, 1957.
180. Starke, H., East German Patent 15,116 (1958); *Chem. Abstr.* **54**, P3464f (1960).
181. Staub, H., *Schweiz. Med. Wochschr.* **92**, 959 (1962).
182. Studer, A., and Tripod, J., *Helv. Physiol. Pharmacol. Acta* **18**, 384 (1960).
183. Sulser, F., Dissertation, Benno Schwabe & Co., Basle (1955).
184. Sycheva, T. P., Kuz'micheva, T. P., Chernyaeva, A. T., Trupp, T. Kh., and Shchukina,
     M. N., *Med. Prom. SSSR* **14**, 13 (1960); *Chem. Abstr.* **54**, 22669g (1960).
185. Sycheva, T. P., and Shchukina, M. N., *Zh. Obshch. Khim.* **30**, 608 (1960); *Chem. Abstr.*
     54, 24783g (1960).
186. Tripod, J., "Symposium on Hypotensive Drugs," p. 47. Pergamon Press, Oxford, 1956.
187. Tripod, J., *Pathol. Biol., Semaine Hôp.* **9**, 511 (1961).
188. Tripod, J., and Bein, H. J., *Helv. Physiol. Pharmacol. Acta* **18**, 394 (1960).
189. Tripod, J., and Meier, R., *Helv. Physiol. Pharmacol. Acta* **12**, C33 (1954).
190. Tripod, J., and Meier, R., *Arch. Intern, Pharmacodyn.* **99**, 104 (1954).
191. Tripod, J., and Meier, R., *Arch. Exptl. Pathol. Pharmakol.* **232**, 470 (1958).
192. Tripod, J., Studer, A., Wirz, E., and Meier, R., *Arch. Intern. Pharmacodyn.* **126**, 126
     (1960).
193. Tripod, J., and Wirz, E., *Arch. Intern. Pharmacodyn.* **105**, 73 (1956).
194. Tripod, J., Wirz, E., and Meier, R., *Arch. Intern. Pharmacodyn.* **116**, 464 (1958).
195. Tripod, J., Wirz, E., and Meier, R., "Studies of Function in Health and Disease"
     (edited by A. S. Marrazzi and M. H. Aprison), p. 1–17, Galesbury State Research
     Hospital Press, Galesbury, Ill., 1960.
196. Vick, J., and Spink, W. W., *Proc. Soc. Exptl. Biol. Med.* **106**, 280 (1961).
197. Walker, H. A., Wilson, S., Atkins, E. C., Garrett, H. E., and Richardson, A. P., *J.
     Pharmacol. Exptl. Therap.* **101**, 368 (1951).
198. Walz, D., and Fallab, S., *Helv. Chim. Acta* **43**, 540 (1960).
199. Walz, D., and Fallab, S., *Helv. Chim. Acta* **44**, 13 (1961).
200. Werle, E., Schauer, A., and Hartung, G., *Klin. Wochschr.* **33**, 562 (1955).
201. Wesley-Hadžija, B., and Abaffy, F., *Croat. Chem. Acta* **30**, 15 (1958); *Chem. Abstr.* **54**,
     2661i (1960).
202. West, J. W., Kobayashi, T., and Anderson, F. S., *Circulation Res.* **10**, 722 (1962).
203. Wezler, K., and Sinn, W., *in* "Das Strömungsgesetz des Blutkreislaufes" *Arzneimittel-
     Forsch.*, **3**, 1–126, 1953.
204. Williams, J. R., Grollman, A., and Harrison, T. R., *J. Clin. Invest.* **18**, 373 (1939).
205. Wilske, K. R., Shalit, I. E., Willkens, R. F., and Decker, J. L., *Arthritis Rheumat.* **8**,
     260 (1965).
206. Wolkerstorfer, H., *Münch. Med. Wochschr.* **101**, 1913 (1959).
207. Woods, J. W., *J. Clin. Invest.* **39**, 1813 (1960).
208. Yeary, R. A., Brahm, C. A., and Miller, D. L., *Toxicol. Appl. Pharmacol.* **7**, 598 (1965).
209. Zsolnai, T., *Biochem. Pharmacol.* **11**, 995 (1962).
210. Zugravescu, I., Petrovanu, M., and Rucinschi, E., *Analele Stiint, Univ. "A.I. Cuza,"
     Iasi, Sect. I* [N.S.] **7**, 169 (1961); *Chem. Abstr.* **59**, 6399g (1963).

CHAPTER VII

Diuretics in the Clinical Treatment of Hypertension

George deStevens

It is now generally accepted that many types of human and experimental hypertension are associated with changes in electrolyte balances, especially as regards sodium ion concentration (44). Consequently, the maintenance of normal blood pressure is associated closely but not exclusively with normal kidney function.

The earliest observations on the role of sodium and other electrolytes in hypertension resulted from the use of a low salt diet in the therapeutic management of patients with high blood pressure. The original advocates of such diets were Ambard and Beaujard (2), and later Allen and Sherrill (1), and also Volhard (48). However, the beneficial effect of these diets was attributed to the restriction of the chloride ion rather than sodium. This misconception was enforced by the observation that the addition of large amounts of salt to the normal diet did not cause an increase in blood pressure either of the normal or the hypertensive patient. It was concluded, accordingly, that the intake of salt was not associated to any great extent with increased blood pressure. This was an unfortunate erroneous notion because it impeded the acceptance of salt-free dietotherapy for many years.

The investigations of Grollman (23) and of Grollman and Harrison (26) demonstrated the effectiveness of maximum sodium restriction in lowering blood pressure first in experimental animals and then in hypertensive patients. Moreover, they showed unequivocally for the first time that it was the sodium rather than the chloride ion which was responsible for the hypotensive effects of salt restriction. In addition, it was revealed that sodium phosphate or sodium bicarbonate, which previously were permitted in the diet of hypertensive patients, counteracted the beneficial effects of a salt-free diet.

Finally, these studies supported the findings of Kempner (34) concerning the effectiveness of rice in lowering blood pressure. Whereas it had been thought previously that the rice per se contained a factor which was responsible for the antihypertensive effect, Grollman (24) was able to show that this effect of rice was due to its low sodium content. Moreover, he concluded that a hypotensive effect could be induced by the use of any salt-restricted diet. However, it should not be surmized from these studies that ingestion of large amounts of salt is responsible for the hypertensive syndrome, but only that salt aggravates and enhances this condition. Several detailed reviews have been written on this subject, to which the reader is referred (25, 43, 44).

For over a decade following the report of Grollman and Harrison (26), low salt dietotherapy was an essential factor in the treatment of high blood pressure. Even the introduction of effective antihypertensives between the years 1952 and 1958 did not alter the necessity of sodium restriction.

Although Megibow and colleagues (40) reported that mercurial diuretics significantly reduced blood pressure in a small group of hypertensive patients, it is surprising that this form of antihypertensive therapy did not gain much favor in the subsequent 10-year period. It was not until the advent of chlorothiazide (1958) and hydrochlorothiazide (1959) that diuretic drugs achieved the prominence they now enjoy in the treatment of hypertension.

The synthesis of chlorothiazide (II) by Novello and Sprague (1957) and the synthesis of hydrochlorothiazide (III) by deStevens and Werner (1958) are shown in Scheme I. This subject has already been thoroughly reviewed (13)

(I)

HCOOH   NaBH₄   CH₂O
                         KMnO₄

(II)   (III)
Chlorothiazide   Hydrochlorothiazide

and for this discussion it need only be noted that these substances are the prototypes of a large variety of compounds synthesized in many laboratories. The mode of action of their active derivatives is quite similar and therefore emphasis will primarily be confined to these two drugs.

The use of chlorothiazide in the treatment of hypertension was first reported independently by Hollander and Wilkins (32) and Freis and Wilson (21). They demonstrated that this compound enhanced the antihypertensive effects of ganglionic blockers and reserpine. In a minority of patients chlorothiazide seemed to be effective when used as the sole antihypertensive agent. Shortly thereafter, Hollander et al. (30) compared the effect of hydrochlorothiazide with chlorothiazide in over 50 hypertensive subjects. In Table I and Fig. 1 the blood pressure responses to these compounds are compared. In a dose

Table I

COMAPARATIVE EFFECTS OF CHLOROTHIAZIDE AND DIHYDROCHLOROTHIAZIDE ON THE BLOOD PRESSURE OF
56 HYPERTENSIVE SUBJECTS[a]

Drugs	Number of cases	Number of responders (B.P. + = 14/9)	Average blood pressure reduction (mm Hg)	Range of blood pressure reduction (mm Hg)	Average diuretic dosage (mg/day)	Diuretic dose range (mg/day)
Chlorothiazide alone	16	7	18/10	20/10–60/25	750	375–1000
Dihydrochlorothiazide alone	16	9	24/14	20/10–70/30	75	37.5–100
Rauwolfia + Hydralazine						
+ Chlorothiazide	32	20	30/16	20/15–60/25	750	375–1000
+ Dihydrochlorothiazide	32	23	37/20	20/15–70/30	75	37.5–100
Ganglion blocker + *Rauwolfia*						
+ Chlorothiazide	8	5	34/16	20/10–80/30	375	375–750
+ Dihydrochlorothiazide	8	6	40/21	20/10–80/40	37.5	37.5–75

[a] From (30).

one-tenth that of chlorothiazide, hydrochlorothiazide alone and in combination with other drugs appeared to be slightly more antihypertensive than
chlorothiazide. Hollander *et al.* (30) reported that in general, about one in ten
subjects appeared to have a definitely greater blood pressure response to
hydrochlorothiazide than to chlorothiazide. Additional clinical studies (18,
29, 47) have indicated that these two drugs as well as other members of the
thiazide and hydrothiazide groups are effective in mild hypertension. Much
discussion and debate have followed on how these compounds act to reduce
blood pressure. It appears that, in general, these compounds cause sodium
depletion which in turn results in a reduction of plasma volume. This subject
has been succinctly reviewed by Corcoran only recently (11).

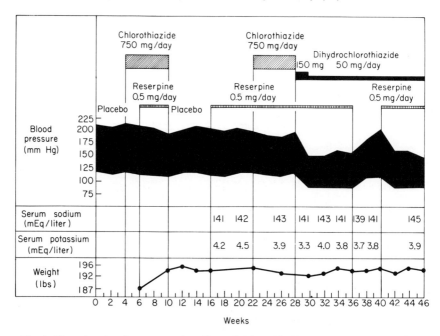

Fig. 1. Chart showing the comparative effects of chlorothiazide and dihydrochlorothiazide
on the blood pressure, serum electrolytes, and weight in a hypertensive patient.

These findings have prompted the study of other diuretics in the treatment of
hypertension. Gifford (22) has evaluated amisometradine (IV) in a group of
patients with mild to moderate, uncomplicated hypertension. The results of
his study are shown in Table II. These patients were treated for periods that
varied from 6 weeks to 6 months at a daily dosage of 1200 mg. A hypotensive
effect was noted in all five patients, but it was less than that observed in the
larger series of patients treated with chlorothiazide and hydrochlorothiazide.

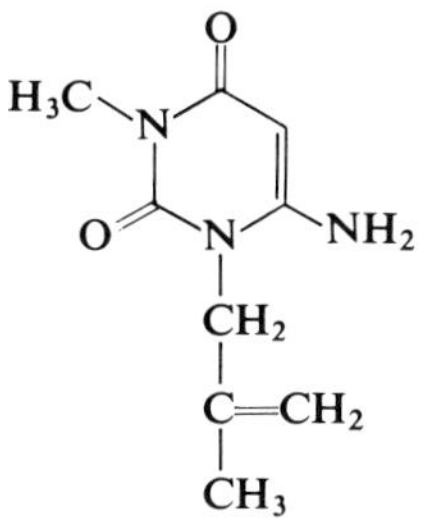

(IV)

Amisometradine

Moreover, Gifford also noted that amisometradine is much less effective in potentiating the effects of either hydralazine or a ganglionic blocking drug than are the thiazide compounds.

Table II

EFFECT OF DIURETIC AGENTS ADMINISTERED IN THE TREATMENT
OF HYPERTENSION[a]

| Diuretic | Patients | Average dose (mg/day) | Average blood pressure (sitting) (mm Hg) | | Percent reduction of mean blood pressure[b] |
			Before treatment	During treatment	
Chlorothiazide	38	1000	187/111	166/102	10.0
Hydrochlorothiazide	20	100	176/104	150/94	12.9
Amisometradine	5	1200	184/106	168/102	6.9

[a] From reference (22).
[b] Mean blood pressure = (systolic + diastolic)/2.

Finnerty *et al.* (17) have reported that acetazolamide (V) has a modest hypotensive effect for relatively short periods when given to women with toxemia of pregnancy. Again the antihypertensive effect of acetazolamide is less than that of thiazides. In addition, carbonic anhydrase inhibitors such

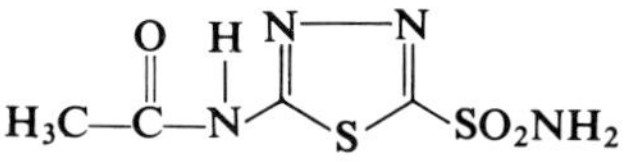

(V)

Acetazolamide

as acetazolamide are rendered ineffective after several days of continuous therapy, and this has made them unsuitable for the prolonged treatment of hypertension.

Ford *et al.* (20) have shown that chlorazinil (VI) and amanozine (VII) enhance

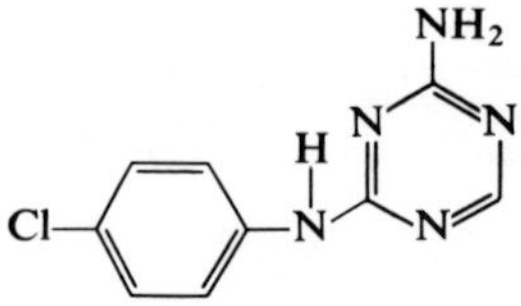

(VI)

Chlorazinil

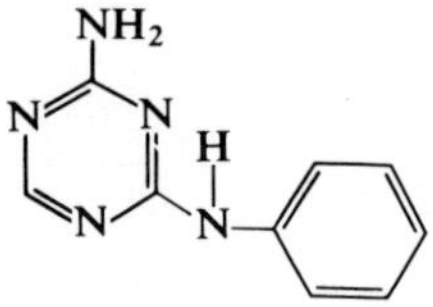

(VII)

Amanozine

the potency of reserpine and mecamylamine, but this effect is less pronounced than that observed with thiazide or mercurial diuretics. Ford has suggested that chlorazinil may have a nephrotoxic effect since it frequently causes elevation of blood urea.

Hollander *et al.* (31) also have reported on the clinical effects of spirono-lactone (VIII) in subjects with uncomplicated essential hypertension. In Fig. 2 are shown the results of one subject of this study.

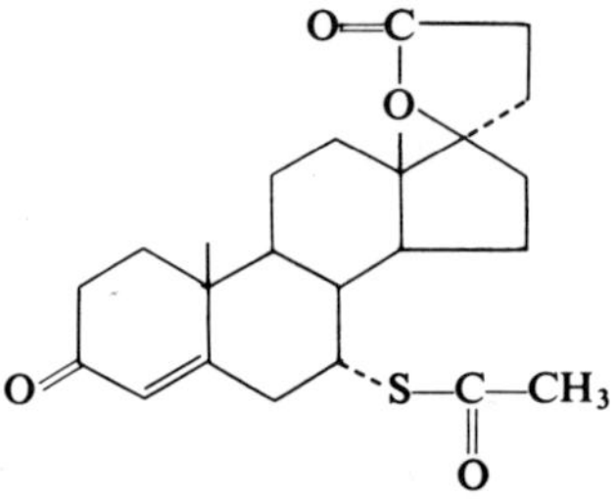

(VIII)

Spironolactone   SC. 9420

A combination of reserpine, hydralazine, and hydrochlorothiazide had produced a moderate reduction in blood pressure. Following the addition of spironolactone, there followed a further reduction in blood pressure with an increase in serum potassium to normal. In the last part of the study satisfactory control of the blood pressure and serum electrolytes was achieved with spirono-lactone alone, as well as in combination with hydrochlorothiazide. This latter combination is useful in those states where hypopotassemia is already a complicating factor. Unlike hydrochlorothiazide, the hypotensive action of spironolactone is gradual in onset, a maximum effect being attained only after 2 or 3 weeks following the administration of the drug. However, extensive

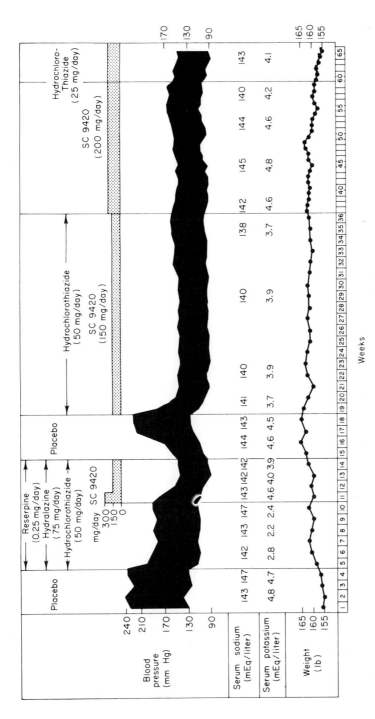

Fig. 2. Clinical effects of spironolactone (SC-9420) and hydrochlorothiazide in a hypertensive patient.

clinical trials with reserpine, hydralazine, hydrochlorothiazide combinations have proved this to be a most effective preparation for reducing high blood pressure. It is presently a most important drug for overcoming moderate-to-severe hypertension.

Hydrochlorothiazide combined with guanethidine (39) has been found to be remarkably effective in eliciting an antihypertensive effect. Schultz (46) reported

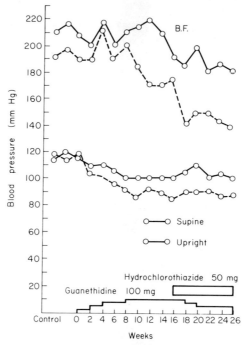

Fig. 3. Clinical effects of guanethidine in combination with hydrochlorothiazide in a hypertensive patient.

his results on a group of 25 patients with moderate-to-severe hypertension receiving daily doses of guanethidine averaging 21–25 mg plus 25 mg of hydrochlorothiazide. In all cases blood pressure reductions were approximately 38/20 mm Hg supine and 44/18 mm Hg standing. This investigator noted that side effects were reduced with the combination and that blood pressure control was smoother especially in the supine position.

Brest and Moyer (7) also observed that the hypotensive potency of guanethidine is markedly enhanced by hydrochlorothiazide. This potentiation is illustrated in Fig. 3. The antihypertensive response obtained with guanethidine was conspicuously potentiated by the concomitant administration of hydrochlorothiazide at the sixteenth week of therapy. Moreover, the daily dosage of guanethidine was reduced by one-half without a blood pressure rise. Similar findings have been recorded by Blanshard and Essigman (5), Ford (19), Klapper and Richard (35), and Maronde et al. (38).

The combination of hydrochlorothiazide and α-methyldopa has also proved useful in the treatment of hypertension. A considerable number of papers have been published on the efficacy of this combination.

Wilson et al. (49) studied the blood-pressure lowering effect of hydrochlorothiazide in combination with α-methyldopa. The individual changes in supine and standing mean arterial pressure in the hypertensive patients under study are shown in Figs. 4 and 5 respectively. It is clearly evident that this combination regimen is more effective than was either drug given alone. A total of 45 patients participated in the study with only 3 patients indicating central nervous symptoms of dizziness, headaches, and sleepiness.

In another study, Mizgala et al. (42) reported that a combination of hydrochlorothiazide (25 mg) and α-methyldopa (125 mg) was useful in reducing elevated blood pressure. Again, minimum side effects were observed. This combination is presently being used widely for the control of moderate and sustained hypertension.

Pargyline, a substance which also behaves as a monoamine oxidase inhibitor, has been used in combination with methychlothiazide (IX) by Bryant et al. (8). They have reported that a greater antihypertensive response was obtained

(IX)   (X)

Methychlothiazide   Chlorthalidone

when this combination was used rather than when the drugs were used separately; in addition, there was a 91% reduction in side effects. The effective daily dosage of the combination was 12.5 mg of pargyline and 10 mg of methychlothiazide.

Chlorthalidone (X) has been studied by a number of investigators for its effect on blood pressure. Howard (33) tested this drug on a total of 86 hypertensive patients for periods ranging from a few weeks up to 8 months. He found that 50 mg per day of chlorthalidone caused significant decreases in systolic and diastolic blood pressure in 82% of the patients previously untreated. Howard also reported that a group of 30 patients transferred from previous therapy with thiazide diuretics combined with reserpine responded better

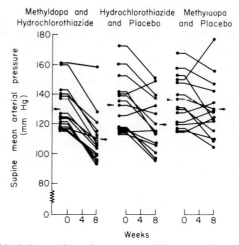

Fig. 4. The individual changes in supine mean arterial pressure between the average of the last 2 weeks of the hydrochlorothiazide control period and the average of the last 3 weeks of the double-blind phase of the trial are shown for each treatment combination. Arrows indicate average values.

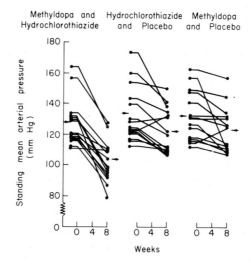

Fig. 5. The individual changes in standing mean arterial pressure are shown for each treatment as in Fig. 4. Arrows indicate average values.

on 50 mg daily of chlorthalidone. Satisfactory clinical response occurred in 81% of these patients.

Bowlus and Langford (6) compared chlorthalidone (50 mg), hydrochlorothiazide (100 mg), and placebo in a double-blind study and could note no differences in the degree and intensity of the antihypertensive effect of these drugs.

On the other hand, Cranston *et al.* (12) compared the antihypertensive action of chlorthalidone (50 mg daily), triamterene (XI) (150 mg daily), and placebo in a double-blind crossover trial: each treatment was given for 6 weeks, and blood pressure was measured at weekly intervals. Chlorthalidone proved effective whereas triamterene alone had very little antihypertensive effect. A combination of the two drugs did not significantly increase the fall in arterial pressure. Triamterene, however, prevented the fall in serum potassium caused by chlorthalidone.

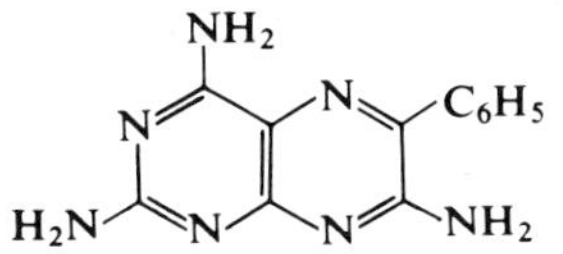

(XI)

Triamterene

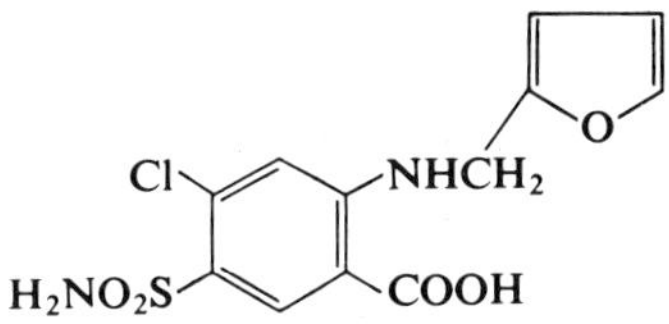

(XII)

Furosemide

A sulfonamide diuretic recently under study is furosemide (XII). This substance is reported to be highly potent, especially with regard to water clearance and chloride excretion. Engelmann (15) has found furosemide plus reserpine to be highly effective in the treatment of hypertension. This combination was excellent, particularly in cases with very high mean initial values of 241/138 mm Hg which showed a systolic decrease by 46 and a diastolic decrease by 34 mm Hg without an increase of the prescribed dose.

Ethacrynic acid [2,3-dichloro-4-(2-methylene-butyryl)-phenoxyacetic acid] (XIII) is a more recent addition to the list of diuretics useful for the treatment of hypertension. This compound, synthesized by Schultz *et al.* (45), was shown

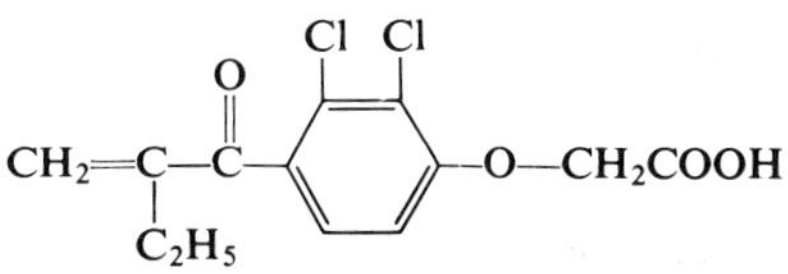

(XIII)

Ethacrynic acid

to be highly effective as a diuretic and saluretic in the dog when administered orally, intravenously, or intramuscularly. Baer *et al.* (3) reported the activity to be comparable to hydrochlorothiazide but unlike the organomercurials and the thiazides, the diuresis and saluresis caused by this drug is very rapid in onset and occurs even in bicarbonate-treated dogs. When ethacrynic acid was superimposed in animals receiving meralluride and chlorothiazide, an additional saluresis was obtained, suggesting that (XIII) has a novel mode of action (4). Clinical trials with this compound have supported the pharmacological findings (16, 27, 28, 37, 41).

Ethacrynic acid has also been studied for its effect on blood pressure. Cannon *et al.* (9) reported that (XIII) at doses of 100 to 200 mg once a day reduces both the standing and supine blood pressures of three of six patients with essential hypertension and added to the effect of guanethidine on the standing blood pressure of another.

Dollery *et al.* (14) noted that ethacrynic acid is as effective as hydrochlorothiazide in the reduction of elevated blood pressure. In a group of eleven hypertensive patients with an average blood pressure of 209/107 mm Hg before treatment, hydrochlorothiazide reduced the average value of blood pressure in the sitting position to 168/95 mm Hg and ethacrynic acid reduced it to 169/94 mm Hg. It was also of interest to note that potassium depletion and hyperuricemia were equally common in patients treated with 100 mg of ethacrynic acid daily and in those given 50 mg of hydrochlorothiazide daily.

Conway and Leonetti (10) have reported that when thiazide therapy is supplemented by ethacrynic acid and dietary restriction of sodium chloride, a substantial additional reduction in blood pressure averaging 48/18 mm Hg was obtained.

In summary then, the effectiveness of the thiazide and hydrothiazide drugs alone or in conjunction with other antihypertensive drugs and with other diuretic agents in the treatment of hypertension had been well established. More than any of the other diuretic drugs presently in use (see Table III), they are most suited for the long-term treatment of hypertension for the following reasons: (1) They are amongst the most potent, orally effective natriuretic and diuretic agents available and thus have a greater hypotensive action than any of the other diuretics when given orally. (2) They are consistently effective, resistance to their action seldom occurring. (3) They are relatively nontoxic. (4) In contrast to the mercurials and the carbonic anhydrase inhibitors, their activity is not affected by changes in the acid-base balance.

The chief disadvantage of treatment with thiazide and hydrothiazide diuretics as well as with furosemide and ethacrynic acid for edema, hypertension, or any other clinical condition is their tendency to cause some potassium depletion. However, this side effect is usually asymptomatic and rarely does the serum potassium level go below 2.5 mEq per liter if the patient has adequate food intake and normal kidney and liver function. Administration of supplements of potassium and the liberal consumption of fluids by patients taking these drugs over any length of time may be a necessary corollary to therapy in some individuals.

Table III

COMPARATIVE ADVANTAGES AND DISADVANTAGES OF VARIOUS DIURETIC AGENTS IN THE TREATMENT OF HYPERTENSION

Diuretic	Hypotensive potency	Effective orally	Resistance develops	Hypopotassemia	Azotemia	Other electrolyte disturbance	Nephrotoxicity
Acetazolamide	+	Yes	+++	+	0	++	0
Amisometradine	+	Yes	+	0	0	0	0
Chlorazinil	+	Yes	0	0	+++	0	?
Mercurials	++	No[a]	0	0	±	++	?
Thiazides	+++	Yes	0	+++	++	0	0
Furosemide	+++	Yes	0	+++	++	0	0
Ethacrynic acid	+++	Yes	0	+++	++	0	0

[a] Oral use is about 50% as effective as parenteral use.

In the past year there has been considerable concern over the use of enteric coated potassium chloride in combination with diuretic agents. It has been reported that in some patients the potassium chloride may be responsible for intestinal lesion or ulceration (36). This has been also referred to stenosis of the small bowel. Careful observation and frequent patient–physician interaction by patients requiring some potassium supplement is a necessary corollary in such antihypertensive therapy.

References

1. Allen, F. M., and Sherrill, W. J., *J. Metab. Res.* **2**, 529 (1922).
2. Ambard, L., and Beaujard, E., *Semaine Med.* **25**, 133 (1905).
3. Baer, J. E., Michaelson, J. K., Russo, H. F., and Beyer, K. H., *Pharmacologist* **4**, No. 2, 158 (1962).
4. Baer, J. E., Michaelson, J. K., Russo, H. F., and Beyer, K. H., *Federation Proc.* **22**, 598 (1963).
5. Blanshard, G., and Essigman, W., *Lancet* **II**, 334 (1961).
6. Bowlus, W. E., and Langford, H. G., *Clin. Pharmacol. Therap.* **5**, 708 (1964).
7. Brest, A. N., and Moyer, J. H., *Symp. Guanethidine (Ismelin), Memphis, Tenn., April 22, 1960,* sponsored by CIBA Pharm. Prod., Summit, New Jersey.
8. Bryant, J. M., Schwartz, N., Torosdag, S., Fertig, H., Fletcher, J., Jr., Schwartz, M. S., and Quan, R. G., *Ann. N.Y. Acad. Sci.* **107**, 1023 (1963).
9. Cannon, P. J., Ames, R. P., and Laragh, J. H., *J. Am. Med. Assoc.* **185**, 854 (1963).
10. Conway, J., and Leonetti, G., *Circulation* **31** (5), 661 (1965).
11. Corcoran, A. C., *in* "Edema" (J. H. Moyer and M. Fuchs, eds.), pp. 387–391. Saunders, Philadelphia, Pennsylvania, 1960.
12. Cranston, W. I., Semmence, A. M., Richardson, D. W., and Barnett, C. F., *Am. Heart J.* **70**, 455 (1965).
13. deStevens, G., "Diuretics." Academic Press, New York, 1963.
14. Dollery, C. T., Parry, E. H. O., and Young, D. S., *Lancet* **I**, 947 (1964).
15. Engelmann, G., *Muench. Med. Wochschr.* **107** (21), 1060 (1965).
16. Folty, E. S., *Federation Proc.* **22**, 598 (1963).
17. Finnerty, F. A., Jr., Buchholz, J. H., and Tuckman, J., *J. Am. Med. Assoc.* **166**, 141 (1958).
18. Ford, R. V., *Ann. N.Y. Acad. Sci.* **88**, 809 (1960).
19. Ford, R. V., *Geriatrics* **16**, 577 (1961).
20. Ford, R. V., Bullock, A. C., and Rochelle, J. B., III, *G. P.* **18**, 116 (1958).
21. Freis, E. D., and Wilson, I. M., *Med. Ann. District Columbia* **26**, 468 and 516 (1957).
22. Gifford, R. W., Jr., *in* "Edema" (J. H. Moyer and M. Fuchs, eds.), pp. 392–397. Saunders, Philadelphia, Pennsylvania 1960.
23. Grollman, A., *J. Am. Med. Assoc.* **129**, 533 (1945).
24. Grollman, A., *J. Am. Dietet. Assoc.* **22**, 864 (1946).
25. Grollman, A., *in* "Edema" (J. H. Moyer and M. Fuchs, eds.), pp. 375–378. Saunders, Philadelphia, Pennsylvania 1960.
26. Grollman, A., and Harrison, T. R., *Proc. Soc. Exptl. Biol. Med.* **60**, 52 (1945).
27. Hagedorn, C. W., Kaplan, A. A., and Hulett, W. H., *Clin. Res.* **12**, 47 (1964).
28. Hagedorn, C. W., Kaplan, A. A., and Hulett, W. H., *New Engl. J. Med.* **272** (28), 1152 (1965).

29. Hejtmancik, M. R., Herrmann, G. R., and Roetz, F. W., *Texas State J. Med.* **54**, 854 (1958).
30. Hollander, W., Chobanian, A. V., and Wilkins, R. W., *in* "Hypertension" (J. H. Moyer, ed.), pp. 570–580. Saunders, Philadelphia, Pennsylvania, 1959.
31. Hollander, W., Chobanian, A. V., and Wilkins, R. W., *Ann. N. Y. Acad. Sci.* **88**, 975 (1960).
32. Hollander, W., and Wilkins, R. W., *BMQ, Boston Med. Quart.* **8**, 69 (1957).
33. Howard, B. E., *Current Therap. Res., Clin. Exptl.* **7**, 304 (1965).
34. Kempner, W., *N. Carolina Med. J.* **5**, 125 (1944).
35. Klapper, M. S., and Richard, L., *Southern Med. J.* **55**, 75 (1962).
36. Lawrason, F. D., Alpert, E., Mohr, F. L., and McMahon, F. G., *J. Am. Med. Assoc.* **191**, 641–644 (1965).
37. Maher, J. F., *in* "Renal Metabolism and Epidemiology of Some Renal Diseases" (J. Metcoff, ed.), pp. 231–244. The Foundation, New York, 1964.
38. Maronde, R. F., Haywood, L. J., and Barbour, B., *Am. J. Med. Sci.* **242**, 228 (1961).
39. Maxwell, R. A., Mull, R. P., and Plummer, A. J., *Experientia* **15**, 267 (1959).
40. Megibow, R. S., Pollak, H., Stollerman, G. H., Roston, E. H., and Bookman, J. J., *J. Mt. Sinai Hosp., N. Y.* **15**, 233 (1948).
41. Melvin, K. E. W., Farrelly, R. O., and North, J. D. K., *Brit. Med. J.* **II**, 1521 (1963).
42. Mizgala, H., Wolf, R. I., and Mendlowitz, J. *J. Mt. Sinai Hosp., N. Y.* **30**, 156 (1963).
43. Moyer, J. H., *in* "Hypertension" (J. H. Moyer, ed.), pp. 299–318. Saunders, Philadelphia, Pennsylvania, 1959.
44. Schroeder, H. A., *in* "Edema" (J. H. Moyer and M. Fuchs, ed.), pp. 379–386. Saunders, Philadelphia, Pennsylvania, 1960.
45. Schultz, E. M., Cragoe, E. J., Jr., Bicking, J. B., Bolhofer, W. A., and Sprague, J. M., *J. Med. Pharm. Chem.* **5**, 660 (1962).
46. Schultz, F. B., *J. Med. Assoc. State Alabama* **31** (6), 1 (1961).
47. Spittel, J. A., Jr., Gifford, R. W., Jr., and Achor, R. W. P., *Proc. Staff Meetings Mayo Clinic* **34**, 256 (1959).
48. Volhard, F., "Handbuch der inn. Med.," Vol. 6, p. 1753. Springer, Berlin.
49. Wilson, W. R., Okun, R., Tetreault, T., and Fallis, N., *J. Am. Med. Assoc.* **185**, 819 (1963).

CHAPTER VIII

Quaternary Ganglionic Blockers

A. Marxer

O. Schier

I. Introduction, 279

II. Chemistry of the Ganglionic Blockers, 279
    A. Symmetrical, Diquaternary Compounds, 280
    B. Asymmetrical, Diquaternary Compounds, 285
    C. Monoquaternary Compounds, 287

III. Pharmacological Effects and Therapeutic Use of Quaternary Ganglionic Blockers, 289
    A. Pharmacological Effects of Ganglionic Blockers, 289
    B. Mechanism of Action, 290
    C. Test Methods, 291
    D. Clinical Results, 291

    Reviews on Pharmacology, 292

    References, 293

I. Introduction

Ganglion is a term applied to collections of nerve cells. The nerves of the autonomic nervous system issuing from the spinal cord or from the brain are made up of so-called preganglionic fibers, which end in a ganglion, and of postganglionic fibers, which run from the ganglion and terminate in the innervated organ. Stimulation of the preganglionic neurons results in the release of acetylcholine at the ganglion. This acetylcholine, in turn, causes depolarization of the synaptic membrane, thereby stimulating the post-ganglionic fiber and consequently the peripheral organ. Ganglionic blockers inhibit nerve-impulse transmission in the ganglion.

II. Chemistry of the ganglionic blockers

Attention has repeatedly been drawn to the fact that progress in the realm of physiology and in methods of biological assay has helped to stimulate research concerned with pharmacology and with pharmaceutical chemistry and vice versa (30).

As long ago as 1914, for example, Burn and Dale (14) discovered that tetraethylammonium chloride (V) blocks impulse transmission in the ganglia of the autonomic nervous system; but they failed to draw from this discovery any conclusions regarding the possibility of treating hypertension, because at that time little detailed knowledge was available concerning either the effects of ganglionic blockade or the nature of hypertension as such. As this knowledge was gradually acquired, it resulted not only in the elaboration of new methods of assay, but also—thanks to the introduction of these new methods—in the development of a wide selection of chemically differing substances.

A. Symmetrical, Diquaternary Compounds

When testing quaternary ammonium salts, chemists and pharmacologists alike have repeatedly been impressed by their toxicity—so impressed, in fact, that they have seldom undertaken more than a few tentative experiments with them. It can also be demonstrated experimentally that quaternization of an active tertiary nitrogen compound often leads to derivatives in which the absolute lethal dose and therapeutic range are significantly smaller. Despite this, however, it was with one of these toxic ammonium compounds, i.e., with tubocurarine (I) that the intensive study of ganglionic blockers began.

Tubocurarine (I), which is in point of fact one of the most toxic of all known substances and was originally employed to poison the tips of arrows, had been in use since the mid-1940's as a muscle relaxant for patients undergoing surgery. Taking tubocurarine as their model, Bovet and his co-workers (12) set about synthesizing simple polyquaternary compounds; this research led to the synthesis of gallamine triethiodide (II). It was Barlow and Ing (6), however, who—simultaneously with Paton and Zaimis (37)—first discovered that, depending on the length of their chain, diquaternary polymethylene compounds exhibit either a predominantly inhibitory effect on motor impulse transmission or a predominantly ganglionic blocking action. Thus, for example, decamethonium (III) has the same chain length between the two quaternary heads (i.e., a chain of 10 members) as tubocurarine and its inhibitory effect on motor impulse transmission is accordingly comparable to that of the latter.

The curarizing activity rapidly diminishes as the chain is shortened, and disappears altogether when there are only eight CH_2 groups between the quaternary centers; in the compounds with seven CH_2 groups it is replaced by a ganglionic blocking effect, which attains its maximum at $n = 6$ (cf. Table I) (37). This highly potent ganglionic blocker, known as hexamethonium (IV), was later introduced for clinical use.

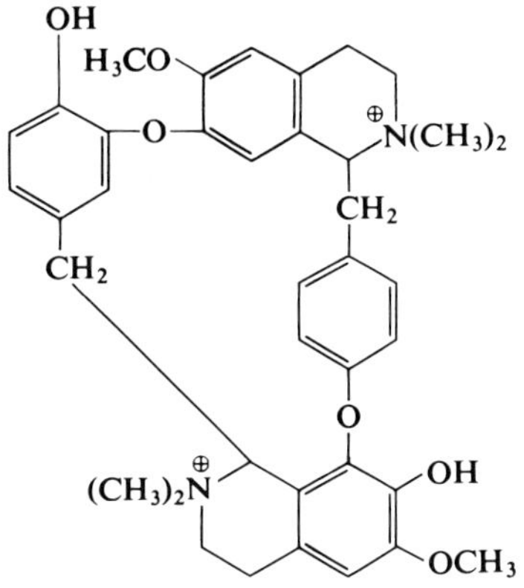

(I)*

Tubocurarine

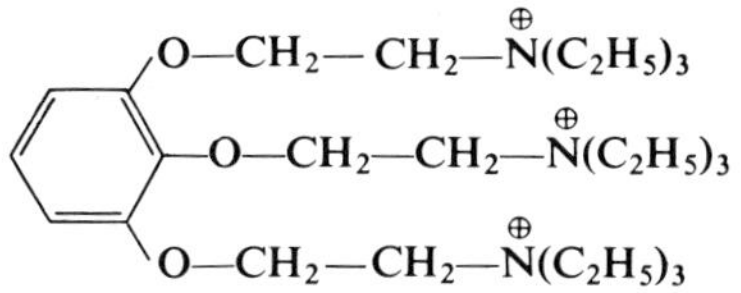

(II)

Gallamine triethiodide

$$(CH_3)_3\overset{\oplus}{N}-(CH_2)_{10}-\overset{\oplus}{N}(CH_3)_3$$

(III)

Decamethonium

$$(CH_3)_3\overset{\oplus}{N}-(CH_2)_6-\overset{\oplus}{N}(CH_3)_3$$

(IV)

Hexamethonium

Table I

INFLUENCE OF CHAIN LENGTH ON GANGLIONIC BLOCKING ACTIVITY

IN COMPOUNDS OF THE $(CH_3)_3\overset{\oplus}{N}-(CH_2)_n-\overset{\oplus}{N}(CH_3)_3$ TYPE

n	2	3	4	5	6	7
Activity	3.0	4.3	5.9	33.3	100	16.7

By way of comparison, the activity of tetraethylammonium bromide (TEA) (V) would be equivalent to 14 units—i.e., only 14% of that of hexamethonium—and according to other authors (20, 31) even less, namely 5%.

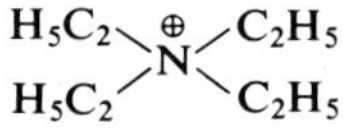

(V)

Tetraethylammonium bromide

* Where the anions in these and subsequent formula are halogens (such as $Cl^{\ominus}$, $Br^{\ominus}$, and $J^{\ominus}$), all displaying similar activity, they have not been specially indicated.

The findings obtained with monoquaternary compounds are not necessarily applicable to diquaternary types. For example, whereas in hexamethonium, replacement of the six methyl groups by ethyl groups (Table II)
results in a loss of ganglionic blocking activity (16), in tetraethylammonium
bromide, replacement of ethyl by methyl gives rise, not to ganglionic blockade,
but to stimulation of the ganglia (20, 31).

Table II

COMPARISON BETWEEN METHYL AND ETHYL SUBSTITUTION AT THE
QUATERNARY NITROGEN

	$R = CH_3$	$R = C_2H_5$
$R \overset{\oplus}{\underset{R}{>}} N \underset{R}{<} R$	Ganglionic stimulation	Ganglionic blockade (intensity 5–14)
$R \overset{\oplus}{\underset{R}{>}} N{-}(CH_2)_6{-}\overset{\oplus}{N}\underset{R}{<}R$	Ganglionic blockade (intensity 100)	Virtually no ganglionic blockade, but, if anything a curarizing effect
$R \overset{\oplus}{\underset{R}{>}} N{-}(CH_2)_{10}{-}\overset{\oplus}{N}\underset{R}{<}R$	Curarizing effect	Ganglionic blockade (intensity 28–30)

It is interesting to note that, in the case of decamethonium, replacement
of the six methyl groups by six ethyl groups results in a kind of ganglionic
blockade (Table II).

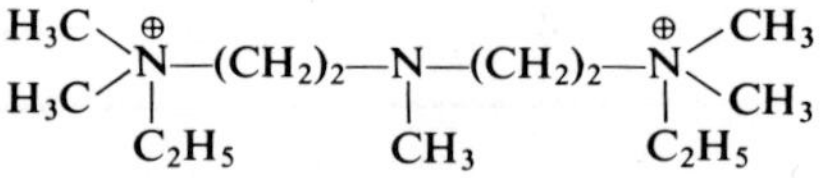

$$H_3C \overset{\oplus}{\underset{C_2H_5}{>}} N{-}(CH_2)_2{-}\underset{CH_3}{N}{-}(CH_2)_2{-}\overset{\oplus}{\underset{C_2H_5}{N}}\underset{CH_3}{<}CH_3$$

(VI)

Azamethonium

At the same time as Barber and Gaimster (5) introduced hexamethonium,
the results of a similar research series undertaken by Marxer and Miescher (26)
were published by Bein and Meier (7). Terminal quaternization of the completely methylated diethylene triamine yielded azamethonium (VI), in which
a third nitrogen function features in place of the two middle CH_2 groups of
hexamethonium.

Besides its use as a hypotensive agent, azamethonium is also employed in
surgery to reduce bleeding at the site of operation to a minimum; in addition,

Table III

AZAMETHONIUM SERIES

(VII)

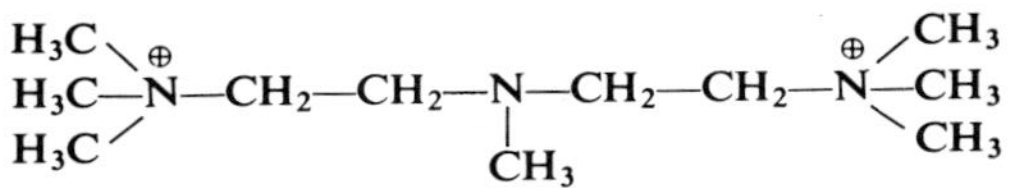

$$H_3C-\overset{\oplus}{\underset{\underset{\textstyle CH_3}{|}}{N}}-CH_2-CH_2-N-CH_2-CH_2-\overset{\oplus}{\underset{\underset{\textstyle CH_3}{|}}{N}}-CH_3$$

Strong activity

(VI)

$$\underset{\textstyle H_3C-H_2C}{H_3C}-\overset{\oplus}{N}-CH_2-CH_2-N-CH_2-CH_2-\overset{\oplus}{N}-CH_2-CH_3$$

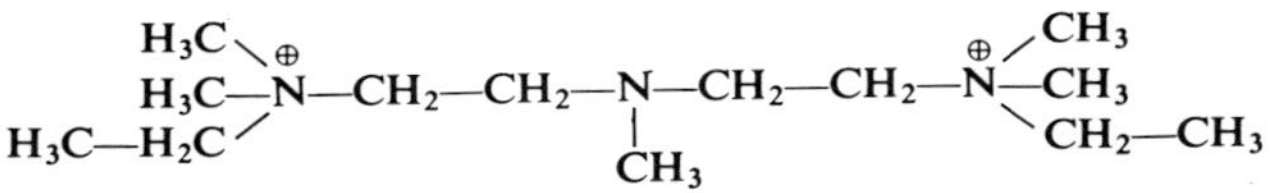

Azamethonium: very strong activity

(VIII)

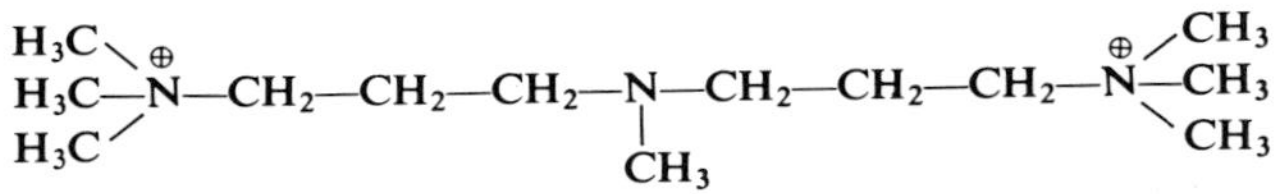

$$H_3C-\overset{\oplus}{N}-CH_2-CH_2-N-CH_2-CH_2-CH_2-\overset{\oplus}{N}-CH_3$$

±

(IX)

$$H_3C-\overset{\oplus}{N}-CH_2-CH_2-N-CH_2-\overset{H}{\underset{CH_3}{C}}-\overset{\oplus}{N}-CH_3$$

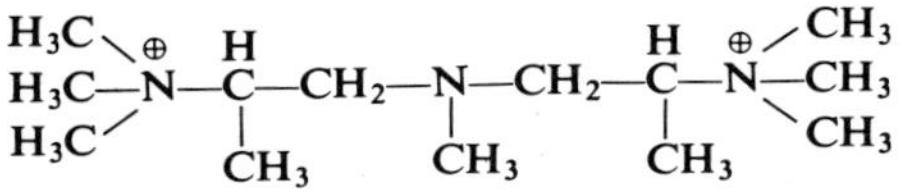

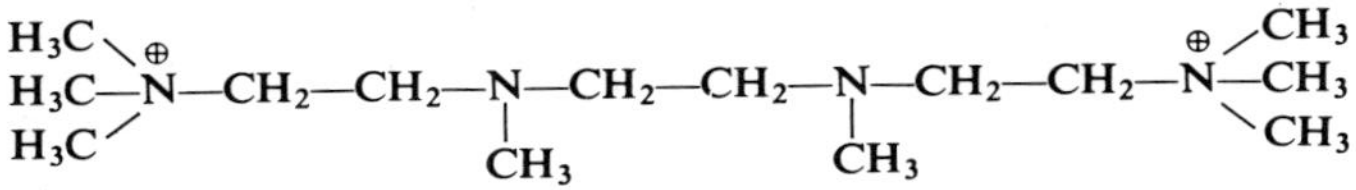

±

(X)

$$H_3C-\overset{\oplus}{N}-CH_2-CH_2-N-CH_2-CH_2-\overset{\oplus}{N}-CH_3$$

± (Curarizing)

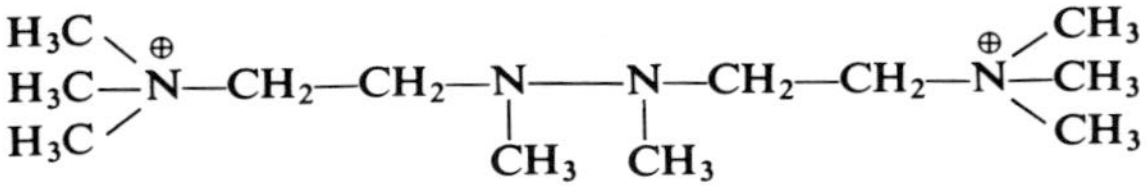

(XI)

$$H_3C-\overset{\oplus}{N}-CH_2-CH_2-N-CH_2-CH_2-\overset{\oplus}{N}-CH_3$$

Slight activity

(XII)

$$H_3C-\overset{\oplus}{N}-CH_2-CH_2-O-CH_2-CH_2-\overset{\oplus}{N}-CH_3$$

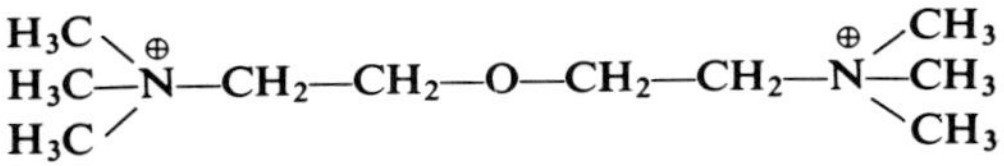

Oxapentonium: Good activity

(XIII)

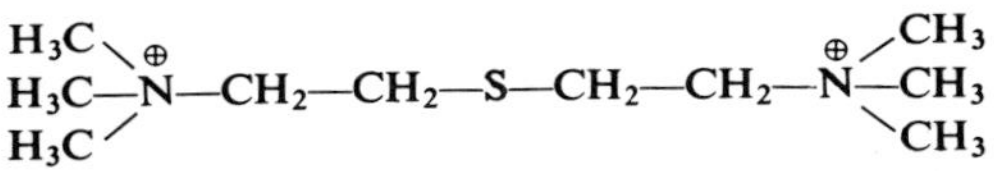

$$H_3C-\overset{\oplus}{N}-CH_2-CH_2-S-CH_2-CH_2-\overset{\oplus}{N}-CH_3$$

Strong activity

it is recognized as an effective form of treatment in cases of embolism, and has likewise been used to suppress spastic pain, e.g., in renal colic.

Listed in Table III are just a few findings—all reported by Bein—from earlier published studies (47) on the problem of relating chemical constitution to pharmacological activity in compounds from the azamethonium series.

Among the various azamethonium compounds featuring at both ends of the chain a heterocyclic nitrogen as quaternary center, a decrease in activity as outlined in Table IV was observed.

Table IV

Azamethonium Series: R—CH$_2$CH$_2$—N—CH$_2$CH$_2$—R
$\qquad\qquad\qquad\qquad\qquad\qquad\quad$ |
$\qquad\qquad\qquad\qquad\qquad\qquad\quad$ CH$_3$

Influence of the quaternary heads (R)

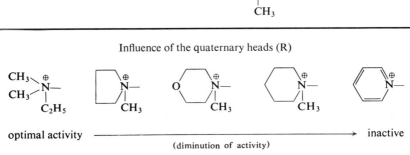

optimal activity ——————————————————————————→ inactive

(diminution of activity)

The oxygen-containing oxapentonium type (XII) has been thoroughly investigated by Fakstorp et al. (17, 18), and (XII) itself has been introduced commercially. Another compound belonging to the same generic conception (oxapentonium) is Diamonal (XIV) (23).

After it had been demonstrated with azamethonium that ganglionic blockade is also possible with other compounds besides those of the hexamethonium type, an intensive and successful quest for new types began in numerous research centers—a quest which was to shed further light on the relationship between chemical constitution and pharmacological activity.

Mason and Wien (27), in particular, were among those who carried out systematic modifications. Wien (55) was able to confirm that in the hexamethonium series, too, optimal activity could be obtained by employing two methyl groups and one ethyl group as substituents for the quaternary nitrogen. It was from a series featuring various heterocyclic quaternary centers that pentolinium tartrate (XV) was obtained; this compound was first synthesized by Libman et al. (24) and, using a different method, by Borowicka et al. (10).

Here, as in the azamethonium series (Table IV), replacement of the two pyrrolidinium residues by piperidinium residues was followed by a decrease in activity.

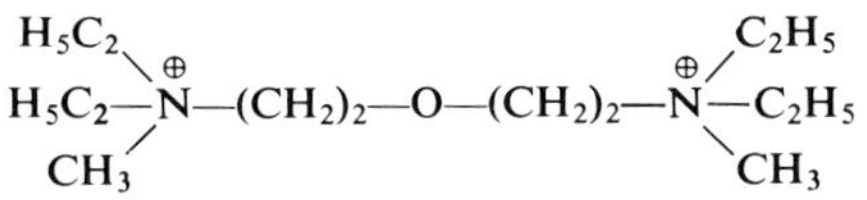

$$H_5C_2-\overset{\overset{H_5C_2}{\underset{CH_3}{\Big|}}}{\overset{\oplus}{N}}-(CH_2)_2-O-(CH_2)_2-\overset{\overset{C_2H_5}{\underset{CH_3}{\Big|}}}{\overset{\oplus}{N}}-C_2H_5$$

(XIV)

Diamonal

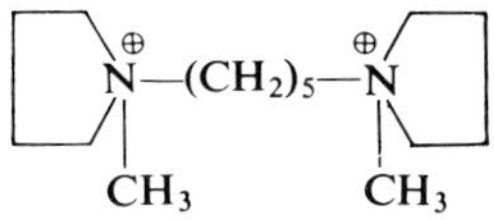

$$\overset{\oplus}{N}-(CH_2)_5-\overset{\oplus}{N}$$
$$\underset{CH_3}{\Big|} \qquad \underset{CH_3}{\Big|}$$

(XV)

Pentolinium tartrate

B. ASYMMETRICAL, DIQUATERNARY COMPOUNDS

When the two quaternary centers in the series so far discussed are replaced by aliphatic or heterocyclic amines of higher molecular weight, the ganglionic blocking activity diminishes or even disappears; in lieu of it, the curarelike activity tends in most instances to become predominant. Quaternary di-iso-quinolinium salts, for example, exert hardly any ganglionic blocking effect. A series of this kind was studied by Smith et al. (48). Among compounds of type (XVI) even those in which $n = 4$–6 displayed only curarizing activity.

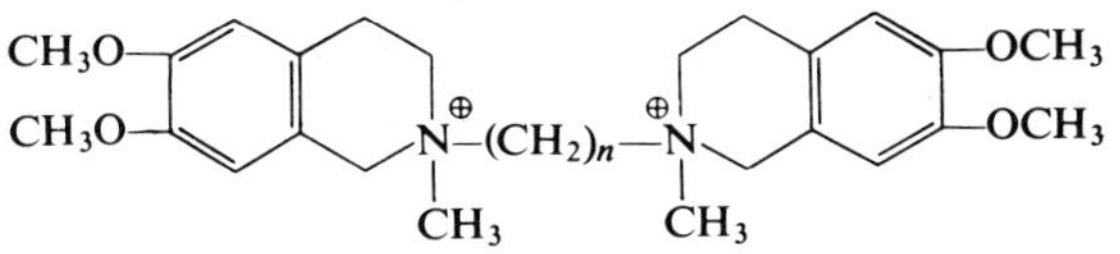

$$CH_3O- \qquad CH_3O- \qquad \overset{\oplus}{N}-(CH_2)_n-\overset{\oplus}{N} \qquad -OCH_3 \quad -OCH_3$$
$$\underset{CH_3}{\Big|} \qquad \underset{CH_3}{\Big|}$$

(XVI)

Simultaneously, however, three research centers subsequently observed that asymmetrical diquaternary amines can be made to carry one quaternary center of higher molecular weight, provided the other quaternary center is of low molecular weight and the chain between the two nitrogen atoms is reduced to 2–3 carbon atoms.

The resulting compounds proved to be optimal ganglionic blockers; moreover, in contrast to the hexamethonium group, they were also fairly well absorbed from the gastrointestinal tract when administered orally.

In chlorisondamine (XVII), the characterizing quaternary center is formed by a tetrachloroisoindoline (2, 44). Chlorisondamine was first described by Plummer et al. and by Maxwell et al. (28, 41). Its effectiveness, even in severe cases of malignant hypertension, was later confirmed by various clinical investigators (46).

Rice and Grogan (19, 43) worked on bicyclic diquaternary compounds and launched, as the best representative from this series, trimethidinium methosulfate (XVIII), which is reported to be particularly well tolerated (9, 22).

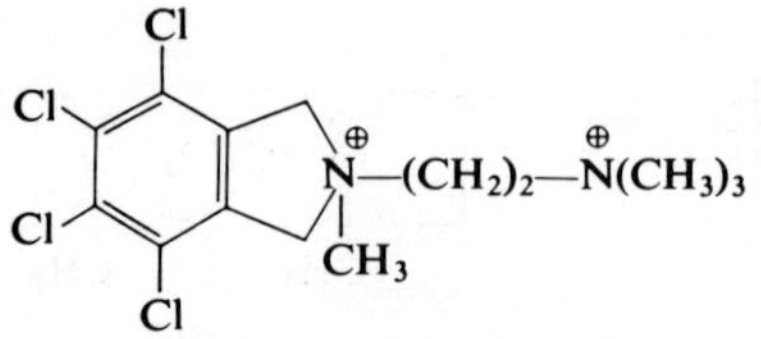

(XVII)

Chlorisondamine

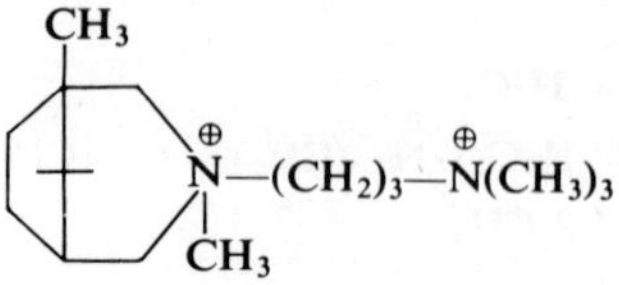

(XVIII)

Trimethidinium

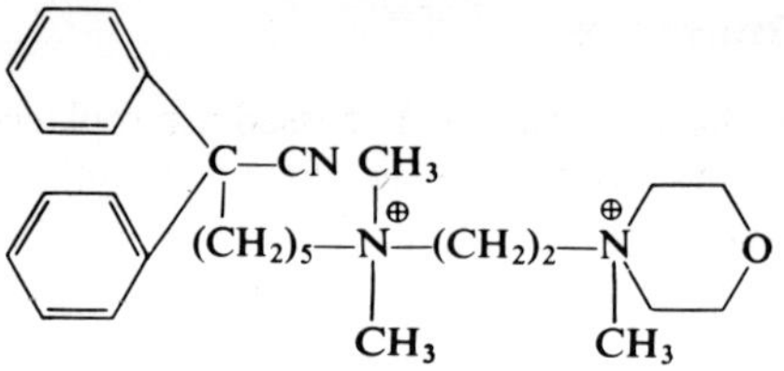

(XIX)

Pentacynium

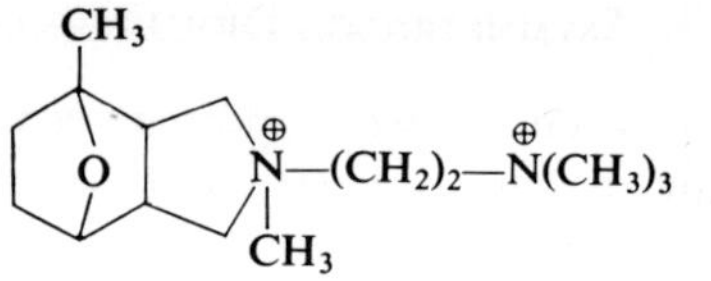

(XX)

Another member of this series of highly active ganglionic blockers is pentacynium (XIX), which contains a diphenylacetonitrile complex and was selected by Adamson *et al.* (1) from a series of homologous compounds. One

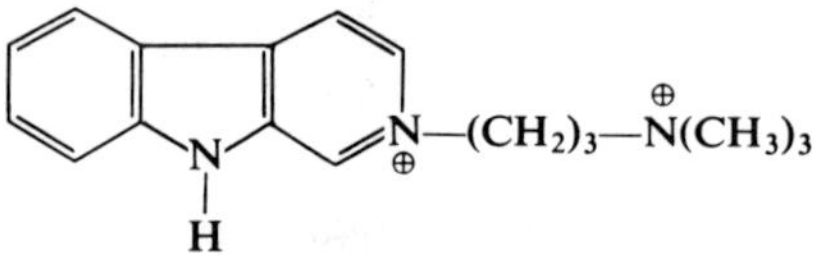

(XXI)

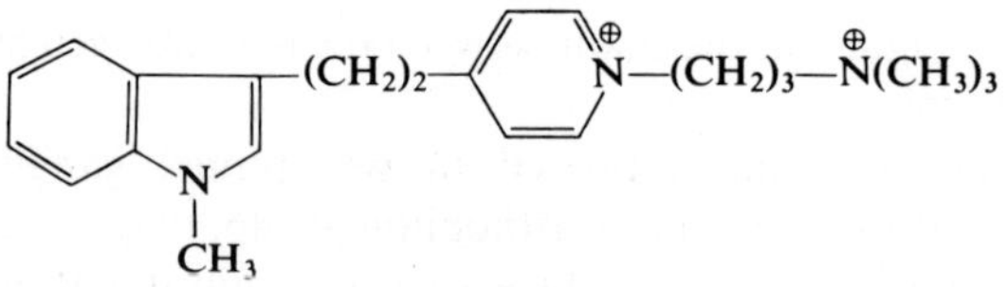

(XXII)

Methindethyrium

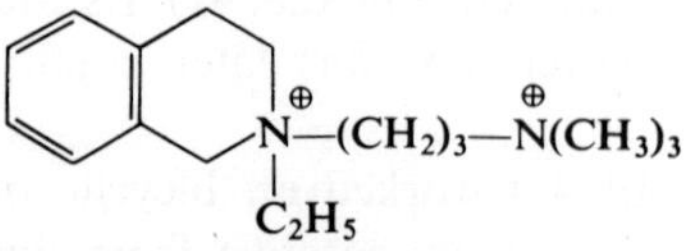

(XXIII)

Ethiquinium

of its most distinctive features emphasized in the literature is its prolonged duration of action when administered subcutaneously (25, 29).

One interesting series, which was studied by O'Malley *et al.* (35), consists of a cross between chlorisondamine and trimethidinium featuring a tricyclic quaternary center with an oxygen bridge (XX).

Before terminating this brief review of the asymmetrical types, reference should also be made to a group of compounds investigated by O'Dell *et al.* (34) which feature a β-carboline structure as a quaternary center (XXI); it is believed that these compounds, none of which has been commercialized, not only block the peripheral ganglia but also combat hypertension by a central action.

When compound (XXI) is separated into an indole and a pyridinium portion, theoretically it yields a type which resulted in the synthesis of methindethyrium (XXII) (34). The latter, too, has proved effective in the treatment of hypertension. It has previously been mentioned that bis-quaternary isoquinolinium compounds of the (XVI) type have exclusively curarelike, but no ganglionic blocking activity. Quaternary compounds with only one isoquinolinium component, however, are highly active ganglionic blockers [e.g. (XXIII), ethiquinium (15)].

C. Monoquaternary Compounds

Unique among the ganglionic blockers is trimetaphane camphorsulfonate, (XXIV), which was derived from starting materials obtained during the synthesis of biotin (42). Its complicated structure, however, appears to have discouraged research chemists from seeking analogs.

(XXIV)	(XXV)
Trimetaphane camphorsulfonate	Bretylium tosylate

An interesting feature of this compound is the presence of sulfur as the charge-carrying heteroatom. Its potency as a ganglionic blocker is roughly equivalent to that of hexamethonium, but its duration of effect is approximately three times as long. Bretylium tosylate (XXV) is said to display hardly any ganglionic blocking action; instead, according to Boura *et al.* (11), its hypotensive effect is due to sympathetic blockade.

The nitrogen atoms in basic esters of the spasmolytic series have been successfully quaternized. Thus, for example, in oxyphenonium and methantheline the diethylamino group which usually appears in the spasmolytics has been replaced by a triethylammonium grouping; but, as in the case of most amines with a high molecular residue which have been quaternized with three ethyl groups, both of these spasmolytics have only a slight ganglionic blocking effect. Some research workers, however, have deliberately set out to achieve a combination of parasympatholytic and ganglionic blocking activity in one and the same molecule. This desideratum has been fulfilled in particular by quaternizing atropine and scopolamine. Whereas scopolamine butylbromide (XXVI) and atropine methylnitrate display a predominantly spasmolytic effect, an extensive series of research studies undertaken by Nador and Gyermek (32) on the one hand, and by Stoll *et al.* (50, 51) as well as Taeschler *et al.* (45, 52) on the other, has resulted in tropinium derivatives endowed with considerable ganglionic blocking activity. From the group studied by Nador came diphenylmethyl atropinium bromide (XXVII) whereas the

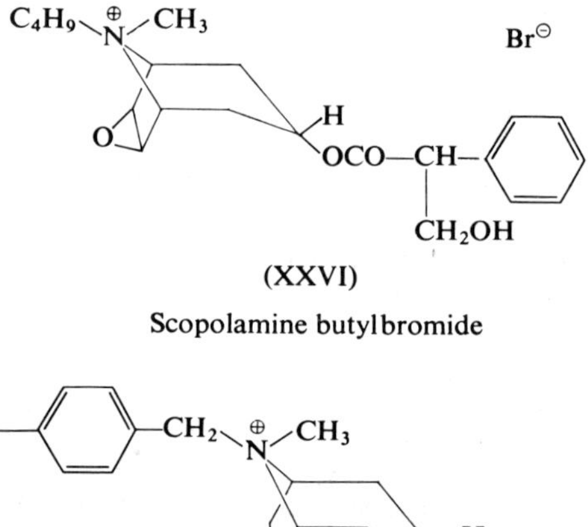

(XXVI)

Scopolamine butylbromide

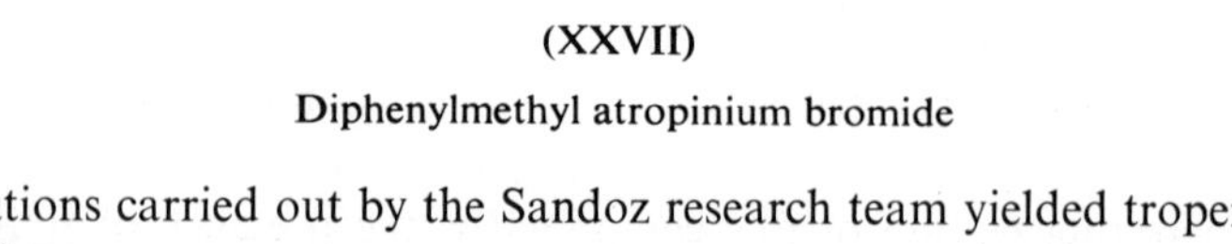

(XXVII)

Diphenylmethyl atropinium bromide

investigations carried out by the Sandoz research team yielded tropenzylium (XXVIII).

A detailed review of this intensively studied group of tropine derivatives has been published by Nador (33).

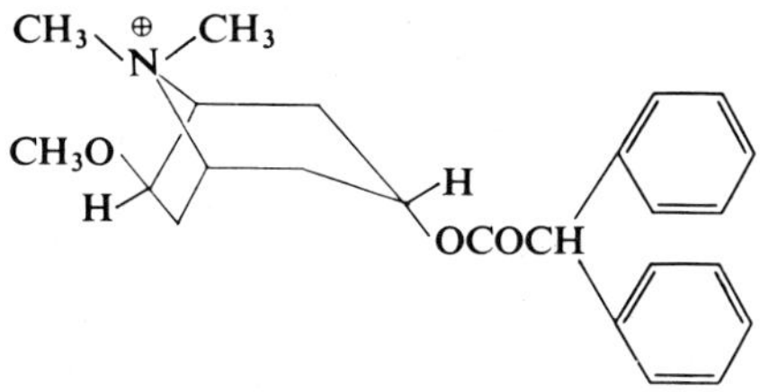

(XXVIII)

Tropenzylium

Another class of ganglionic blocking substances, whose activity is attributable not to quaternary centers but simply to tertiary amines, is described in detail in Chapter IX of this book.

III. Pharmacological effects and therapeutic use of quaternary ganglionic blockers

A. PHARMACOLOGICAL EFFECTS OF GANGLIONIC BLOCKERS

Some of the effects produced by ganglionic blockade on organs with predominantly sympathetic or parasympathetic innervation are indicated in the following list:

Sympathetic blockade
- Arterioles — Vasodilatation, hypotension, increased peripheral blood flow
- Veins — Vasodilatation, decrease in venous return, reduction in cardiac output
- Sweat glands — Anhydrosis

Parasympathetic blockade
- Eye — Mydriasis (iris), cycloplegia (*M. ciliaris*)
- Salivary glands — Xerostomia
- Heart — Tachycardia
- Gastrointestinal tract — Decrease in tone and motility, constipation
- Urinary bladder — Retention of urine

The effects produced on the arterioles and veins have an important bearing on the control of blood-pressure levels. The ganglionic blockers act on ganglionic transmission in the entire autonomic nervous system.

Even in the early days of the ganglionic blockers, close attention was already paid to the question of their selectivity. Paton and Zaimis (38) found that pentamethonium exerted a more marked effect on the superior cervical ganglion in the cat than on the guinea pig ileum, but this comparison in two target organs with varying degrees of sensitivity does not permit any conclusions to be drawn as to the selectivity of the ganglionic blocker. Perry and Wilson (40) compared the effect of five ganglionic blockers on sympathetic and parasympathetic ganglia supplying the same target organ, namely the cat heart. Pentamethonium displayed a more pronounced effect on the parasympathetic nervous system than on the sympathetic, whereas no difference was observed in the case of the other ganglionic blockers. Clinical studies, however, failed to provide any confirmation of pentamethonium's selectivity.

It has admittedly been demonstrated that differences occur in the response of individual ganglia and even of individual groups of cells in a ganglion (54) to ganglionic blockers, but these differences seem to be relatively slight (3, 36). All ganglionic blockers, for example, first block salivary gland secretion. This may be due to the "accessibility" of the ganglia or to structural differences in the various ganglia.

B. Mechanism of Action

An impulse produced in the presynaptic axon leads, upon reaching the axon ends, to the release of acetylcholine. Acetylcholine acts as a chemical mediator, crosses the synaptic gap, and reacts with receptors on the membrane of the ganglionic cells. This results in an increase in the permeability of the membrane for sodium, potassium, and other ions of similar size, in ion exchange, and thus in local depolarization of the membrane. If this depolarization attains a critical value, an impulse is elicited, which is conducted via the postsynaptic axon and acts on the target organ.

A number of substances are known which are capable of suppressing one of the processes involved in impulse conduction. Local anesthetics such as cocaine, for instance, inhibit impulse conduction in the presynaptic axon (49). Other substances, such as botulinum toxin, prevent the release of acetylcholine (4, 13).

In the case of all the antihypertensive ganglionic blockers which have been subjected to detailed study, it has been found that these drugs do not affect the release of acetylcholine at the preganglionic nerve endings, but do influence the action of acetylcholine on the ganglionic cells. The ganglionic blockers probably become bound to the acetylcholine receptors and thereby competitively prevent acetylcholine from acting on the ganglionic cells. Additional evidence in favor of a competitive inhibition is the fact that the effect of the ganglionic blockers can be abolished by large amounts of acetylcholine.

It must be emphasized, however, that the mechanism of action of the ganglionic blockers is considerably more complex than might appear from this simple picture of an acetylcholine antagonism. In the perfused superior cervical ganglion of the cat, for example, the effect of ganglionic blockers is reversed in the absence of potassium ions: the ganglionic blockers then potentiate the effect of acetylcholine and themselves exert a stimulant action on the ganglion. One noteworthy exception is azamethonium, which does not display any stimulant effect of its own on the ganglion in this experimental procedure (39). Since the depolarization of a ganglion is brought about by the displacement of ions, it will readily be understood that potassium ions constitute an important factor. In addition, the release of acetylcholine is markedly influenced by inorganic cations (21).

It is impossible within the confines of this article to give a detailed account of the pharmacology of the ganglionic blockers, and the reader is therefore referred in this connection to the reviews quoted in the bibliography.

C. TEST METHODS

Compare the articles by A. J. Plummer and G. E. Lee in this volume, Chapters II and IX.

D. CLINICAL RESULTS

It was in the 1950's in particular that the ganglionic blockers were used on a large scale in the treatment of severe forms of hypertension. Their hypotensive effect is largely orthostatic in nature and is thus much more pronounced when the patient stands or sits than when he lies down. The lack of autonomic nervous regulation involves a risk of acute episodes of postural hypotension and calls for special precautions.

Careful attention must be paid to the dosage, which has to be adapted to the needs of the individual patient. Tolerance may develop following prolonged administration. Irregular absorption is also a point to be watched. Ammonium compounds, in general, are poorly absorbed; in the case of the ganglionic blockers, an additional factor is that blockade of the parasympathetic ganglia reduces gastrointestinal motility.

The extensive effects exerted by the antihypertensive ganglionic blockers on the autonomic nervous system may give rise to adverse secondary reactions— e.g., diminution in gastrointestinal tone and motility, taking the form of constipation and, in some cases, paralytic ileus. In addition, inhibition of the parasympathetic nervous system may cause disorders of accommodation and paralysis of the urinary bladder.

These side effects are provoked by inhibition of parasympathetic ganglia. It is not surprising, therefore, that in recent years the ganglionic blockers have been superseded by antihypertensive agents which either act selectively on the sympathetic nervous system or display a different mechanism of action altogether. Short-acting ganglionic blockers are still used intravenously to control hypertensive crises.

The quaternary ganglionic blockers employed in therapy differ from one another chiefly in respect of dosage and duration of effect, as can be seen from the following list of recommended dosages:

Azamethonium: single oral dose 100–400 mg; intramuscular or intravenous administration: initial dose 20–50 mg, subsequently rising to 100 mg or more three to four times daily.

Chlorisondamine: initial oral dose 12.5 mg twice daily, maintenance dose up to 200 mg or more daily; subcutaneous or intramuscular administration: initial dose 1–2.5 mg, subsequently rising to 5 mg once or twice daily.

Hexamethonium: oral treatment: initial dose 125 mg four times daily, maintenance dose up to 3000 mg or more daily; subcutaneous or intravenous administration: initial dose 1.25–2.5 mg, subsequently rising to 50 mg or more four times daily.

Pentolinium: oral treatment: initial dose 20 mg three times daily, maintenance dose up to 500 mg or more daily; subcutaneous or intramuscular administration: initial dose of 2.5 mg, subsequently rising to 20 mg or more three to four times daily.

Trimetaphane: administered only by intravenous drip infusion; dose usually 1–4 mg per minute.

Trimethidinium: oral treatment: initial dose 20 mg twice daily, maintenance dose up to 450 mg or more daily.

An extensive double-blind study undertaken with chlorisondamine, pentolinium, and the nonquaternary ganglionic blocker mecamylamine failed to reveal any essential differences between these compounds in respect to therapeutic effect or secondary reactions (53).

Acknowledgment

We are greatly indebted to Professor H. J. Bein for his suggestions regarding the pharmacological aspects of this paper. Our thanks are also due to Mr. H. D. Philps and Mr. I. C. W. Bigland for their help in translating the manuscript.

Reviews on pharmacology

The literature on the ganglionic blockers is so vast today that it is almost impossible to obtain a clear picture of everything that has been written on these compounds. More than 600 papers have been published on azamethonium alone. In one of these papers Bein and Meier (8) review the effects and consequences of ganglionic blockade in connection with anesthesiology and the control of shock. The reader is referred in particular to the following surveys that have appeared in the literature.

Aviado, D. M., Hemodynamic effects of ganglion blocking drugs. *Circulation Res.* **8**, 304–314 (1960). 62 references.

Bennett, M. V. L., Nervous function at the cellular level. *Ann. Rev. Physiol.* **26**, 289–340 (1964). 268 references.

Eccles, J. C., The mechanism of synaptic transmission. *Ergeb. Physiol., Biol. Chem. Exptl. Pharmakol.* **51**, 299–430 (1961). Approx. 400 references.

Moe, G. K., and Freyburger, W. A., Ganglionic blocking agents. *Pharmacol. Rev.* **2**, 61–95 (1950). 258 references.

Paton, W. D. M., Transmission and block in autonomic ganglia. *Pharmacol. Rev.* **6**, 59–67 (1954). 24 references.

Paton, W. D. M., and Zaimis, E. J., The methonium compounds. *Pharmacol. Rev.* **4**, 219–253 (1952). 187 references.

Perry, W. L. M., Transmission in autonomic ganglia. *Brit. Med. Bull.* **13**, 220–226 (1957). 55 references.

Trendelenburg, U., Pharmacology of autonomic ganglia. *Ann. Rev. Pharmacol.* **1**, 219–238 (1961). 246 references.

Volle, R. L., Pharmacology of the autonomic nervous system. *Ann. Rev. Pharmacol.* **3**, 129–152 (1963). 245 references.

Volle, R. L., Modification by drugs of synaptic mechanisms in autonomic ganglia. *Pharmacol. Rev.* **18**, 839–894 (1966). 174 references.

References

1. Adamson, D. W., Billinghurst, J. W., and Green, A. F., *Nature* **177**, 523 (1956).
2. Allen, M. J., and Ocampo, J., *J. Electrochem. Soc.* **103**, 452 and 682 (1956).
3. Alonso-de Florida, F., Cato, J., Ramirez, L., and Pardo, E. G., *J. Pharmacol. Exptl. Therap.* **129**, 433 (1960).
4. Ambache, N., *J. Physiol. (London)* **108**, 127 (1949); **113**, 1 (1951).
5. Barber, H. J., and Gaimster, K., *J. Pharm. Pharmacol.* **3**, 663 (1951).
6. Barlow, R. B., and Ing, H. R., *Nature* **161**, 718 (1948); *Brit. J. Pharmacol.* **3**, 298 (1948).
7. Bein, H. J., and Meier, R., *Experientia* **6**, 351 (1950); *Schweiz. Med. Worchschr.* **81**, 446 (1951).
8. Bein, H. J., and Meier, R., *Anaesthesist* **3**, 25 (1954).
9. Bilecki, G., *Med. Klin. (Munich)* **51**, 1516 (1956).
10. Borowicka, M., Sédivý, Z., and Protiva, M., *Chem. Listy* **49**, 777 (1955).
11. Boura, A. L. A., Green, A. F., McCoubrey, A., Laurence, D. R., Moulton, R., and Rosenheim, M. L., *Lancet* **II**, 17 (1959).
12. Bovet, D., Depierre, F., and de Lestrange, Y., *Compt. Rend.* **225**, 74 (1947).
13. Brooks, V. B., *J. Physiol. (London)* **123**, 501 (1954); **134**, 264 (1956).
14. Burn, J. H., and Dale, H. H., *J. Pharmacol. Exptl. Therap.* **6**, 417 (1914).
15. Cavallito, C. J., and O'Dell, T. B., *J. Am. Pharm. Assoc.* **47**, 169 (1958).
16. Chou, T. C., and De Elio, F. J., *Brit. J. Pharmacol.* **2**, 268 (1947).
17. Fakstorp, J., Christianssen, J., and Pedersen, J. G. A., *Acta Chem. Scand.* **7**, 134 (1953).
18. Fakstorp, J., Poulsen, E., Richter, W., and Schilling, M., *Acta Pharmacol. Toxicol.* **11**, 319 (1955).
19. Grogan, C. H., and Rice, L. M., *J. Org. Chem.* **22**, 1223 (1957).
20. Gyermek, L., and Nador, K., *Acta Physiol. Acad. Sci. Hung.* **3**, 183 (1952).
21. Hutter, O. F., and Kostial, K., *J. Physiol. (London)* **124**, 234 (1954); **129**, 159 (1955).
22. Kühns, K., Liebeskind, H., and Müller, W., *Aerztl. Wochschr.* **11**, 1053 (1956).
23. Lenke, D., *Anaesthesist* **5**, 47 (1956).

24. Libman, D. D., Pain, D. L., and Slack, R., *J. Chem. Soc.* (*London*) p. 2305 (1952).
25. Locket, S., *Brit. Med. J.* **II**, 116 (1956).
26. Marxer, A., and Miescher, K., *Helv. Chim. Acta* **34**, 924 (1951).
27. Mason, D. F. J., and Wien, R., *Brit. J. Pharmacol.* **10**, 124 (1955).
28. Maxwell, R. A., Plummer, A. J., and Osborne, M. W., *Circulation Res.* **4**, 276 (1956).
29. McKendrick, C. S., and Jones, P. O., *Lancet* **I**, 340 (1958).
30. Miescher, K., *Angew. Chem.* **65**, 273 (1953).
31. Nador, K., and Gyermek, L., *Acta Physiol. Acad. Sci. Hung.* **2**, 95 (1952).
32. Nador, K., and Gyermek, L., *Arzneimittel-Forsch.* **8**, 336 (1958); *Arch. Intern. Pharmacodyn.* **113**, 1 (1957).
33. Nador, K., *Progr. Drug Res.* **2**, 358 (1960).
34. O'Dell, T. B., Luna, C., and Napoli, M. D., *J. Pharmacol. Exptl. Therap.* **114**, 306 (1955).
35. O'Malley, W. E., Winkler, G., Rice, L. M., and Geschickter, C. F., *J. Am. Pharm. Assoc., Sci. Ed.* **46**, 346 (1957).
36. Pardo, E. G., Cato, J., Gijon, E., and Alonso-de Florida, F., *J. Pharmacol. Exptl. Therap.* **139**, 296 (1963).
37. Paton, W. D. M., and Zaimis, E. J., *Nature* **161**, 718 (1948); *Brit. J. Pharmacol.* **4**, 381 (1949).
38. Paton, W. D. M., and Zaimis, E. J., *Brit. J. Pharmacol.* **6**, 155 (1951); *Pharmacol. Rev.* **4**, 219 (1952).
39. Perry, W. L. M., and Reinert, H., *J. Physiol.* (*London*) **126**, 101 (1954).
40. Perry, W. L. M., and Wilson, C. W. M., *Brit. J. Pharmacol.* **11**, 81 (1956).
41. Plummer, A. J., Trapold, J. H., Schneider, J. A., Maxwell, R. A., and Earl, A. E., *J. Pharmacol. Exptl. Therap.* **115**, 172 (1955).
42. Randall, L. O., Peterson, W. G., and Lehmann, G., *J. Pharmacol. Exptl. Therap.* **97**, 48 (1949).
43. Rice, L. M., and Grogan, C. H., *J. Org. Chem.* **22**, 185 (1957).
44. Rosen, W. E., Toohey, V. P., and Shabica, A. C., *J. Am. Chem. Soc.* **79**, 3167 (1957).
45. Rothlin, E., Taeschler, M., Konzett, H., and Cerletti, A., *Experientia* **10**, 142 (1954).
46. Scheu, H., and Spühler, O., *Schweiz. Med. Wochschr.* **87**, 117 (1957).
47. Schlittler, E., Druey, J., and Marxer, A., *Progr. Drug Res.* **4**, 297 (1962).
48. Smith, C. M., Pelikan, E. W., Maramba, L. R., and Unna, K. R., *J. Pharmacol. Exptl. Therap.* **108**, 317 (1953).
49. Stämpfli, R., *Physiol. Rev.* **34**, 101 (1954).
50. Stoll, A., and Jucker, E., *Angew. Chem.* **66**, 376 (1954).
51. Stoll, A., Lindenmann, A., Jucker, E., *Helv. Chim. Acta* **36**, 1506 (1953); Stoll, A., Jucker, E., and Lindenmann, A., **38**, 571 (1955).
52. Taeschler, M., Konzett, H., and Cerletti, A., *Schweiz. Med. Wochschr.* **90**, 136 (1960).
53. Veterans Administration Cooperative Study on Antihypertensive Agents, *Arch. Internal Med.* **106**, 81 (1960).
54. Volle, R. L., *J. Pharmacol. Exptl. Therap.* **135**, 54 (1962).
55. cf. Wien, R., *Progr. Med. Chem.* **1**, 53 (1961).

CHAPTER IX

Non-Quaternary Ganglionic Blockers

G. E. Lee

I. Introduction, 295

II. Chemistry and Structure–Activity Relationships of Amine Ganglionic Blockers, 297
   A. Tertiary Di- and Tetramines, 297
   B. Amino Isocamphanes, 298
   C. Polyalkylpiperidines, 305
   D. Cycloalkylamines, 317
   E. Monoamines, 319

III. Pharmacology, 322
   A. Methods of Test, 322
   B. Mode of Action, 323

IV. Excretion, Distribution, and Metabolism, 324
   A. Excretion of Mecamylamine, 324
   B. Excretion and Distribution of Pempidine, 325

V. Clinical Studies, 326
   A. Mecamylamine, 326
   B. Pempidine, 327

   References, 328

I. Introduction

The first clinically useful ganglion-blocking drugs were bis quaternary salts. The most widely used of these were hexamethonium and pentolinium. These bis quaternary salts had, however, certain properties which made them unsuitable particularly for the treatment of mild or moderate hypertension. These disadvantages were the disturbing side effects associated with ganglionic blockade and included: constipation, dry mouth, impotence, blurring of vision, difficulty with micturition and blockade of the reflex adjustment of blood pressure which normally occurred when the patient assumed the erect position. Occasionally, this latter effect, termed postural hypotension, was so severe that there was insufficient blood flow to the brain and the patient fainted. Another feature of all ganglion-blocking drugs was that the blood pressure fluctuated considerably from very low to very high values. Despite careful adjustment of the dose, this fluctuation could not be prevented entirely. In an attempt to prevent these peaks of pressure, therapeutic doses were increased, but this had the result that the patient might at times be unable to stand erect because of postural hypotension. Quaternary ammonium bases are poorly absorbed from the gastrointestinal tract. In the case of hexamethonium and pentolinium, less than 10% of the ingested dose is actually absorbed. Further, even when a quaternary salt reaches the blood stream, it is likely to be rapidly excreted, for it will be filtered by the glomerulus of the kidney, but it is unlikely to be reabsorbed into the blood stream by the tubule. Research in the field of ganglion-blocking agents, therefore, was directed toward improving absorption. It was hoped that the fluctuations in blood pressure and the severity of the side effects associated with pentolinium would be overcome if the blocking agent was completely absorbed.

In 1953 Norton and Phillips (45) discovered powerful ganglionic blocking properties in a bis tertiary amine, 1-methyl-3(4-dimethylaminobutyl)piperidine (I). Plummer et al. (51) likewise found considerable ganglion-blocking activity in a group of tetramines (II) which can be regarded as tertiary amine derivatives of azamethonium. The most active member of the group had blocking activity comparable with hexamethonium.

The first nonquaternary blocking agent of clinical significance was the secondary amine, mecamylamine, 3-methylamino isocamphane (IV) (3).

In terms of dose required to produce a particular degree of ganglion block, this compound was at least as active as hexamethonium (62), but its effects persisted for from three to five times as long. In spite of this and in spite of the lack of any obvious chemical resemblance to hexamethonium, mecamylamine appeared to be acting in essentially the same way, blocking transmission in ganglia.

Two research teams, Spinks and Young (58) and Lee et al. (31), independently discovered the high ganglion-blocking activity of pempidine (1,2,2,6,6-pentamethylpiperidine, XXI). Mecamylamine and pempidine are approximately equiactive as ganglion-blocking agents with similar long durations of activity. Both compounds contain saturated rings with a nitrogen atom surrounded by methyl groups. In mecamylamine the nitrogen atom is exocyclic and secondary, but in pempidine it is endocyclic and tertiary. This grouping of a nitrogen atom surrounded by methyl groups was later to be found in a number of cyclic (e.g., penhexamine) and open ring (e.g., penbutamine, XXXV) ganglion-blocking agents. Mecamylamine and pempidine are both strong bases, are well absorbed from the gastrointestinal tract, and produce a long-lasting ganglionic blockade.

The disturbing side effects produced by these nonquaternary ganglion-blocking agents, however, remained a definite nuisance. Patients complained not only of the side reactions produced by sympathetic blockade, such as weakness and faintness in the erect position due to postural hypotension, but also of parasympathetic blocking effects which included constipation, dryness of the mouth, failure of visual accommodation, difficulty in emptying the urinary bladder, and impotence.

Therefore the search was continued for compounds which would block the sympathetic system selectively, leaving parasympathetic functions undisturbed. As a result of this search, a number of new compounds with interesting properties have been developed.

The first of these, bretylium, a compound claimed to produce only post-ganglionic blockade, was examined with great interest by both pharmacologists and clinicians. Although an advance in the treatment of hypertension, bretylium was soon superseded by guanethidine, a compound considered to act on blood pressure by completely new and still-disputed mechanisms.

An even more recent advance is α-methyldopa, an inhibitor of dihydroxy-phenylalanine (dopa) decarboxylase, which is being widely used clinically although the mechanism by which it causes a reduction in the blood pressure is obscure.

II. Chemistry and structure–activity relationships of amine ganglionic blocking agents

A. TERTIARY DI- AND TETRAMINES

While exploring a series of compounds related to 1-methyl-3(4'-dimethyl-aminobutyl)piperidine (I), Norton and Phillips (45, 47) (Scheme I), found that powerful ganglion-blocking activity was possessed by certain tertiary amines.

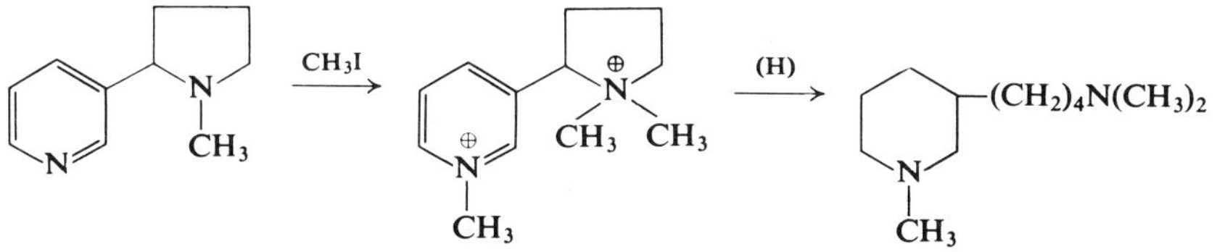

Scheme I

They found that these compounds were as potent as hexamethonium as ganglion-blocking agents but were much less toxic. They hoped that these tertiary amines lacking the quaternary groups of hexamethonium might have fewer side effects.

As no clinical or detailed pharmacological papers have appeared on these compounds, it is not possible to say whether they had clinical activity.

$(C_2H_5)_2N\!-\!(CH_2)_2\!-\!NH_2 + 2Cl(CH_2)_2N(C_2H_5)_2 \longrightarrow$

$$(C_2H_5)_2\!-\!N\!-\!(CH_2)_2N \begin{array}{l} \diagup (CH_2)_2N(C_2H_5)_2 \\ \diagdown (CH_2)_2\!-\!N(C_2H_5)_2 \end{array} \xrightarrow{\quad CH_3I \quad}$$

(II)

$$\longrightarrow \left[\begin{array}{c} CH_3 \\ | \\ (C_2H_5)_2N\!-\!(CH_2)_2 \end{array} \right]_3^{3+} N \cdot (I^-)_3$$

(III)

Scheme II

During an investigation of some tris quaternary salts, (Scheme II) (40, 51), it was discovered that whereas the methiodide (III) was devoid of ganglion-blocking activity, the hydrochloride (II) displayed a high order of ganglion-blocking activity.

B. Amino Isocamphanes

The first clinically useful nonquaternary blocking agent was mecamylamine (IV). This compound was prepared (60) by treating racemic camphene with hydrogen cyanide under strongly acidic conditions (Scheme III). Instead of

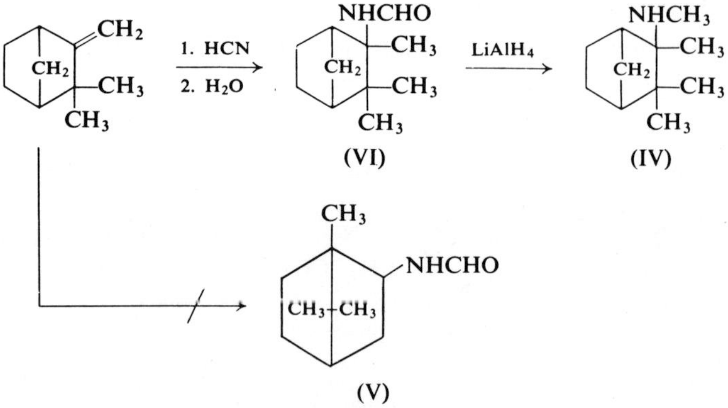

Scheme III

the expected N-formyl isobornylamine (V), 3-formamidoisocamphane (VI) was obtained. Lithium aluminium hydride reduction of this compound gave 3-methylaminoisocamphane (IV), mecamylamine, which showed a significant degree of ganglion-blocking activity. Notwithstanding its chemical dissimilarity to hexamethonium, it was very close in its pharmacological action except that it possessed an inherently longer duration of action combined with an almost quantitative absorption following oral administration.

This reaction of hydrogen cyanide with camphene to give the norcamphane structure (VI) rather than the isomeric N-formylisobornylamine (V) was unexpected. A direct comparison with the melting points of authentic bornyl and isobornylmethylamines confirmed that the product (IV) obtained was different.

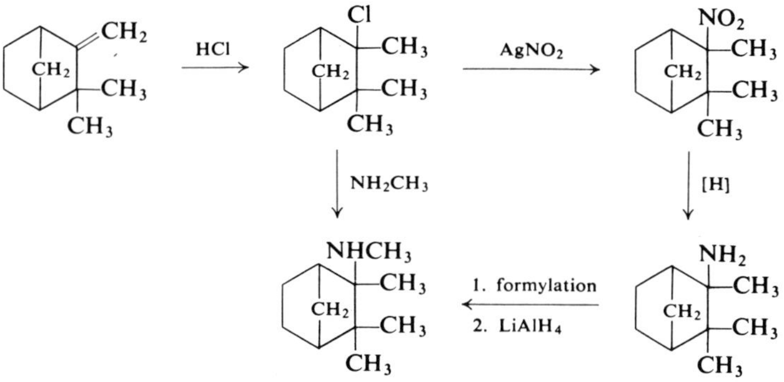

Scheme IV

Repetition of the work of Hückel and Nerdel (27) (Scheme IV) using racemic camphene gave the primary amine (VII). This was methylated to give a sample of mecamylamine identical with that obtained by the alternative route (Scheme III).

Since mecamylamine showed a degree of ganglion-blocking action equivalent to that of hexamethonium, it was of interest to examine some closely related compounds in order to see if the already high level of activity could be further improved.

Two groups of workers, Stone et al. (64) and Edge et al. (17), have investigated structure–activity relationships in this series. Unfortunately, a comparison of results by various researchers in this field is very difficult due to the extremely long action of the compounds. In fact, Edge et al. consider that greater reliance is to be placed on potency estimates of compounds with a duration of action of the order of hexamethonium than to those with a duration of action of the order of that of mecamylamine.

A summary of the results obtained by Edge et al. is given in Table I from which it is evident that the angular methyl groups at R_3 and R_5 are most important for high ganglion-blocking activity. This early structure–activity conclusion proved to be of great importance to Edge et al. in their later work on pempidine and related compounds.

Table I

GANGLION-BLOCKING ACTIVITY OF SOME CONGENERS OF MECAMYLAMINE[a]

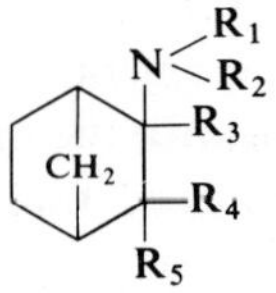

R_1	R_2	R_3	R_4	R_5	Activity[b]
CH_3	CH_3	CH_3	CH_3	CH_3	100
H	CH_3	CH_3	CH_3	CH_3	120
H	H	CH_3	CH_3	CH_3	50
CH_3	CH_3	CH_3	CH_3	H	50
H	CH_3	CH_3	CH_3	H	35
H	CH_3	CH_3	H	H	25
H	CH_3	C_2H_5	H	H	25
H	CH_3	H	CH_3	CH_3	15

[a] From Edge et. al. (17).

[b] $\dfrac{\text{Dose mg/kg of hexamethonium producing } 80\% \text{ block of cat nictitating membrane}}{\text{Dose mg/kg of test compound producing } 80\% \text{ block of cat nictitating membrane}} \times 100$

See Section III, A for test methods.

The synthetic routes used by Edge et al. for the preparation of the mecamyl-amine congeners was different from that used by Stone et al. in that it involved the use of a Diels–Alder reaction to form the norcamphane ring.

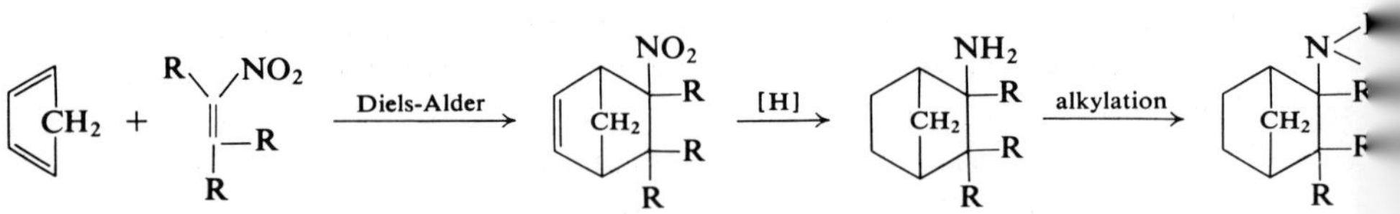

Scheme V

By using the appropriate nitro alkene (VIII), they were able to prepare a range of mecamylamine congeners (Scheme V) (32). Unfortunately, owing to steric hindrance at the Diels–Alder stage, they were unable to prepare mec-amylamine itself.

Stone et al. carried out a similar survey, but concentrated on varying the nitrogen substituents (R_1, R_2 in IX and X, Scheme VI) and the alkyl group (R_3 in XI, Scheme VII) on the carbon atom carrying the nitrogen (Table II).

Activity (a) in Table II is a measure of the compound's ability to cause the pupils of mice to dilate (see Section III, A). The amount of compound (milligrams per kilogram) required to dilate the pupil to a predetermined diameter is quoted. Compounds found to have high activity in the pupil dilation test were examined in the cat nictitating membrane test (see Section III, A), activity (b) in Table II. The dose range required to produce from 20 to 80% reduction of contractions of the nictitating membrane induced by preganglionic nerve stimulation is quoted.

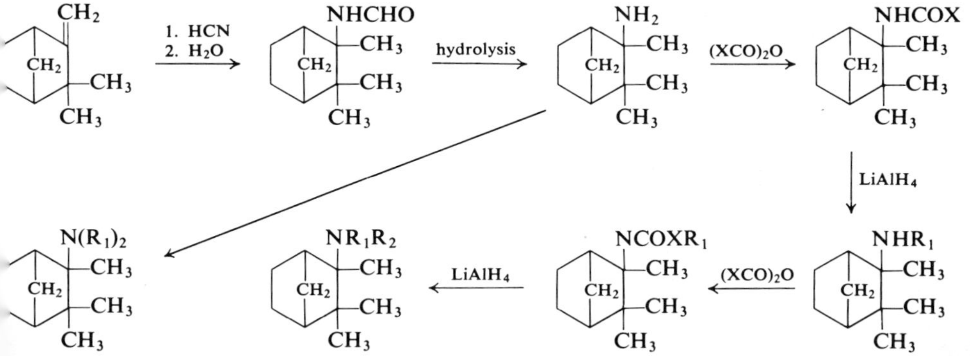

Scheme VI

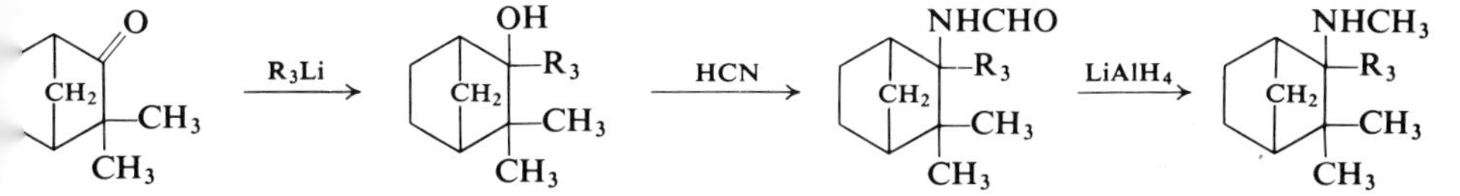

Scheme VII

Although a direct comparison of activities obtained by different authors in this series of long-acting compounds is difficult, there is in general a fair correlation of results, except for one compound in Table I (R_1, $R_3 = H$; R_2, R_4, $R_5 = CH_3$) and Table II (R_1, $R_3 = H$; $R_2 = CH_3$). Rubinstein et al. (54) report a much higher activity in the cat nictitating membrane test than that given by Edge et al. (17) (Table III).

A partial explanation for this lack of correlation may lie in the stereochemistry of these bicyclic compounds.

Stone et al. have separated the isomers (Scheme IX) which show an activity variation, the exo isomer being more active than the endo. It is probable that the methods of synthesis used by Edge et al. (Scheme VIII) and Rubinstein

Table II

GANGLION-BLOCKING ACTIVITIES OF SOME CONGENERS OF MECAMYLAMINE[a]

R_1	R_2	R_3	Activity (a)[b] (mg/kg)	Activity (b)[c] (mg/kg)
H	H	CH_3	5.2	
H	CH_3	CH_3	1.3	0.25–1.0
H	C_2H_5	CH_3	1.6	
CH_3	CH_3	CH_3	1.5	0.25–1.0
C_2H_5	C_2H_5	CH_3	3.8	
H	$(CH_2)_2CH_3$	CH_3	7.5	
H	$(CH_2)_4CH_3$	CH_3	13.5	
H	$-CH(CH_3)_2$	CH_3	5.2	
H	$CH_2CH{=}CH_2$	CH_3	8.5	
H	$(CH_2)_2C(CH_3)_3$	CH_3	43	
H	C_6H_{13}	CH_3	40	
H	$C_6H_5CH_2$	CH_3	83	
H	$C_6H_5CH_2CH_2$	CH_3	36	
H	$C_6H_5CH_2CH_2CH_2$	CH_3	37	
H	CH_3	C_2H_5	7.0	
H	CH_3	C_3H_7	50	
H	CH_3	H	2.9	

[a] From Stone, C. A. *et al.* (64).
[b] Mouse pupil dilation test.
[c] Cat nictitating membrane test.

Table III

GANGLION-BLOCKING ACTIVITY OF
2-METHYLAMINO-3,3-DIMETHYLBICYCLO-2,2,1-HEPTANE

Activity (a)[a]	Activity (b)[b]	Activity (hexamethonium = 100)	Reference
2.9	endo 1–2.0		(64)
4.6	exo	15	(17)
		300	(54)

[a] Mouse pupil dilation test. See Table II.
[b] Cat nictitating membrane test. See Table II.

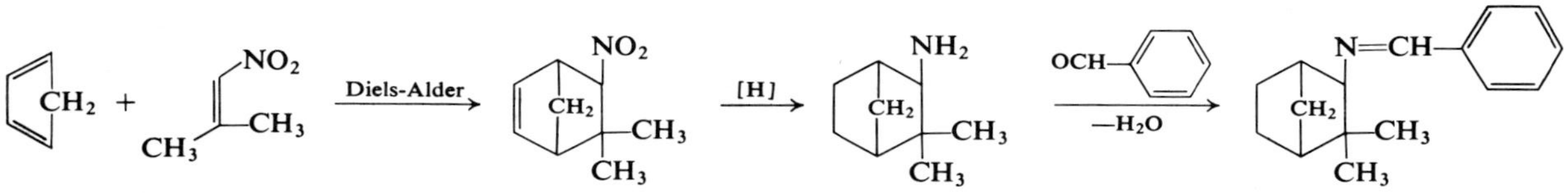

Scheme VIII

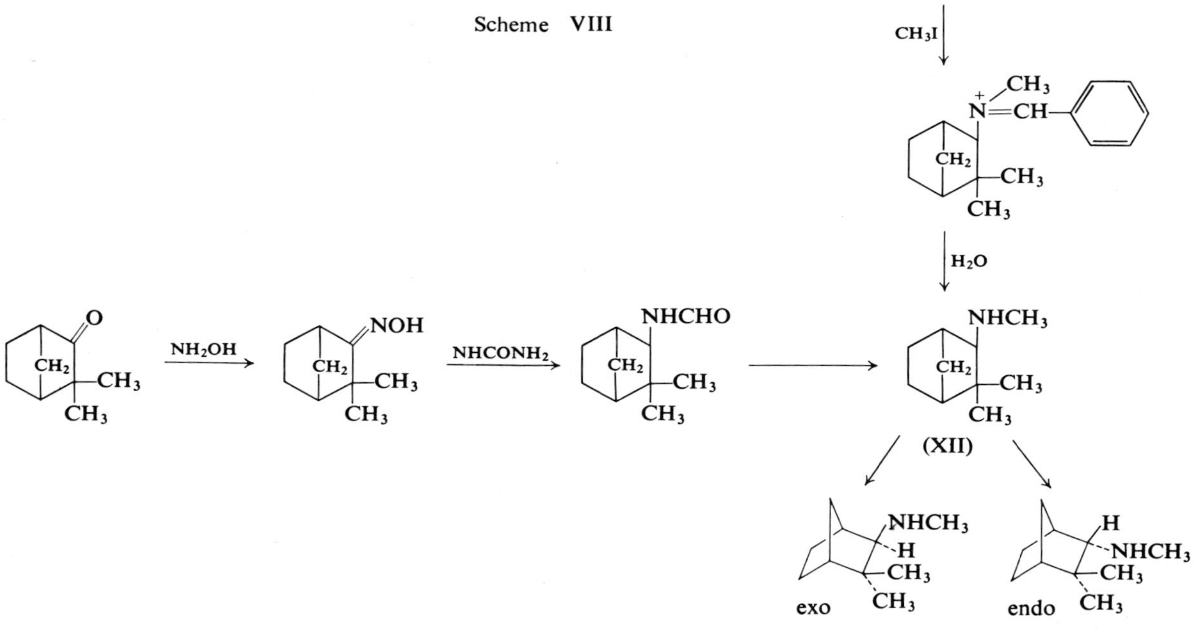

Scheme IX

et al. (not described) have given the endo (XIIb) and exo (XIIa) isomers respectively. Even so, the figure 300 (hexamethonium $= 100$), obtained by Rubinstein is still high compared with those obtained by the other workers.

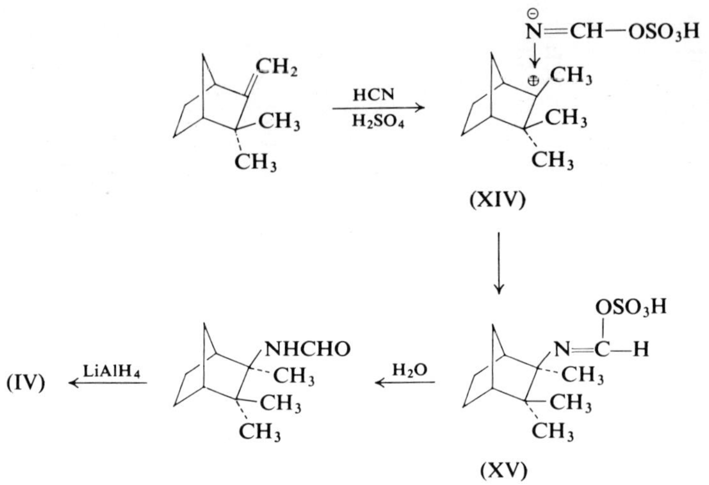

Scheme X

Mecamylamine itself (IV) (Scheme III) was isolated in only one form. This would arise because the conformation of the carbonium ion (XIV) would favor the formation of the exo form of the intermediate (XV) (Scheme X).

Stone *et al.* also investigated the ganglion-blocking activity of optical isomers of mecamylamine. They were able to separate *dl*-mecamylamine into the pure *d* and *l* forms. This resolution was carried out by fractional crystallization of the *d*-camphor sulfonate salt. The *d*-mecamylamine was found to have the same ganglion-blocking activity as *dl*-mecamylamine. No activity figures are given for the *l*-mecamylamine but since the *d*- and *dl*- forms are equiactive, the *l*- form must have a similar level of activity.

The structure–activity relationships of mecamylamine and its various derivatives indicate that the highly basic amino group ($pK_a \simeq 12.3$) must be hindered to a critical degree by the surrounding alkyl substituents. Of the hindering groups, the alkyl substituents in the angular position, on the carbon adjacent to the nitrogen-bearing carbon atom and the bridge methylene are all significant. If the hindrance is too large, then activity is diminished.

The difference in activity of the two geometric isomers (XIIa, XIIb) may also be explained on the basis of critical hindrances. In the exo isomers (XIIa) the methylamino group lies in the same plane as the bridge methylene whereas in the endo isomers (XIIb) the methylamino group lies below the bridge methylene and in fact tends to lie within the cage created by the bridge. This suggests that the endo isomer is less active because the hindrance is more than optimum.

C. POLYALKYLPIPERIDINES

The introduction of mecamylamine stimulated researches by other workers and resulted in the production of another useful compound for the treatment of hypertension, pempidine, 1,2,2,6,6-pentamethylpiperidine (XXI). This discovery was made independently by two groups, working along similar but quite distinct lines of approach.

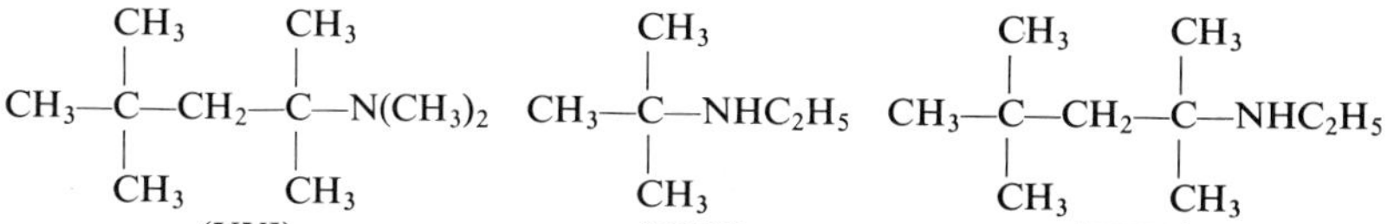

$$
\begin{array}{cccc}
& \text{CH}_3 \quad \text{CH}_3 & \text{CH}_3 & \text{CH}_3 \quad \text{CH}_3 \\
& | \qquad | & | & | \qquad | \\
\text{CH}_3-\text{C}-\text{CH}_2-\text{C}-\text{N(CH}_3)_2 & \text{CH}_3-\text{C}-\text{NHC}_2\text{H}_5 & \text{CH}_3-\text{C}-\text{CH}_2-\text{C}-\text{NHC}_2\text{H}_5 \\
& | \qquad | & | & | \qquad | \\
& \text{CH}_3 \quad \text{CH}_3 & \text{CH}_3 & \text{CH}_3 \quad \text{CH}_3 \\
& \text{(XVI)} & \text{(XVII)} & \text{(XVIII)}
\end{array}
$$

Spinks et al. (59) studied the ganglion-blocking action of a variety of secondary and tertiary bases in which the nitrogen atom was sterically hindered by being closely surrounded by alkyl groups, e.g., (XVI), (XVII), (XVIII).

From a consideration of the results on some 2400 compounds, Spinks et al. decided that high ganglion-blocking activity would be found in simple bases in which the nitrogen atom was linked to two tertiary carbon atoms.

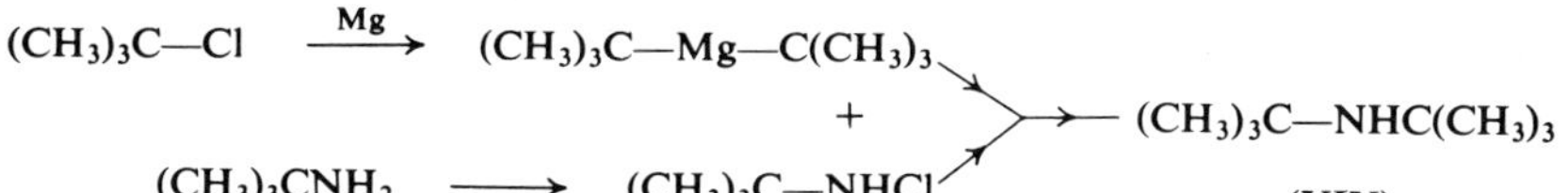

$$(CH_3)_3C-Cl \xrightarrow{\text{Mg}} (CH_3)_3C-Mg-C(CH_3)_3$$
$$+$$
$$(CH_3)_3CNH_2 \longrightarrow (CH_3)_3C-NHCl$$
$$\longrightarrow (CH_3)_3C-NHC(CH_3)_3 \quad \text{(XIX)}$$

Scheme XI

$$(CH_3)_3C-Cl \rightarrow (CH_3)_3C-MgCl \rightarrow (CH_3)_3C-NO$$
$$+$$
$$(CH_3)_3CMgCl$$
$$\longrightarrow (CH_3)_3CNC(CH_3)_3$$
$$\qquad\qquad\qquad | \;\; OH$$
$$\Big\downarrow \text{Sn/HCl}$$
$$(CH_3)_3CNHC(CH_3)_3$$

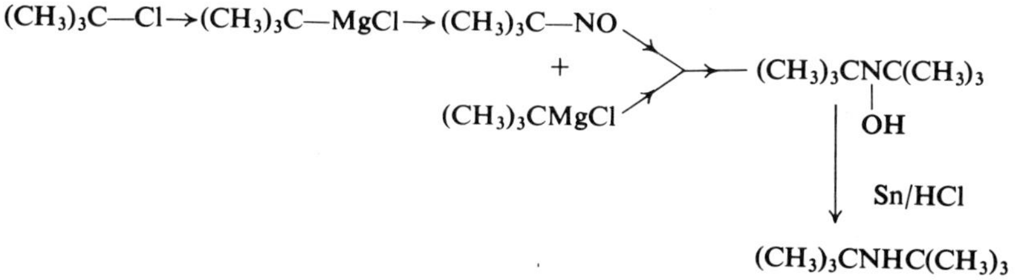

(XIX)

Scheme XII

The preparation of the simplest compound of this type, ditertiary butylamine (XIX), is extremely difficult (28) (Scheme XI) (29) (Scheme XII) and the yield is low; furthermore, compounds containing two tertiary butyl groups are characterized by low stability (10, 11). However, a cyclic analog of ditertiary

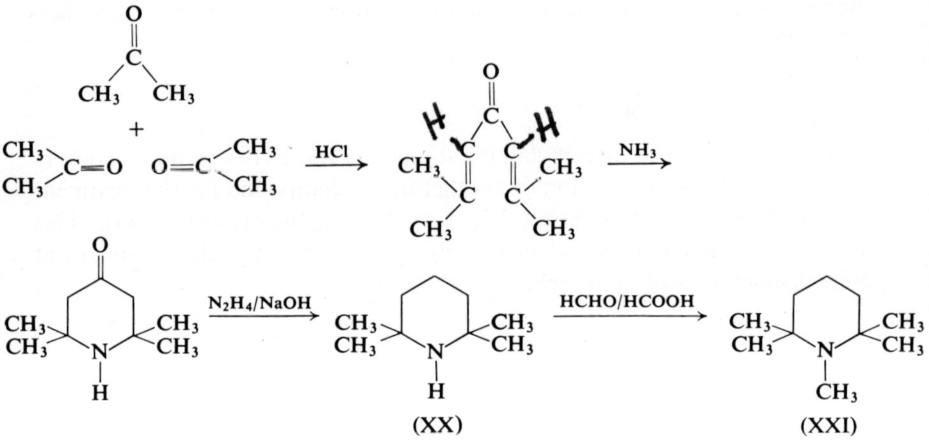

Scheme XIII

butylamine, 2,2,6,6-tetramethylpiperidine (XX), was readily accessible (Scheme XIII) and stable.

Ganglion-blocking activity*

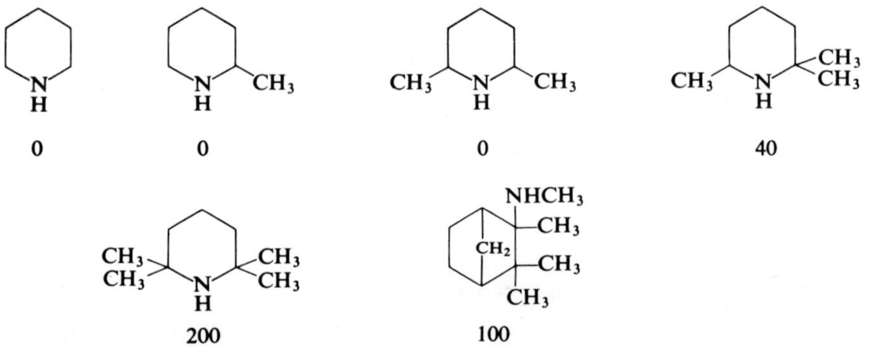

Spinks *et al.* found that 2,2,6,6-tetramethylpiperidine (XX), was about twice as active as mecamylamine as a ganglionic blocker in the cat nictitating membrane preparation. They also investigated the less heavily alkylated piperidines (XXII) (Scheme XIV) and found, as with mecamylamine, that the activity increased as did the number of methyl groups on the carbon atoms adjacent to the nitrogen atom.

Although Spinks *et al.* found 2,6-dimethylpiperidine (XXIII) (Scheme XV) to have no ganglion-blocking activity, Gyermek and Nador (22) report an activity of twice that of tetraethylammonium. Syrneva (65) claims that it is

* Hexamethonium = 100.

five to seven times more active than tetraethylammonium and is useful in the treatment of high blood pressure at 100–200 mg per day.

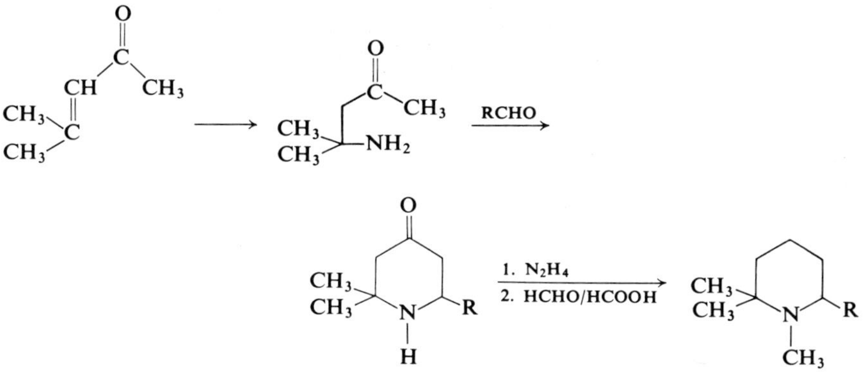

Scheme XIV

The tertiary amines (Table IV) proved to be even more active, reaching a peak at the *N*-ethyl compound. This again paralleled the work on mecamylamine where excessive hindrance could cause a fall in activity. The *N*-methyl derivative, pempidine, was chosen for clinical evluation because the more active *N*-ethyl compound showed an effect on the pituitary and testis in chronic toxicity studies.

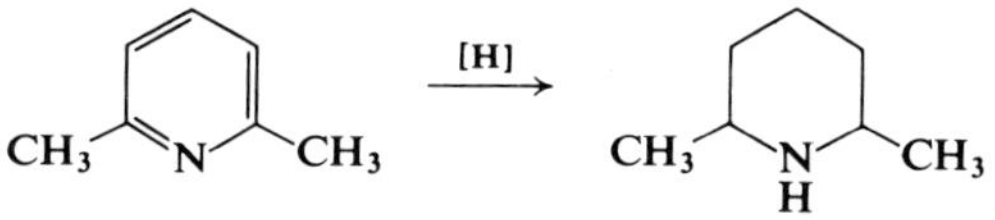

Scheme XV

That two research groups have quite independently and contemporaneously followed similar lines is of sufficient interest to merit an account of how Lee *et al.* (31) also arrived at 1,2,2,6,6-pentamethylpiperidine.

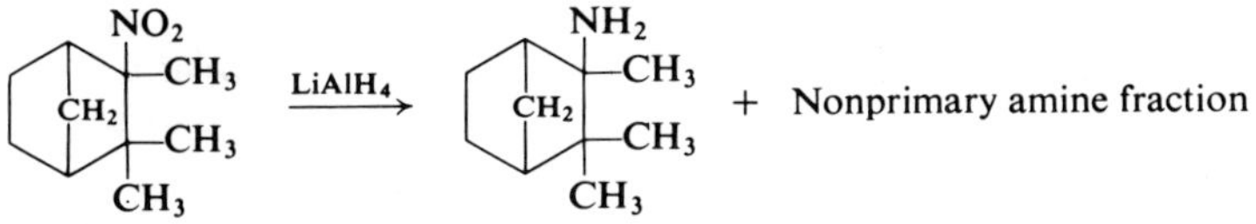

Scheme XVI

Table IV

GANGLIONIC BLOCKING ACTIVITY OF A SERIES OF
N-ALKYL 2,2,6,6-TETRAMETHYLPIPERIDINES

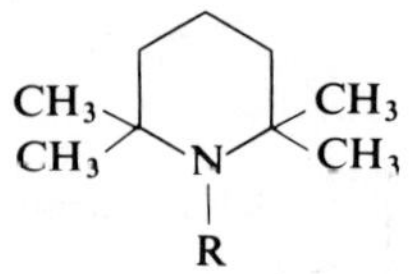

R	Activity (mecamylamine = 100)
H	200
CH_3	250
C_2H_5	300
nC_3H_7	200
nC_4H_9	150
$CH_2 \cdot CH = CH_2$	120
$CH_2C_6H_5$	15

While repeating some work of Gaillot *et al.* (20), who used lithium aluminum hydride to reduce the nitroisocamphane (XXIV) (Scheme XVI) prepared

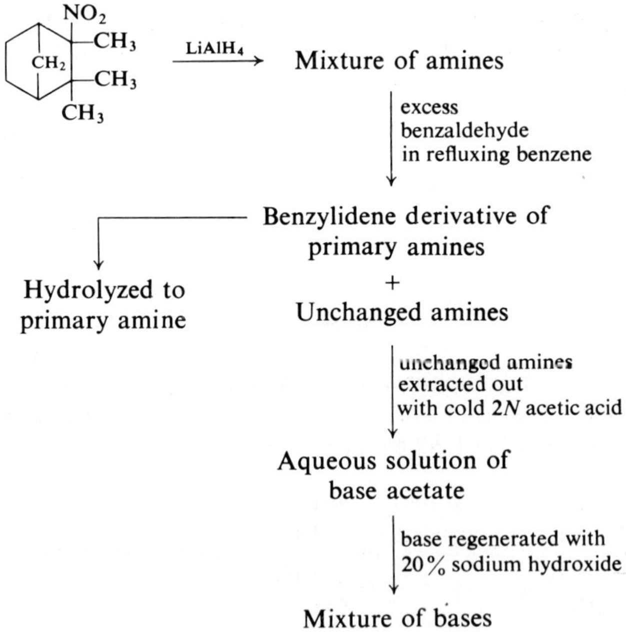

Scheme XVII

by the method of Hückel and Nerdel (27) (Scheme IV), Lee *et al.* observed that the amine fraction formed contained a large proportion that was not primary amine (Scheme XVII) (33).

Properties of mixture of bases

1. Vaporphase chromatography, two components ratio 70:30.
2. I.R. spectrum, no band at 6.3 μ $\therefore$ no —NH_2 grouping.
3. Mixture of bases does not react with benzaldehyde $\therefore$ no NH_2 grouping.
4. Bases separated by preparative vaporphase chromatography.

Properties of separate bases

1. Both analyzed for $C_{10}H_{20}N$.
2. Both formed monohydrochlorides $C_{10}H_{20}N \cdot HCl$, having a band at 6.3 μ corresponding to —$\overset{+}{N}H_2$.
3. Molecular weight of bases $\simeq 150$ (elevation b.p. of benzene).
4. Neither compound had any small *N*-alkyl groups (Hertzig–Meyer).
5. No band in I. R. spectrum of base corresponding to —NH_2 in either compound.
6. I.R. spectrum of both isomers too different to be considered simple geometric isomers.
7. $[\alpha]_D^{20}$ for both bases between $+1°$ and $-1°$ and probably zero.
8. Monomethylation with formic acid–formaldehyde in each case gave an amine, the hydrobromides of which had no 6.3 μ band $\therefore$ both tertiary amines.

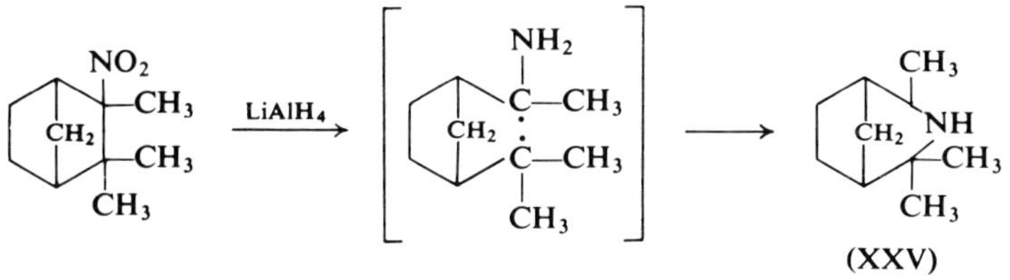

Scheme XVIII

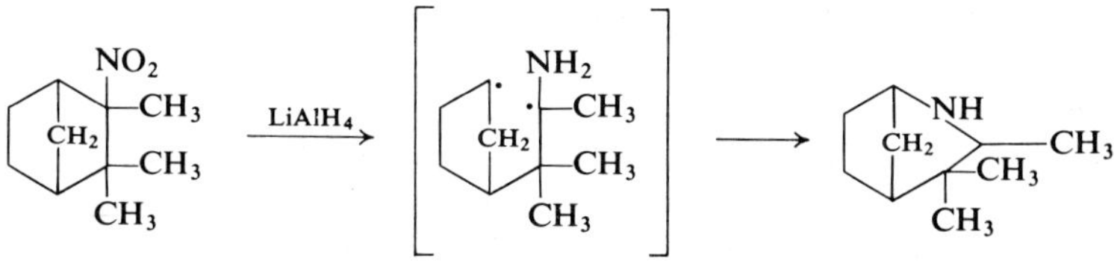

Scheme XIX

Investigation of this nonprimary amine fraction led them to the conclusion that a ring enlargement reaction had taken place to give two secondary amines (XXV) (Scheme XVIII) and (XXVI) (Scheme XIX).

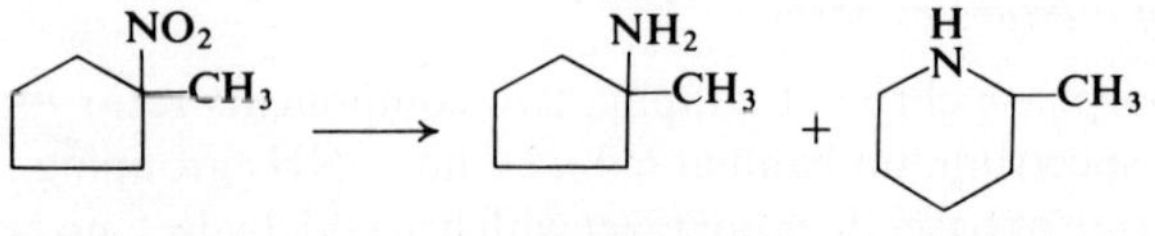

| (XXVII) | (XXVIII) | (XXIX) |

Scheme XX

Evidence that such a ring enlargement was indeed feasible was provided by model experiments in which Lee *et al.* (30) have shown that 1-nitro-1-methyl-cyclopentane (XXVII) does in fact yield not only 1-amino-1-methylcyclo-pentane (XXVIII) but also a substantial proportion of 2-methylpiperidine (XXIX), (Scheme XX).

Ganglion-blocking activity[*]

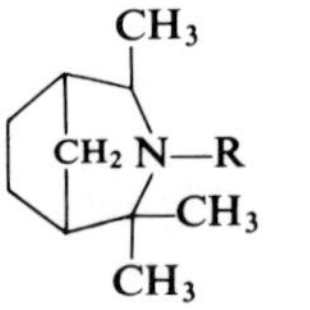

R=H,   134
R=CH₃,   100

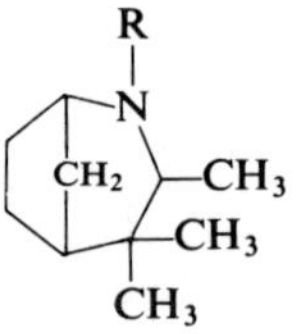

R=H,   75
R=CH₃,   40

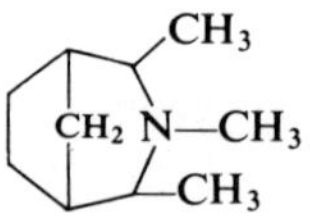

50

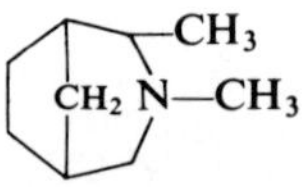

25

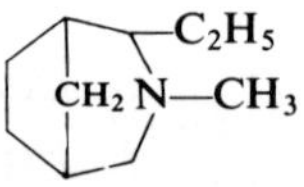

25

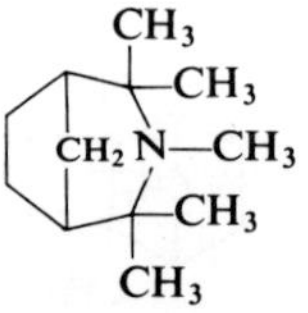

(XXX)

A study of the structure–activity relationships among the above bicyclo-(3,2,1)azaoctanes (synthesized via Scheme XVI) led Lee *et al.* to the conclusion that the activity increased regularly with the number of methyl groups on the two carbon atoms adjacent to the nitrogen atom. This led to an unsuccessful attempt to prepare the fully methylated bicycloaza-3,2,1-octane (XXX), but they were able to prepare the desethylene-bridged compound 1,2,2,6,6-pentamethylpiperidine (pempidine), and found it to have ganglion-blocking activity of the same order and duration as mecamylamine.

* Hexamethonium = 100.

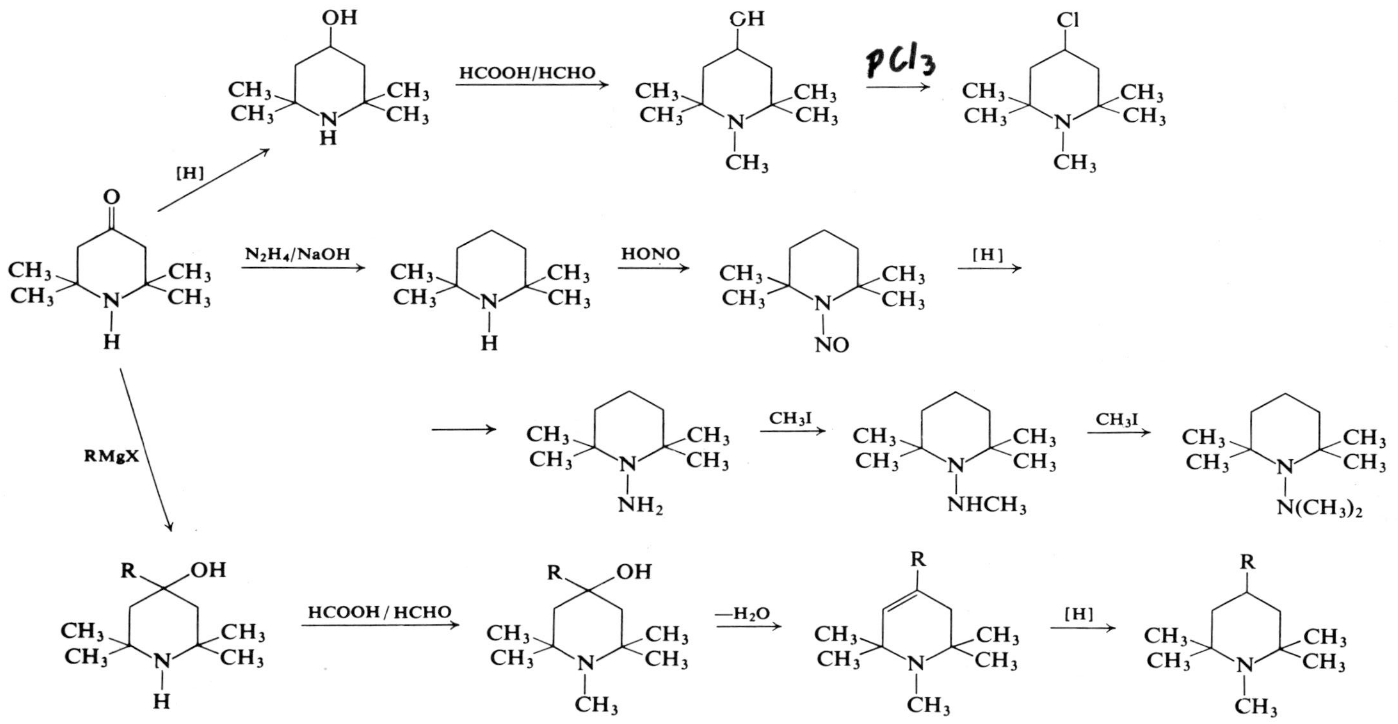

Scheme XXI

311

Bretherick *et al.* (7) examined some 150 congeners of pempidine, many of which exhibited a level of ganglion-blocking activity similar to that of pempidine.

Some of the synthetic routes employed are set out in Scheme XXI. Not unexpectedly, when the nitrogen atom was substituted by groups which reduced the basic strength, the activity was largely eliminated (e.g., —NO, Table V, No. 2, —OH, No. 12).

Table V

ACTIVITY ON THE PREGANGLIONICALLY STIMULATED NICTITATING MEMBRANE
OF THE CAT AND TOXICITY IN THE MOUSE OF 34 CONGENERS OF PEMPIDINE

Compound number	Structure of compound	Activity Potency[a]	Activity Duration[b]	LD_{50} (mg/kg) I.V.	LD_{50} (mg/kg) Oral
1	Pempidine	1.35	long	39.5	275
2	R=H	2.0	long	32.5	220
	R=—C_2H_5	2.0	long	24.4	148
	R=—NO	0.04	long	25.0	300
	R=—NH_2	1.4	short	44.3	261
	R=—$NHCH_3$	1.2	long	25.0	235
	R=—$N(CH_3)_2$	0.03	long		
	R=—N=CH_2	1.75	long	57.0	396
	R=—N=CH·CH_3	1.0	long		
3	R=—Cl	1.0	long		
	R=—Br	1.0	short	51.0	172
4		1.0	long	17.7	127

[a] Hexamethonium=1.0.
[b] Short=similar to hexamethonium: long=similar to pempidine.

Table V—*continued*

Compound number	Structure of compound	Activity		LD$_{50}$(mg/kg)	
		Potency[a]	Duration[b]	I.V.	Oral
5	(structure) R = H	2.3	long	79.0	460
	R = —C$_2$H$_5$	1.0	long	13.2	82
	R = —(CH$_2$)$_3$N(CH$_3$)$_2$	1.0	medium	41.0	460
	R = —C≡CH	1.0	medium	30.0	330
6	(structure) R = H	1.0	long	34.0	230
	R = —CH$_3$	1.0	short	58.0	165
7	(structure)	1.0	medium		
8	(structure)	1.0	short		
9	(structure)	1.4	short	40.0	310
10	(structure)	1.4	short	53.8	210
11	(structure)	(none detected)			

Table V—continued

Compound number	Structure of compound	Activity		LD$_{50}$(mg/kg)	
		Potency[a]	Duration[b]	I.V.	Oral
12	(ring structure) R=H	0.5	long	63.0	450
	R=—CH$_3$	0.5	long	72.0	316
	R=—C$_2$H$_5$	2.0	long	51.0	360
	R=—C$_3$H$_7$	0.5	long	30.4	200
	R=—OH	0.025	medium		
13	(structure)	1.0	long		
14	(structure with C$_2$H$_5$)	0.75	medium		
15	(structure with H)	0.05	very short		
16	(structure with NH, CH$_3$)	0.4	short	99.0	1970
17	CH$_3$—C—NH—C—CH$_3$ (with CH$_3$ groups)	1.4	long		
18	(structure with N$^{\oplus}$)	3.0	very short	11.0	186
19	(structure with S$^{\oplus}$)	1.0	very short	6.55	140

[a] Hexamethonium=1.0.

[b] Short=similar to hexamethonium: long=similar to pempidine.

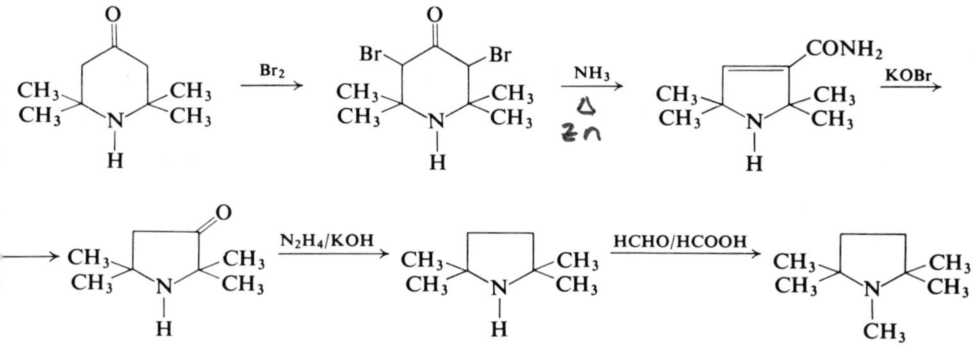

Scheme XXII

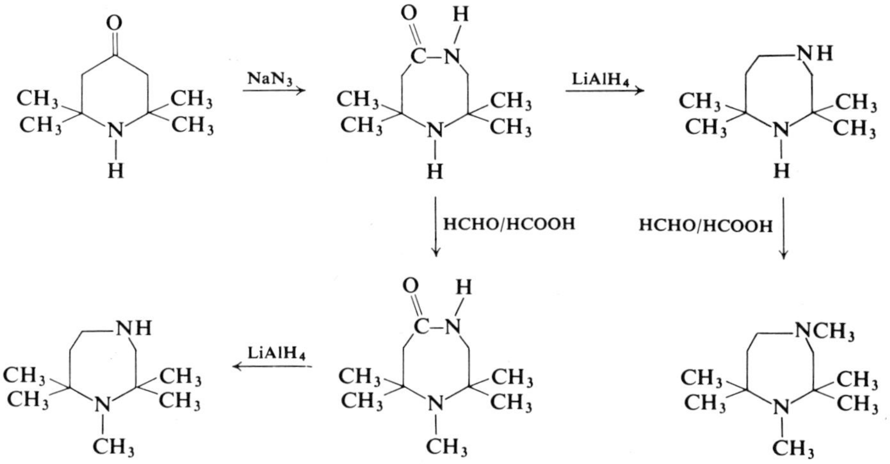

Scheme XXIII

Activity was not confined to derivatives of piperidine; those of pyrrolidine (Scheme XXII) (6) and azacycloheptane (Scheme XXIII) (8) had similar ganglion-blocking properties.

In the piperidine series, at least three methyl groups in the 2 and 6 positions were required for ganglion-blocking activity. Among the pyrrolidines on the other hand, four methyl groups in the 2 and 5 positions were necessary for a useful level of activity (Table V, No. 15 and No. 12, R = H).

Examination of molecular models led Bretherick et al. to conclude that the fourth of these methyl groups was required because the smaller bond angles in the pyrrolidine ring caused a reduction in shielding due to a displacement of the methyl groups in the 2 and 5 positions away from the nitrogen atom as compared with the spatial orientation of the corresponding methyl groups in pempidine. Corroboration that such an effect can influence activity was provided by the reduced level of activity of the pyrroline (Table V, No. 14) as compared with the pyrrolidine (Table V, No. 12, $R = C_2H_5$), the double bond in the pyrroline (Table V, No. 14) evidently caused a further displacement of the methyl groups in the 2,2,5,5-positions away from the nitrogen atom. Furthermore, ditertiary butylamine (Table V, No. 17) in which the ring is absent and α-C-methyl substitution is a maximum, has an activity similar to that of pempidine.

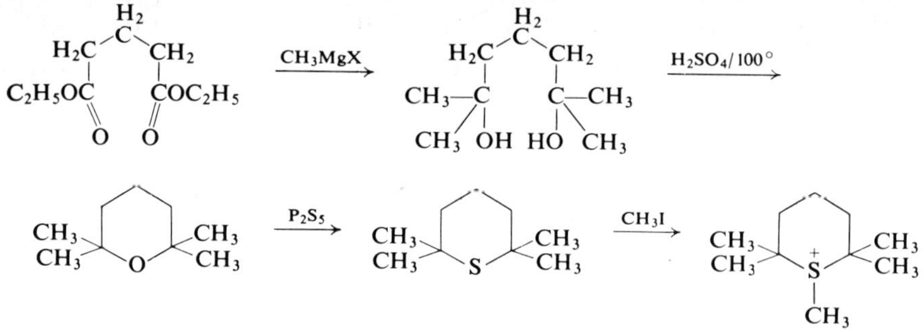

$$
\begin{array}{ccc}
\underset{\substack{\text{H}_2\text{C} \quad \text{CH}_2 \\ \text{C}_2\text{H}_5\text{OC} \quad \text{COC}_2\text{H}_5 \\ \parallel \qquad \parallel \\ \text{O} \qquad \text{O}}}{\overset{\text{H}_2}{\text{C}}} & \xrightarrow{\text{CH}_3\text{MgX}} & \underset{\substack{\text{H}_2\text{C} \quad \text{CH}_2 \\ \text{CH}_3-\text{C} \quad \text{C}-\text{CH}_3 \\ \text{CH}_3 \; \text{OH} \; \text{HO} \; \text{CH}_3}}{\overset{\text{H}_2}{\text{C}}} & \xrightarrow{\text{H}_2\text{SO}_4/100°}
\end{array}
$$

$$
\text{(ring, O, } CH_3 \times 4) \xrightarrow{\text{P}_2\text{S}_5} \text{(ring, S, } CH_3 \times 4) \xrightarrow{\text{CH}_3\text{I}} \text{(ring, } S^+-CH_3, CH_3 \times 4)\ \textbf{(XXXI)}
$$

Scheme XXIV

Conversion of pempidine into its quaternary salt (Table V, No. 18) increased its ganglionic blocking activity but greatly diminished its duration of action. The sulfonium analog (Scheme XXIV, XXXI), as is frequently observed in a ganglion-blocking series, also had an appreciable level of activity.

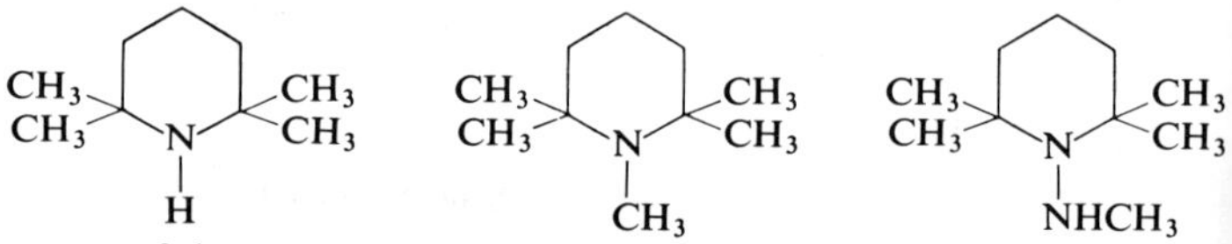

	Structure 1 (N–H)	Structure 2 (N–CH₃)	Structure 3 (N–NHCH₃)
Clinical dose*	3.4	4.2	4.2
Ganglion-blocking activity (duration).†	200 (long)	135 (long)	120 (long)

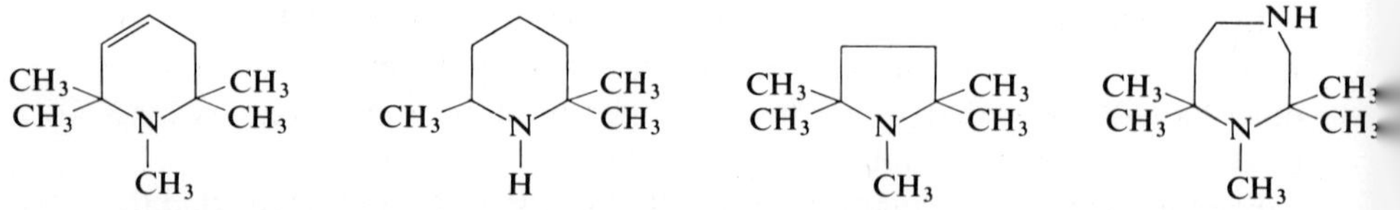

	Structure (pyridine, N–CH₃)	Structure (N–H)	Structure (pyrrolidine, N–CH₃)	Structure (azepine, N–CH₃, –NH)
	6.25	18.2	21.6	21.4
	230 (long)	140 (short)	50 (long)	40 (short)

* As base, milligrams per patient.
† Hexamethonium = 100. Hexamethonium—short, mecamylamine—long.

Smirk and Hodge (57) studied the effect of the six pempidine analogs listed above in comparison with pempidine in hypertensive patients to find the dose which reduced the blood pressure in the standing posture to the near normal level. All six compounds and pempidine appeared to be typical ganglionic blocking drugs and most of the usual parasympathetic side effects have been encountered among them.

In general, the values obtained by Bretherick *et al.* in the preganglionically stimulated nictitating membrane test in the cat correlate reasonably well with the clinically obtained figures. The duration of action was smaller for each of these substances, being usually from 4 to 8 hours. However, it is interesting to note that 2,2,6-trimethylpiperidine, which was short-acting in the cat was long-acting in the human hypertensive subject.

No delayed toxic manifestations as seen with mecamylamine (mental disturbances and tremors) were encountered with the above series of compounds or with pempidine.

D. Cycloalkylamines

1. *Cyclohexylamines*

(XXXII)   (XXXIII)

An obvious simplification of the mecamylamine structure (XXXII), the removal of the methylene bridge to give (XXXIII), has been investigated by at least two groups of workers. Stone *et al.* (62) who were responsible for the work on mecamylamine, and Protiva *et al.* (52) have both investigated the alkyl cyclohexylamines.

Once again, the direct comparison of results is extremely difficult. Stone *et al.* used a scheme whereby the dose in milligrams per kilogram needed to achieve a specified response was recorded whereas Protiva *et al.* observed the effect produced by a selected dose. The results from these systems can usually be compared when the same standard is used. In this example, although Stone *et al.* and Protiva *et al.*, have both used mecamylamine as standard, Stone *et al.* consider penhexamine (Table VI, R_1, R_2, R_3, R_4, $R_5 = CH_3$; R_6, $R_7 = H$) to be about half as active as mecamylamine whereas Protiva *et al.* consider penhexamine and mecamylamine to be equiactive.

This situation could, of course, arise if a supramaximal dose of mecamylamine had been used by Protiva *et al.* in their comparison tests. Since Stone

Table VI

GANGLION-BLOCKING ACTIVITY OF SOME AMINO CYCLOHEXYLAMINES

R_1	R_2	R_3	R_4	R_5	R_6	R_7	Stone et al. (62) Activity (a)[a]	activity (b)[b]	Protiva et al. (52)[c]
		Mecamylamine					1.3	0.25–1.0	75–100%
H	H	H	CH₃	H	H	H	4.8		50–75%
H	H	H	CH₃	CH₃	H	H	21		
H	H	CH₃	H	CH₃	H	H			50–75%
H	CH₃	CH₃	H	H	H	H			0
CH₃	CH₃	H	H	H	H	H			25–50%
H	H	CH₃	CH₃	CH₃	H	H			75–100%
H	CH₃	H	CH₃	CH₃	H	H			25–50%
CH₃	CH₃	CH₃	H	H	H	H			5–25%
CH₃	CH₃	H	H	CH₃	H	H	3.1		75–100%
CH₃	CH₃	H	H	H	CH₃	H			0
CH₃	CH₃	CH₃	CH₃	H	H	H			25–50%
CH₃	CH₃	H	CH₃	CH₃	H	H			75–100%
CH₃	CH₃	H	H	H	CH₃	CH₃			50–75%
CH₃	CH₃	CH₃	CH₃	CH₃	H	H			75–100%
CH₃	CH₃	CH₃	CH₃	H	CH₃	H			50–75%

[a] Mouse pupil dilation test. See Table II.
[b] Cat nictitating membrane test. See Table II.
[c] Degree of ganglion block achieved by dose at 5 mg per kilogram i.v. to cat under chloralose anesthesia.

et al. demonstrated an 80% reduction of contractions of the preganglionically stimulated cat nictitating membrane at 0.25 to 1 mg per kilogram i.v., it is probable that 5 mg per kilogram i.v. in the cat used as by Protiva et al. was supramaximal.

2. Cyclobutylamines

Pircio et al. (50) investigated the pharmacological properties of a new series of cyclobutanes and found that trans-3-dimethylamino-2,2,4,4-tetramethylcyclobutanol (XXXIV) had ganglion-blocking activity.

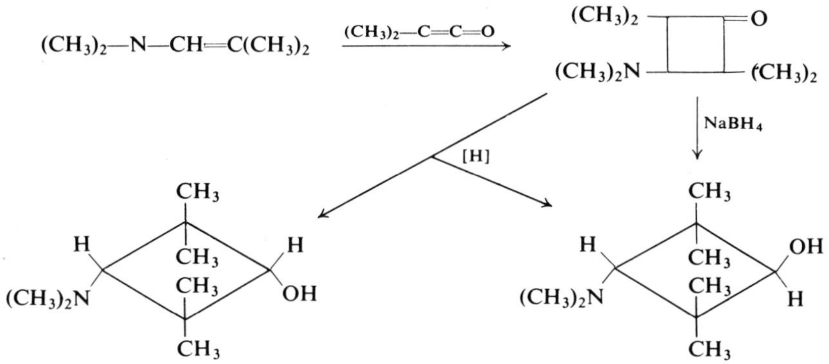

$(CH_3)_2$—N—CH=$C(CH_3)_2$ $\xrightarrow{(CH_3)_2-C=C=O}$

$(CH_3)_2$ ⊐=O
$(CH_3)_2N$ ⊐ $(CH_3)_2$

NaBH₄ (as $NaBH_4$)

[H]

CH₃
H ... CH₃ ... H
$(CH_3)_2N$ ... CH₃ ... OH
CH₃

cis isomer

CH₃
H ... CH₃ ... OH
$(CH_3)_2N$ ... CH₃ ... H
CH₃

trans isomer

Scheme XXV

The trans isomer was as active as hexamethonium in lowering the blood pressure after intravenous injection, but only half as effective in blocking the contraction of the nictitating membrane. The cis isomer was less active. No reports of clinical activity have been found.

E. MONOAMINES

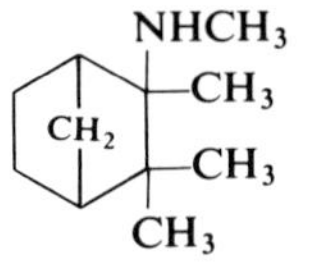

NHCH₃
CH₂ —CH₃
—CH₃
CH₃

Mecamylamine

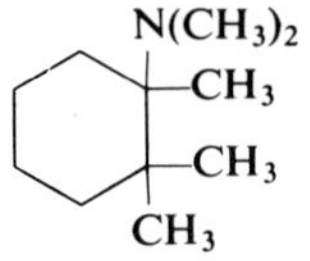

N(CH₃)₂
—CH₃
—CH₃
CH₃

Penhexamine

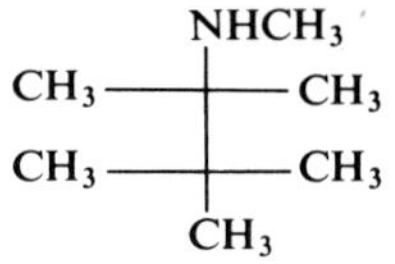

NHCH₃
CH₃— —CH₃
CH₃— —CH₃
CH₃

Penbutamine

(XXXV)

A further simplification of the structure of mecamylamine in which the ring was removed entirely (XXXV) was investigated by Vejdelek and Trcka (66).

Simple amines of this type were investigated by Spinks et al. (59) during their approach to pempidine and by Bretherick et al. (7) after their work on pempidine, but apart from the difficultly accessible ditertiary butylamine, nothing of great interest was found.

Vejdelek and Trcka used the synthetic route of Scheme XXVI to investigate a series of heavily substituted amines (XXXVI). They found that the compounds most closely related to mecamylamine were the most active (Table VII).

Using the general method of Scheme XXVII, Hiltman et al. (25) prepared a series of hindered amines (XXXVII) related to fragments of pempidine rather than to mecamylamine (Table VIII).

Two points of interest emerge from the compounds reported by Hiltmann et al.

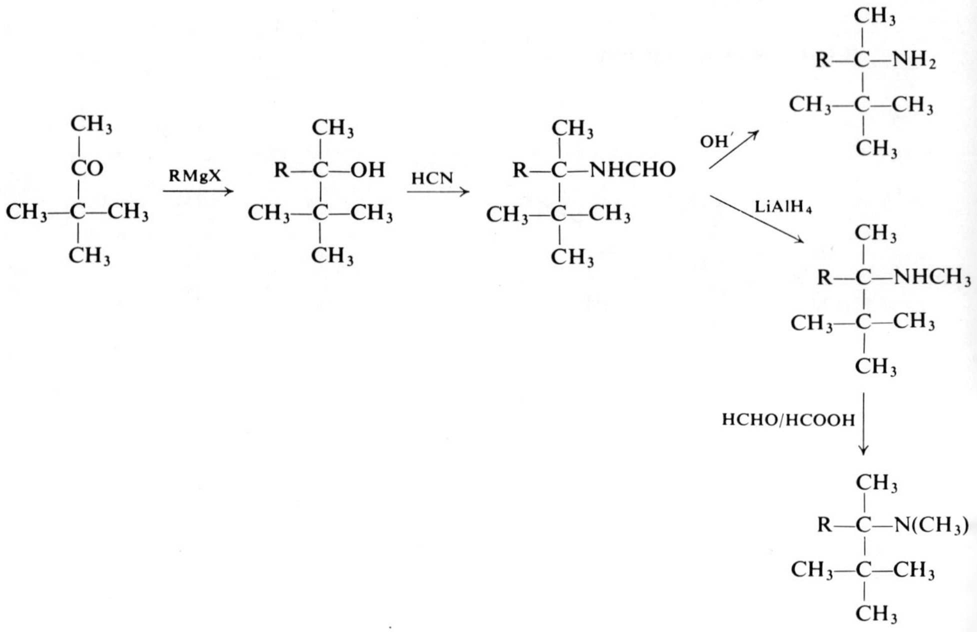

Scheme XXVI showing:

$$CH_3-\underset{\underset{CH_3}{|}}{\overset{\overset{CH_3}{|}}{C}}-\underset{}{CO} \xrightarrow{RMgX} CH_3-\underset{\underset{CH_3}{|}}{\overset{\overset{CH_3}{|}}{C}}-\underset{}{R}{-}OH$$

$CH_3-\overset{CH_3}{\underset{CH_3}{C}}-CO$ $\xrightarrow{RMgX}$ $R-\overset{CH_3}{\underset{CH_3-\overset{CH_3}{C}}{C}}-OH$ $\xrightarrow{HCN}$ $R-\overset{CH_3}{\underset{CH_3-\overset{CH_3}{C}}{C}}-NHCHO$

OH' → $R-\overset{CH_3}{\underset{CH_3-\overset{CH_3}{C}}{C}}-NH_2$

LiAlH$_4$ → $R-\overset{CH_3}{\underset{CH_3-\overset{CH_3}{C}}{C}}-NHCH_3$

HCHO/HCOOH ↓

$R-\overset{CH_3}{\underset{CH_3-\overset{CH_3}{C}}{C}}-N(CH_3)$

(XXXVI)

Scheme XXVI

Table VII

GANGLION-BLOCKING ACTIVITY OF A SERIES OF
NONCYCLIC AMINE FRAGMENTS OF MECAMYLAMINE[a]

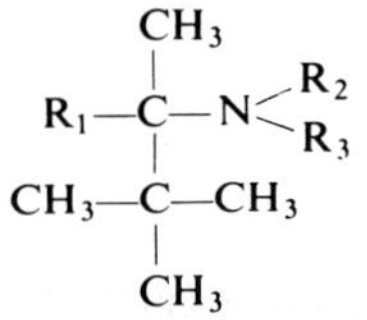

$$R_1-\overset{CH_3}{\underset{CH_3-\overset{CH_3}{C}}{C}}-N\overset{R_2}{\underset{R_3}{\diagdown}}$$

R_1	R_2	R_3	Ganglion-blocking activity
CH_3	CH_3	CH_3	150–200
CH_3	H	H	60–80
CH_3	CH_3	H	100–125
Mecamylamine			100
Dimecamine[b]			100–140
Penbutamine			190–200

[a] From Vedjelek. Z. J. and Trcka, V. (66).
[b] N-methyl mecamylamine. cf. Table II.

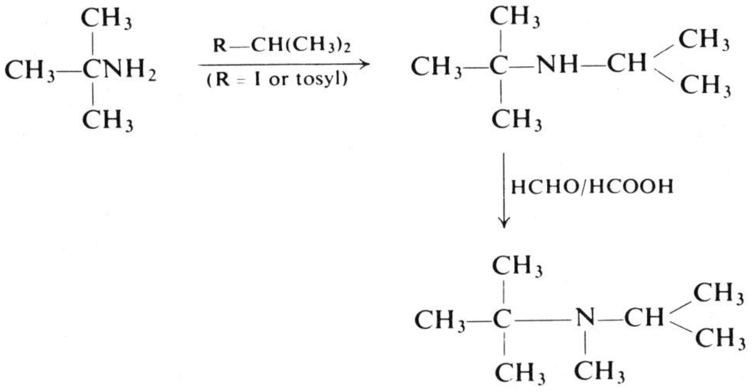

$$CH_3-\underset{\underset{CH_3}{|}}{\overset{\overset{CH_3}{|}}{C}}NH_2 \xrightarrow[\text{(R = I or tosyl)}]{R-CH(CH_3)_2} CH_3-\underset{\underset{CH_3}{|}}{\overset{\overset{CH_3}{|}}{C}}-NH-CH\overset{CH_3}{\underset{CH_3}{<}}$$

$$\downarrow \text{HCHO/HCOOH}$$

$$CH_3-\underset{\underset{CH_3}{|}\ \ \underset{CH_3}{|}}{\overset{\overset{CH_3}{|}}{C}}\underset{}{----}N-CH\overset{CH_3}{\underset{CH_3}{<}}$$

(XXXVII)

Scheme XXVII

(1) Whereas Bretherick *et al.* find the open chain secondary amine, ditertiarybutylamine, equiactive with the cyclic tertiary amine, pempidine, and less active than cyclic secondary 2,2,6,6-tetramethylpiperidine, Hiltmann *et al.*

Table VIII

GANGLION-BLOCKING ACTIVITY OF SOME CONGENERS OF
DITERTIARY BUTYLAMINE[a]

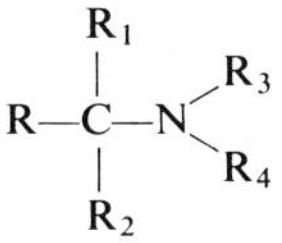

$$\underset{\underset{R_2}{|}}{R-\overset{\overset{R_1}{|}}{C}}-N\overset{R_3}{\underset{R_4}{<}}$$

R	R_1	R_2	R_3	R_4	Activity[b]
CH_3	CH_3	CH_3	iC_3H_7	H	0.1–0.5
CH_3	CH_3	CH_3	iC_3H_7	CH_3	1
CH_3	CH_3	CH_3	$CH\overset{CH_3}{\underset{C_2H_5}{<}}$	H	1
CH_3	CH_3	CH_3	$CH\overset{CH_3}{\underset{CH_2OH}{<}}$	H	< 10
CH_3	CH_3	CH_3	$CH\overset{CH_3}{\underset{CH_2OCH_3}{<}}$	H	> 5
CH_3	CH_3	C_2H_5	iC_3H_7	H	1
CH_3	CH_3	iC_3H_7	CH_3	CH_3	<5
C_2H_5	C_2H_5	C_2H_5	iC_3H_7	H	<5
CH_3	CH_3	CH_2OH	iC_3H_7	CH_3	10
		Mecamylamine			1
		Pempidine			1

[a] From Hiltman *et. al.* (25).
[b] Dose in milligrams per kilogram i.v. to cat under chloralose anesthesia to produce a specified level of ganglion block.

consider the open chain secondary amine, tertiary butylisopropylamine, much more active than the cyclic tertiary amine pempidine which both Bretherick *et al.* and Spinks *et al.* find considerably more active than the cyclic secondary amine 2,6,6-trimethylpiperidine. A possible explanation is that when the piperidine ring is opened, as in ditertiary butylamine, the restraining effect of the ring is lost and the nitrogen atom becomes too hindered and this results in a lower ganglion-blocking activity than is shown by tertiary butylisopropylamine, which may have the maximal amount of hindrance of the nitrogen atom.

(2) The second point of interest is that in this series, as in the piperidine series, the secondary amine is more active than the tertiary amine. This is in contrast to the penbutamine and mecamylamine series where the secondary amine is less active or at least only just as active as the tertiary amine.

III. Pharmacology

A. METHODS OF TEST

The blood pressure of an animal is dependent on the peripheral vascular resistance and on the cardiac output. Peripheral resistance can be lowered by causing a reduction in sympathetic vasoconstrictor tone. Such a reduction in tone may be brought about by a ganglion blocker. The first of these to be examined in great detail was hexamethonium. This compound has the property of selectively blocking transmission at the preganglionic nerve ending, leaving postganglionic transmission unaffected. Hexamethonium competes with the chemical mediator, acetylcholine, released from the nerve endings in the ganglia, preventing it from exciting the nerve cells. It does not inhibit or modify the release of acetylcholine at the ganglionic synapse.

Compounds suspected of having ganglion-blocking properties can be tested for their ability to block the effect of preganglionic excitation of the cervical sympathetic nerve of the anesthetized cat. Intravenous injection of a ganglion blocker prevents transmission through the superior cervical ganglion, the indicator for this response being the inhibition of the contraction of the nictitating membrane, the third eyelid of the cat. Electrical stimulation of the preganglionic fibers of the cervical sympathetic nerve causes a sustained contraction of this nictitating membrane. When a ganglionic blocker is administered intravenously, transmission through the superior cervical ganglion is blocked, which results in a relaxation of the membrane.

The potencies of various ganglion-blocking compounds can be compared in this manner by simply finding the dose of the new compound which will produce the same degree of block as that produced by a standard dose of hexamethonium. This screening method was widely used and was very useful for dealing with short-acting compounds. Although the number of animals used was not large from a statistical point of view, it was possible to compare several drugs in the same preparation. When, however, the compounds became much longer acting (e.g., mecamylamine, pempidine, about 8 hours), it was no longer easy to compare two long-acting compounds in the same preparation. It was possible to compare each compound with a short-acting standard and most workers used hexamethonium as that standard. This procedure still required one preparation per compound and most experimenters turned to alternative procedures for routine screening.

It was known that the intraperitoneal administration of ganglion-blocking agents to mice caused an increase in pupil diameter. This increase in diameter was proportional to the potency of the ganglion-blocking agent. The experimental procedure normally used was that described by Pulewka (53). Briefly, pupil diameters were measured with an ocular micrometer at 5, 10, 20, 40, and 80 minutes after intraperitoneal administration of the compound under test. The amount of compound required to dilate the pupils to a standard diameter was estimated graphically from the dose-response line.

A second method was devised by Stone et al. (63) who have shown that mice can be protected from the convulsant effects of nicotine if they are pretreated with a ganglion-blocking agent. The following test procedure was employed. Several groups of ten mice were pretreated intraperitoneally with various doses of the test compound, 30 minutes prior to the rapid intravenous injection of nicotine. Immediately following the injection, the mice were placed on an elevated platform. If the injected mouse remained on this platform for 15 seconds it was considered protected from the excitatory and clonic convulsive phase of nicotine-induced convulsions. Untreated mice injected with saline remained on the platform indefinitely, untreated mice injected with nicotine ran off the platform within 5 seconds and the proportion of treated mice remaining on the platform was directly related to the magnitude of the dose of ganglion-blocking agent.

Any compound showing a high activity in the pupil diameter and antagonism of nicotine convulsions tests was then examined in the cat nictitating membrane test.

B. MODE OF ACTION

Although the structure of mecamylamine is entirely different from that of hexamethonium, its action as a competitive antagonist to acetylcholine in autonomic ganglia appears to be similar (36, 62). However, other workers (4) have suggested that the fall in blood pressure in man is a result of the actions of mecamylamine at several sites in the body. Bennet et al. (4) using the cat nictitating membrane, the tibialis anterior muscle of the cat, and the isolated mammalian heart and intestine, deduced that the effects of mecamylamine on autonomic ganglia and effects at the neuromuscular junction were not produced by competition with acetylcholine. They also showed that mecamylamine had a direct action on the intestine and heart, and an action on the central nervous system. It was proposed that the compound alters the physiological state of the ganglion cell and of the muscle fiber, resulting in a modified response of the structures to acetylcholine. The fall in blood pressure in man was therefore the result of actions of mecamylamine at several sites in the body.

The experimental findings of Spinks *et al.* (59) and of Corne and Edge (12) on the mechanism of action of pempidine suggest that the latter compound may also act at several sites. Since both mecamylamine and pempidine readily enter cells, an intracellular action has been suggested. On the other hand, the competitive interference with synaptic transmission, as found with hexamethonium and pentolinium, is probably extracellular.

The long duration of action of pempidine and mecamylamine prompted Corne and Edge to draw attention to several mechanisms which might be responsible for the ganglion-blocking activity. Although the opinion that these amines act intracellularly was not rejected, these authors suggested that, by virtue of the slow release of the amines from the ganglion cell body, the acetylcholine membrane receptors might be blocked in the same way as has been postulated for the quaternary ammonium compounds.

It is also possible that their prolonged effects may even be due to stronger binding at the membrane receptors themselves. Since mecamylamine is excreted into the stomach and absorbed by the small intestine, it undergoes a phase of excretion and absorption which may also contribute to the prolonged action of this compound.

Other evidence on the action of mecamylamine has been provided by the experiments of Payne and Rowe (49), who showed that carbon dioxide inhalation increased the plasma concentration of mecamylamine and enhanced its hypotensive effect. One explanation advanced was that carbon dioxide, by lowering the plasma pH, brought about the transfer of mecamylamine from the cells into the extracellular spaces, resulting in greater activity. This is evidence against an intracellular site of action.

Recent work has shown that mecamylamine and pempidine do not alter the rate of formation of acetylcholine. Gardiner (21) found that neither amine had any effect on acetylcholine formation when choline acetylase preparations from guinea pig brain were used. Parkinson (48) likewise came to the same conclusion using choline acetylase from rabbit brain.

IV. Excretion, distribution, and metabolism

A. EXCRETION OF MECAMYLAMINE

Although mecamylamine is strongly basic, it is completely absorbed when given by mouth. It is highly ionized (pK_a 11.4) (3) but the unionized fraction is lipid soluble and is readily diffusible.

Allanby and Trounce (1) have investigated the excretion of mecamylamine after intravenous and oral administration to hypertensive patients. The method of estimation of amines devised by Brodie and Udenfriend (9) was used to estimate the urinary concentration of mecamylamine. The drug was extracted from alkalinized urine by shaking with ethylene dichloride. This extract when mixed with methyl orange formed a chromagen which was measured colorimetrically. The urinary excretion of mecamylamine after an oral dose of 15 mg per kilogram reached about 50% in the first 12 hours, rising to 65% of the total ingested after about 60 hours. After a similar intravenous dose, about 90% was excreted in the urine in 60 hours. The renal excretion of mecamylamine has been shown to be pH dependent, and alkalinization of the urine by the administration of sodium bicarbonate produced a very low excretion of mecamylamine. This was considered to be due to reabsorption of mecamylamine by the renal tubule under the alkaline conditions. Acidification of the urine by the administration of ammonium chloride, however, gave a normal excretion of mecamylamine, over 50% of an oral dose being recovered in 24 hours.

Milne *et al.* (37) have investigated the absorption, distribution, and excretion of mecamylamine in rats after intraperitoneal injection. The highest concentrations were noted in the spleen; decreasing concentrations were found in liver, lungs, kidney, heart, and skeletal muscle. This is attributed to the fixation of the drug by intracellular protein and may explain the more gradual and prolonged action as compared with quaternary ammonium compounds which do not penetrate cells to any extent and concentrate in extracellular fluid (15).

B. EXCRETION AND DISTRIBUTION OF PEMPIDINE

Pempidine is also a strong base (pK_a 11) and under physiological conditions (pH 8) it exists almost entirely (99.9%) in the ionized form. It can also be estimated colorimetrically (44) by coupling with methyl orange using the method of Brodie and Udenfriend. The technique is rather insensitive but could be used to measure the amount of pempidine in urine from rats which had received the drug orally. However, the methyl orange method could not detect the very low plasma concentrations of pempidine attained after oral administration of the drug in amounts which were effective clinically, 0.25–0.50 mg base per kilogram. Use was therefore made of the fact that eosin dissolved in xylene is nonfluorescent. Addition of pempidine produces a fluorescence which is proportional to the concentration of pempidine. The technique is extremely sensitive, 0.001 μg per milliliter being detectable with relatively simple equipment. The method was successfully applied to plasma and tissue studies but could not be applied to urine because of interfering substances which quench the fluorescence.

When given orally at 1–10 mg per kilogram, pempidine was rapidly absorbed

(14) and the peak plasma concentration attained in about 30 minutes was proportional to the dose. The amount in the plasma was small compared with the dose, the pempidine being widely distributed throughout the body tissues. One hour after dosing, the highest concentrations were found in the kidney, spleen, and liver of rats. After 4 hours the drug was concentrated mainly in the spleen, as with mecamylamine, presumably owing to a rapid turnover of red cells. The placenta afforded no barrier to pempidine, which rapidly penetrated into fetal tissue.

Pempidine and mecamylamine were both found in the cerebrospinal fluid but pempidine disappeared more rapidly than mecamylamine. This particular penetration is considered to account for the appearance of tremors as seen with amine ganglion-blocking drugs. Quaternary compounds are considered not to penetrate into the central nervous system and this may account for the absence of the tremor side effect with these compounds.

Pempidine was excreted rapidly in urine during the 24 hours following oral administration, the rate of excretion in the first 7 hours being almost twice that of mecamylamine. At doses approaching those used in clinical practice, 45% of the drug appeared in the urine within 24 hours (70–80% with larger doses) but very little of the drug was recovered subsequently. The renal excretion is pH dependent but this effect is less marked than that with mecamylamine. No metabolites of mecamylamine and pempidine have been reported.

V. Clinical studies

A. MECAMYLAMINE

The first publication on mecamylamine was by Stein *et al.* (60) in 1956. This was mainly a chemical paper but it did disclose the clinical activity of the compound. Stone *et al.* (61, 62) and Milne *et al.* (39) followed with complete descriptions of the pharmacological properties of the compound. The first clinical papers (18, 19, 41–43) soon followed and it was quickly evident that this new nonquaternary ganglion-blocking agent was effective in the treatment of hypertension. Initial doses were of the order of 10–40 mg per day. After oral administration, the onset was within 15 to 60 minutes and the effect lasted for from 12 to 48 hours. Some tolerance was noted after 2 weeks but with slightly increased doses the drug continued to control blood pressure. Mecamylamine was claimed to have a greater uniformity and certainty of action when administered orally than the then currently available quaternary ganglion-blocking drugs. Most of the side effects seen were due to the concurrent blockade of both sympathetic and parasympathetic systems. These side effects (16) were chiefly gastrointestinal, though blurring of vision, dryness of mouth, and urinary retention were frequently observed. Reserpine was recommended as an adjuvant to keep these side effects to a minimum (56).

Two side effects were, however, much more serious and could only be reversed by complete withdrawal of the compound. The first of these was caused by blockade of the parasympathetic system. In its mildest form it was manifested as constipation (47) but if untreated this could quickly become a paralytic ileus. Treatment of the constipation by senna or cascara preparations was recommended for nine out of ten patients being treated with mecamylamine (2).

The second side effect which had not been observed with the quaternary ganglion-blocking agents was a coarse tremor (23, 34). This was considered to be a central effect as it was normally accompanied by mental disturbance, confusion, and vivid hallucinations which were a consequence of the ability of the strongly basic tertiary amine mecamylamine to penetrate into the central nervous system. The only effective course of action with this particular side effect was to stop the drug, after which the side effect slowly disappeared.

B. PEMPIDINE

The structure of pempidine is in some ways very similar to and in some ways different from mecamylamine, but in its pharmacological actions it seemed to be almost the same. It was, however, in the excretion studies that the clue to the differences, which were later to be clinically demonstrated, was first clearly shown. Harington et al. (24) considered that pempidine was more rapidly excreted from the body than mecamylamine. A greater proportion of a dose of pempidine was available for excretion because it entered body cells less freely than did mecamylamine and almost none was bound to plasma protein. About 70% of a single dose of pempidine was excreted within 24 hours and if toxic symptoms from overdosage occurred, these were likely to be of shorter duration than in the case of mecamylamine. Thus, during the initial stages of therapy, the dose of pempidine could safely be increased rapidly so that final control of the high blood pressure could be rapidly achieved.

Nevertheless, the usual side effects seen with powerful ganglion-blocking agents were observed with pempidine. The more rapid excretion of pempidine normally necessitated dosing four times per day as compared with twice per day with mecamylamine (5). Paralytic ileus could still be caused, particularly when a thiazide diuretic was used in conjunction with pempidine (26).

Most authors found pempidine a satisfactory ganglion-blocking agent [e.g., Mathisen (35), Croll et al. (13), Milne (38)], and in a double-blind trial, Sinclair (55) found mecamylamine and pempidine very similar and effective drugs for hypertensive diseases.

Smirk and Hodge (57) (Section II, C) examined a number of close relatives of pempidine but concluded that although several of them were very potent ganglion-blocking agents, they showed no advantage over pempidine.

No clinical papers have appeared concerning the other ganglion-blocking drugs which are mentioned in this chapter; it is not possible, therefore, to discuss them in relation to human therapy.

Acknowledgment

Sections III, IV, and V were prepared with the assistance of M. F. Cuthbert, M.B., B.S.

References

1. Allanby, K. D., and Trounce, J. R., *Brit. Med. J.* **II**, 1219 (1957).
2. Allanby, K. D., *Practitioner* **180**, 488 (1958).
3. Baer, J. E., Paulson, S. F., Russo, H. F., and Beyer, K. H., *J. Pharmacol. Exptl. Therap.* **116**, 2 (1956).
4. Bennet, G., Tyler, C., and Zaimis, E., *Lancet* **II**, 218 (1957).
5. Botha, P. W. A., *S. African Med. J.* **33**, 769 (1959).
6. Bretherick, L., and Wragg, W. R., British Patent 857,426 (1958).
7. Bretherick, L., Lee, G. E., Lunt, E., Wragg, W. R., and Edge, N. D., *Nature* **184**, 1707 (1959).
8. Bretherick, L., and Wragg, W. R., personal communication (1959).
9. Brodie, B. B., and Udenfriend, S., *J. Biol. Chem.* **158**, 705 (1945).
10. Brown, H. C., Barbaras, G. K., Berneis, H. L., Bonner, W. H., Johannesen, R. B., Grayson, M., and Nelson, K. L. R., *J. Am. Chem. Soc.* **75**, 2 (1953).
11. Brown, H. C., and Barbaras, G. K., *J. Chem. Phys.* **14**, 114 (1946).
12. Corne, S. J., and Edge, N. D., *Brit. J. Pharmacol.* **13**, 339 (1958).
13. Croll, F. J. T., Bauer, G. E., Raftos, J., Goldnick, R. B., and Young, A. A. *Med. J. Australia* **48**, 98 (1961).
14. Dollery, C. T., Emslie-Smith, D., and Muggleton, D. F., *Brit Med. J.* **I**, 521 (1960).
15. Dollery, C. T., *in* "Absorption and Distribution of Drugs" (T. B. Binns, ed.), pp. 157–164. Livingstone, Edinburgh and London, 1964.
16. Doyle, A. E., Murphy, E. A., and Neilson, G. H., *Brit. Med. J.* **II**, 1209 (1956).
17. Edge, N. D., Corne, S. J., Lee, G. E., and Wragg, W. R., *Brit. J. Pharmacol.* **15**, 207 (1960).
18. Ford, R. V., Madison, J. C., and Moyer, J. H., *Am. J. Med. Sci.* **232**, 129 (1956).
19. Freis, E. D., and Wilson, I. M., *Abstr. Sci. Session Am. Heart Assoc.* **28**, 41 (1955).
20. Gaillot, P., Baget, J., and Sarret, P., Belgian Patent 558,352 (1957).
21. Gardiner, J. E., *Nature* **184**, B.A. 71 (1959).
22. Gyermek, L., and Nador, K., *J. Pharm. Pharmacol.* **9**, 209 (1957).
23. Harington, M., and Kincaid-Smith, P., *Lancet* **I**, 499 (1958).
24. Harington, M., Kincaid-Smith, P., and Milne, M. D., *Lancet* **II**, 6 (1958).
25. Hiltmann, R., Wollweber, H., Wirth, W., and Gösswald, R., *Angew. Chem.* **72**, 1001 (1960).
26. Hobolth, N., *Ugeskrift Laeger* **121**, 504 (1959).
27. Hückel, W., and Nerdel, F., *Ann. Chem.* **528**, 57 (1937).
28. Klages, F., Nober, G., Kircher, F., and Bock, M., *Ann. Chem.* **547**, 1 (1941).
29. Klages, F., and Sitz, H., *Ber. Deut. Chem. Ges.* **92**, 2606 (1959).
30. Lee, G. E., Lunt, E., Wragg, W. R., and Barber, H. J., *Chem. & Ind. (London)* p. 417 (1958).
31. Lee, G. E., Wragg, W. R., Corne, S. J., Edge, N. D., and Reading, H. W., *Nature* **181**, 1717 (1958).
32. Lee, G. E., and Wragg, W. R., British Patent 827,831 (1958).

33. Lee, G. E., and Wragg, W. R., unpublished observation (1959).
34. Lennox, J. A., *Lancet* I, 798 (1958).
35. Mathisen, H. S., *Nord. Med.* **62**, 1805 (1959).
36. McIsaac, R. J., and Millerschoen, N. R., *J. Pharmacol. Exptl. Therap*, **139**, 18 (1963).
37. Milne, M. D., Muehrcke, R. C., Rowe, G. G., and Somers, K., *Clin. Res. Proc.* **5**, 293 (1957).
38. Milne, M. D., *Practitioner* **182**, 366 (1959).
39. Milne, M. D., Rowe, G. G., Somers, K., Muehrcke, R. C., and Crawford, M. A., *Clin. Sci.* **16**, 599 (1957).
40. Mizzoni, R. H., Hennessey, M. A., and Scholz, C. R., *J. Am. Chem. Soc.* **76**, 2414 (1954).
41. Moyer, J. H., Dennis, E., Ford, R., and Caplovitz, C., *Abstr. Sci. Session Am. Heart Assoc.* **28**, 85 (1955).
42. Moyer, J. H., Ford, R., Dennis, E., and Hardley, C. A., *Proc. Soc. Exptl. Biol. Med.* **90**, 402 (1955).
43. Moyer, J. H., Heider, C., and Dennis, E., *J. Am. Med. Assoc.* **164**, 1879 (1957).
44. Muggleton, D. F., and Reading, H. W., *Brit. J. Pharmacol.* **14**, 202 (1959).
45. Norton, S., and Phillips, A. P., *Nature* **172**, 867 (1953).
46. Nussbaum, H. E., Leff, W. A., Mattia, V. D., and Hillman, E., *Am. J. Med. Sci.* **234**, 150 (1957).
47. Phillips, A. P., *J. Am. Chem. Soc.* **77**, 1693 (1955).
48. Parkinson, J., *Nature* **184**, 554 (1959).
49. Payne, J. P., and Rowe, G. G., *Brit. J. Pharmacol.* **12**, 457 (1957).
50. Pircio, A. W., Wilson, A., Kuna, S., Hasek, R. H., and Martin, J. C., *Nature* **201**, 1037 (1964).
51. Plummer, A. J., Schneider, J. A., and Barrett, W. E., *Arch. Intern. Pharmacodyn.* **97**, 1 (1954).
52. Protiva, M., Rajsner, M., Trcka, V., Vanecek, M., and Vejdelek, Z. J., *Experientia* **15**, 54 (1959).
53. Pulewka, P., *Arch. Exptl. Pathol. Pharmakol.* **168**, 307 (1932).
54. Rubinstein, K., Pedersen, J. G. A., and Fakstorp, J., *Experientia* **14**, 222 (1958); Rubinstein, K., Elming, N., and Fakstorp, J., *Acta Chem. Scand.* **17**, 2079 (1963).
55. Sinclair, K., *Scot. Med. J.* **6**, 397 (1961).
56. Smirk, F. H., and McQueen, E. G., *Brit. Med. J.* I, 422 (1957).
57. Smirk, F. H., and Hodge, J. V., *New Zealand Med. J.* **59**, 253 (1960).
58. Spinks, A., and Young, E. H. P., *Nature* **181**, 1397 (1958).
59. Spinks, A., Young, E. H. P., Farrington, J. A., and Dunlop, D., *Brit. J. Pharmacol.* **13**, 501 (1958).
60. Stein, G. A., Sletzinger, M., Arnold, H., Gaines, W. A., Reinhold, D., and Pfister, K., III, *J. Am. Chem. Soc.* **78**, 1514 (1956).
61. Stone, C. A., Torchiana, M. L., O'Neill, G. Q., and Beyer, K. H., *J. Pharmacol. Exptl. Therap.* **116**, 54 (1956).
62. Stone, C. A., Torchiana, M. L., Navarro, A., and Beyer, K. H., *J. Pharmacol. Exptl. Therap.* **117**, 169 (1956).
63. Stone, C. A., Meckelnberg, K. L., and Torchiana, M. L., *Arch. Intern. Pharmacodyn.* **117**, 419 (1958).
64. Stone, C. A., Torchiana, M. L., Meckelnberg, K. L., Stavorski, J., Sletzinger, M., Stein, G. A., Ruyle, W. V., Reinhold, D. F., Gaines, W. A., Arnold, H., and Pfister, K., III, *J. Med. Pharm. Chem.* **5**, 665 (1962).
65. Syrneva, In. I., *Med. Prom. SSSR* **6**, 42 (1957).
66. Vejdelek, Z. J., and Trcka, V., *Experientia* **15**, 215 (1959).

CHAPTER X

Adrenergic Blocking Agents

L. H. Werner
W. E. Barrett

I. Introduction, 331
II. Phenethylamine Derivatives, 333
III. Derivatives of Benzodioxan, 334
    A. Chemistry, 335
    B. Structure–Activity Relations, 337
    C. Compounds with Ring Systems Related to Benzodioxan, 342
IV. β-Haloethylamine Adrenergic Blocking Agents, 344
    A. Structure–Activity Relations, 344
    B. Mode of Action of β-Haloethylamine Adrenergic Blockers, 349
V. Derivatives of Phenylpiperazine, 353
    A. Structure–Activity Relations, 353
    B. Chemistry, 355
VI. Substituted Imidazolines, 357
    A. Structure–Activity Relations, 357
    B. Chemistry, 360
VII. Miscellaneous Compounds with α-Adrenergic Blocking Activity, 361
    A. Dibenzazepines, 361
    B. Tetrahydronaphthalenes, 361
    C. Tetrahydroisoquinolines and Miscellaneous Compounds, 362
VIII. Ergot Alkaloids, 362
    A. Introduction, 362
    B. Structure–Activity Relationship and Chemistry, 363
IX. Adrenergic β-Receptor Blocking Agents, 364
X. Pharmacology and Clinical Application of α- and β-Adrenergic Blocking Agents, 368
    A. Derivatives of Benzodioxan, 368
    B. β-Haloethylamine—α-Adrenergic Blocking Drugs, 369
    C. Derivatives of Phenylpiperazine, 372
    D. Substituted Imidazolines, 372
    E. Ergot Alkaloids, 376
    F. β-Adrenergic Blocking Compounds, 379
References, 384

I. Introduction

Historically, the first hypotensive agents available were α-adrenergic blocking agents. Their action could be readily detected in the experimental animal because of their property of reversing the pressor effect of epinephrine and of markedly reducing the blood pressure rise produced by norepinephrine. The effect of adrenergic blocking agents on the body should theoretically resemble the effects of cutting the sympathetic nerve supply. The sympathetic fibers arise in the central nervous system from nerve cells situated in the hypothalamic area near the pituitary gland, and pass to the peripheral organs via a relay (synapse) in the closely linked chain of sympathetic ganglia. In the ganglia the processes of one nerve cell are transmitted to other cells via a synapse. The nerve fibers leading from the spinal cord to the ganglion are anatomically preganglionic. The passage of nerve impulses in the preganglionic fibers releases acetylcholine at the synapse and they are therefore termed cholinergic nerve fibers. The nerve fibers leading from the ganglia to the tissues are postganglionic; they have been named adrenergic nerves since impulses traveling along these fibers release norepinephrine at the sympathetic myoneural junction, i.e., adrenergic receptor site.

Experimentally, electrical stimulation of the sympathetic nerve fibers leads to a rise in blood pressure due to vasoconstriction, an acceleration of the heart rate, and increased secretion of an adrenergic hormonal mixture of approximately 20% norepinephrine and 80% epinephrine into the blood, by the medulla of the adrenal gland (88).

HO—⟨benzene⟩—CH—CH$_2$NH$_2$
     |
HO   OH

Norepinephrine
(Noradrenaline)

HO—⟨benzene⟩—CH—CH$_2$NHCH$_3$
     |
HO   OH

Epinephrine
(Adrenaline)

HO—⟨benzene⟩—CH—CH$_2$NHCH(CH$_3$)$_2$
     |
HO   OH

Isoproterenol

⟨benzene⟩—CH—CH$_2$NHCH$_3$
     |
HO   OH

Phenylephrine

Epinephrine and related compounds produce adrenergic effects which are both excitatory and inhibitory. Ahlquist (3, 142) has proposed that there are two principal types of receptors, for convenience termed alpha and beta. The responses attributed to α-receptor activation are primarily excitatory, with the exception of intestinal relaxation. The responses attributed to β-receptor activation are primarily inhibitory, with the exception of the myocardial stimulant effect.

Epinephrine is the most effective α-receptor activator, being more potent than norepinephrine and much more active than isoproterenol which has practically no action on α receptors; the latter, however, is the most potent activator of the β receptors.

Adrenergic responses can be decreased by drugs which act through a variety of mechanisms. The present discussion, however, will be limited to those drugs that act directly on the responding or effector cells. Drugs of this type are called α- and β-adrenergic receptor blocking agents respectively. Substances which can prevent a sympathoadrenal discharge by blocking nervous impulses at the ganglia (ganglionic blockers), and adrenergic neuron blocking drugs such as guanethidine and related compounds are not discussed in this chapter. The terms adrenolytic, sympatholytic, or adrenergic blockade, unless otherwise qualified, refer to α-adrenergic receptor blockade.

It had been hoped that adrenergic blocking agents would prove particularly effective as antihypertensives by preventing the contraction of the smooth muscle of the vascular walls elicited by epinephrine and norepinephrine. To date, these expectations have not been fulfilled; however, a number of clinically useful drugs have been developed in this field. Their main application lies in their use as peripheral vasodilators and as diagnostic aids in suspected cases of phaeochromocytoma.

Over 60 years ago, in 1906, Sir Henry Dale (53) first observed α-adrenergic blockade brought on by the action of ergot and clearly defined its action in blocking responses to circulating epinephrine and sympathetic nerve stimulation. Subsequent progress in this field has been slow. The use of adrenergic blocking agents in research and therapy has been handicapped by the lack of specificity and incompleteness of action. The adrenergic inhibitors represent a heterogeneous collection of different chemical classes of compounds and will be discussed in groups. This survey is not intended to be exhaustive but should convey an impression of the scope of the work done in this field.*

II. Phenethylamine derivatives

Bovet and co-workers (31) in Fourneau's laboratory at the Institut Pasteur in Paris studied a large number of substituted phenethylamines, phenoxyethylamines, and N-phenyl-1,2-diaminoethanes, as it had been found that certain compounds, closely related to epinephrine, ephedrine, and other adrenergic drugs (sympathomimetics) were adrenergic blocking agents (sympatholytics). This is illustrated by the following two compounds.

$OCH_2CH_2NHCH_3$

OH

Sympathomimetic
1180F

$OCH_2CH_2NHCH_3$

OH

Sympatholytic
1086F

* For further discussion of some of these subjects see reference (241a).

These phenoxyethylamine derivatives were, however, relatively weakly active, doses of 10–20 mg per kilogram given intravenously were required, and even at these elevated doses only some of the effects of epinephrine were blocked (34). These simpler compounds, however, can be viewed as the starting points for other, more potent groups of adrenergic blocking agents, as is shown in Chart I.

Chart I

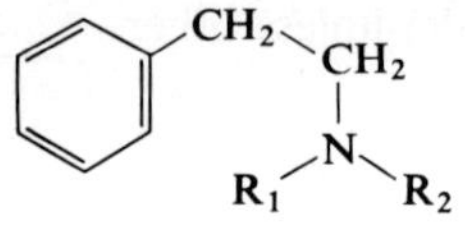

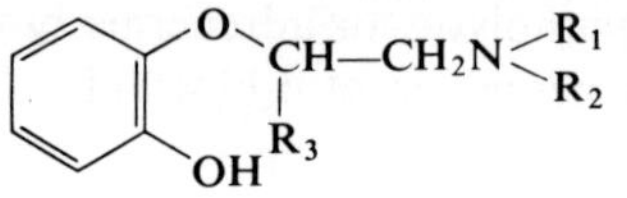

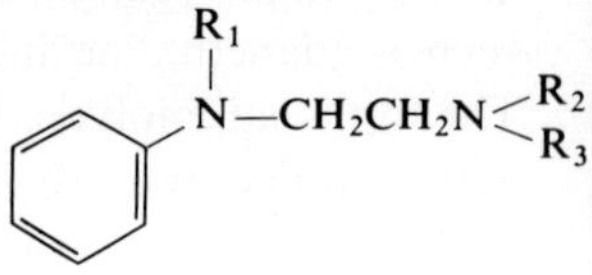

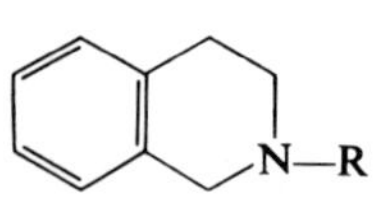

1,2,3,4-Tetrahydro-
isoquinolines

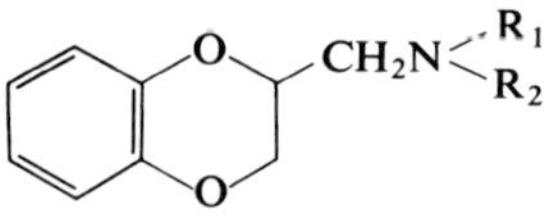

1,4-Benzodioxans

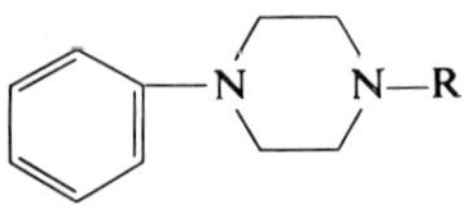

1-Phenylpiperazines

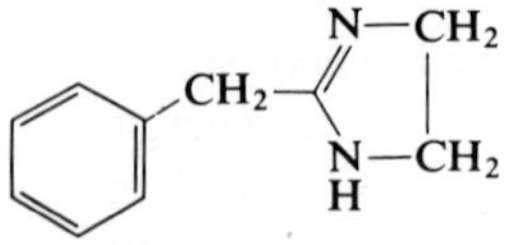

2-Benzylimidazoline
tolazoline

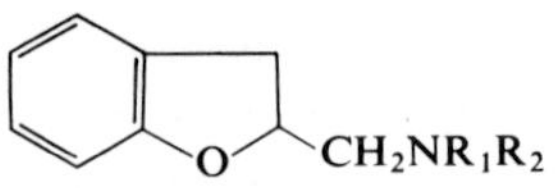

2,3-dihydrobenzofurans

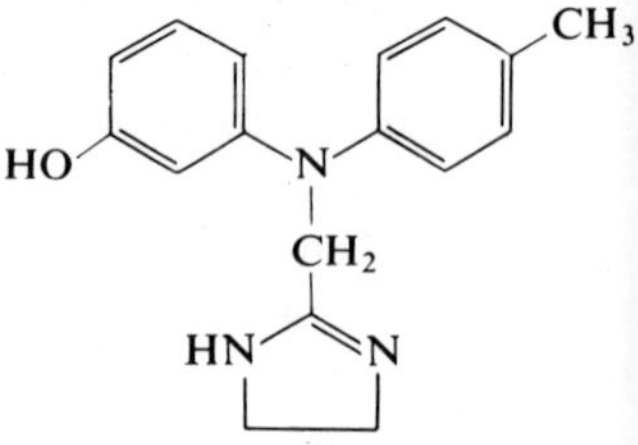

Phentolamine

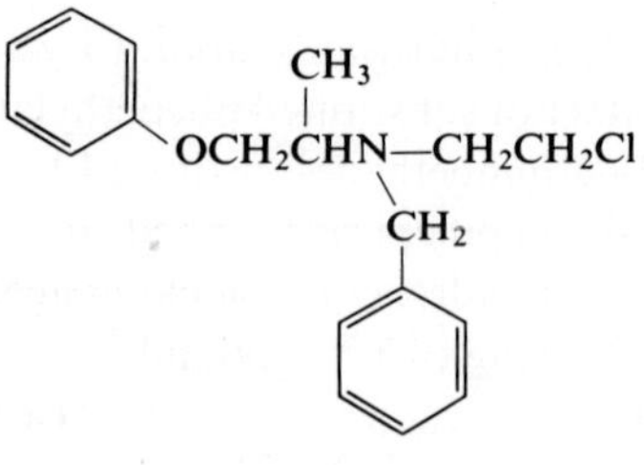

Phenoxybenzamine

III. Derivatives of benzodioxan

The first benzodioxan derivative with pronounced α-adrenergic blocking activity was found by Fourneau et al. (70, 72) in 1933. This compound, 2-

(diethylaminomethyl)-1,4-benzodioxan or Prosympal* (883F), led to the preparation of a large number of related compounds.

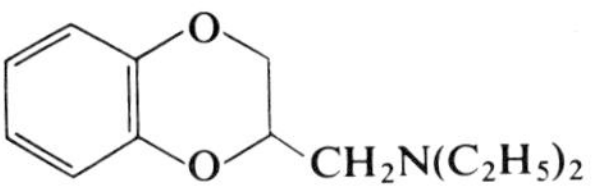

Prosympal (883F)

A. CHEMISTRY

The procedures outlined below (Schemes I and II) have been used in the synthesis of benzodioxan derivatives having substituents in various positions (97, 134, 164, 242).

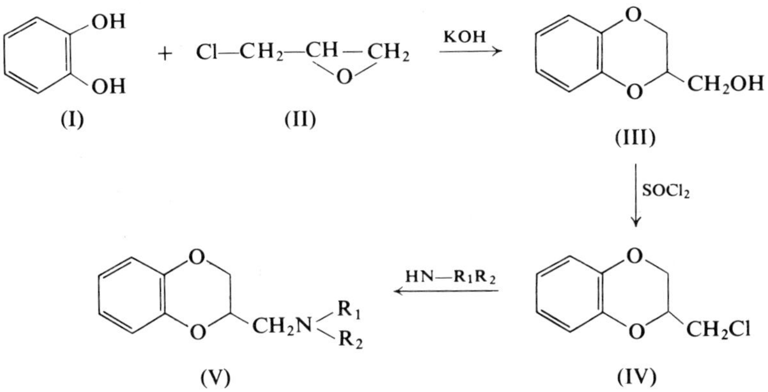

Scheme I

The application of either of the procedures shown in Scheme I or II, to a substituted pyrocatechol generally yields a mixture of the two possible isomers. Methods for the separation of the isomers, e.g., Mills and Rathbun (164), or for the synthesis of individual isomers (77) such as the 6- and 7-hydroxy-2-substituted 1,4-benzodioxans have been developed. A novel procedure for the preparation of 2-chloromethyl-8-alkoxy-1,4-benzodioxan (XVb) has been described by Schmidt (220) and is outlined in Scheme III.

Syntheses for the preparation of 5,6,7- and 8-acyl-2-substituted-1,4-benzodioxans have been worked out by Funke et al. (75).

One peculiarity in the preparation of 2-aminomethyl benzodioxan derivatives is the difficulty with which the 2-chloromethyl group reacts with amines—conditions such as 4–10 hours at 150°C are required (97).

* No generic name available.

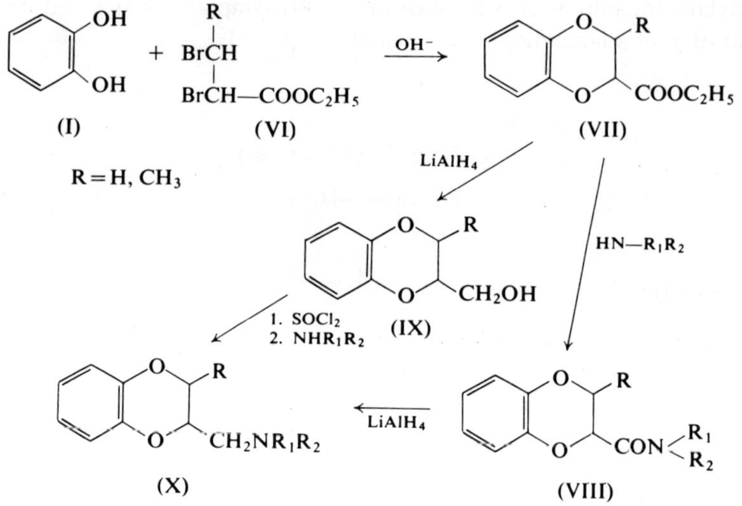

Scheme II

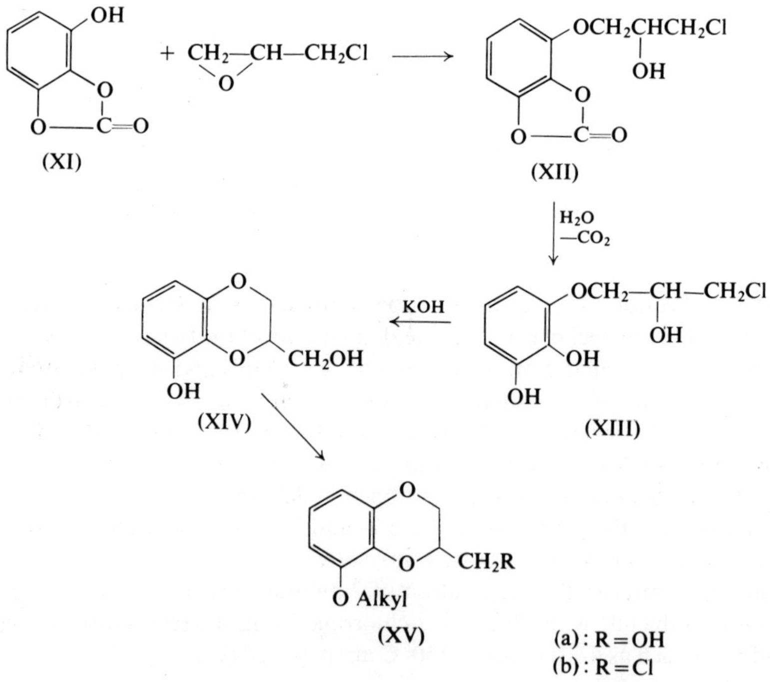

Scheme III

B. STRUCTURE–ACTIVITY RELATIONS

The first study of analogs of Prosympal was made by Bovet and Simon (30) in 1937. The compounds were studied for adrenolytic activity, sedative effects, and toxicity. Their findings are summarized in Table I.

Table I*

Compound number	R	Adrenolytic dose mg/kg i.v.[a]	Sedative effect[b]
1	$-NH_2$	5	−
2	$-NHCH_3$	5	±
3	$-NHC_2H_5$	1	+ +
4	$-NHC_3H_7(n)$	2	+ +
5	$-NHC_4H_9(n)$	2	+ +
6	$-NHC_5H_{11}(n)$	2–5	+
7	$-NHC_4H_9(iso)$	10	+ +
8	$-NHCH_2CH=CH_2$	2	+ +
9	$-N(CH_3)_2$	2	−
10	$-N(C_2H_5)_2^c$	1–2	+ +
11	$-N(C_3H_7)_2(n)$	2–5	+
12	$-N(C_4H_9)_2(n)$	> 30	−
13	$\begin{array}{c} CH_3 \\ \vert + \\ -N-(C_2H_5)_2 I^\ominus \\ {}_d \end{array}$	Inactive	
14		1	+ +
15		2–5	±

* Data from Bovet and Simon (30).

[a] Dose resulting in inversion of pressor effect of epinephrine.

[b] Prolongation of hexobarbital sleeping time.

[c] Prosympal, 883F.

[d] Piperoxan, 933F.

Table I—*continued*

Compound number	R	Adrenolytic dose mg/kg i.v.[a]	Sedative effect[b]
16		1–2	±
17		1–2	±
18		5	±

In the series where R = NH-alkyl (Table I) the toxicity increased from methyl through amyl, the adrenolytic activity reached a maximum when the alkyl group equaled ethyl and propyl. In the R = NR$_1$R$_2$ series, the diethylamino derivative, Prosympal, was the most toxic and also the most active compound.

As is shown in Table II and III, substitution of the benzene ring in position 6 or 7 decreased the adrenolytic activity (33) (compounds 19–22).

Later, however, Marini-Bettolo *et al.* (150) reported marked sympatholytic activity for other 7-substituted derivatives (compounds 23–26).

Funke *et al.* (76) showed that the 7-acyl derivatives, compounds 31–34 (Table III), were devoid of adrenolytic activity.

A series of 5- and 8-alkoxy-2-substituted aminomethyl-1,4-benzodioxans were studied by Mills *et al.* (162) and Schmidt (219) in relation to their psychosedative and blood-pressure lowering effects. Some of the compounds they prepared are shown in Table IV.

This study was prompted by the observation that many well-known adrenergic blocking agents at high doses produced behavioral changes in laboratory animals similar to those produced by reserpine and chlorpromazine (165).

Table II

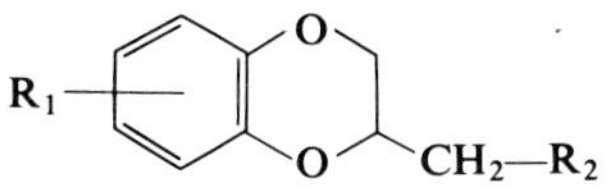

Compound number	R_1	R_2	Adrenolytic dose mg/kg i.v.[a]	Reference
10	H—	—N(C$_2$H$_5$)$_2$	1–2	(30)
19	6- or 7-CH$_3$O—	—N(C$_2$H$_5$)$_2$	5	(33)
20	6- or 7-C$_2$H$_5$O—	—N(C$_2$H$_5$)$_2$	10	(33)
21	6- or 7-CH$_2$=CHCH$_2$—	—N(C$_2$H$_5$)$_2$	20	(33)
22	6- or 7-I—	—N(C$_2$H$_5$)$_2$	20	(33)
23	7-HO—	—NHCH$_3$		(150)
24	7-CH$_3$O—	—NH$_2$	Marked activity	(150)
25	7-Cl—	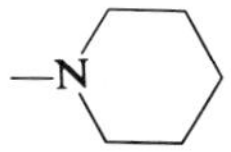 —N⟨piperidine⟩		(150)
26	7-Cl—	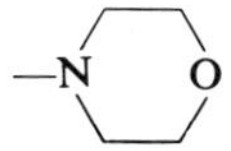 —N⟨morpholine⟩O		(150)
27	H—	—HNCH$_2$CH$_2$OH	1	(150)
28	7-Cl—	—HNCH$_2$CH$_2$OH	>10	(150)
29	7-Cl—	—N—CH$_2$CH$_2$OH | C$_2$H$_5$	>10	(150)
30	7-Cl—	—N—CH$_2$CH$_2$OH | C$_3$H$_7$(i)	>10	(150)

[a] Dose resulting in inversion of pressor effect of epinephrine.

Table III

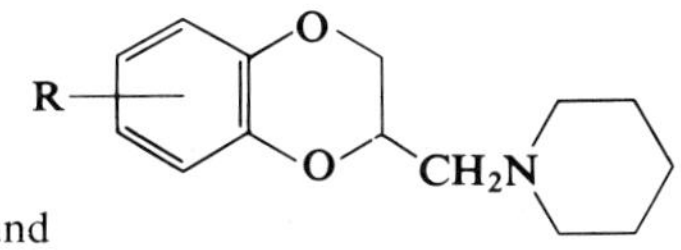

Compound number	R	Adrenolytic activity[a]	Reference
31	6- or 7-C$_6$H$_5$CO—	Inactive or very weakly active	(76)
32	7-C$_6$H$_5$CH$_2$CO—	Inactive or very weakly active	(76)
33	7-C$_6$H$_5$CH$_2$CH$_2$CO—	Inactive or very weakly active	(76)
34	7-C$_6$H$_5$CH$_2$CH$_2$CH$_2$CO—	Inactive or very weakly active	(76)

[a] Dose resulting in inversion of pressor effect of epinephrine.

L. H. Werner and W. E. Barrett

Unfortunately, no data on the adrenergic blocking effects of these compounds are available, but it can be assumed that the blood-pressure lowering effect is a direct measure of the adrenolytic effect of these compounds. It can be seen that the introduction of a 5-ethoxy group (compound 36) eliminated the activity whereas the ethoxy group in the 8 position (compound 37) enhanced it slightly. Additional substitution in position 5 by chlorine again lowered the activity (compound 41). Compound 35, Quiloflex*, has been introduced in Germany as a centrally acting muscle relaxant. The parmacology of this compound was studied by Klupp and Streller (133) and Henatsch *et al.* (111).

Table IV

Compound number	R_1	R_2	Blood pressure cat i.v.[a]	Reference
5	H—	—$NHC_4H_9(n)$	III	(161)
35	H—	—$NHCH_2CH_2CH_2OCH_3$[b]	III	(162, 133)
36	5-C_2H_5O—	—$NHC_4H_9(n)$	0	(162)
37	8-C_2H_5O—	—$NHC_4H_9(n)$	III	(162)
38	8-C_2H_5O—	—NHC_2H_5	IV	(162)
39	8-C_2H_5O—	—$NHCH_2CH_2CH_2OCH_3$	III	(162, 219)
40	8-C_2H_5O—	—$NH(CH_2)_5CH_3$	III	(162)
41	5-Cl-8-C_2H_5O	—$NHC_4H_9(n)$	I	(162)
42	8-C_2H_5O—	—NH—⬠	0	(162)

a Classification of blood pressure data: I, Less than 20% fall at 0.5 mg per kilogram. II, 20–40% fall at 0.5 mg per kilogram. III, More than 40% fall at 0.5 mg per kilogram. IV, More than 40% fall at 0.1 mg per kilogram.

b Quiloflex (Dr. K. Thomae, Germany).

Table V lists the adrenolytic activity of a number of benzodioxan derivatives incorporating an amide function as reported by Gatti *et al.* (80).

Compound 44, 1205 I.S., was of particular interest in this group. The adrenolytic dose was comparable to that of Prosympal (883F) and phentolamine. It caused only slight tachycardia and other mild side effects. The preparation of this type of compound was described by Marini-Bettolo *et al.* (35, 140, 149) and Rossi *et al.* (209).

Numerous other variations of the side chain attached at the 2 position of the

* No generic name available.

benzodioxan nucleus, e.g., derivatives of 2-(2-aminoethyl)- and 2-(3-amino-propyl)benzodioxan, have been studied (81, 152, 166, 222).

Table V

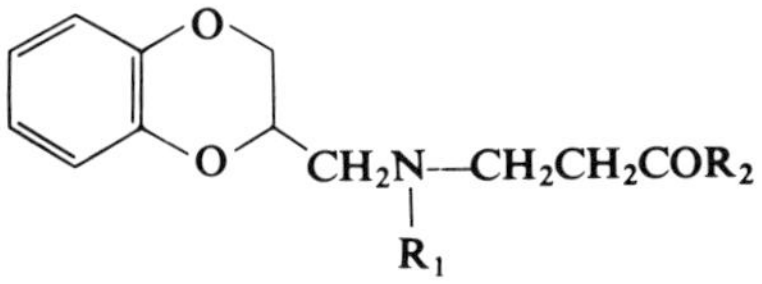

Compound number	R_1	R_2	Adrenolytic activity mg/kg i.v.[a]	Reference
43	H	$-NH_2$	0.5	(80)
44	H	$-NHCH_3$[b]	0.5	(80)
45	H	$-N(CH_3)_2$	0.5	(80)
46	H	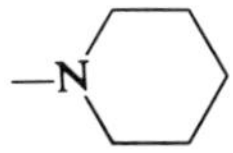	1	(80)
47	CH_3	$-NHCH_3$	5	(80)
48	CH_3	$-N(CH_3)_2$	2	(80)

[a] Dose resulting in inversion of pressor effect of epinephrine.
[b] 1205 I.S.

It would appear that none of these compounds had any outstanding properties. Swain (238) studied a group of benzodioxan derivatives, including dibozane (XVI), which was found to be a very potent adrenolytic agent (200). Gunn (98) reported that in hypertensive patients it produced a drop in blood pressure with moderately severe side effects.

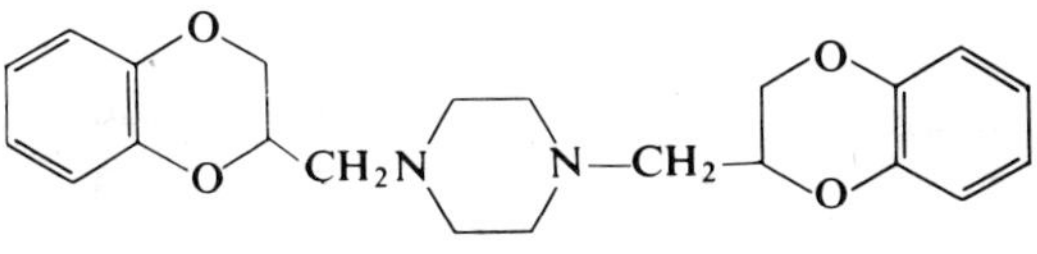

(XVI)
Dibozane

A few other derivatives of benzodioxan which are of some interest have been reported. They are listed in Table VI.

Table VI

Compound number	R	Remarks	Reference
49	—NHCH$_2$CH$_2$O— (with OCH$_3$)	Strong adrenolytic	(65)
50	—NHNHCH$_2$C$_6$H$_5$	Strong adrenolytic monoamine oxidase inhibitor	(36)
51	(piperidine N with CH$_2$, NHCOCH$_3$, C$_6$H$_5$)	Adrenolytic peripheral vasodilator (Acetoxatrine)	(215)
52	(spiro structure with C$_6$H$_5$, N, NH, O, NH)	Weakly adrenolytic, produces catalepsy (Spiroxamide)	(185)
53	—NH—C—NH$_2$ (C=NH)	Hypotensive	(10)
54	(imidazoline ring, N, N—H)	Adrenolytic peripheral vasodilator	(136)
55	(piperazine-piperidine with CONH$_2$)	Weakly adrenolytic	(248)

C. Compounds with Ring Systems Related to Benzodioxan

The pronounced sympatholytic activity of the benzodioxan derivatives stimulated interest in related ring systems. In 1938 Benoit and Bovet (23) reported a group of such compounds (e.g., compounds 56–59, Table VII). Fourneau et al. (71) also studied several 2-aminomethyl dihydrobenzofurans (e.g., compound 60). All of these compounds were considerably less potent adrenolytics than the corresponding benzodioxan derivative, Prosympal.

Table VII

Compound number	Structure	Adrenolytic dose mg/kg i.v.[a]	Reference
56		2–10	(23)
57		20	(23)
58		20	(23)
59		Very weak	(23)
60		Weak	(71)
61			(13)
62			(82)
63			(82)

[a] Dose resulting in inversion of pressor effect of epinephrine.

Baines *et al.* (13) prepared a series of 2-substituted 1,3-benzodioxoles, (e.g., compound 61); it, too, was less active than the corresponding benzodioxan derivative in blocking the effect of epinephrine. Derivatives of 1,5-benzo-dioxepanes (82) of the general structures 62 and 63 have also been prepared. Again, these compounds do not appear to have any properties which would make them therapeutically useful.

In spite of the very large number of derivatives of benzodioxan and related compounds that have been prepared, only Prosympal, compound 10, pipero-xan, compound 14, and to a limited extent dibozane (XVI), have found clinical application.

IV. β-Haloethylamine adrenergic blocking agents

The β-haloethylamine blockers have been studied in great detail; more than 800 substances have been prepared and among these some of the most potent α-adrenergic blockers have been found. The blocking activity of the first member of this series, Dibenamine,* *N*-(2-chloroethyl)dibenzylamine hydro-chloride (XVII), was discovered by the keen observations of Nickerson and Goodman (182) during a screening procedure.

(XVII)
N-(2-Chloroethyl)-dibenzylamine hydrochloride
Dibenamine

Nickerson and Goodman found that Dibenamine blocked and reversed the vasopressor response to doses of epinephrine ranging from 0.1 to 10 mg per kilogram, this blocking action persisting for 3–4 days following a single injec-tion. As a result of these findings, numerous congeners of Dibenamine were prepared and studied by Nickerson and Gump (183). This field was reviewed in 1956 by Ullyot and Kerwin (244), covering literature up to 1952.

A. STRUCTURE–ACTIVITY RELATIONS

The following tentative generalizations regarding structural requirements for adrenergic blocking activity in the Dibenamine series have been made, based on more than 200 compounds (183): (a) The compound must be a tertiary amine. (b) It must include at least one β-haloalkylamino group capable

* No generic name available.

Table VIII

$$\text{C}_6\text{H}_5\!-\!\underset{\underset{\text{R}_1}{|}}{\text{CH}_2\text{N}}\!-\!\text{R}_2$$

Compound number	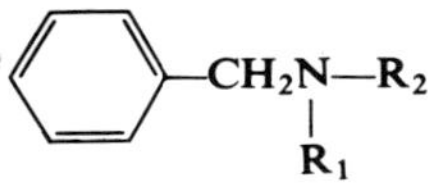 R_1	R_2	Activity	LD_{50} (approx.) mg/kg s.c.	Reference
64	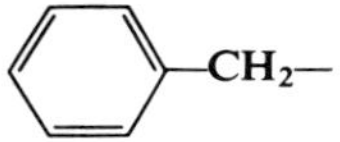 $\text{C}_6\text{H}_5\text{CH}_2-$	$-\text{CH}_2\text{CH}_2\text{Cl}$	+ + (Dibenamine)	800	(183)
65	H	$-\text{CH}_2\text{CH}_2\text{C}$	– –	500	(183)
66	C_2H_5-	$-\text{CH}_2\text{CH}_2\text{Cl}$	+ +	75	(183)
67	$\text{C}_6\text{H}_5\text{OCH}_2\underset{\underset{\text{CH}_3}{|}}{\text{CH}}-$	$-\text{CH}_2\text{CH}_2\text{Cl}$	+ + + (Phenoxybenzamine)		
68	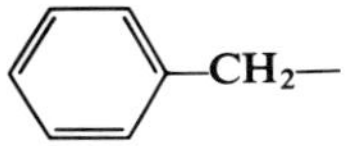 $\text{C}_6\text{H}_5\text{CH}_2-$	$-\text{CH}_2\text{CH}_2\text{CH}_2\text{Cl}$	–	850	(183)
69	$\text{C}_6\text{H}_5\text{CH}_2-$	$-\text{CH}_2\underset{\underset{\text{CH}_3}{|}}{\text{CHCl}}$	+ +	500	(183)
70	$\text{C}_6\text{H}_5\text{CH}_2-$	$-\text{CH}_2\underset{\underset{\text{CH}_3}{|}}{\overset{\overset{\text{CH}_3}{|}}{\text{C}}}-\text{Cl}$	+ +	1000	(183)
71	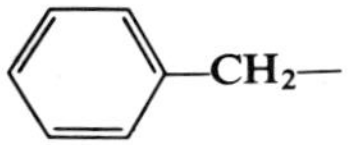 $\text{C}_6\text{H}_5\text{CH}_2-$	$-\text{CH}_2\text{CH}_2\text{OH}$	– –	1000	(183)
72	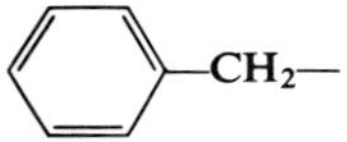 $\text{C}_6\text{H}_5\text{CH}_2-$	$-\text{CH}_2\text{CH}_2\text{N}(\text{C}_2\text{H}_5)_2$	– –	100	(183)

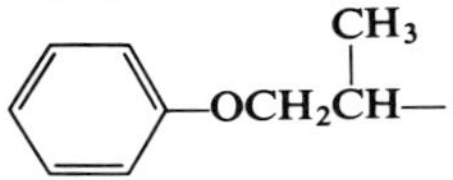

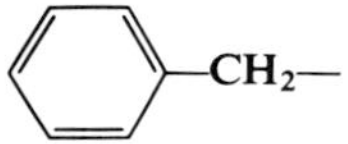

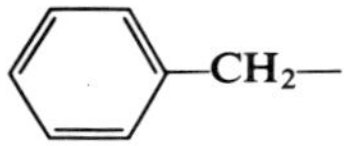

345

Table IX[a]

$$R_1 \diagdown N-CH_2CH_2Cl$$
$$R_2 \diagup$$

Compound number	R_1	R_2	Activity (Dibenamine = ++)	LD_{50} (approx.) mg/kg s.c.
73	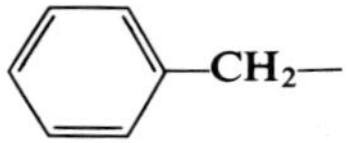 ![phenyl-CH₂—]	C_2H_5-	++	75
74	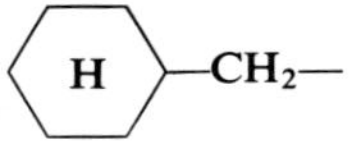 ![cyclohexyl(H)-CH₂—]	C_2H_5-	$--$	75
75	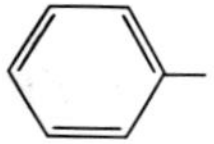 ![methylphenyl]	C_2H_5-	$--$	400
76	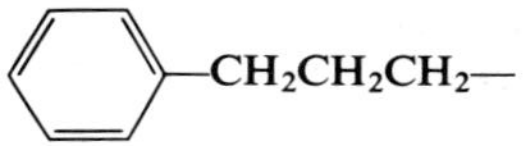 ![phenyl-CH₂CH₂CH₂—]	C_2H_5-	$--$	40
77	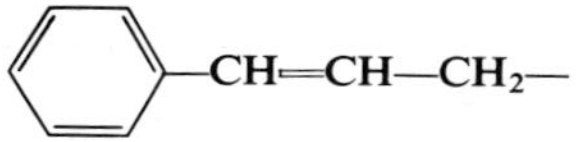 ![phenyl-CH=CH-CH₂—]	C_2H_5-	++	50
78	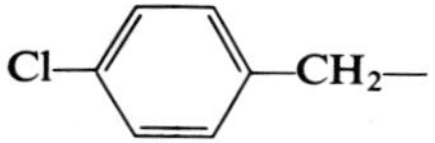 ![Cl-phenyl-CH₂—]	C_2H_5-	+	100

346

No.	Structure	Structure	Rating	Value
79	3-Cl-C$_6$H$_4$-CH$_2$-	C$_2$H$_5$-	+ + +	200
80	4-CH$_3$O-C$_6$H$_4$-CH$_2$-	CH$_3$-	+	50
81	2-OCH$_3$-C$_6$H$_4$-CH$_2$-	CH$_3$-	+ +	150
82	2-CH$_3$-C$_6$H$_4$-CH$_2$-	4-CH$_3$-C$_6$H$_4$-CH$_2$-/C$_2$H$_5$-	+ +	100
83	4-CH$_3$-C$_6$H$_4$-CH$_2$-	4-CH$_3$-C$_6$H$_4$-CH$_2$-	+ +	1000 (v. sl. sol.)
84	4-C$_2$H$_5$-C$_6$H$_4$-CH$_2$-	4-C$_2$H$_5$-C$_6$H$_4$-CH$_2$-	– –	1000 (v.sl.sol.)
85	4-C$_2$H$_5$-C$_6$H$_4$-CH$_2$-	C$_2$H$_5$-	– –	25

^{a} Data from Nickerson and Gump (183).

347

of forming an intermediate ethylenimmonium derivative with loss of halogen. (c) It must include an unsaturated ring structure attached to the nitrogen in certain specific ways. An attempt will be made to illustrate these requirements in Tables VIII and IX.

The adrenergic blocking activity of these compounds was determined in cats anesthetized with pentobarbital or urethane and prepared for direct carotid pressure recording. Actual reversal of the blood pressure response to epinephrine was selected as the criterion of activity because mere reduction of the pressor response could have resulted from a number of nonspecific factors. The compounds were administered by slow intravenous injection. From the data in the tables it is apparent that activity and toxicity do not run parallel.

The first requirement, that the compound must be a tertiary amine, is illustrated by compounds 64, 65 and 66 (Table VIII). Compound 64, N-(2-chloroethyl)dibenzylamine, (Dibenamine) had a 2+ activity. Compound 66, in which one of the benzyl groups has been replaced by an ethyl group, retained the activity. However, the secondary amine N-(2-chloroethyl)benzylamine, compound 65, was inactive.

The second requirement stated that the compound must include at least one β-haloalkylamine group. This is shown by compounds 68–72 (Table VIII). Branching of the side chain as in compounds 69 and 70, while retaining a distance of two carbon atoms between the nitrogen and chlorine atom, did not destroy the activity; compounds in which the chlorine had been replaced by bromine, iodine, or a sulfonic acid ester group retained their activity.

Considering the third requirement that the compound must contain an aromatic ring structure attached to the nitrogen, we note that compound 74, in which the nitrogen is substituted by an ethyl and a cyclohexylmethyl group, was inactive, whereas the corresponding N-benzyl-N-ethyl analog, compound 73, was highly active. The N,N dialkyl analogs were also inactive. None of the compounds with two saturated substituents had any activity. The aniline derivative, compound 75, was inactive presumably because it is a very weak base and as such not able to displace the chlorine of the β-chloroethyl group to form an ethylenimmonium ion under physiological conditions (see Section IV, B). Compound 76, a γ-phenylpropyl analog, was inactive whereas compound 77, the corresponding cinnamyl analog, again showed activity.

Substituents on the benzene ring, depending on their nature and position, had a varying effect on the adrenergic blocking activity, as evidenced by compounds 78–85.

The benzyl group, nevertheless, could be replaced by related aromatic groups such as benzhydryl, 1-naphthylmethyl, 9-fluorenyl, and 2-thenyl, as in compounds 87–91 (Table X), without complete loss of activity. Quaternary compounds, such as compound 92, were inactive (129).

Fellows et al. (64) found that replacement of one of the benzyl groups in

Dibenamine, compound 64 (Table VIII), by a phenoxy-2-propyl group as in phenoxybenzamine, compound 67, greatly enhanced the oral activity.

Analogs of phenoxybenzamine have been studied and the structure–activity relationship of this group of compounds (general formula XVIII) has been reported in detail (64).

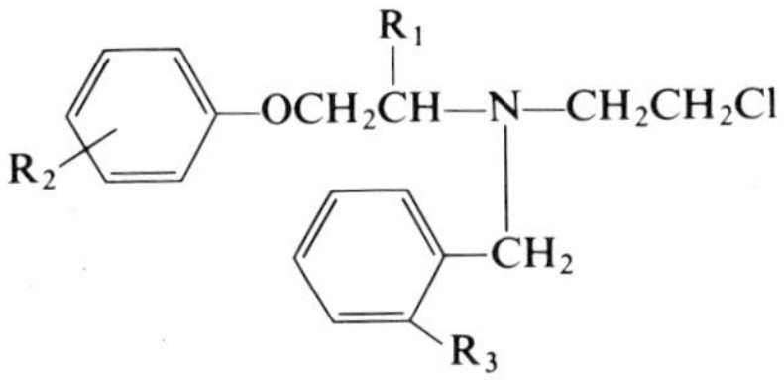

$R_1 = H, CH_3$
$R_2 = H$, alkyl, aryl, halogen
$R_3 = H, CH_3, C_3H_7$

(XVIII)

Substituents were introduced at R_1, R_2, and R_3. The most favorable properties i.e., high intravenous adrenergic blocking activity and outstanding oral activity, were found for phenoxybenzamine, where $R_1 = CH_3$ and $R_2 = R_3 = H$.

Numerous other analogs of Dibenamine have been prepared by other investigators, e.g., Campbell *et al.* (42), Wheatley *et al.* (254), Hunter *et al.* (117), Kerwin and Ullyot (130), Belleau (18, 20), Schipper *et al.* (218), Nickerson *et al.* (183), Cheney (47), and deStevens (58).

Compound (XIX) (218) was of interest, as in contrast to Dibenamine, it contains two haloalkyl groups and has shown high activity.

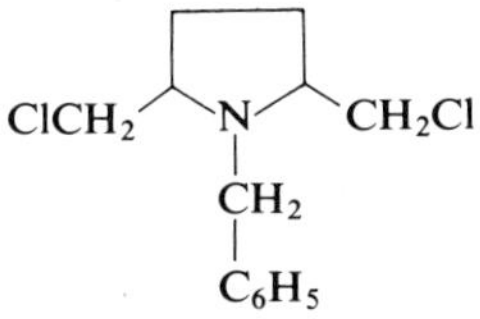

(XIX)

B. Mode of Action of β-Haloethylamine Adrenergic Blockers

Kerwin *et al.* (129) have stated that in considering the structure–activity relationship of compounds which block a normal function of the autonomic nervous system, attention is usually focused on the geometry of the molecule. The presence of certain groups or atoms provides a means for loose attachment to cellular surfaces through electrostatic or van der Waals forces. It is assumed that continued adherence of the blocking drug prevents the approach of stimulant molecules. In contrast, the β-haloethylamines may block the effects of epinephrine by a definite chemical reaction. The initial phase of adrenergic blockade by these compounds is competitive and may well depend solely on

Table X

$$R_1 \diagdown N - CH_2CH_2Cl$$
$$R_2 \diagup$$

Compound number	R₁	R₂	Activity (Dibenamine = + +)	LD₅₀ (approx.) mg/kg s.c.	Reference
87		C_2H_5-	+ +	500	(183)
88		C_2H_5-	+ + +	100	(183)

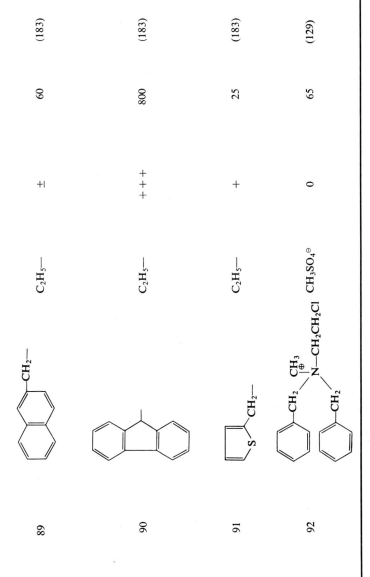

89	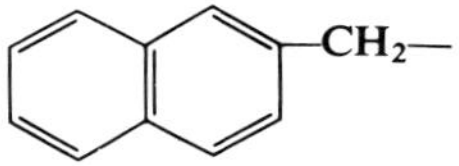	C_2H_5—	±	60	(183)
90	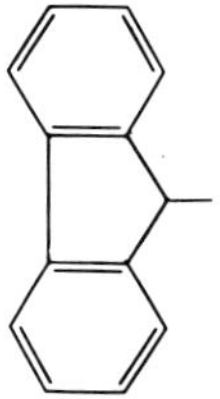	C_2H_5—	+++	800	(183)
91		C_2H_5—	+	25	(183)
92	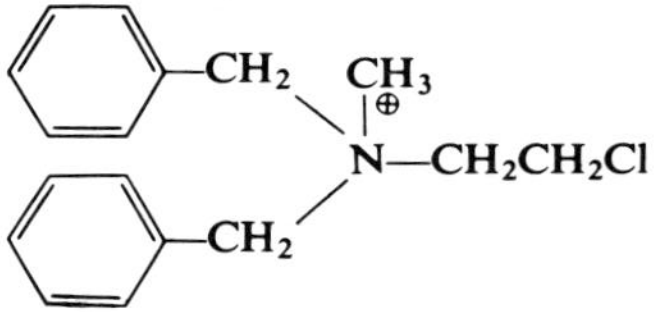	$CH_3SO_4^{\ominus}$	0	65	(129)

the stereochemistry and physical properties of the molecule. This stage is followed by a prolonged noncompetitive blockade which is thought to be caused by alkylation of some tissue constituent of the sympathetic receptors.

Considerable evidence has been presented by Nickerson (183) that the alkylating agent is not the β-haloethylamine (XX) per se but the ethylenimmonium ion (XXI) formed from it.

$$R_1{\diagdown}{>}N{-}CH_2CH_2Cl \longrightarrow \quad R_1{\diagdown}\overset{\oplus}{N}{<}\underset{CH_2}{\overset{CH_2}{\diagup}} \quad Cl^{\ominus}$$

$$\text{(XX)} \qquad\qquad\qquad\qquad \text{(XXI)}$$

Belleau *et al.* (17, 19, 21) in particular have studied the mode of action of Dibenamine and its congeners. Using *N,N*-dimethyl-β-chlorophenethylamine (XXII) in their studies, they have postulated that the alkylation reaction proceeds by way of the open-chain carbonium ion (XXIV).

$$\text{(XXII)} \qquad\qquad\qquad\qquad\qquad \text{(XXIII)}$$

$$\text{(XXIV)}$$

Compound (XXII) was reported briefly by Nickerson and Gump (183) and studied in greater detail by Ferguson and Wescoe (66).

Although a great number of compounds have been prepared in this group of adrenergic blockers, only phenoxybenzamine has found clinical application.

Compound No. 67

It has been found especially effective in peripheral vascular diseases characterized by excessive vasospasm. In the treatment of hypertension the undesirable side effects usually outweigh the benefits obtainable.

V. Derivatives of phenylpiperazine

Derivatives of phenylpiperazine have been studied extensively, especially in connection with their possible tranquilizing effects. In this section, however, only compounds with pronounced adrenergic blocking activity will be reviewed.

A. Structure–Activity Relations

Bovet (32) was the first to report the adrenolytic properties of N-phenyl-piperazine (XXV) and of 1-methyl-4-phenylpiperazine (XXVI); however,

(XXV)   (XXVI)

doses of 5–10 mg per kilogram i.v. were required to produce inversion of the blood pressure response to epinephrine. Subsequently, Roth (210) studied a series of aryl- and aralkyl-substituted piperazines of the general structure (XXVII) for adrenolytic, antihypertensive, and antihistaminic activity and

(XXVII)

R_1 = phenyl, 2-pyridyl,
benzyl, diphenylmethyl
R_2 = CH_3, C_2H_5, C_3H_7

found 1-methyl-4-phenylpiperazine (XXVI) to be the most effective adrenergic blocker of this group.

Research in the field of phenylpiperazines and related compounds has been quite extensive during the past decade and a number of interesting activities have been found among these compounds. Details may be found in the following publications and patents. Pollard and Wicker (194) and Parcell (188) have described 1-(hydroxyalkyl)- and 1-(dihydroxyalkyl)-4-phenylpiperazines; 1-(N-ethylanilino)ethyl-4-phenylpiperazines and related compounds were reported by Bach et al. (12). Ratouis et al. (201) and Mills et al. (163) have prepared a series of substituted 1-phenethyl-4-phenylpiperazines with pronounced adrenolytic activity, e.g., (XXVIII). Related compounds are described in Boissier et al. (29) (see also 145, 224).

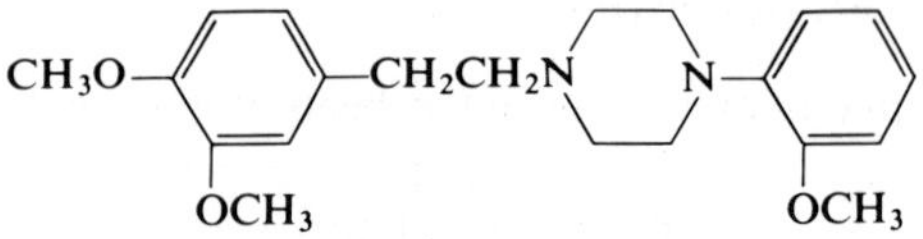

(XXVIII)

Mull *et al.* (174) have prepared an extensive series of phenylpiperazine derivatives differing from those described above in that an alkoxy group is attached to the alkyl group of the aralkyl moiety linked to the phenylpiperazine. Some of these compounds are shown in Table XI. Compound 95 had

Table XI

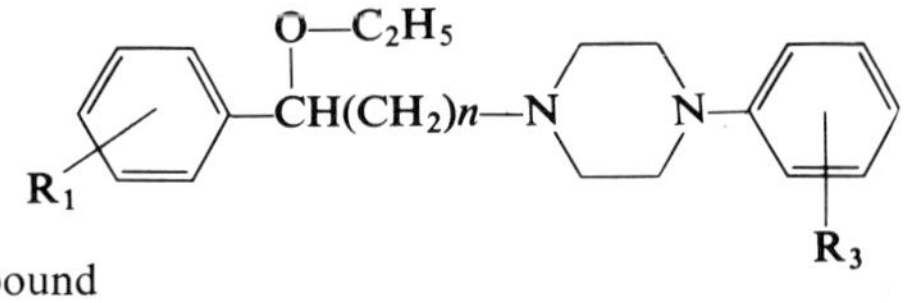

Compound number	R_1	n	R_3	Reference
93	H—	1	—H	(174)
94	H—	1	—2-OCH$_3$	(174)
95	4-CH$_3$—	2	—2-CH$_3$	(174)
96	H—	2	—3-CH$_3$	(174)
97	4-Cl—	2	—H	(174)

pronounced adrenolytic activity; at 50 μg per kilogram, it reversed the pressor response of epinephrine in the anesthetized dog. The corresponding $R_3 = 3$- or 4-methyl and 3- or 4-methoxy derivatives were less active. Compound 96 produced only a slight augmentation of the pressor response to intravenously administered *l*-epinephrine but did give a marked increase in the response produced by norepinephrine and angiotensin amide. The compound also had a marked hypotensive effect in unanesthetized dogs at 4 mg per kilogram orally. Compounds 94 and 97 did not show a marked adrenolytic effect; however, anti-inflammatory activity was found in the rat granuloma pouch test and in the cotton pellet test.

An extensive study of phenylpiperazine derivatives comprising 35 compounds characterized by being either amides of a polymethoxybenzoic acid or of an alkanoic acid was made by Hayao and Schut (107). Most of these compounds had a marked adrenolytic effect; one of these (XXIX) was studied as an antianxiety drug (123).

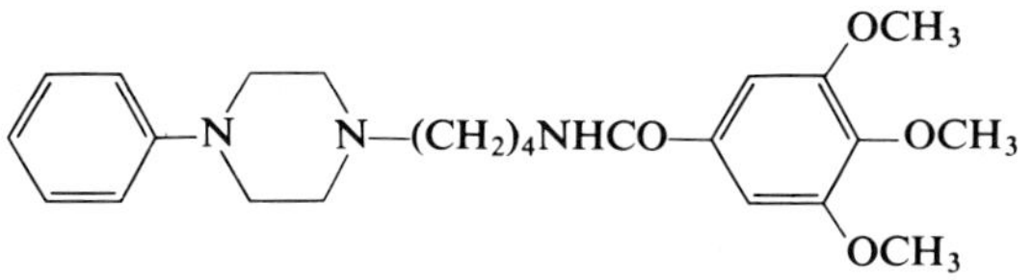

(XXIX)   (MA 568) (Miles)

The phenylpiperazine moiety has also been linked to other heterocycles such as indole, e.g., (XXX) (8, 256) and tetrazole, e.g., (XXXI) (206) and has yielded compounds with interesting α-adrenergic blocking activity.

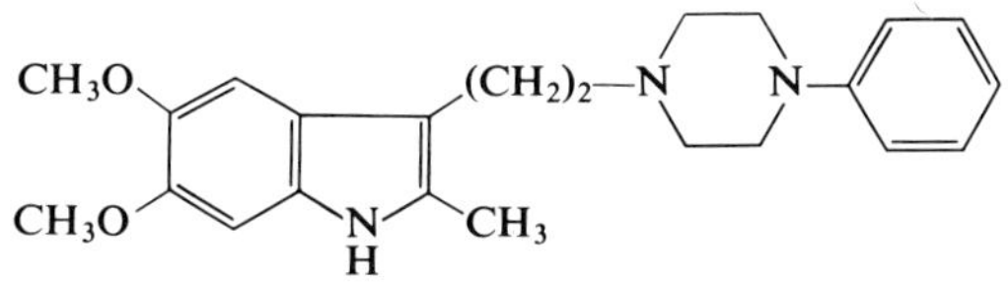

(XXX)
Oxypertine

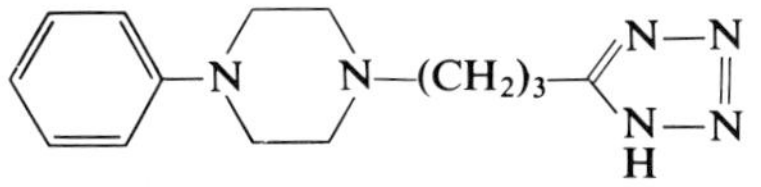

(XXXI)
Phenpiperazole

Numerous other phenylpiperazines have been prepared and studied, in particular as psychosedative drugs as has been discussed by Morren et al. (172). Nevertheless, haloanisone (XXXII) is at this time the only phenylpiperazine derivative which has found clinical application (109).

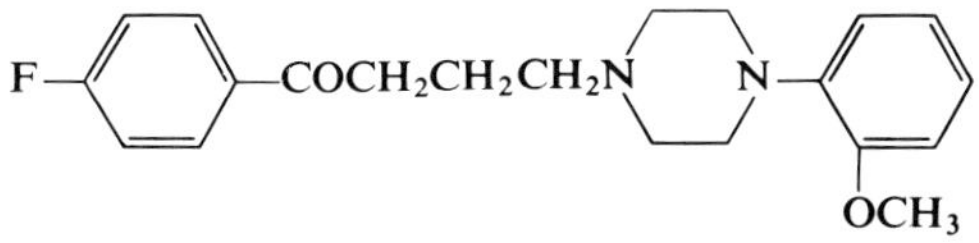

(XXXII)
Haloanisone

B. CHEMISTRY

In general 1-substituted 4-phenylpiperazines are prepared by reaction of a substituted 1-alkylhalide with the phenylpiperazine moiety as described by Mull et al. (174) and Ratouis (201) and shown in Scheme IV. An alternate approach consists in the reaction of a substituted alkanoic acid chloride with the desired phenylpiperazine followed by reduction, e.g., with lithium aluminum hydride as outlined by Archer *et al.* (8) (Scheme V).

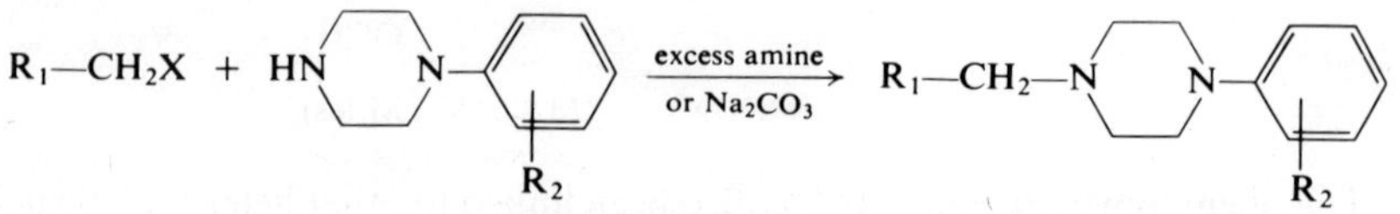

Scheme IV

Ratouis *et al.* (201) have also described procedures for the preparation of the phenylpiperazine moiety. This is shown in Schemes VI and VII.

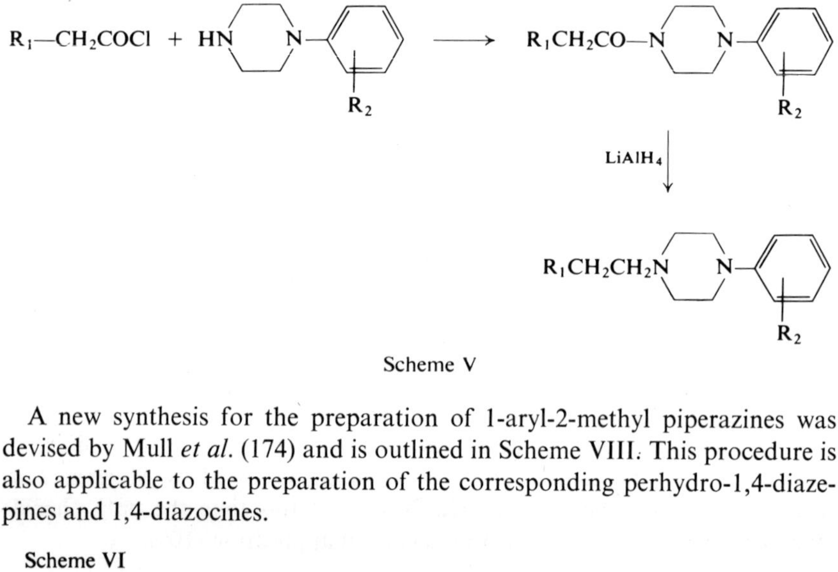

Scheme V

A new synthesis for the preparation of 1-aryl-2-methyl piperazines was devised by Mull *et al.* (174) and is outlined in Scheme VIII. This procedure is also applicable to the preparation of the corresponding perhydro-1,4-diazepines and 1,4-diazocines.

Scheme VI

Scheme VII

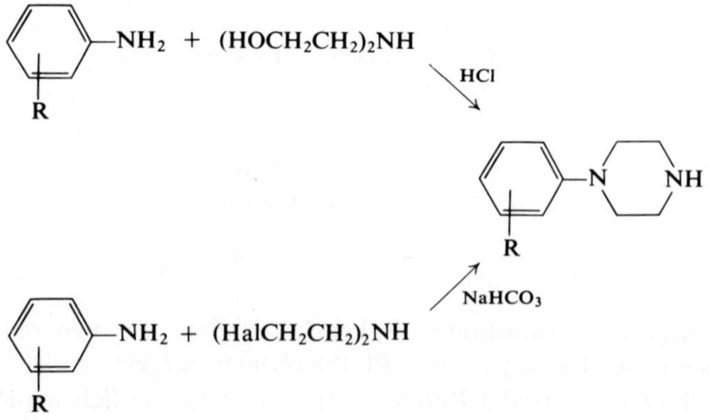

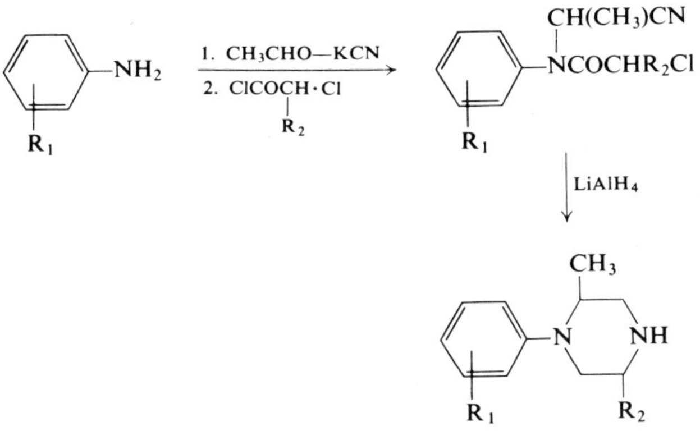

Scheme VIII $R_2 = H, CH_3$

VI. Substituted imidazolines

A STRUCTURE–ACTIVITY RELATIONS

Research in the field of imidazoline derivatives has yielded a number of clinically useful drugs. This group of compounds has been studied extensively by Sonn (228), Hartmann and Isler (104), and Urech *et al.* (245). Compound (XXXIII), tolazoline, was of particular interest as a potent adrenolytic and vasodilator (49, 104, 158, 159). Analogs of tolazoline have been prepared by Cavallini *et al.* (44) and Faust and Sahyun (63). Urech *et al.* (245) reported a

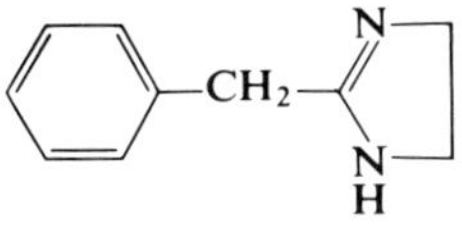

(XXXIII)

Tolazoline

series of derivatives of 2-aminomethyl imidazolines, among which antazoline, an antihistaminic, and phentolamine, an adrenergic blocker, were found. Representative members of this group are listed in Table XII.

Phentolamine, compound 108, was studied pharmacologically by Meier *et al.* (160) and found to be a potent adrenergic blocker at doses of 0.1–1 mg per kilogram administered subcutaneously or intravenously.

The imidazolinylmethyl derivatives of phenothiazine and phenoxazine (XXXIV) have also been prepared and studied by Miescher and Marxer (161) and Nieschulz *et al.* (186) and found to have adrenolytic properties. Analogous carbazole derivatives, prepared by Hartmann and Studer (105) had sympathomimetic activity.

Imidazolinylalkylindoles (61, 137, 156, 217) e.g. (XXXV) and 2-arylamino-imidazoline derivates (118) have been synthesized and screened pharmaco-

Table XII[a]

Compound number	R_1	R_2	Remarks
99	C_2H_5-	$-C_2H_5$	
100	$H-$	$-C_6H_5$	
101	$H-$	(phenyl with R_3)	$R_3 = HO, Cl, CH_3, OCH_3$ etc.
102	$H-$	(naphthyl)	
103	(cyclohexyl)	$-C_6H_5$	
104	(benzyl)$-CH_2-$	$-C_6H_5$	Antazoline
105	(benzyl)$-CH_2-$	$-CH_2-$(phenyl)	
106	C_6H_5-	$-C_6H_5$	
107	$HO-$(phenyl)$-$	(phenyl)$-OH$	
108	(phenyl, OH)	(phenyl)$-CH_3$	Phentolamine

[a] From Urech *et al.* (245).

logically. These compounds, in general, had adrenolytic properties; some were also vasoconstrictors.

In this connection it is of interest that Najer *et al.* (175) prepared a number of isosteric amino-oxazolines; (XXXVI) and (XXXVII) were strong vasoconstrictors; whereas compound (XXXVIII) was an adrenolytic vasodilator.

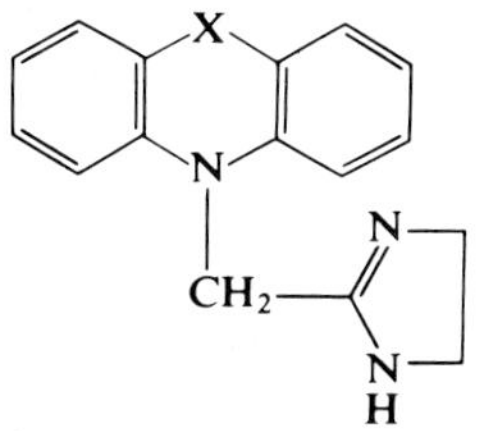

(XXXIV)

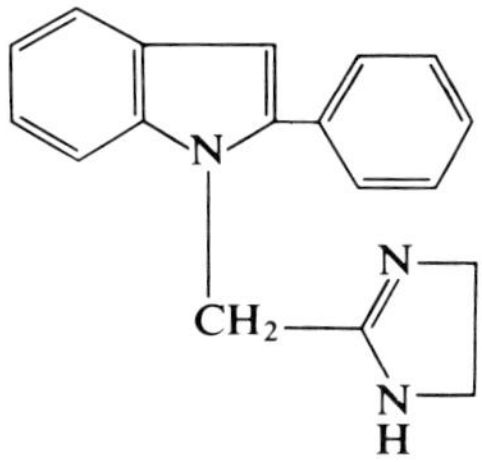

(XXXV)

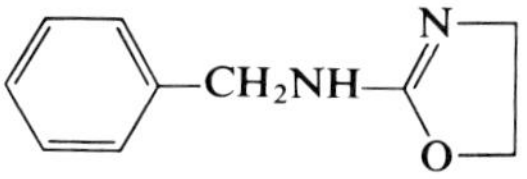

(XXXVI) 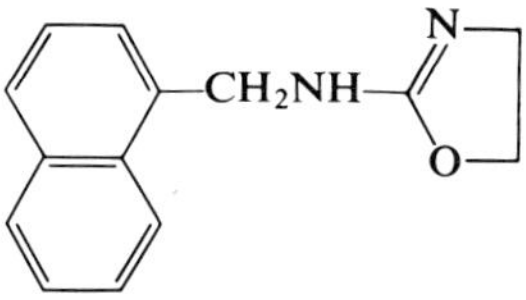   (XXXVII)

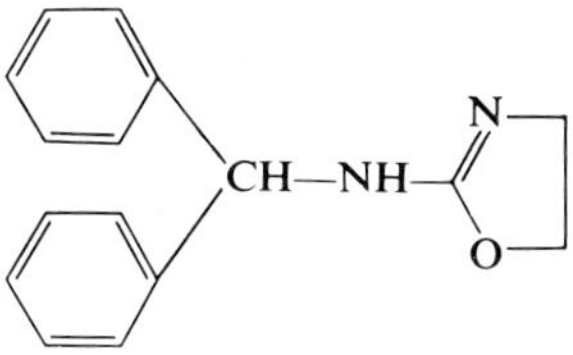

(XXXVIII)

Recently Hoefke and Kobinger (115a) have described a new blood pressure
lowering imidazoline derivative, St 155 (Catapresan ®). Although this compound is a relatively weak adrenolytic, compared to phentolamine (Compound
108), it lowers blood pressure at very low doses in animals and in man; this

clonidine

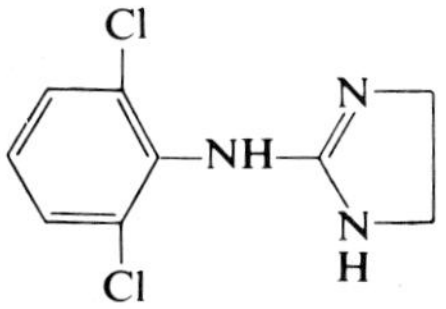

St 155

tends to indicate a highly specific mechanism of action (91a). Favorable clinical results with this compound have been reported by Grabner *et al.* (87a).

B. Chemistry

Derivatives of 2-aminomethylimidazolines have been prepared by two routes: (a) reaction of a secondary amine with 2-chloromethylimidazoline according to Urech *et al.* (245), or (b) by cyanomethylation of an appropriate secondary amine followed by conversion of the cyanogroup to the imidazoline ring by treatment with 1,2-diaminoethane in the presence of a trace of hydrogen sulfide (105, 120) (Scheme IX). Furthermore, a nitrile can be converted to the

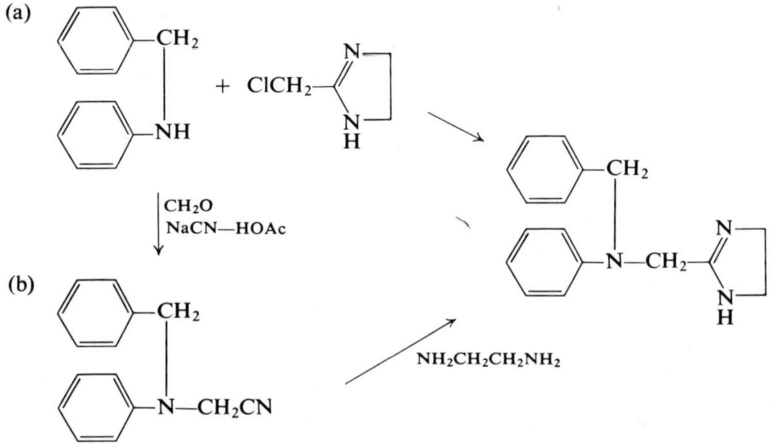

Scheme IX

imidazoline ring via the iminoether. This procedure has been used by Klarer and Urech (132) to prepare 2-chloromethylimidazoline and also, for example, to prepare tolazoline from phenylacetonitrile (Scheme X).

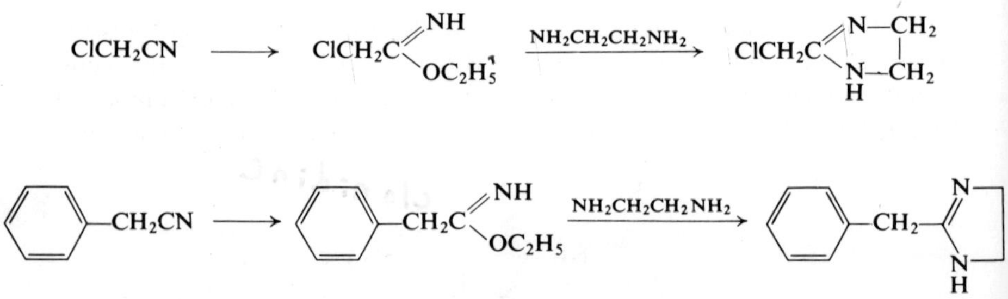

Scheme X

VII. Miscellaneous compounds with α-adrenergic blocking activity

A. DIBENZAZEPINES

The search for new types of compounds with an antagonistic action against epinephrine led Wenner (252) to a series of 6,7-dihydro-5-*H*-dibenz[*c,e*]-azepines (XXXIX).

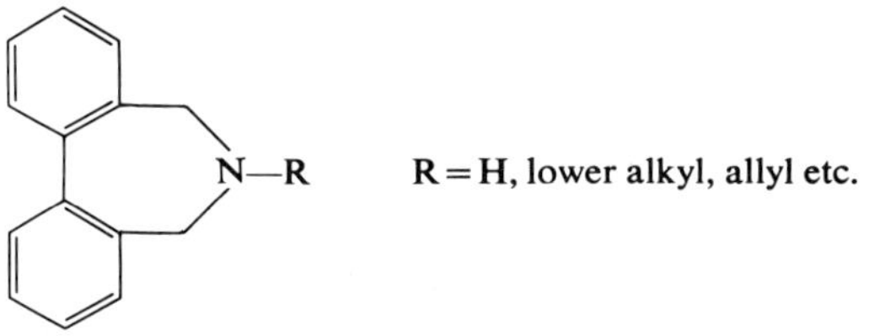

R = H, lower alkyl, allyl etc.

(XXXIX)

The most active α-adrenergic blocker in this group was the 6-allyl-derivative, azapetine (XI). This compound was prepared by bromination of bi-*o*-tolyl followed by reaction with allylamine (Scheme XI).

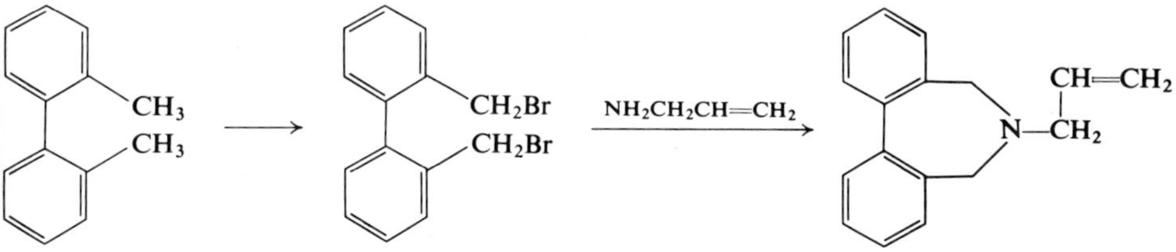

(XL)
Azapetine

Scheme XI

B. TETRAHYDRONAPHTHALENES

An extensive series of tetrahydro-1- and 2-naphthylamines (1, 43, 50 151) including (XLI) 621 I.S. was studied by a group at the Istitute Superiore di Sanità in Rome. Many of these compounds had adrenolytic and oxytocic

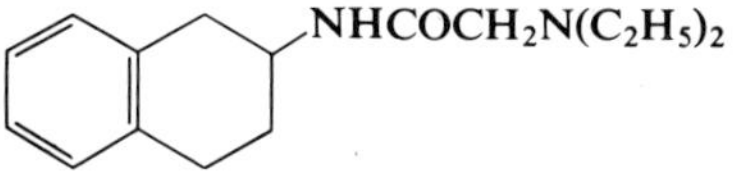

$NHCOCH_2N(C_2H_5)_2$

(XLI)   621 I.S.

activity. Compound 621 I.S. was of greater interest as an oxytocic rather than as an adrenergic blocker and was found to be clinically effective (37).

C. Tetrahydroisoquinolines and Miscellaneous Compounds

Tetrahydroisoquinolines with adrenolytic activity were prepared by a number of groups, e.g., Hjort *et al.* (115), Landi-Vittory and Marini-Bettolo (141), Cook *et al.* (52) (e.g., XLII), and Schmutz (221). Adrenolytic activity has also been claimed for certain pyrimidine (208), quinoline- (25, 26), and bis pyridyl (122) compounds. Yelnosky *et al.* (257) have reported α-adrenergic blockade

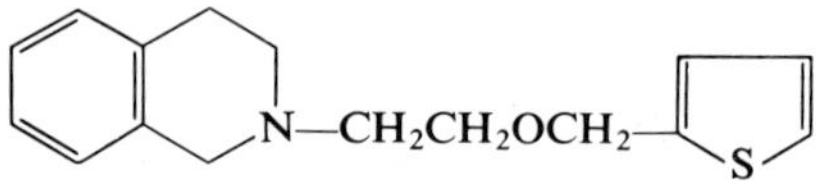

(XLII)

for droperidol (XLIII) at very low doses, as has also been found for certain other neuroleptic drugs, e.g., chlorpromazine.

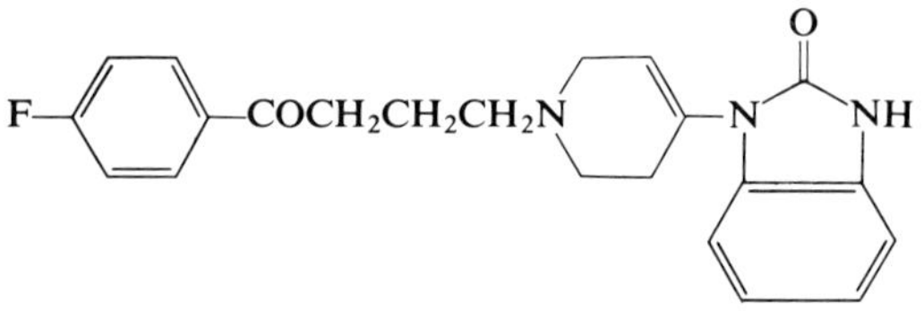

Droperidol
(XLIII)

VIII. Ergot alkaloids

A. Introduction

Early interest in the ergot alkaloids was largely stimulated by their oxytocic and adrenergic blocking activity. The term ergot or *Secale cornutum* indicates the dark brown pegs projecting from the ripening ears of rye in place of rye grains. These growths are caused by an infection of the rye inflorescence with the fungus *Claviceps purpurea*. As early as 1582 ergot was used in small doses by midwives as a proved method of inducing labor as described by Adam Lonitzer in his *Kräuterbuch*. However, not until 1922 was a homogeneous, crystalline alkaloid with the typical biological activity of ergot isolated by Stoll (235, 236). To date, the structures of approximately two dozen ergot alkaloids, counting the stereoisomeric forms as a single alkaloid, have been elucidated.

A number of drugs of considerable therapeutic value have been found among the ergot alkaloids* and their derivatives, e.g., ergonovine and methylergo-novine as oxytocics, ergotamine and methysergide for the treatment of

---

* See also a very recent review by Hofmann (115b) and Stoll and Hofmann (235).

migraine, and lysergic acid diethylamide (LSD-25) which has been used as an experimental tool in psychotherapy. A combination of dihydroergocristine, dihydroergocryptine, and dihydroergocornine in equal proportions is the only derivative of ergot which has found clinical application (16) as an adrenolytic for the treatment of peripheral and cerebral vascular disorders and of essential hypertension.

B. STRUCTURE–ACTIVITY RELATIONSHIP AND CHEMISTRY

All ergot alkaloids contain the same tetracyclic ring system (XLIV) which Jacobs and Gould (121) have called ergoline. The ergot alkaloids can be divided

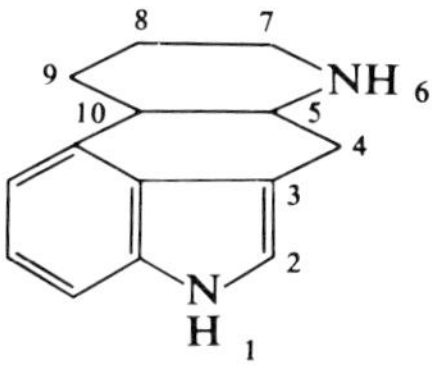

(XLIV)

into two main groups: the lysergic acid derivatives of the amide type (XLV) (including the peptide-type alkaloids) and the so-called clavine alkaloids (XLVI). Only derivatives belonging to the first group will be considered here.

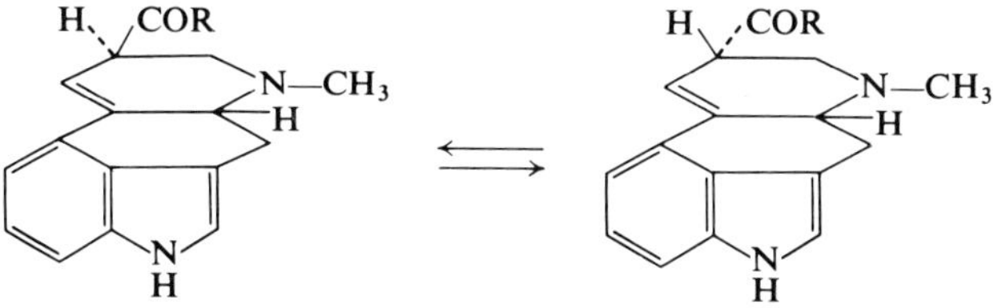

(XLVa)
Lysergic acid derivatives

(XLVb)
Isolysergic acid derivatives

$R = NH-CH-CH_3$
$\quad\quad\quad\quad |$
$\quad\quad\quad CH_2OH$ = Ergonovine (amide alkaloid)

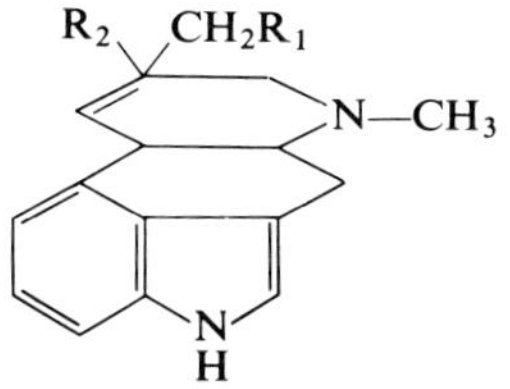

(XLVI)
Clavine group
$R_1 = R_2 = H$: Agroclavine

The alkaloids of the lysergic acid series occur in pairs of interconvertible isomers; one is levorotatory (lysergic acid derivatives) and is physiologically active. The names of these derivatives end in -ine. The other member of the pair is dextrorotatory (isolysergic acid derivatives), shows no biological activity, and has a name ending in -inine, e.g., ergotamine and ergotaminine. Lysergic acid and isolysergic acid are epimeric at C-8 (XLV a + b) as was shown by Stoll *et al.* (234).

As mentioned before, the only therapeutically useful adrenolytic in this group is a mixture of three peptide-type derivatives of dihydrolysergic acid, namely, dihydroergocornine, dihydroergocristine, and dihydroergocryptine methane sulfonates (XLVII). Hydrogenation of the 9,10-double bond present in the ergotoxine group (ergocornine, ergocristine, and ergocryptine) practically eliminates the classical effects of ergot, i.e., vasoconstriction, oxytocic activity, and central sympathetic stimulation, and enhances the adrenolytic action characterized by vasodilatation, lowering of blood pressure, and a certain sedative effect (235).

(XLVII)

Dihydroergocristine   Dihydroergocryptine   Dihydroergocornine

IX. Adrenergic β-receptor blocking agents

It has been well established that the classical adrenergic blocking drugs such as phenoxybenzamine or phentolamine do not effectively antagonize the myocardial responses to catecholamines. Although blockage of the excitatory effects of sympathomimetic amines have been reported for a great number of compounds, relatively few compounds have been found that antagonize the inhibitory effects of these amines. Astrom (9) in 1949 studied the antisympathetic action of a number of phenethylamine derivatives and showed that some were capable of blocking the inhibitory effects of epinephrine; these compounds were, however, themselves pressor amines of varying potency. In 1957 Powell and Slater (195) reported that dichloroisoproterenol (XLVIII) selectively blocked some of the inhibitory effects of epinephrine and isoproterenol and itself was virtually devoid of excitatory action. Later work by

$$Cl-\underset{Cl}{\bigcirc}-CH-CH_2NHCH(CH_3)_2$$
$$\overset{|}{OH}$$

(XLVIII)
Dichloroisoproterenol (DCI)

Furchgott (79), however, showed that dichloroisoproterenol also had appreciable sympathomimetic effects, depending on the organs studied. Four analogs (XLIX and L) of dichloroisoproterenol were studied by Van Deripe and Moran (246). The results suggested a difference in cardiac and vasodilator

$$Cl-\underset{Cl}{\bigcirc}-\overset{\overset{R}{|}}{\underset{\underset{OH}{|}}{C}}-CH_2NHCH(CH_3)_2 \qquad\qquad CH_3-\bigcirc-\overset{\overset{R}{|}}{\underset{\underset{OH}{|}}{C}}-CH_2-NHCH(CH_3)_2$$

R=CH₃, C₂H₅ \qquad\qquad R=H, CH₃
(XLIX) \qquad\qquad L

$$Cl-\bigcirc-\overset{R}{\underset{OH}{C}}-CH_2NHCH(CH_3)_2 \qquad CH_3-\bigcirc-\overset{R}{\underset{OH}{C}}-CH_2-NHCH(CH_3)_2$$

R=CH$_3$, C$_2$H$_5$ \qquad\qquad R=H, CH$_3$
(XLIX) \qquad\qquad L

receptors and a need for further evaluation of the present β-receptor classification.

Stanton *et al.* (232) studied a group of related compounds (LI to LIII), which were α-adrenergic receptor blockers, and β-receptor stimulators (LI and LIII); methoxyisoxsuprine (LII), however, also showed weak β-receptor blocking activity. Isoxsuprine (LI) has found application as a vasodilator (127).

$$HO-\bigcirc-CH-\overset{\overset{CH_3}{|}}{CH}-NHCHCH_2O-\bigcirc$$
$$\quad\quad\overset{|}{OH}\quad\quad\quad\overset{|}{CH_3}$$

(LI)
Isoxsuprine

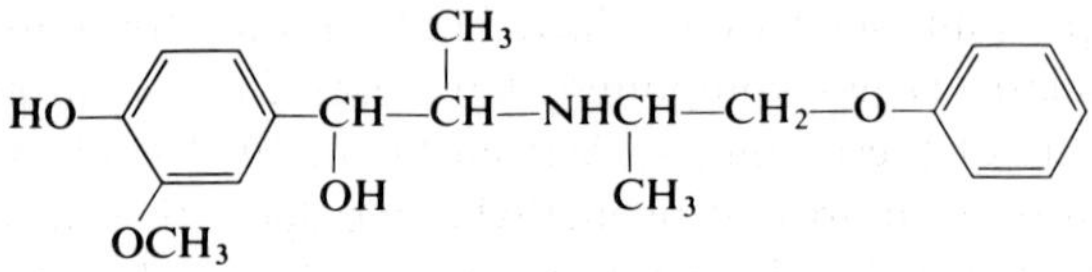

$$HO-\underset{OCH_3}{\underset{|}{\bigcirc}}-\underset{OH}{\underset{|}{CH}}-\underset{CH_3}{\overset{CH_3}{\underset{|}{CH}}}-NHCH-CH_2-O-\bigcirc$$

(LII)

Methoxyisoxsuprine

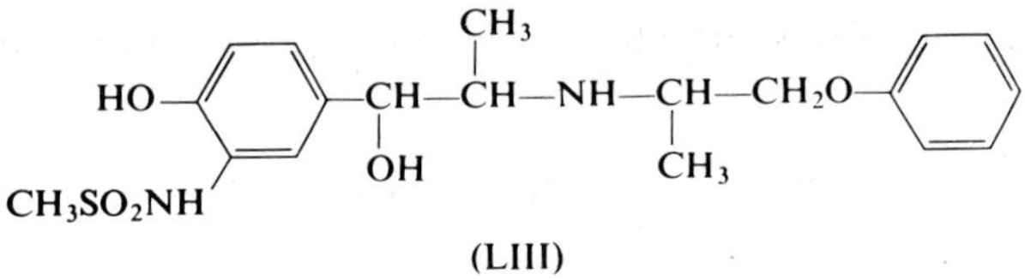

$$HO-\underset{CH_3SO_2NH}{\bigcirc}-\underset{OH}{\underset{|}{CH}}-\overset{CH_3}{\underset{|}{CH}}-NH-\underset{CH_3}{\underset{|}{CH}}-CH_2O-\bigcirc$$

(LIII)

MJ 1991

Recently, two other compounds, (LIV) and (LV) have been reported as specific β-adrenergic blockers by Dungan and Lish (60). These compounds were about four times as active as dichloroisoproterenol.

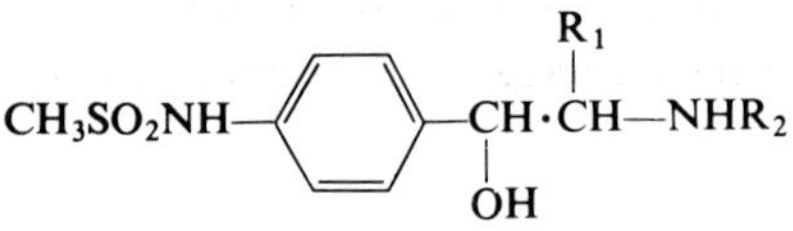

$$CH_3SO_2NH-\bigcirc-\overset{R_1}{\underset{OH}{\underset{|}{CH}}}\cdot\underset{}{CH}-NHR_2$$

(LIV)   MJ 1999: $R_1 = H$; $R_2 = CH\begin{smallmatrix}CH_3\\CH_3\end{smallmatrix}$

(LV)   MJ 1998: $R_1 = CH_3$; $R_2 = CH_3$

Black and Stephenson (27), continuing the search for a more specific β-receptor blocker, described the pharmacological properties of a new β blocker, pronethalol (nethalide LVI), in 1962. This compound appeared to be free of intrinsic sympathomimetic activity; it did, however, have certain cancerogenic properties in mice. Further work by Black *et al.* (28) resulted in a related compound, propranolol (LVII), which had no carcinogenic potential.

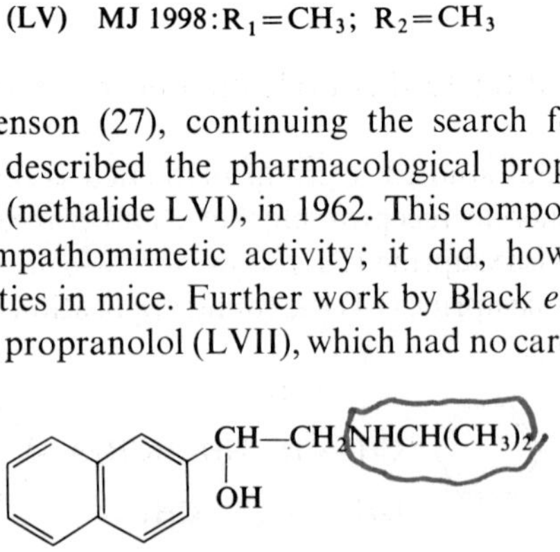

$$\underset{OH}{\underset{|}{CH}}-CH_2NHCH(CH_3)_2$$

(LVI)

Pronethalol (Nethalide)

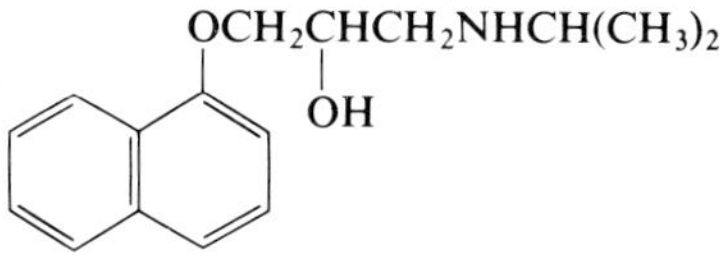

$$OCH_2CHCH_2NHCH(CH_3)_2$$

(LVII)
Propranolol

Investigating certain pyrroline derivatives, Honkomp and Buckley (116) found that compound (LVIII) had a pronounced blocking effect on β receptors. More than eighty somewhat related pyrrolidines were prepared by Gould *et al.*

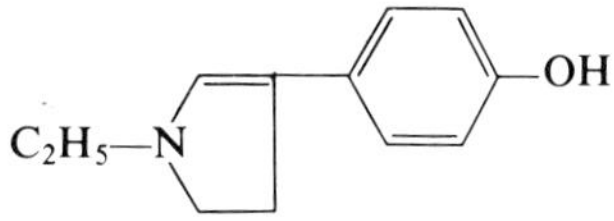

(LVIII)

(87). Although these compounds did not have a strong α- or β-adrenergic blocking effect, they found that compound (LIXa) had significant coronary vasodilator activity and compound (LIXb) depressed intestinal smooth muscle activity markedly; compound (LX) was a bronchodilator.

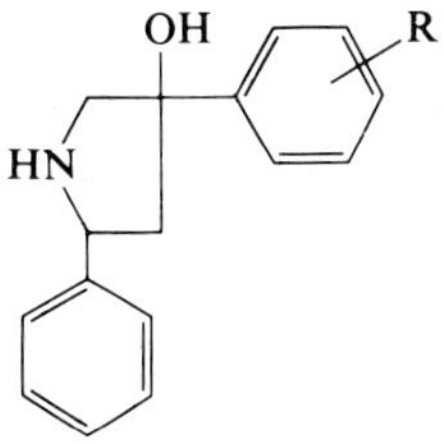

(LIX) 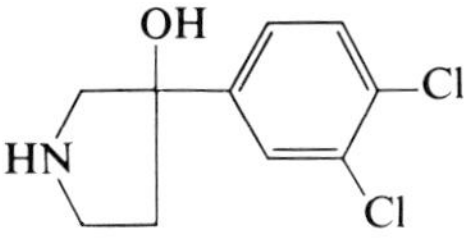   (LX)

(a) R = 3,4-dichloro
(b) R = 4-chloro

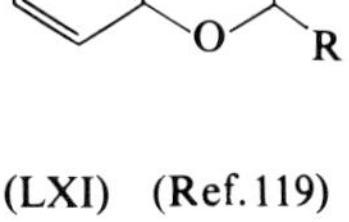

(LXI)   (Ref. 119) 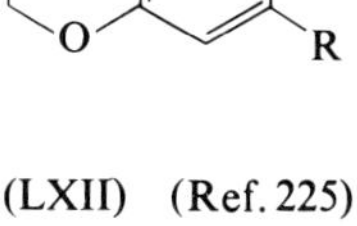   (LXII)   (Ref. 225) 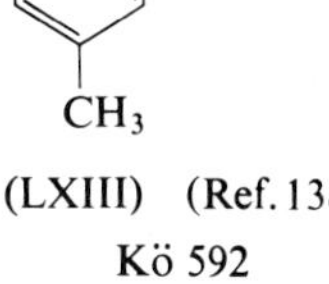   (LXIII)   (Ref. 138)

Kö 592

$$R = CH—CH_2NCH(CH_3)_2$$
$$OH$$

A few additional compounds with β-adrenergic blocking activity have appeared recently in the literature, e.g., compounds (LXI–LXIII).

In addition, Burns and Lemberger (41) have studied a compound, butoxamine (LXIV), which appears to be a specific antagonist of the metabolic actions of epinephrine and thus differs in its effects from the other α- and β-receptor blockers described.

(LXIV)
Butoxamine

Interest in the field of β-adrenergic receptor blockers has grown considerably in the past few years and no doubt other types of specific β-receptor blockers will be found.

X. Pharmacology and clinical application of α- and β-adrenergic blocking agents

The great early interest in the α-adrenergic blockers was spurred by the hope that they might be of use for lowering elevated blood pressure by curbing sympathetic overactivity. As time has passed, it has become apparent that substances which interfere with the liberation of endogenous norepinephrine from sympathetic nerve endings are more effective than those which block the pressor influence of exogenously administered catecholamines. Moreover, such large doses of α blockers are required to block sympathetic vasoconstriction that side effects overshadow the desired activity. Nevertheless, the study of the circulatory effects of the α blockers represents an important intermediate step in the quest for antihypertensive agents.

A. Derivatives of Benzodioxan

Piperoxan, 933F, (No. 14, Table I) which is a typical member of the benzodioxan series, is an α-adrenergic blocking compound (70). The blockade produced by this substance is of the competitive type. In addition, the benzodioxan derivatives appear to produce a vasoconstriction of the peripheral blood vessels by means of a direct effect on the smooth muscle of such structures. These substances also appear to cause a stimulation of the central sympathetic centers (176).

As a result of these multiple sites of action, the benzodioxan blockers may cause a rise in blood pressure due to an increase in peripheral tone of the blood vessels and to a stimulation of central sympathetic centers. The response to injected epinephrine is reversed and that produced by norepinephrine is decreased. The reflex-induced pressor response produced by occlusion of the common carotid arteries and the pressor response evoked by stimulation of the central end of the vagi are inhibited, presumably by virtue of the α-adrenergic blocking activity (92).

The benzodioxan derivatives, like the other synthetic α-adrenergic blocking drugs, do not inhibit the positive inotropic or chronotropic effects produced by epinephrine, norepinephrine, or stimulation of the cardiac sympathetic nerves (57, 92). The resultant tachycardia has interfered with their use as antihypertensive agents.

Piperoxan may decrease coronary blood flow but may not inhibit the increased blood flow induced by epinephrine (92, 176, 180). In the vascular bed of the skeletal muscle, vasoconstrictor activity evoked by epinephrine, norepinephrine, and sympathetic nerve stimulation is inhibited. The decreased renal blood flow induced by epinephrine is also inhibited by piperoxan; renal blood flow *per se* may be decreased by the injection of piperoxan (230). Cerebral blood flow is not significantly altered (92).

The action of the benzodioxan blockers on the central nervous system is somewhat complex; they appear to cause a stimulation of sympathetic and vagal activity and depress to some extent the cardiovascular reflexes (180). A sedative effect has been observed in experimental animals.

The benzodioxan derivatives and the other synthetic α-adrenergic blocking drugs increase intestinal motility apparently by a direct action on the smooth muscle. They also depress the myocardium in a manner similar to that produced by quinidine (176, 180).

Piperoxan has been employed in the treatment of and diagnosis of phaeochromocytoma, but it has been replaced by less toxic drugs for this purpose.

B. β-HALOETHYLAMINE—α-ADRENERGIC BLOCKING DRUGS

The β-haloethylamine series of compounds has been extensively studied by Nickerson et al. (176, 177), by Ullyott and Kerwin (244), and by Graham (89).

Reports of several studies (78, 183) indicate that phenoxybenzamine (No. 67, Table VIII) produces its initial α-adrenergic blocking action in a competitive manner and involves a competition with the α-adrenergic stimulating substances for receptor sites. Later the blockade becomes noncompetitive, one in which the law of mass action equilibrium between phenoxybenzamine and the α-adrenergic stimulating substances no longer obtains. The α-adrenergic stimulating substances are no longer able to alter or overcome the α-adrenergic blockade (178).

Phenoxybenzamine (No. 67, Table VIII) and Dibenamine (compound XVII) prevent or inhibit the α-adrenergic stimulating activity of the catecholamines on smooth muscle and the exocrine glands. Inhibition of sympathetic nerve stimulation is less effective. These drugs are essentially devoid of β-adrenergic blocking activity. In addition to the α-adrenergic blocking activity, phenoxybenzamine and Dibenamine inhibit the responses produced by injection of 5-hydroxytryptamine, histamine, and, in high doses, the responses elicited by acetylcholine. The antihistaminic activity of Dibenamine is rather weak while that exhibited by phenoxybenzamine is considerable. Rate of onset of α-blockade is slow and progressive; experimentally it occurs 1–2 hours after the intravenous administration of Dibenamine and within 1 hour after the administration of phenoxybenzamine. Experimentally, at least, this type of α-adrenergic blockade can persist for several days.

Intravenous doses of phenoxybenzamine and Dibenamine administered slowly usually do not produce a hypotensive response in laboratory animals or in healthy normovolemic individuals in the recumbent position. The response produced in patients with essential hypertension is variable. The major effect of these drugs becomes manifested when some form of stress is placed on the cardiovascular system of treated individuals. Thus a change from the supine to the erect position produces an orthostatic hypotension. Other forms of stress that normally do not result in a change in blood pressure produce a hypotensive effect in the patient with adrenergic blockade; examples of this type of stress would be a slight degree of hypovolemia, hypercapnia, and normal analgesic doses of morphine or meperidine.

The effect of phenoxybenzamine on regional blood flows appears to depend upon the degree of vasoconstriction present in the region at the time of the administration of the drug. In a cold environment the degree of vasoconstriction is high in both the muscular and cutaneous vascular beds, and under these conditions phenoxybenzamine produces an increase in blood flow in both vascular beds. Conversely, in the presence of a warm environment or during muscular exercise, vasoconstriction does not appear to be a prominent factor and phenoxybenzamine produces little change in blood flow. Hypovolemia tends to produce an increased vasoconstriction in the splanchnic and renal vascular beds, and under such conditions an α-adrenergic blocking drug induces an increase in regional blood flow. For this reason the combination of adrenergic blockade with measures for increasing the blood volume have been proposed for the treatment of shock.

Phenoxybenzamine and the other β-haloethylamine compounds do not inhibit the inotropic and chronotropic effects of the sympathomimetic amines. A tachycardia is usually observed after the administration of phenoxybenzamine (171, 176).

While the β-haloethylamine adrenergic blocking drugs do not block the

β-adrenergic effects of epinephrine in the heart, they do inhibit certain types of cardiac arrhythmias. The arrhythmias induced by cyclopropane-epinephrine or chloroform-epinephrine administration are inhibited to varying degrees by phenoxybenzamine or Dibenamine. The spontaneously occurring arrhythmias induced by cyclopropane are inhibited by Dibenamine, but those observed after coronary artery occlusion and those obtained during hypothermia are not eliminated by these drugs (59, 168, 181, 184).

The β-haloethylamine compounds, and in particular phenoxybenzamine, appear to have a definite effect on the central nervous system. These drugs can produce nausea, vomiting, increased respiratory efforts, and an increase in motor activity. Convulsions can be produced by large intravenous doses. In man, oral doses produce a miosis, sedation, tiredness, and lethargy. A loss of time perception may also occur. The evidence reported by Nickerson (180) indicates that the substances produced by hydrolysis of the haloethylamines do not produce α-adrenergic blockade but do produce the central nervous system stimulant effects obtained with the β-haloethylamine compounds.

The α-adrenergic blocking compounds do not inhibit to a significant degree the relaxation of the intestine produced by epinephrine or isoproterenol but can inhibit the effect produced by phenylephrine (5: p. 2). In general, these compounds block the stimulation of the salivary glands produced by α-adrenergic stimulating agents and antagonize the mydriasis induced by α-adrenergic stimulating compounds. The stimulation of the sweat glands produced by α-adrenergic stimulation is also inhibited (99, 229).

Phenoxybenzamine and other β-haloethylamines are absorbed from the gastrointestinal tract; it has been estimated that 20–30% of an oral dose of phenoxybenzamine is absorbed. Phenoxybenzamine has a high affinity for lipids and tends to accumulate in the neutral fat (40) from which there is a slow release from the twelfth to the ninety-sixth hour after intravenous administration, but the release from fat stores does not appear to be a major facet of the pharmacological activity when the compound is administered in low doses which eventuate in adrenergic blockade (179). Agarwal and Harvey (2) found that adrenergic blockade persisted for 3–4 days, although no drug could be demonstrated in blood in cross-circulation experiments. In the dog it is dealkylated and yields the N-phenoxyisopropyl-N-benzylamine derivative (40). The drug is not hydrolyzed to the corresponding alcohol.

The only practical route of administration of the β-haloethylamine compounds is the intravenous route since local irritation precludes their use by other parenteral routes.

Phenoxybenzamine has been employed in the treatment of peripheral vascular disease, e.g., Raynaud's disease, causalgia, and the frostbite syndrome. In addition, it has been used to treat individuals with arteriosclerosis obliterans and thromboangiitis obliterans and other vascular diseases where a high level of α sympathetic tone is thought to be present. Although theoretically suitable, the side effects of this series have interfered with their successful use in the management of hypertension.

C. DERIVATIVES OF PHENYLPIPERAZINE

Haloanisone (compound XXXII) is one of the butyrophenones described by Janssen (124) which have been added to the clinical armamentarium in the field of psychiatry and anesthesiology. This compound appears to possess a wide range of neuroplegic activities which are similar to those possessed by the phenothiazine drugs. In general, haloanisone produced in various experimental animals (dogs, mice, rats) an inhibition of both spontaneous motor activity and induced motor activity. It decreased the compulsory gnawing produced in rats by the intravenous injection of amphetamine or apomorphine (172). Its tranquilizing activity was demonstrated in dogs and rats by obtaining the dose of haloanisone which inhibited the avoidance reaction or response in 50% of the animals in a jumping box experiment. The drug potentiated the pentobarbital sleeping time in mice and also produced an analgesic effect in mice in the same dosage range required to inhibit avoidance behavior in rats and dogs (172). It also appears to have a pronounced antiemetic effect in dogs.

Haloanisone had been found to possess a pronounced α-adrenergic blocking activity and some of the untoward reactions observed in man are reported to be due to this type of activity (172). The drug has been studied in a double-blind type of experiment in man, and it was found that chlorpromazine and haloanisone yielded the same results (55). Hypotensive reactions were observed following the administration of haloanisone and this may be the result of the α blocking activity (55, 56, 216). It appears to be effective in the treatment of psychomotor agitations encountered in psychiatry.

The intravenous LD_{50} value of haloanisone in rats suggests that it is slightly more toxic than chlorpromazine and approximately three times as toxic as perphenazine (172).

It is interesting to recall that Bovet and Simon (30) found in the benzodioxan series that piperoxan (933F) possessed both α-adrenergic blocking activity and sedative activity. This sedative type of activity appears to be also a characteristic of haloanisone.

D. SUBSTITUTED IMIDAZOLINES

1. *Phentolamine*

Phentolamine (No. 108, Table XII), an imidazoline derivative, is employed in clinical practice as a diagnostic aid for the determination of the presence of phaeochromocytoma. The original report describing the α-adrenergic blocking activity was presented by Meier *et al.* (160).

Following the parenteral or oral administration of phentolamine, the pressor response produced by injected *l*-epinephrine is reversed, that produced by *l*-norepinephrine is greatly decreased, and the pressor response elicited by stimulation of the sympathetic nerves is inhibited or greatly attenuated, although the doses required to achieve this effect are usually greater than those necessary to reverse the pressor effect produced by injected *l*-epinephrine (250).

Phentolamine produces its α-adrenergic blockade by means of a competitive type of inhibition, a competition for α-receptor sites with the catecholamines. As a result of this type of pharmacological action, a considerable reduction in mean arterial blood pressure may be observed in man and experimental animals following parenteral administration. Orthostatic hypotension has been observed in both normal and hypertensive individuals.

The drug has not been successful as an orally active antihypertensive agent because of the gastrointestinal side effects encountered and secondly because of the development of tolerance or refractoriness to its antihypertensive effects (172a).

Because of its α-adrenergic blocking effects, coupled with its intrinsic safety and minimal tendency for false positive tests, phentolamine has achieved wide acceptance as a diagnostic agent for the detection of phaeochromocytoma (62, 83, 96, 110, 131, 139, 211, 223).

In addition to the inhibitory effects on catecholamines, the synthetic α-adrenergic blocking drugs inhibit to various degrees the pressor response induced by occlusion of the common carotid arteries and the pressor response induced by stimulation of the central end of the severed vagus nerve (176). The hypertensive responses elicited by asphyxia and anoxia are also antagonized by these agents.

Phentolamine injected directly into the vascular beds of muscle or skin produces a transient vasodilatation (125, 204). The α-adrenergic blockade induced by phentolamine persists for a much longer period than does the vasodilatation and does not appear to be a factor in this transient vasodilatation. Following the administration of phentolamine, the epinephrine-induced vasoconstriction was converted to vasodilatation in the muscle vascular beds and the pressor responses induced by norepinephrine and phenylephrine were decreased, but all three adrenergic drugs still produced a vasoconstrictive effect in the vascular bed of the skin (125). A 10-fold increase in dose was required to produce an inhibition of the vasoconstrictor effect of these adrenergic drugs in the vascular bed of the skin, although phentolamine produced a transient increase in blood flow *per se* (125).

Recently Taylor *et al.* (240) have reported that the intravenous administration of 5 mg of phentolamine produced an increase in cardiac output and heart rate, a decrease in peripheral resistance, and a decrease in mean arterial blood pressure both in normotensive and hypertensive individuals. The hypotensive effect of phentolamine was reported to be due to a decrease in general vascular resistance; this occurred in the presence of an increase in cardiac output but without a consistent change in stroke volume (240).

Phentolamine usually produces some degree of tachycardia in experimental animals and man. The increase in heart rate appears to occur as a result of a reflex compensatory mechanism activated by the hypotensive response. In addition, phentolamine has a direct stimulatory effect on the heart (11). Unpublished results obtained in our laboratories indicated phentolamine possessed an indirect (β-adrenergic) stimulating effect and that this pharmacological activity could account for the positive inotropic and chronotropic effects observed with phentolamine (15a).

Phentolamine produces an increase in the peristaltic activity of the intestine. In experimental animals, the oral administration of large doses of phentolamine produces vomiting and diarrhea (241). This agent will block the inhibition or relaxation produced by the catecholamine phenylephrine, an amine which possesses mainly an α-adrenergic stimulating action.

Large oral doses of phentolamine produced a marked depression of the blood sugar levels in dogs (241). However, the α-adrenergic blocking drug phenoxybenzamine (No. 67, Table VIII) has been reported to be ineffective in inhibiting the epinephrine-induced hyperglycemia in the dog (154). The hypoglycemic response produced by phentolamine is thought to be one of the mechanisms by which it produces its toxic effects in animals. Intravenous infusion of glucose restored the blood glucose levels to normal and terminated the hypoglycemic coma induced by phentolamine in dogs (241).

Phentolamine is readily absorbed from the gastrointestinal tract (241). Following the intravenous administration of a large dose (15 mg per kilogram) to dogs, phentolamine was found to rapidly disappear from the blood. One hour after administration less than 2 μg per liter was detected in the plasma (203). These same authors reported that 10% of the administered dose was excreted in the urine in 12 hours and an additional 10% as a conjugated form. Following oral administration, 3–5% of free phentolamine was recovered from the urine. Richardson et al. (203) did not find a correlation between the plasma concentration of the drug and biological activity but found some agreement between the urinary excretion of phentolamine and biological activity.

2. Tolazoline

Experimental studies in animals have indicated that tolazoline (compound XXXIII) produces a hypotensive effect by virtue of its effect on the adrenergic system (113, 157), which results in peripheral vasodilatation (158). The site of action of tolazoline appears to be on the α-adrenergic receptor in the vascular smooth muscle (95). Numerous experiments have demonstrated that it will reverse or abolish the pressor response induced by injected epinephrine (4, 6,

48, 173, 258). Ahlquist (4) also noted that tolazoline appeared to possess some sympathomimetic activity as well as cholinergic and histaminelike activity. The effect of tolazoline on the heart is one of stimulation both in the intact animal and in the isolated perfused heart. The cardiac stimulation results in an increase in cardiac output and this increase in output can result in an increase in arterial pressure, even though peripheral vasodilatation is present (4).

Moore et al. (169) found that when tolazoline was injected into the femoral artery of anesthetized dogs it reversed the vasoconstriction produced by epinephrine. Johnson et al. (125) observed that tolazoline caused a vasodilatation in the vascular beds supplying the muscle and skin regions and reversed the vasoconstriction produced by epinephrine in the muscle vascular bed.

Grassi Bertazzi and De Gennaro (90, 91) observed that tolazoline increased gastric activity. Yonkman and Chess (258) have obtained evidence that the increased intestinal motility observed after the administration of tolazoline appeared to be due to the cholinergiclike activity of the drug.

Hendrix et al. (112) have suggested that tolazoline appeared to produce its vasodilatation by virtue of a block of sympathetic receptors in the vascular smooth muscle and also by means of a direct histaminelike effect on small blood vessels.

Tolazoline has been employed in various vascular disorders; Raynaud's disease (95); causalgia-type of pain (95, 207); peripheral arteriosclerosis to decrease abnormal degrees of vascular tone (167, 202); peripheral vascular disease associated with diabetes mellitus (68, 73, 135, 146, 207). Van Itallie et al. (247) found that tolazoline increased peripheral blood flow in normal individuals and patients with peripheral vascular disease; Lynn (147) also reported the drug to be effective in producing a vasodilatation in the hands and feet with little effect on the calf region of the leg. It has also been employed to treat the early phases of frostbite (69, 73). Although originally considered an antihypertensive agent, its cardiac stimulatory effects have mitigated against it for this purpose.

Tolazoline is readily absorbed from the gastrointestinal tract. Century et al. (45) reported that in rats the drug was found in the greatest concentrations in the liver and kidneys. It is rapidly excreted in the urine of both dog and man in an unchanged form and the half life of a single dose has been estimated to be 2 hours in both man and dog (39).

3. *Azapetine*

Randall and Smith (199) have described the pharmacological activity of azapetine (compound XL). In many respects the cardiovascular activity of this agent is similar to that ascribed to tolazoline. Azapetine appears to possess both a direct dilating effect on the smooth muscle of the vascular system and an α-adrenergic blocking activity.

Experimental evidence has been obtained by Johnson *et al.* (125) which indicates that azapetine produced a vasodilatation in the vascular beds of the cutaneous and muscular regions. This compound prevented the vasoconstrictor effect induced by epinephrine and converted the constrictor response to a vasodilatation in the muscular vascular bed, but the vasoconstriction evoked by epinephrine in the vascular region of the skin remained. Large doses of azapetine were required to inhibit the vasoconstriction produced in the vascular areas of the skin by epinephrine, norepinephrine, and phenylephrine. The vasoconstriction produced by epinephrine in the vascular bed of skeletal muscle was more readily inhibited by azapetine than was the vasoconstriction induced by norepinephrine and phenylephrine.

Deal and Green (54) have reported that the vasoconstriction evoked in the mesenteric vascular bed by epinephrine and norepinephrine was inhibited by azapetine. The response produced by epinephrine was converted to one of slight vasodilatation.

Large doses of azapetine were observed by Denison *et al.* (57) to inhibit the vasodilatation induced by epinephrine, norepinephrine, and isoproterenol in the coronary arterial system of anesthetized dogs. Green and Denison (94) noted the absence of effects of synthetic α-adrenergic blocking drugs on cerebral vessels since they found epinephrine and norepinephrine to be without an effect on cerebral arterioles.

Azapetine as well as tolazoline and piperoxan inhibited the vasoconstriction induced in the renal vascular bed by epinephrine. Larger doses of the adrenergic blocking drugs were required to inhibit the effects produced by norepinephrine. The work of Handley and Moyer (101) indicated that azapetine did not depress glomerular filtration rate, the renal plasma flow, or the maximum rate of tubular transport of glucose.

Azapetine, like the other synthetic α-adrenergic blocking drugs, does not inhibit the effect of epinephrine upon the mammalian heart.

Green (93) has obtained evidence in man that azapetine will produce vasodilatation in both the hands and feet when vasoconstriction has been induced by exposure to a cold environment.

Azapetine is absorbed following oral administration. Experimentally the drug appears to be stored in a temporary manner in fatty depots of tissues, from which it is slowly released. Little is excreted by the kidney (198), for only 5–10% was recovered from the urine of dogs and rats.

E. ERGOT ALKALOIDS

The pharmacological activity of the ergot alkaloids has been reviewed in several reports (153, 180, 212, 213). The natural peptide-type ergot alkaloids and the hydrogenated alkaloids possess α-adrenergic blocking activity. In general, these pharmacological actions are similar to those described for the synthetic α-blocking compounds but certain differences in action are apparent. In general it is these differences, not the similarities, which will be emphasized.

The natural peptide-type ergot alkaloids tend to produce a hypertensive response in animals by means of a direct vasoconstricting effect on the arteries. This effect, reported by Dale (53), can be demonstrated upon the isolated vessels of the rabbit ear, and by means of the pressor effect, obtained in pithed cats (21). In contrast, the hydrogenated alkaloids tend to produce a hypotensive response.

The ergot alkaloids reverse the pressor response evoked by injected epinephrine. Large doses are required to inhibit the pressor responses induced by sympathetic nerve stimulation or norepinephrine. In this respect, they resemble the activity described for other synthetic α-adrenergic blocking drugs of the competitive type.

In experimental animal studies the ergot alkaloids will inhibit the pressor responses induced by a stimulation of the central end of the severed vagus nerve, by carotid occlusion, and those responses induced by anoxia and asphyxia. It has been suggested (176) that these responses are inhibited by an action of the ergot alkaloids upon the central nervous system.

The ergot alkaloids produce a bradycardia in experimental animals by a direct stimulation of the brain stem; the bradycardia can be eliminated by vagotomy. In addition, although both ergotamine and dihydroergotamine appear to increase cerebral blood flow, ergotamine appears to cause coronary vasoconstriction by a direct effect on these vessels.

Additional evidence for the effect of the ergot alkaloids upon the central nervous system is found in the experimental results which indicate that elimination of the vasomotor centers and of the sympathetic efferent tracts inhibits the hypotensive effect observed with the alkaloids (176, 212). In man the depression of the vasomotor center results in a decrease in peripheral sympathetic tone and this in turn appears to be responsible for the hypotension and decreased reflex vasomotor activity (14). At least this appears to be true for the preparation produced by Stoll and Hofmann (235).

It is the hydrogenated alkaloids which possess a more pronounced α-adrenergic blocking activity, hypotensive activity, and vasodilating activity than the unsaturated alkaloids. The direct vasoconstrictor activity appears to have been greatly attenuated by the reduction of the double bond in the lysergic acid part of the molecule.

Hayes et al. (108) and Barcroft et al. (14) noted that the hydrogenated alkaloids did not produce a hypotensive effect in normotensive patients but did in the hypertensive patient.

Following the intravenous administration of dihydroergocornine in man,

Freis *et al.* (74) observed the following effects: blood flow through the limb (leg and arm) was usually increased in the presence of a concomitant decrease in blood pressure, although in some cases blood flow in these regions remained unchanged or decreased; blood flow through the hepatic-portal circulation exhibited a variable response but usually decreased; the renal blood flow exhibited an initial decrease followed by a return to the control levels or to levels higher than the control values and as a result glomerular filtration rate decreased then increased in parallel with the renal blood flow. The hydro-genated alkaloids appeared to increase, to some degree, the tubular reabsorp-tion of water (74). The cardiac output in man was either not changed or exhibited a slight increase in response to the hypotension observed. Thus total peripheral resistance was decreased. A bradycardia was observed but it was not inhibited by the administration of atropine. The blood flow in the cutaneous bed, as measured by digital skin temperature, was increased in the presence of a warm but not a cold ambient temperature. The opposite effect has been reported to occur with phenoxybenzamine.

Barcroft *et al.* (14) also observed a peripheral vasodilatation in man. The cutaneous circulation to the hands and feet was increased by the dihydrogenated alkaloids, while the blood flow to the muscular vascular beds of the leg was not significantly increased. These authors concluded that the alkaloids produce a slight blockade of the peripheral sympathetic system but appeared to produce their principal effect by an inhibition of the vasomotor centers. In addition, they noted that the alkaloids did not produce a significant inhibition of the effects of epinephrine or norepinephrine on the blood pressure or blood flow in man in doses which influenced peripheral blood flow.

Barcroft *et al.* (14) also obtained evidence of a direct vasoconstricting effect produced by the hydrogenated alkaloids.

Both ergotamine and the dihydrogenated alkaloids appear to cause a stimulation or augmentation of peristaltic activity of the gastrointestinal tract both in man and experimental animals.

Ergotamine has found clinical application in the treatment of migrainous headaches. Evidence available indicates that the alkaloid reduces the severity of the headache by producing a reduction in the amplitude of the pulsations of the cranial artery, particularly branches of the external carotid arteries (255).

The amide alkaloids which are usually devoid of α-adrenergic blocking activity are orally active, highly potent stimulants of uterine motility. The natural peptide-type ergot alkaloids are active in this respect following paren-teral administration but are ineffective by the oral route. The dihydrogenated alkaloids are active on the human pregnant uterus.

The alkaloids generally are poorly absorbed from the gastrointestinal tract although the amide alkaloids, ergonovine and methylergonovine, appear to be readily absorbed (38). Evidence presented by Barcroft *et al.* (14) for man and Rothlin (213) and Cerletti *et al.* (46) for animals indicates that the alkaloids are very rapidly removed from the blood stream.

The natural peptide-type ergot alkaloids, the dihydrogenated alkaloids, and the amide alkaloids (ergonovine) all have been reported to inhibit the hyperglycemia induced by epinephrine. Only the natural peptide-type ergot alkaloids (ergotamine) and the dihydrogenated alkaloids possess α-adrenergic blocking activity; ergonovine lacks α-adrenergic blocking activity (106). Thus this inhibition of the epinephrine-induced hyperglycemia does not appear to be related to α-adrenergic blocking activity but may be related to a possible β-adrenergic blocking activity.

F. β-ADRENERGIC BLOCKING COMPOUNDS

In 1948 Ahlquist (3) published his concept that the adrenergic receptors could be divided into two groups, namely α and β receptors. Ten years later Powell and Slater (195) described the pharmacological properties of dichloroisoproterenol (DCI) (XLVII), which in essence produced an inhibition of the β receptors. Later, Moran and Perkins (171) reported that DCI produced an inhibition of the cardiac or positive inotropic effects produced by epinephrine, norepinephrine, isoproterenol, and that evoked by stimulation of the central sympathetic nerves. In addition, these authors also observed the β-adrenergic stimulating effects of DCI *per se*, although this β-adrenergic stimulating activity is of a short duration and is soon followed by β blockade. The positive inotropic effects of digoxin, theophylline, and calcium chloride were not inhibited by DCI (171).

Powell and Slater (195) noted that DCI produced an increase in femoral arterial flow and decreased the vasodilatation obtained with isoproterenol. The rather marked intrinsic β-adrenergic stimulating activity of DCI did not permit this agent to be employed in extensive clinical trials.

In 1962 Black and Stephenson (27) described the β-adrenergic blocking activity of pronethalol (LVI). Pronethalol appears to possess considerably less intrinsic β-adrenergic stimulating activity than does DCI. Like DCI, pronethalol was found to decrease cardiac rate and myocardial contractile force. The inotropic and chronotropic responses produced by epinephrine and isoproterenol were inhibited. Pronethalol was found to produce tumors of the thymus when given to mice in a chronic toxicity study and thus the clinical trials of this agent were curtailed.

Recently Black *et al.* (28) have described the activity of propranolol (LVII), a compound related to pronethalol which appears to be devoid of a tumorinducing potential. Propranolol has been reported to be approximately ten times as potent as pronethalol in terms of β-adrenergic blockade.

During the past year and a half a number of papers have appeared which have described various aspects of the pharmacological activity of propranolol in both man and experimental animals.

Levy and Richards (144) have obtained evidence which indicated that the *dl*-mixture and *d*-isomers of propranolol as well as the *l*-isomer of MJ-1999 (LIV) produced a significant decrease in the heart rate of both the electrically driven rabbit atria and the isolated rabbit atria. In contrast, the *dl*-form and the *d*- and *l*-isomers of pronethalol did not produce a significant decrease in heart rate. The *dl*-form and the *d*-isomer of MJ-1999 also failed to produce a significant decrease in heart rate. DCI produced a significant increase in heart rate. These authors concluded that there did not appear to be a simple relationship between β-adrenergic blocking activity and a direct chronotropic activity. Previous work by Levy and Richards (143) had indicated that propranolol, pronethalol, and MJ-1999 did not inhibit the positive inotropic response induced by ouabain.

Vogel *et al.* (249) have reported that the *l*-isomer of propranolol is more potent as a β blocking drug than the *d*-isomer. The *d*-isomer of propranolol appeared to possess very little β blocking activity. The *l*-propranolol derivative produced heart failure or a depression of ventricular function in the experimental lambs under study. The activity of *dl*-propranolol was intermediate between that observed with the *l*- and *d*-isomers. In heart failure induced by coarctation of the main pulmonary artery, β blockade was not well tolerated, suggesting a contraindication in right-sided heart failure.

The work of Sekiya and Vaughan-Williams (222a) has indicated that pronethalol would reduce the toxicity of ouabain. Pronethalol was also reported to be a potent local anesthetic agent with an activity twice that of procaine (84). Recently, Morales-Aguilera and Vaughan-Williams (170) have reported that propranolol is approximately twice as potent as procaine in terms of local anesthetic activity and about equal in potency to pronethalol and lidocaine. These authors also obtained evidence which indicated that propranolol was more potent than either pronethalol or lidocaine in raising the electrical threshold of the isolated rabbit atria, in reducing the maximum driving frequency of the atria, and more effective in decreasing the contractions of the atria. A study of the effect of propranolol on the cardiac action potentials recorded by means of intracellular electrodes indicated that this β blocking drug did not produce a change in resting potential, but did decrease the rate of rise of the action potential and decreased the so-called "overshoot." Repolarization was significantly shortened or decreased. Pronethalol produced essentially the same results but was less potent than propranolol (170). These authors also observed that their results were not consistent with the suggestion of West and Amory (252a) that the antiarrhythmic drugs act by a prolongation of the duration of the action potential since propranolol produced a significant decrease in the duration of the action potential. It is assumed that in the studies conducted by Morales-Aguilera and Vaughan-Williams (170) the *dl*-form of propranolol was employed. From the recent work of Levy and Richards (144), it would appear that the direct effect of propranolol on contraction and possibly the cardiac action potential was due to the activity of the *d*-isomer and not due to the β-adrenergic blocking activity of the *l*-isomer.

Propranolol has been administered to patients whose cardiac arrhythmias have been converted to a normal sinus rhythm by means of a direct-current shock therapy, in an effort to prevent the reversion to atrial fibrillation (243). In this clinical situation it failed to maintain normal sinus rhythm.

In patients with a variety of cardiac arrhythmias, Ginn *et al.* (86) reported that propranolol produced a decrease or slowing of sinus tachycardia, effected a conversion of paroxysmal atrial tachycardia to a normal rhythm, and inhibited the ventricular ectopic beats produced by digitalis.

Whalen *et al.* (253) reported that propranolol administered to dogs with a surgically induced heart block, in whom heart rates were fixed, produced a decrease in cardiac output, stroke volume, mean systolic ejection rate, and systolic blood pressure. Total peripheral resistance increased.

Benfey and Varma (22) reported that propranolol inhibited the sympathomimetic effects of butyrylcholine and tyramine in a noncompetitive manner but inhibited norepinephrine in a competitive manner. Propranolol also increased the concentration of ouabain required to produce digitalis intoxication in anesthetized guinea pigs. These authors concluded that the antagonism of ouabain-induced arrhythmias by propranolol and pronethalol was not related to β-adrenergic blockade. Lucchesi (146a) had also suggested previously that the antiarrhythmic activity of pronethalol was not dependent upon β-adrenergic blockade. Roberts *et al.* (205) noted that the action of pronethalol on ventricular escape and on the arrhythmia induced by acetylstrophanthidin appeared to be similar to that produced by agents which block the release of catecholamines from nerve endings (reserpine, choline 2,6 xylyl ether). In addition, Roberts *et al.* (205) have presented evidence that pronethalol depressed the post-tetanic potentiation of the soleus muscle contraction observed in the cat, indicating a depressant action at the nerve endings. Again, one must assume that the racemic mixture of pronethalol was employed and it is difficult to determine if the *l*-isomer or the *d*-isomer is responsible for this depressant action at the nerve ending.

Recently, Parratt and Grayson (190) have observed that in dogs treated with propranolol, myocardial blood flow was decreased and the resistance in the myocardial vascular bed was increased. In addition, dogs treated with propranolol exhibited a marked increase in resistance to blood flow within the myocardium when the dogs were subjected to hemorrhage. These effects were thought to be due to the sympathetic vasoconstrictor action of epinephrine on α-adrenergic receptors and an inactivation of sympathetic vasodilating nerves produced by the β blocking drugs. Essentially similar results were obtained with pronethalol where a decrease in myocardial blood flow and an increase in resistance was observed (189). In these experiments pronethalol reduced the vasodilatation produced by isoproterenol and reversed that obtained with epinephrine. Chiong et al. (51) have reported that in anesthetized dogs pronethalol produced an initial increase in oxygen consumption, an increase in the right ventricular systolic pressure, a decrease in blood pressure, total peripheral resistance, and in the hematocrit. Thirty minutes after the intravenous injection of pronethalol the only changes reported by these authors was a decrease in arterial blood pressure and a decrease in stroke work. Pronethalol significantly decreased or inhibited the effect of epinephrine on cardiac output, heart rate, stroke volume, and stroke work. Chiong et al. (51) concluded that pronethalol inhibited the epinephrine-induced responses which were mediated via the β receptors.

In unanesthetized dogs Wallace et al. (251) found that propranolol did not produce any effect on the conduction in the Purkinje system or upon ventricular activation. Pronethalol was found to prolong the ventricular activation time in unanesthetized dogs. This drug also produced an increase in heart rate and a decrease in A-V conduction time. Atropine prevented the increase in heart rate but not the decrease in A-V conduction time. This effect of pronethalol was thought to be due to some intrinsic sympathomimetic activity and antivagal activity. In anesthetized dogs, barbiturate anesthesia produced an increase in ventricular activation time and this effect appeared to be augmented by β-adrenergic blocking drugs. Both propranolol and pronethalol did not alter cardiac diastolic threshold values and Wallace et al. (251) have suggested that the antiarrhythmic activity of these β blocking drugs does not appear to be related to changes in cardiac excitability.

Prichard (196, 197) has presented evidence that both pronethalol and propranolol produce a slight but significant degree of hypotension after chronic oral administration in man.

Harris et al. (102) have very recently studied the effect of propranolol on the epinephrine-induced hemodynamic responses in man. Results obtained by these authors in ten normal unanesthetized male subjects indicated that propranolol produced a bradycardia and a decrease in cardiac output and stroke volume. Mean arterial pressure was not altered but the drug induced an increase in right atrial pressure and an increase in total peripheral resistance. The hemodynamic responses produced by epinephrine were reversed. Heart rate, cardiac output, and stroke volume were decreased while mean arterial and right atrial pressures were increased. Total peripheral resistance was increased. In addition, the hemodynamic effects of small doses of isoproterenol were inhibited but the β blockade produced by propranolol could be overcome by the infusion of large doses of isoproterenol (102).

Harrison and Griffin (103) reported that propranolol inhibited the iso-proterenol-induced increase in free fatty acids in man. Pilkington *et al.* (193) have presented evidence indicating that propranolol was able to inhibit the increase in plasma free fatty acids induced in man by the intravenous infusion of nine sympathomimetic compounds. Previous work by Pilkington (192) indicated that pronethalol but not phenoxybenzamine would inhibit the increase in fatty acids.

The β-adrenergic blocking compounds have been studied in a variety of clinical conditions, some of the more important of which are angina pectoris, cardiac arrhythmias, myocardial infarction, Parkinsonism, and hyperten-sion.

Efforts to establish the value of the β-adrenergic blocking drugs in the treat-ment of angina pectoris have been the subject of numerous papers (7, 15, 24, 58a, 85, 100, 128, 148, 231). In the majority of the reports, the use of the β-adrenergic blocking drugs appeared to result in a biologically significant improvement as judged by the increase in effort or activity tolerance exhibited by patients with a proved history of angina pectoris. MacAlpin *et al.* (148) noted that the β blocking drugs appeared to augment the antianginal effects of glyceryl trinitrate. However, Srivastava *et al.* (231) and Besterman *et al.* (24) did not observe a significant antianginal effect in patients treated with β-blocking drugs.

Following the suggestion of Black and Stephenson (27) that pronethalol might be useful in the treatment of cardiac arrhythmias, Stock and Dale (233) employed pronethalol in the treatment of various cardiac arrhythmias. Their work suggested that this drug appeared to be useful in controlling the rapid irregular ventricular rate observed in atrial fibrillation. Pronethalol also ap-peared to afford some protection against various types of extrasystoles both atrial and ventricular in origin. Rowlands *et al.* (214) and Fiene *et al.* (67) have obtained evidence for the control of ventricular rate.

Arrhythmias arising as a result of digitalis intoxication appear to be amen-able to treatment with the β blocking drugs (191, 226, 239).

Ventricular extrasystoles which have occurred during anesthesia have been successfully treated with the β blocking drugs (24, 126, 191).

Tachycardia of various types arising presumably as a result of increased sympathetic activity has been controlled by use of the β-adrenergic blocking drugs (24, 86). In contrast to these results, Stock and Dale (233) and Rowlands *et al.* (214) were not successful in treating tachycardia with the β blocking drugs. Atrial flutter does not appear to lend itself to treatment with these agents (233).

Snow (227) has studied the effect of propranolol in patients with acute myocardial infarction. Although the sample size was small, the group treated with propranolol appeared to have a better survival rate than did the untreated control group. The potential role of β-adrenergic blocking drugs in this clinical condition is still in the exploratory stage.

Several reports have indicated that both propranolol and pronethalol appear to have a significant biological effect in controlling tremors in patients with Parkinsonism (114, 187, 237).

Clinical experience to date appears to indicate two major areas which may result in contraindications for these drugs; (a) heart failure and (b) broncho-spasm. An inhibition on decrease in sympathetic activity produced by the β blocking drugs may actually result in the initiation of heart failure (196, 233). Sympathetic stimulation of the β-adrenergic receptors results in a broncho-dilatation, and thus a blockade of these receptors by the β blocking drugs may result in a bronchospasm, (155, 214) a state which is especially undesirable in depressed circulatory conditions.

Some of the confusing effects reported for propranolol as well as for the other β-adrenergic blocking drugs probably will be resolved when the d- and l-isomers of the β blocking compounds are made available for extensive experimental and clinical investigation. Preliminary evidence presented by Levy and Richards (144) and evidence presented at the recent New York Academy of Sciences meeting on β-adrenergic blocking drugs suggests that the d-isomer or propranolol and other β blockers may be the active antiarrhythmic component of the racemic mixture while the l-isomer appears to possess the potent β-adrenergic blocking activity observed with propranolol, pronethalol, and the other β-adrenergic blocking drugs.

Prichard (197) and Prichard and Gillam (196) have observed a moderate hypotensive effect in two groups of hypertensive patients treated with prone-thalol and propranolol. The exact role of β-adrenergic blocking drugs in the treatment of hypertension has yet to be determined.

References

1. Adank, K., Chiavarelli, S., and Pirelli, A. M., *Rend. Ist. Super. Sanita* **16**, 133 (1953); *Chem. Abstr.* **48**, 7847 (1954).
2. Agarwal, S. L., and Harvey, S. C., *J. Pharmacol. Exptl. Therap.* **117**, 106 (1956).
3. Ahlquist, R. P., *Am. J. Physiol.* **153**, 586 (1948).
4. Ahlquist, R. P., Huggins, R. A., and Woodbury, R. A., *J. Pharmacol. Exptl. Therap.* **89**, 271 (1947).
5. Ahlquist, R. P., and Levy, B., *J. Pharmacol. Exptl. Therap.* **127**, 146 (1959).
6. Ahlquist, R. P., and Woodbury, R. A., *Federation Proc.* **5**, 161 (1946).
7. Alleyne, G. A. O., Dickinson, C. J., Dornhorst, A. C., Fulton, R. M., Green, K. G., Hill, I. D., Hurst, P., Laurence, D. R., Pilkington, T. R. E., Prichard, B. N. C., Robinson, B. F., and Rosenheim, M. L., *Brit. Med. J.* **II**, 1226 (1963).
8. Archer, S., Wylie, D. W., Harris, L. S., Lewis, T. R., Schulenberg, J. W., Bell, M. R., Kullnig, R. K., and Arnold, A., *J. Am. Chem. Soc.* **84**, 1306 (1962).
9. Astrom, A., *Acta Physiol. Scand.* **18**, 295 (1949).
10. Augstein, J., and Green, S. M., *Nature* **201**, 628 (1964).
11. Aviado, D. M., *Ann. Internal Med.* [N.S.] **62**, 1050 (1965).

12. Bach, F. L., Jr., Brabander, H. J., and Kushner, S., *J. Am. Chem. Soc.* **79**, 2221 (1957); U.S. Patent 2,794,804 (1957) to American Cyanamid Co.; *Chem. Abstr.* **51**, 16,527 (1957).
13. Baines, M. W., Cobb, D. B., Eden, R. J., Fielden, R., Gardner, J. N., Roe, A. M., Tertiuk, W., and Willey, G. L., *J. Med. Chem.* **8**, 81 (1965).
14. Barcroft, H., Konzett, H., and Swan, H. J. C., *J. Physiol. (London)* **112**, 273 (1951).
15. Barnett, A. J., and Brandstater, M. E., *Med. J. Australia* **1**, 714 (1964).
15a. Barrett, W. E., unpublished results (1965, 1966).
16. Bechgaard, P., and Paulsen, L., *Acta Med. Scand.* **145**, 189 (1953).
17. Belleau, B., and Triggle, D. J., *J. Med. Pharm. Chem.* **5**, 636 (1962).
18. Belleau, B., U.S. Patent 2,807,628 (1957) to Corega Chem. Co.; *Chem. Abstr.* **52**, 2940 (1958).
19. Belleau, B., *J. Med. Pharm. Chem.* **1**, 327 and 343 (1959).
20. Belleau, B., and Cooper, P., *J. Med. Chem.* **6**, 579 (1963).
21. Belleau, B., *Proc. 1st Intern. Pharmacol. Meeting, Stockholm, 1961* Vol. 7, p. 75. Pergamon Press, Oxford, 1962.
22. Benfey, B. G., and Varma, D. R., *Brit. J. Pharmacol.* **26**, 3 (1966).
23. Benoit, G., and Bovet, D., *Bull. Sci. Pharmacol.* **45**, 97 (1938).
24. Besterman, E. M., and Friedlander, D. H., *Postgrad. Med. J.* **41**, 526 (1965).
25. Bickerton, R. K., Halliday, R. P., and Rockhold, W. T., *Pharmacologist* **6**, 180 (1964)
26. Bickerton, R. K., Dailey, R. F., Rockhold, W. T., and Buller, R. H., *J. Pharmacol. Exptl. Therap.* **144**, 218 (1964).
27. Black, J. W., and Stephenson, J. S., *Lancet* **II**, 311 (1962).
28. Black, J. W., Crowther, A. F., Shanks, R. G., Smith, L. H., and Dornhorst, A. C., *Lancet* **I**, 1080 (1964).
29. Boissier, J. R., Ratouis, R., and Dumont, C., *J. Med. Chem.* **6**, 541 (1963).
30. Bovet, D., and Simon, A., *Arch. Intern. Pharmacodyn.* **55**, 15 (1937).
31. Bovet, D., and Simon, A., *Ann. Physiol. Physicochim. Biol.* **12**, 705 (1936); Bovet, D., Simon, A., and Druey, J., *Arch. Intern. Pharmacodyn.* **56**, 33 (1937).
32. Bovet, D., and Bovet-Nitti, F., "Medicaments du Systeme Nerveux Vegetatif," p. 247. Karger, Basel, 1948.
33. Bovet, D., and Bovet-Nitti, F., "Medicaments du Systeme Nerveux Vegetatif," p. 271. Karger, Basel, 1948.
34. Bovet, D., and Bovet-Nitti, F., "Medicaments du Systeme Nerveux Vegetatif," p. 216. Karger, Basel, 1948.
35. Bovet, D., and Marini-Bettolo, G. B., U.S. Patent 2,725,386 (1955); *Chem. Abstr.* **50**, 13,100 (1956).
36. Bovet-Nitti, F., Orsingher, O., Landi-Vittory, R., and Bovet, D., *Compt. Rend.* **252**, 614 (1961).
37. Bravo, R. R., *Rend. Ist. Super. Sanita* **15**, 1008 (1952); *Chem. Abstr.* **47**, 8259 (1953).
38. Brazeau, P., *in* "Pharmacological Basis for Therapeutics" (L. S. Goodman and A. Gilman, eds.), 3rd ed., p. 878. Macmillan, New York, 1965.
39. Brodie, B. B., Aronow, L., and Axelrod, J., *J. Pharmacol. Exptl. Therap.* **106**, 200 (1952).
40. Brodie, B. B., Aronow, L., and Axelrod, J., *J. Pharmacol. Exptl. Therap.* **111**, 21 (1954).
41. Burns, J. J., and Lemberger, L., *Federation Proc.* **24**, 298 (1965).
42. Campbell, K. N., Ackerman, J. F., and Campbell, B. K., *J. Am. Chem. Soc.* **71**, 2905 (1949).
43. Cavalla, J. F., and Marini-Bettolo, G. B., *Gazz. Chim. Ital.* **84**, 927 (1954).
44. Cavallini, G., Mille, E., Grumelli, E., Massarani, E., and Nardi, D., *Farmaco (Pavia)*, *Ed. Sci.* **11**, 633 (1956).

45. Century, B., Ellinwood, L. E., Kohli, J. D., and Coon, J. M., *J. Pharmacol. Exptl. Therap.* **109**, 318 (1953).
46. Cerletti, A., Bircher, R., and Rothlin, E., *Helv. Physiol. Pharmacol. Acta* **7**, 7c (1949).
47. Cheney, L. C., U.S. Patent 2,548,652 (1951) to Bristol Laboratories Inc.; *Chem. Abstr.* **45**, 8039 (1951).
48. Chess, D., and Yonkman, F. F., *Federation Proc.* **4**, 114 (1945).
49. Chess, D., and Yonkman, F. F., *Proc. Soc. Exptl. Biol. Med.* **61**, 127 (1946).
50. Chiavarelli, S., Landi-Vittory, R., Mazzadro, M., and Palazzo, G., *Rend. Ist. Super. Sanita* **15**, 862 (1952); *Chem. Abstr.* **48**, 4489 (1954); Chiavarelli, S., and Marini-Bettolo, G. B., *Gazz. Chim. Ital.* **82**, 86 (1952).
51. Chiong, M. A., Binnion, P. F., and Hatcher, J. D., *Can. J. Physiol. Pharmacol.* **43**, 411 (1965).
52. Cook, D. L., Lawler, C. A., and Cusic, J. W., *J. Pharmacol. Exptl. Therap.* **120**, 269 (1957).
53. Dale, H. H., *J. Physiol. (London)*, **34**, 163 (1906).
54. Deal, C. P., Jr., and Green, H. D., *Circulation Res.* **4**, 38 (1956).
55. Deberdt, R., *Acta Neurol. Psychiat. Belg.* **60**, 663 (1960).
56. Delay, J., Deniker, P., Leyrie, J., and Donnet, J. L., *Ann. Medico-Psychol.* **118**, 749 (1960).
57. Denison, A. B., Jr., Bardhanabaedya, S., and Green, H. D., *Circulation Res.* **4**, 653 (1956).
58. deStevens, G., U.S. Patent 3,000,946 (1961) to CIBA Pharmaceutical Products Inc.; *Chem. Abstr.* **56**, 8641 (1962).
58a. Dornhorst, A. C., and Robinson, B. F., *Lancet* **II**, 314 (1962).
59. Dresel, P. E., and Sutter, M. C., *Circulation Res.* **9**, 1284 (1961).
60. Dungan, K. W., and Lish, P. M., *Federation Proc.* **23**, 124 (1964).
61. Ehrhart, G., and Leditschke, H., U.S. Patent 2,752,358 (1956) to Hoechst A.-G.; *Chem. Abstr.* **51**, 2873 (1957).
62. Emlet, J. R., Grimson, K. S., Bell, D. M., and Orgain, E. S., *J. Am. Med. Assoc.* **146**, 1383 (1951).
63. Faust, J. A., and Sahyun, M., U.S. Patent 2,919,274 (1959) to Sahyun Laboratories; *Chem. Abstr.* **54**, 6768 (1960).
64. Fellows, E. J., McLean, R. A., Macko, E., Kerwin, J. F., Hall, G. C., Milnes, F. J., Witt, I. H., and Ullyot, G. E., *J. Pharmacol. Exptl. Therap.* **110**, 463 (1959).
65. Fenton, H., Green, P. N., Shapero, M., and Wilson, C., *Nature* **206**, 725 (1965).
66. Ferguson, F. G., and Wescoe, W. C., *J. Pharmacol. Exptl. Therap.* **100**, 100 (1950).
67. Fiene, T. J., Griffin, J. R., and Harrison, D. C., *Circulation* **32**, Suppl. II, II-84 (1965).
68. Fishman, J., *U.S. Armed Forces Med. J.* **2**, 815 (1951).
69. Fishman, J., *U.S. Armed Forces Med. J.* **2**, 957 (1951).
70. Fourneau, E., and Bovet, D., *Arch. Intern. Pharmacodyn.* **46**, 178 (1933).
71. Fourneau, E., Bovet, D., and Maderni, P., *Compt. Rend. Soc. Biol.* **115**, 1215 (1934).
72. Fourneau, E., Maderni, P., and de Lestrange, Y., *J. Pharmacol. Chim.* **18**, 185 (1933); Fourneau, E., and Bovet, D., *Compt. Rend. Soc. Biol.* **113**, 388 (1933).
73. Frank, N., Strazza, J. A., Jr., and Helsper, J. T., *Ann. Internal Med.* [N.S.] **35**, 19 (1951).
74. Freis, E. D., Stanton, J. R., Litter, J., Culbertson, J. W., Halperin, M. H., Moister, F. C., and Wilkins, R. W., *J. Clin. Invest.* **28**, 1387 (1949).
75. Funke, A., U.S. Patent 2,887,484 (1959) to Société des usimes chimiques Rhône-Poulenc; *Chem. Abstr.* **53**, 20,098 (1959); Funke, A., Paulsen, A., and Cibrario, N., *Compt. Rend.* **245**, 1935 (1957); Funke, A., and Paulsen, A., *Gazz. Chim. Ital.* **91**, 1268 (1961); *Compt. Rend.* **246**, 784 (1958).

76. Funke, A., Cibrario, N., and Jacob, J., *Compt. Rend.* **244**, 813 (1957).
77. Funke, A., Paulsen, A., and Gombert, R., *Bull. Soc. Chim. France* p. 1644 (1960).
78. Furchgott, R. F., *J. Pharmacol. Exptl. Therap.* **111**, 265 (1954).
79. Furchgott, R. F., *Pharmacol. Rev.* **11**, 429 (1959).
80. Gatti, G. L., and Bovet, D., *Arch. Intern. Pharmacodyn.* **105**, 317 (1956).
81. Gatti, G. L., Percori-Giraldi, J., Landi-Vittory, R., and Beguin, M., *Boll. Soc. Ital. Biol. Sper.* **35**, 1851 (1959); *Chem. Abstr.* **56**, 13501 (1962).
82. Geigy, A. G., I.R. French Patents 1,312,889 and 1,312,891 (1962).
83. Gifford, R. W., Jr., Roth, G. M., and Kvale, W. F., *J. Am. Med. Assoc.* **149**, 1628 (1952).
84. Gill, E. W., and Vaughan-Williams, E. M., *Nature* **201**, 199 (1964).
85. Gillam, P. M. S., and Prichard, B. N. C., *Brit. Med. J.* **II**, 337 (1965).
86. Ginn, W. M., Jr., Irons, G. V., Jr., and Orgain, E. S., *Circulation* **32**, Suppl. II, II-97 (1965).
87. Gould, W. A., Lish, P. M., Wu, Y. H., Roth, H. R., Lobeck, W. G., Jr., Berdahl, J. M., and Feldkamp, R. F., *J. Med. Chem.* **7**, 60 (1964).
87a. Grabner, G., Michalek, R., Pokorny, D., and Vormittag, E., *Arzneimittel-Forsch.* **16**, 1174 (1966).
88. Graham, J. D. P., *Mfg. Chemist* **26**, 391 (1955).
89. Graham, J. D. P., *Progr. Med. Chem.* **2**, 132 (1962).
90. Grassi-Bertazzi, C., and De Gennaro, A., *Folia Med.* (*Naples*) **28**, 525 (1942).
91. Grassi-Bertazzi, C., and De Gennaro, A., *Riv. Patol. App. Respirat.* **29**, 49 (1942).
91a. Graubner, W. and Wolf, M., *Arzneimittel-Forsch.* **16**, 1055 (1966).
92. Green, H. D., *in* "Pharmacology in Medicine" (V. A. Drill, ed.), 2nd ed. p. 419. McGraw-Hill, New York, 1958.
93. Green, H. D., *Circulation* **15**, 47 (1957).
94. Green, H. D., and Denison, A. B., Jr., *Circulation Res.* **4**, 565 (1956).
95. Grimson, K. S., Reardon, M. J., Marzoni, F. A., and Hendrix, J. P., *Ann. Surg.* **127**, 968 (1948).
96. Grimson, K. S., Longino, F. H., Kernodle, C. E., and O'Rear, H. B., *J. Am. Med. Assoc.* **140**, 1273 (1949).
97. Grün, A., U.S. Patent 2,366,102 (1944) to I. R. Geigy A. G.; *Chem. Abstr.* **40**, 2271 (1946).
98. Gunn, C. G., *J. Lab. Clin. Med.* **42**, 810 (1953).
99. Haimovici, H., *J. Appl. Physiol.* **2**, 512 (1950).
100. Hamer, J., Grandjean, T., Melendez, L., and Sowton, G. E., *Brit. Med. J.* **II**, 720 (1964).
101. Handley, C. A., and Moyer, J. H., *J. Pharmacol. Exptl. Therap.* **110**, 277 (1954).
102. Harris, W. S., Schoenfeld, C. D., Brooks, R. H., and Weissler, A. M., *Am. J. Cardiol.* **17**, 484 (1966).
103. Harrison, D. C., and Griffin, J. R., *Clin. Res.* **13**, 209 (1965).
104. Hartmann, M., and Isler, H., *Arch. Exptl. Pathol. Pharmakol.* **192**, 141 (1939).
105. Hartmann, M., and Studer, S., U.S. Patent 2,569,415 (1951) to CIBA Pharmaceutical Company; *Chem. Abstr.* **46**, 9616 (1952).
106. Harvey, S. C., Wang, C. Y., and Nickerson, M., *J. Pharmacol. Exptl. Therap.* **104**, 363 (1952).
107. Hayao, S., and Schut, R. N., *J. Org. Chem.* **26**, 3414 (1961).
108. Hayes, D. W., Wakim, K. G., Horton, B. T., and Peters, G. A., *J. Clin. Invest.* **28**, 615 (1949).
109. Hekimian, L., Friedhoff, A. J., and Handley, P., *Current Therap. Res.* **5**, 437 (1963).
110. Helps, E. P. W., Robinson, K. C., and Ross, E. J., *Lancet* **II**, 267 (1955).

111. Henatsch, H. D., Langrehr, D., and Kaese, H. J., *Arzneimittel-Forsch.* **10**, 876 (1960).
112. Hendrix, J. P., Reardon, M. J., and Marzoni, F. A., *Federation Proc.* **6**, 338 (1947).
113. Herman, J., Jourdon, F., and Bonnet, V., *Compt. Rend. Soc. Biol.* **135**, 1653 (1941).
114. Herring, A. B., *Lancet* **II**, 892 (1964).
115. Hjort, A. H., and Fassett, D. W., *J. Pharmacol. Exptl. Therap.* **63**, 253 (1938); Hjort, A. H., DeBeer, E. J., Buck, J. S., and Randall, L. O., *ibid.* **76**, 64 (1942).
115a. Hoefke, W., and Kobinger, W., *Arzneimittel-Forsch.* **16**, 1038 (1966).
115b. Hofmann, A., "Die Mutterkornalkaloide." Enke, Stuttgart, 1964.
116. Honkomp, L. J., and Buckley, J. P., *Federation Proc.* **23**, 125 (1964).
117. Hunter, W. T., Buck, J. S., Gubitz, F. W., and Bolen, C. H., *J. Org. Chem.* **21**, 1512 (1956).
118. Hutcheon, D. E., Scriabine, A., Ling, J. S., P'an, S. Y., and Bloom, B. M., *Arch. Intern. Pharmacodyn.* **147**, 146 (1964).
119. I.C.I. Ltd., French Patent 3579 M (1964).
120. Isler, H., Schellenberg, H., and Urech, E., U.S. Patent 2,505,248 (1950) to CIBA Pharmaceutical Company; *Chem. Abstr.* **44**, 6888 (1950).
121. Jacobs, W. A., and Gould, R. G., Jr., *J. Biol. Chem.* **120**, 141 (1937).
122. Jandhyala, B. S., Vogin, E. E., and Buckley, J. P., *J. Pharm. Sci.* **54**, 727 (1965).
123. Janecek, J., Schiele, B. C., Bellville, T. P., Vestre, N. D., and Raths, O., *J. New Drugs* **5**, 51 (1965).
124. Janssen, P. A. J., *Arzneimittel-Forsch.* **11**, 819 and 932 (1961).
125. Johnson, H. D., Green, H. D., and Lanier, J. T., *J. Pharmacol. Exptl. Therap.* **108**, 144 (1953).
126. Johnstone, M., *Brit. J. Anaesthesia* **36**, 224 (1964).
127. Kaindl, F., Samuels, S. S., Selman, D., and Shaftel, H., *Angiology* **10**, 185 (1959).
128. Keelan, P., *Brit. Med. J.* **I**, 897 (1965).
129. Kerwin, J. F., Hall, G. C., Macko, E., McLean, R. A., Fellows, E. J., and Ullyot, G. E., *J. Am. Chem. Soc.* **73**, 5681 (1951).
130. Kerwin, J. F., and Ullyot, G. E., U.S. Patent 2,774,770 (1956) to S. K. and F. Laboratories; *Chem. Abstr.* **51**, 8134 (1957).
131. Kirkendall, W. M., Liechty, R. D.. and Culp D. A., *Arch. Internal Med.* **115**, 529 (1965).
132. Klarer, W., and Urech, E., *Helv. Chim. Acta* **27**, 1762 (1944).
133. Klupp, H., and Streller, I., *Arzneimittel-Forsch.* **9**, 604 (1959).
134. Koo, J., Avakian, S., and Martin, G. J., *J. Am. Chem. Soc.* **77**, 5373 (1955); Koo, J., *J. Org. Chem.* **26**, 339 (1961).
135. Kramer, D. W., GP II, No. 3, 59 (1950).
136. Krapcho, J., and Lott, W. A., U.S. Patent 2,979,511 (1961) to Olin-Mathieson Chem. Corp.; *Chem. Abstr.* **55**, 18,780 (1961).
137. Küng, H. L., and Schindler, W., *Experientia* **15**, 66 (1959).
138. Kuschinsky, G., and Rahn, K. H., *Arch. Exptl. Pathol. Pharmakol.* **252**, 50 (1965).
139. Kvale, W. F., Roth, G. M., Manger, W. M., and Priestley, J. T., *J. Am. Med. Assoc.* **164**, 854 (1957).
140. Landi-Vittory, R., and Marini-Bettolo, G. B., *Rend. Ist. Super. Sanita* **19**, 109 (1956); *Chem. Abstr.* **54**, 22,653 (1960).
141. Landi-Vittory, R., and Marini-Bettolo, G. B., *Gazz. Chim. Ital.* **84**, 908 (1954).
142. Levy, B., and Ahlquist, R. P., *in* "Drill's Pharmacology in Medicine" (J. R. DiPalma, ed.), 3rd ed., p. 463. McGraw-Hill, New York, 1965.
143. Levy, J. V., and Richards, V., *Proc. Soc. Exptl. Biol. Med.* **119**, 278 (1965).
144. Levy, J. V., and Richards, V., *Clin. Res.* **14**, 126 (1966).

145. Eli Lilly and Co., British Patent 836,753 (1960); *Chem. Abstr.* **54**, 24,812 (1960).
146. Lippmann, H. I., *Angiology* **3**, 69 (1952).
146a. Lucchesi, B. R., *J. Pharmacol. Exptl. Therap.* **145**, 286 (1964).
147. Lynn, R. B., *Lancet* **II**, 676 (1950).
148. MacAlpin, R. N., Kattus, A. A., and Winfield, M. E., *Circulation* **31**, 869 (1965).
149. Marini-Bettolo, G. B., Landi-Vittory, R., and Bovet, D., *Gazz. Chim. Ital.* **83**, 144 (1953).
150. Marini-Bettolo, G. B., Landi-Vittory, R., and Bovet, D., *Croat. Chem. Acta* **29**, 363 (1957); *Chem. Abstr.* **53**, 16,137 (1959); Marini-Bettolo, G. B., Renzi, L., Landi-Vittory, R., and Bovet, D., *Gazz. Chim. Ital.* **87**, 1303 (1957).
151. Marini-Bettolo, G. B., Frediani, H. A., and Chiavarelli, S., *Rend. Ist. Super. Sanita* **15**, 850 (1952); *Chem. Abstr.* **48**, 4489 (1954); Marini-Bettolo, G. B., Chiavarelli, S., and Bovet, D., *Gazz. Chim. Ital.* **80**, 281 (1950); **81**, 587 (1951); Marini-Bettolo, G. B., Landi-Vittory, R., and Bovet, D., *Rend. Ist. Super. Sanita* **15**, 844 (1952); *Chem. Abstr.* **48**, 4489 (1954); Marini-Bettolo, G. B., and Falco, M. R., *Rend. Ist. Super. Sanita* **15**, 826 and 837 (1952); *Chem. Abstr.* **48**, 4487 (1954).
152. Marini-Bettolo, G. B., Renzi, L., Milani, C., and Bovet, D., *Rend Ist. Super Sanita* **22**, 201 (1959); Milani, C., Landi-Vittory, R., and Marini-Bettolo, G. B., *Rend. Ist. Super. Sanita* **22**, 207 (1959); Landi-Vittory, R., Milani, C., and Marini-Bettolo, G. B., *ibid.* p. 217; Renzi, L., Milani, C., and Marini-Bettolo, G. B., *ibid.* p. 225, *Chem. Abstr.* **54**, 1522-24 (1960); Renzi, L., Alvarado, F. H., Fraschetti, F., and Marini-Bettolo, G. B., *Gazz. Chim. Ital*, **90**, 269 (1960).
153. Maxwell, R. A., *in* "Drill's Pharmacology in Medicine" (J. R. DiPalma, ed.), 3rd ed., p. 502. McGraw-Hill, New York, 1965.
154. Mayer, S., Moran, N. C., and Fain, J., *J. Pharmacol. Exptl. Therap.* **134**, 18 (1961).
155. McNeill, R. S., *Lancet* **II**, 1101 (1964).
156. Mechelke, K., and Nusser, E., *Experientia* **15**, 69 (1959).
157. Meier, R., and Meyer, R *Schweiz. Med. Wochschr.* **71**, 1206 (1941).
158. Meier, R., and Muller, R., *Schweiz. Med. Wochschr.* **69**, 1271 (1939).
159. Meier, R., and Muller, R., *Schweiz. Med. Wochschr.* **71**, 554 (1941).
160. Meier, R., Yonkman, F. F., Craver, B. N., and Gross, F., *Proc. Soc. Exptl. Biol. Med.* **71**, 70 (1949).
161. Miescher, K., and Marxer, A., U.S. Patent 2,485,212 (1949) to CIBA Pharmaceutical Company; *Chem. Abstr.* **44**, 2472 (1950).
162. Mills, J., Boren, M. M., Buting, W. E., Cannon, W. N., and Soper, Q. F., *Abstr. Papers, 132nd Meeting, Am. Chem. Soc., New York, 1957* p. 7-O.
163. Mills, J., Boren, M. M., and Easton, N. R., *Abstr. Papers, 132nd Meeting. Am. Chem. Soc., New York, 1957* pp. 9-O to 11-O; Mills, J., U.S. Patent 2,927,924 (1960) to Eli Lilly and Co.; *Chem. Abstr.* **54**, 14,280 (1960).
164. Mills, J., and Rathbun, R. C., U.S. Patent 2,922,744 (1960) to Eli Lilly and Co.; *Chem. Abstr.* **54**, 17,426 (1960).
165. Mills, J., Rathbun, R. C., and Slater, I. H., *Abstr. Papers, 132nd Meeting, Am. Chem. Soc., New York, 1957* p. 6-O.
166. Misiti, D., De Marchi, F., Rosnati, V., and Bovet, D., *J. Med. Pharm. Chem.* **5**, 1285 (1962); Rosnati, V., De Marchi, F., and Misiti, D., *Gazz. Chim. Ital.* **91**, 1365 (1961).
167. Mitchell, R. H., Rutledge, A. H., and Davenport, E., *Am. Practitioner Dig. Treat.* **2**, 311 (1951).
168. Moe, G. K., Malton, S. D., Rennick, B. R., and Freyburger, W. A., *J. Pharmacol. Exptl. Therap.* **94**, 319 (1948).
169. Moore, P. E., Richardson, A. W., and Green, H. D., *J. Pharmacol. Exptl. Therap.* **106**, 14 (1952).

170. Morales-Aguilera, A., and Vaughan-Williams, E. M., *Brit. J. Pharmacol.* **24**, 332 (1965).
171. Moran, N. C., and Perkins, M. E., *J. Pharmacol. Exptl. Therap.* **124**, 223 (1958); **133**, 192 (1961).
172. Morren, H. G., Bienfet, V., and Reyntjens, A. M., *in* "Psychopharmacological Agents" (M. Gordon, ed.), Vol. 4; pt. 1, p. 251. Academic Press, New York, 1964.
172a. Moyer, J. H., and Caplovitz, C., *Am. Heart J.* **45**, 602 (1953).
173. Mueller, F., *Meeting Swiss Physiol. Soc. 1942* p. 45.
174. Mull, R. P., Tannenbaum, C., Dapero, M. R., Bernier, M., Yost, W., and deStevens, G., *J. Med. Chem.* **8**, 332 (1965).
175. Najer, H., Chabrier, P., and Giudicelli, R., *Bull. Soc. Chim. France* p. 352 (1959).
176. Nickerson, M., *Pharmacol. Rev.* **1**, 27 (1949).
177. Nickerson, M., and Nomaguchi, G. M., *J. Pharmacol. Exptl. Therap.* **101**, 379 (1951).
178. Nickerson, M., *Pharmacol. Rev.* **9**, 246 (1957).
179. Nickerson, M., *Arch. Intern. Pharmacodyn.* **140**, 237 (1962).
180. Nickerson, M., *in* "Pharmacological Basis of Therapeutics" (L. S. Goodman and A. Gilman, eds.), 3rd. ed. p. 546. Macmillan, New York, 1965.
181. Nickerson, M., and Brown, H. O., *Anesthesiology* **12**, 216 (1951).
182. Nickerson, M., and Goodman, L. S., *J. Pharmacol. Exptl. Therap.* **89**, 167 (1947); see also Eisleb, O., U.S. Patent 1,949,247 (1934) to Winthrop Chem. Co.; *Chem. Abstr.* **28**, 2850 (1934).
183. Nickerson, M., and Gump, W. S., *J. Pharmacol. Exptl. Therap.* **97**, 25 (1949).
184. Nickerson, M., and Nomaguchi, G. M., *J. Pharmacol. Exptl. Therap.* **95**, 1 (1949).
185. Niemegeers, C. J. E., Verbruggen, F. J., Van Nueten, J. M., and Janssen, P. A. J., *Intern. J. Neuropharmacol.* **2**, 349 (1963).
186. Nieschulz, O., Popendiker, K., and Scheuermann, R., *Arzneimittel-Forsch.* **6**, 36 (1956).
187. Owen, D. A. L., and Marsden, C. D., *Lancet* **II**, 1259 (1965).
188. Parcell, R. F., U.S. Patent 2,833,770 (1958) to Parke-Davis and Co.; *Chem. Abstr.* **52**, 15,600 (1958).
189. Parratt, J. R., *Brit. J. Pharmacol.* **24**, 601 (1965).
190. Parratt, J. R., and Grayson, J., *Lancet* **I**, 338 (1966).
191. Payne, J. P., and Senfield, R. M., *Brit. Med. J.* **I**, 603 (1964).
192. Pilkington, T. R. E., Lowe, R. D., Robinson, B. F., and Titterington, E., *Lancet* **II**, 316 (1962).
193. Pilkington, T. R. E., Lowe, R. D., Foster, R., Robinson, B. F., and Antonis, A., *J. Lipid Res.* **7**, 73 (1966).
194. Pollard, C. B., and Wicker, T. H., U.S. Patent 2,575,122 (1951) to Parke-Davis and Co.; *Chem. Abstr.* **46**, 5095 (1952).
195. Powell, C. E., and Slater, I. H., *J. Pharmacol. Exptl. Therap.* **122**, 480 (1958).
196. Prichard, B. N. C., and Gillam, P. M. S., *Brit. Med. J.* **II**, 725 (1964).
197. Prichard, B. N. C., *Brit. Med. J.* **I**, 1227 (1964).
198. Randall, L. O., Roe, M. D., and Iliev, V., *Arch. Intern. Pharmacodyn.* **102**, 207 (1955).
199. Randall, L. O., and Smith, T. H., *J. Pharmacol. Exptl. Therap.* **103**, 10 (1951).
200. Rapela, C. E., and Green, H. O., *J. Pharmacol. Exptl. Therap.* **132**, 29 (1961).
201. Ratouis, R., Boissier, J. R., and Dumont, C., *J. Med. Chem.* **8**, 104 and 271 (1965).
202. Reedy, W. J., *J. Lab. Clin. Med.* **37**, 365 (1951).
203. Richardson, A. P., Jones, P. S., and Walker, H. A., *J. Pharmacol. Exptl. Therap.* **98**, 28 (1950).
204. Roberts, G., Richardson, A. W., and Green, H. D., *J. Pharmacol. Exptl. Therap.* **105**, 466 (1952).

205. Roberts, J., Ehrreich, S., and Levitt, B., *Federation Proc.* **24**, 1421 (1965).
206. Rodriguez, R., Hong, E., Vidrio, H., and Pardo, E. G., *J. Pharmacol. Exptl. Therap.* **148**, 54 (1965).
207. Rogers, M. P., *J. Am. Med. Assoc.* **140**, 272 (1949).
208. Rorig, K. J., U.S. Patent 2,704,285 (1955) to G. D. Searle; *Chem. Abstr.* **50**, 1932 (1956).
209. Rossi, G. V., and Smith, T. H. F., *J. Am. Pharm. Assoc.* **46**, 472 (1957); Rossi, G. V., and Rosenthal, M. E., *ibid.* **48**, 409 (1959).
210. Roth, L. W., *J. Pharmacol. Exptl. Therap.* **110**, 157 (1954).
211. Roth, G. J., Flock, E. V., Kvale, W. F., Wangh, J. M., and Ogg, J., *Circulation* **21**, 769 (1960).
212. Rothlin, E., *Helv. Physiol. Pharmacol. Acta* **2**, C 248 (1944).
213. Rothlin, E., *Bull. Schweiz. Akad. Med. Wiss.* **2**, 249 (1947).
214. Rowlands, D. J., Howitt, G., and Markman, P., *Brit. Med. J.* **I**, 891 (1965).
215. Schaper, W. K. A., Jageneau, A. H. M., and Janssen, P. A. J., *Arzneimittel-Forsch.* **13**, 597 (1963).
216. Scherrer, P., and Dermenghem, J. F., *Ann. Medico-Psychol.* **120**, 623 (1962).
217. Schindler, W., and Häfliger, F., U.S. Patent 2,751,393 (1956) to J. R. Geigy AG.; *Chem. Abstr.* **51**, 4440 (1957); U.S. Patent 2,808,413 (1957) to J. R. Geigy AG.; *Chem. Abstr.* **52**, 2926 (1958).
218. Schipper, E., Boehme, W. R., Graeme, M. L., Siegmund, E., and Chinery, E., *J. Med. Pharm. Chem.* **4**, 79 (1961).
219. Schmidt, G., German Patent 1,118,218 (1961); *Chem. Abstr.* **56**, 7331 (1962).
220. Schmidt, G., U.S. Patent 3,101,345 (1963) to Dr. Karl Thomae, G.m.b.H., Biberach Germany; German Patent 1,137,035 (1962); *Chem. Abstr.* **58**, 7949 (1963).
221. Schmutz, J., Swiss Patent 322,652 (1958) to A. Wander AG.; *Chem. Abstr.* **54**, 2370 (1960); British Patent 774,649 (1957); *Chem. Abstr.* **51**, 16,565 (1957).
222. Schreibman, M., Miller, C. E., Shelver, W. H., and Vacik, J. H., *J. Pharm. Sci.* **53**, 985 (1964).
222a. Sekiya, A., and Vaughan-Williams, E. M., *Brit. J. Pharmacol.* **21**, 473 (1963).
223. Shaw, G., *Scot. Med. J.* **1**, 89 (1956).
224. Shepard, E. R., and Morrison, D. E., U.S. Patent 2,596,058 (1960) to Eli Lilly and Co.; *Chem. Abstr.* **57**, 15,077 (1962).
225. Siphar S. A., French Patent 3635 M (1964).
226. Sloman, G., Robinson, J. S., and McLean, K., *Brit. Med. J.* **I**, 895 (1965).
227. Snow, P. J. D., *Lancet* **II**, 551 (1965).
228. Sonn, A., U.S. Patent 2,161,938 (1939) to CIBA Ltd.; *Chem. Abstr.* **33**, 7316 (1939).
229. Sonnenschein, R. R., *Proc. Soc. Exptl. Biol. Med.* **71**, 654 (1949).
230. Spencer, M. P., Denison, A. B., Jr., and Green, H. D., *Circulation Res.* **2**, 537 (1954).
231. Srivastava, S. C., Dewar, H. A., and Newell, D. J., *Brit. Med. J.* **II**, 724 (1964).
232. Stanton, H. C., Dungan, K. W., and Lish, P. M., *Federation Proc.* **24**, 612 (1965).
233. Stock, J. P. P., and Dale, N., *Brit. Med. J.* **II**, 1230 (1963).
234. Stoll, A., Hofmann, A., and Troxler, F., *Helv. Chim. Acta* **32**, 506 (1949).
235. Stoll, A., and Hofmann, A., *in* "Alkaloids" (R. H. F. Manske, ed.), Vol. VIII, p. 725. Academic Press, New York, 1965.
236. Stoll, A., *Schweiz. Apotheker-Ztg.* **60**, 458 and 374 (1922).
237. Strang, R. R., *J. Neurol., Neurosurg., Psychiatr.* [N.S.] **28**, 404 (1965).
238. Swain, A. P., U.S. Patent 2,695,294 (1954); *Chem. Abstr.* **49**, 14,039 (1955).
239. Taylor, R. R., Johnstone, C. I., and Jose, A. D., *New Engl. J. Med.* **271**, 877 (1964).
240. Taylor, S. H., Sutherland, G. R., MacKenzie, G. J., Staunton, H. P., and Donald, K. W., *Circulation* **31**, 741 (1965).

241. Trapold, J. H., Warren, M. R., and Woodbury, R. A., *J. Pharmacol. Exptl. Therap.* **100**, 119 (1950).

241a. Triggle, D. J., "Chemical Aspects of the Autonomic Nervous System." Academic Press, New York, 1965.

242. Trefouel, J., and Dunant, Y., *Bull. Sci. Pharmacol.* **42**, 459 (1935).

243. Tsolakas, T. C., Davies, J. P. H., and Oram, S., *Lancet* **II**, 1064 (1964).

244. Ullyot, G. E., and Kerwin, J. K., *in* "Medicinal Chemistry" (F. F. Blicke and C. M. Suter, eds.), Vol. II, p. 234. Wiley, New York, 1956.

245. Urech, E., Marxer, A., and Miescher, K., *Helv. Chim. Acta* **33**, 1386 (1950).

246. Van Deripe, D. R., and Moran, N. C., *Federation Proc.* **24**, 712 (1964).

247. Van Itallie, T. B., and Clark, C. W., Jr., *Circulation* **3**, 820 (1951).

248. Van de Westeringh, C., Van Daele, P., Hermans, B., Van der Eycken, C., Boey, J., and Janssen, P. A. J., *J. Med. Chem.* **7**, 619 (1964).

249. Vogel, J., Overy, H., Brammell, H., Page, H., and Paton, B., *Clin. Res.* **14**, 129 (1966).

250. Walker, H. A., Heymans, C., Wilson, S., and Richardson, A. P., *J. Pharmacol. Exptl. Therap.* **98**, 33 (1950).

251. Wallace, A. G., Troyer, W. G., Lesage, M. A., and Zotti, E. F., *Circulation Res.* **18**, 140 (1966).

252. Wenner, W., *J. Org. Chem.* **16**, 1475 (1951); **17**, 523 and 1451 (1952).

252a. West, T. C., and Amory, D. W., *J. Pharmacol. Exptl. Therap.* **130**, 182 (1960).

253. Whalen, R. E., Thompson, H. K., Jr., Morris, J. J., Jr., and McIntosh, H. D., *Clin. Res.* **14**, 86 (1966).

254. Wheatley, W. B., Fitzgibbon, W. E., Cheney, L. C., and Binkley, S. B., *J. Am. Chem. Soc.* **72**, 1655 (1950).

255. Wolff, H. G., "Headache and Other Head Pain." Oxford Univ. Press, London and New York, 1948.

256. Wylie, D. W., and Archer, S., *J. Med. Pharm. Chem.* **5**, 932 (1962).

257. Yelnosky, J., Katz, R., and Dietrich, E. V., *Toxicol. Appl. Pharmacol.* **6**, 37 (1964).

258. Yonkman, F. F., and Chess, D., *Proc. Soc. Exptl. Biol. Med.* **61**, 127 (1946).

CHAPTER XI

Chemistry and Pharmacology of Monoamine Oxidase Inhibitors

Hollis G. Schoepke

Leo R. Swett

I. Introduction, 393

II. Hydrazines, 394

III. Nonhydrazines, 398
  A. Harmala Alkaloids, 398
  B. Bretylium and Guanethidine-type Compounds, 399
  C. Tryptamine Derivatives, 402
  D. Cyclopropylamines, 403
  E. Propynylamines, 405

IV. Mechanism of Action, 412

V. Side Effects and Toxic Reactions, 420

  References, 424

I. Introduction

Monoamine oxidase (MAO) is the enzyme which is responsible for the deamination of a wide variety of amines. The development of knowledge of this enzyme has been the subject of many research reports and reviews such as those of Blaschko (15, 16), Axelrod (6, 7), Pletscher et al. (120), and Kopin (89). Inhibitors of the activity of MAO comprise a biochemical class which has in common the ability to produce a number of pharmacological effects, the most common of which have resulted in a clinical usefulness as antidepressants. Whereas a number of compounds of diverse chemical structures have been put into this class of "MAO inhibitors" and have a common enzyme inhibitory action, like all drugs, many of their pharmacological actions differ quantitatively from each other to a significant degree. They also often have important qualitatively different pharmacological actions, depending on the particular compound in question and on the net effect of their action on all organ systems of the body.

During the early clinical trials of these compounds as antidepressants, postural hypotension was observed as a frequent but not consistent side effect. Consequently, other derivatives and new inhibitors were prepared and often examined specifically as antihypertensive agents. Of these, only pargyline used alone or in combination with the diuretic methyclothiazide, is available to the medical profession as an antihypertensive at the present time.

This chapter will discuss primarily the chemistry and pharmacology of MAO inhibitors, insofar as they relate to antihypertensive effects. Major emphasis will be placed on those which have undergone some investigation as antihypertensive agents in animals and/or man. Proposed theories of the mechanism of action of this interesting group of compounds and their toxic reactions will also be discussed.

It has been traditional to divide the MAO inhibitors into two classifications, hydrazines and nonhydrazines. Although the hydrazines have found their eventual clinical use as antidepressants rather than antihypertensives, they are an important consideration in the historical development of the subject.

II. Hydrazines

In 1957, iproniazid was introduced for the treatment of tuberculosis and found to have a pronounced euphoric effect. This observation eventually led to its use in the treatment of depression. Since Zeller et al. (157) had already reported that iproniazid was a potent MAO inhibitor, a new enzymatic approach was available to the pharmacologist in the search for psychotherapeutic drugs. The chemistry of hydrazines began to grow explosively. Added impetus was given with the observation that a significant hypotensive effect was noted in many patients treated with iproniazid. This effect, coupled with the information that certain hydrazine derivatives such as hydrazinophthalazine (hydralazine) had been shown to be useful blood-pressure lowering agents (40, 83, 125), challenged the chemist to synthesize more effective hydrazine derivatives.

In sifting through the wealth of pharmacological data these compounds have produced, it is evident that there exists a very marked difference between the relative potencies of the compounds studied in different animal species. This is best explained by differences in absorption, penetration of the drugs into cells, and metabolism, as well as particular properties of the enzyme systems involved. This has been illustrated by Rowe (123) who reported that the reserpine antagonist potency of nialamide was the same as iproniazid in rats and guinea pigs but three times stronger in dogs, twelve times stronger in cats, and ten times stronger in mice. Reserpine antagonism was used to measure antidepressant activity. Attempts to find a relation or correlation between inhibition of MAO and pharmacological activity are numerous. Crumpton (42) found that within a series of hydrazide derivatives there was a good correlation between the influence on monoamine metabolism in animals and its clinical effect on humans (mental depression, angina pectoris, blood pressure regulation), although pointing out that the ability of the MAO inhibitor to penetrate certain tissues and the resulting intracellular concentration may determine the degree of block. In one of the first attempts to correlate MAO inhibition and hypotensive activity, Schuler and Wyss (126) found that the intensity of the inhibitory effect of MAO *in vitro* by numerous hydrazine derivatives allowed a differentiation between hypotensive and pharmacologically inactive derivatives (with little inhibitory effect). Subsequent work by others has tended to confirm that the central actions of these compounds are probably related to inhibition of MAO; however, the effects on blood pressure do not seem to exhibit this causal relationship. Theories on the mechanism of the antihypertensive effects of these compounds are discussed in more detail in Section IV of this chapter.

In Table I, Zbinden *et al.* (156) summarized the clinical effects of various hydrazine MAO inhibitors on blood pressure which had been investigated prior to 1960. All of these compounds were marketed but two were subsequently withdrawn because of adverse reactions. Iproniazid produced cases of severe and frequently fatal hepatitis, and pheniprazine was removed because of hepatitis and toxic amblyopia. Subsequently, other derivatives of iproniazid such as N^2-benzylpivalic acid hydrazide (I) (Tersavid, RO4-1634) were studied for cardiovascular activity. Tersavid had four times the hypotensive activity of iproniazid in the anesthetized dog (1).

$$\text{\Large\bigcirc}\!\!-\!\!CH_2NHNH\overset{\displaystyle O}{\overset{\|}{C}}\!\!-\!\!C(CH_3)_3$$

(I)

$$HOCH_2\!\!-\!\!\underset{\underset{NH_2}{|}}{CH}\!\!-\!\!\overset{\overset{\displaystyle O}{\|}}{C}\!\!-\!\!NH\!\!-\!\!NH\!\!-\!\!CH\!\!<\!\!\overset{CH_3}{\underset{CH_3}{}}$$

(II)

Another hydrazine derivative, N^2-isopropyl-DL-serine hydrazide (II) was reported to be an antihypertensive in man (104). The effect was primarily orthostatic but supine pressure was significantly reduced also. These responses were potentiated by the simultaneous administration of chlorothiazide. They related the hypotensive effects to an inhibition of arteriolar constriction without any change in venomotor tone; however, it is doubtful if the orthostatic effect could be produced without any effects on the venous circulation. The

Table I

CLINICAL EFFECTS OF VARIOUS MONOAMINE OXIDASE INHIBITORS ON BLOOD PRESSURE[a]

Compound	Average daily dose (mg)	Effectiveness (compared with iproniazid)	Structure
Iproniazid	50 (10–150)	Mild to moderate drop of blood pressure in 20–50% of the patients. Marked postural hypotension in about 4–19% of the cases.	
Isocarboxazid	15 (10–30)	Hypotensive effect less frequent and usually less severe than after iproniazid.	
Pheniprazine		Marked hypotensive effect, often greater than after iproniazid.	

Phenelzine	45 (–120)	Ph–CH$_2$CH$_2$NHNH$_2$	Hypotensive effect less frequent and usually less severe than after iproniazid.
Nialamide	75 (–150)	pyridyl–C(=O)–NHNHCH$_2$CH$_2$C(=O)–NHCH$_2$–Ph	Mild drop in blood pressure less frequent than after iproniazid. Only rare cases of severe postural hypotension reported.
Isoniazid	150–300	pyridyl–C(=O)–NHNH$_2$	No effect on blood pressure.

[a] From Zbinden et al. (156).

397

antihypertensive effect was attributed by Maxwell *et al.* (104) almost solely to a decreased peripheral resistance.

A short-acting MAO inhibitor, N^2-*p*-dimethylaminobenzyl-[5-methylisoxazolyl-3]-carbonyl hydrazide, (III), demonstrated only minor antihypertensive effectiveness when employed alone. When combined with hydrochlorothiazide, an additive antihypertensive effect was seen (20). None of these agents have

(III)

survived more than initial clinical trials as antihypertensives.

In the succeeding years, hundreds of hydrazine derivatives were prepared. Although we could not hope to list them all, certain contributions to the chemistry of these compounds were outstanding (2, 10, 36, 48, 56–58, 122, 158).

III. Nonhydrazines

A. HARMALA ALKALOIDS

Harmine   Harmaline   Harman

Harmaline, harmine, and other harmala alkaloids have been used therapeutically for more than 25 years. Gunn (73) discussed the hypotensive activities of these alkaloids. There was some evidence of utility in the therapy of angina pectoris and Parkinsonism. This was several years before MAO was known. In 1958, Udenfriend *et al.* (143) found that certain harmala alkaloids were among the most potent reversible inhibitors of MAO. The mode of enzyme inhibition and the central nervous system effects of the harmala alkaloids were further studied by Pletscher and Besendorf (118) and Pletscher *et al.* (119). They noted the relatively short duration of MAO inhibition in contrast to the hydrazines and the antagonism between the two at the same receptor site on the enzyme MAO.

Sjoerdsma *et al.* (130) described the effect of harmaline on hypertensive patients. When five hypertensives were given a dosage of 75 mg every 8 hours for 7–14 days there was a marked inhibition of 5-hydroxytryptamine (serotonin) metabolism to 5-hydroxyindoleacetic acid in the absence of any significant effect on blood pressure. It was of interest that maximal inhibition with harmaline was apparent after only one dose, as compared to a slow onset of inhibition seen with iproniazid. There was no evidence of enzyme inhibition the day after harmaline therapy was discontinued.

These results would suggest that a decrease in blood pressure does not coincide with MAO inhibition; however, in the case of the harmala alkaloids other factors must be considered. Metabolism studies have shown that these alkaloids are very poorly absorbed from the gut. Inhibition could be quite complete in the gut, but inconsequential elsewhere.

Other investigators (73, 116) have shown a marked hypotensive effect in man by intravenous administration of the harmala alkaloids. Work with this class of drugs has been complicated by marked toxicity such as visual hallucinations, neurological changes, numbness, etc.

B. BRETYLIUM AND GUANETHIDINE-TYPE COMPOUNDS

Although bretylium and guanethidine will be covered elsewhere in this book, it is appropriate to mention them briefly here, since there is some evidence to suggest that both they and the MAO inhibitors may lower blood pressure by a closely related mechanism. Both guanethidine and bretylium block efferent adrenergic transmission peripheral to the ganglia without parasympathetic blockade, producing a similar net hemodynamic effect. However, guanethidine decreases the norepinephrine content of peripheral tissues, whereas bretylium does not have this action at normal dose levels. Guanethidine, at least in its early phases, blocks the release of adrenergic transmitter in a manner similar to the adrenergic neuron-blocking action of bretylium. Boura et al. (17) demonstrated a bretyliumlike effect for guanethidine on an isolated smooth muscle preparation. The effect of bretylium on the respiration of brain slices and certain enzyme systems has been investigated by McCoubrey (106) who found it to be a weak MAO inhibitor, a property which is probably unrelated to its hypotensive effect in man.

Boura et al. (18) studied a series of benzyl and phenethyl guanidines and found them to be powerful adrenergic neuron-blocking agents and thus having the capability of lowering blood pressure. One of these compounds was later reported by Gessa et al. (61) to be a potent MAO inhibitor. They also found that a number of MAO inhibitors such as iproniazid, pheniprazine, phenelzine, nialamide, and others unrelated in structure such as pargyline, tranylcypromine, and harmaline, acted like bretylium in preventing guanethidine from depleting heart norepinephrine in rats. They postulated that the hypotensive action of MAO inhibitors was due to a bretyliumlike action at certain sympathetic nerve endings. In a related study, Axelrod et al. (8) demonstrated that certain MAO

Table II
In vitro Inhibition of Monoamine Oxidase by Benzyl and Phenethylguanidines[a]

Compound	% Inhibition			Structure
	$5 \times 10^{-4}\ M$	$5 \times 10^{-5}\ M$	$5 \times 10^{-6}\ M$	
392C60[b]	100	100	70	2-Cl-C6H4-CH2-N=C(NHCH3)2
Bethanidine	75	27	0	C6H5-CH2-N=C(NHCH3)2
59-323	100	61	0	2-Br-C6H4-CH2-N=C(NH2)2
200C58	68	15	0	C6H5-CH2-N=C(NH2)2
62-418	49	8	0	3-HO-C6H4-CH2-N=C(NH2)2
62-108	100	88	40	2-Br-C6H4-CH2-CH2-N=C(NH2)2
62-103	0	0	0	3,4,5-(CH3O)3-C6H2-CH2-N=C(NH2)2

58-176	67	19	
247C58	80	23	
62-127	30	19	
PIH[b]	100	100	78
Bretylium	82	24	0
Guanethidine	0	0	0

[a] From Kuntzman and Jacobson (92).
[b] % Inhibition of MAO at lower concentrations of PIH and B.W. 392C60 was as follows:

	$1.0 \times 10^{-6}\,M$	$1.5 \times 10^{-6}\,M$	$2.0 \times 10^{-6}\,M$
B.W. 392C60	31	40	50
PIH	40	53	60

inhibitors prevented the release of norepinephrine-^{3}H from its binding sites in the heart.

These findings prompted Kuntzman and Jacobson (92) to study the effect of these compounds on MAO activity *in vitro* and *in vivo*. Table II relates their *in vitro* data.

This study demonstrated that these guanidines are competitive and reversible inhibitors of MAO and that *N-o*-chlorobenzyl-*N'N''*-dimethylguanidine sulfate (B.W. 392C60) was as potent an MAO inhibitor *in vitro* as phenylisopropyl hydrazine (PIH, JB516, pheniprazine), whereas its dechlorinated congener *N*-benzyl-*N'N''*-dimethylguanidine sulfate (B.W. 467C60, bethanidine), had little activity. The inhibition produced by B.W. 392C60 was competitive and reversible while that produced by PIH was noncompetitive and irreversible. Compounds containing bromine in the *ortho* position were about ten times more active as MAO inhibitors than compounds without *ortho* substitution. Methylation of the nitrogens of the guanidine groups had little effect on the MAO inhibition produced (bethanidine and B.W. 200C58), whereas substituents on the *meta* or *para* position tended to decrease the degree of MAO inhibition.

These guanidines and certain "MAO inhibitors" thus had the common property of inhibiting MAO and preventing norepinephrine release. Kuntzman and Jacobson as well as Gessa *et al.* concluded that the ability to block the sympathetic nervous system by these drugs was unrelated to their ability to inhibit MAO since there did not appear to be a significant correlation between MAO inhibition on one hand and adrenergic neuron blockade and hypotension on the other.

C. Tryptamine Derivatives

It has been suggested that serotonin plays an important role in such conditions as mental disease (23, 55, 151), hypertension (115, 152), inflammatory processes (51, 133, 142), and gastrointestinal functions (29, 148). Clinical effectiveness in schizophrenia by increasing brain serotonin, with the administration of its precursor, 5-hydroxytryptophan, was reported by Woolley (150). The mechanistic picture became confused when it was shown by Shore *et al.* (127) that the MAO inhibitor iproniazid increased serotonin brain levels and was useful in depression. Spector *et al.* (134) found a rise in brain norepinephrine after administration of iproniazid as well. On the other hand, three *Rauwolfia* alkaloids (reserpine, deserpidine, and rescinnamine) which decrease brain serotonin (22) and norepinephrine (79) cause sedation.

In order to more completely study the effects of indole-containing compounds, Heinzelman *et al.* (74) prepared a series of α-alkyl-tryptamines and tryptophans, on the hypothesis that such compounds would act either like serotonin, or as serotonin antagonists similar to 1-benzyl-2-methyl-5-methoxytryptamine (BAS) (153).

From this work evolved α-ethyltryptamine [(IV), etryptamine]. This compound has been previously prepared by Snyder and Katz (132), who studied the conversion of such amines to substances containing the β-carboline nucleus.

(IV)

Only a few reports are available concerning the pharmacology of etryptamine (70, 71, 101, 102). It is an MAO inhibitor of the competitive type and differs from iproniazid *in vivo* as inhibition of MAO by etryptamine is reversible. In cats, etryptamine produced a central "sympatheticlike" excitation and depressed sympathetic transmission in autonomic ganglia, but not in the spinal cord or the ascending somatosensory system. Ganglionic transmission was depressed (40%) but not completely blocked, even in doses twice that required to produce gross changes in behavior. Mean arterial blood pressure increased moderately in these experiments. The onset was immediate and the rise was gradual. The elevated blood pressure was maintained for several hours in spite of the simultaneously developing ganglionic depression, suggesting the possibility of an indirect effect of etryptamine by releasing and/or accumulating epinephrine peripherally. The pressor response induced by etryptamine was apparently not due to release of catecholamines since the response was obtained in reserpinized as well as normal animals. Little is known of the action of etryptamine on blood pressure in man. It was introduced as an antidepressant and its specific study as an antihypertensive has not been reported. Toxicity problems such as agranulocytosis necessitated its withdrawal from the market.

D. CYCLOPROPYLAMINES

trans-2-Phenylcyclopropylamine (tranylcypromine) was first prepared by Burger and Yost (30) as an amphetamine substitute and later was found to be a potent MAO inhibitor (140, 141). Although hypotension was noted in many clinical trials in depressed patients, other investigators (37, 95) found it produced increased blood pressure in man.

This discovery prompted Kaiser *et al.* (85) to prepare numerous analogs, homologs, isomers, and derivatives of this drug.

Analogs of 2-phenylcyclopropylamine were prepared according to Scheme I.

Scheme I

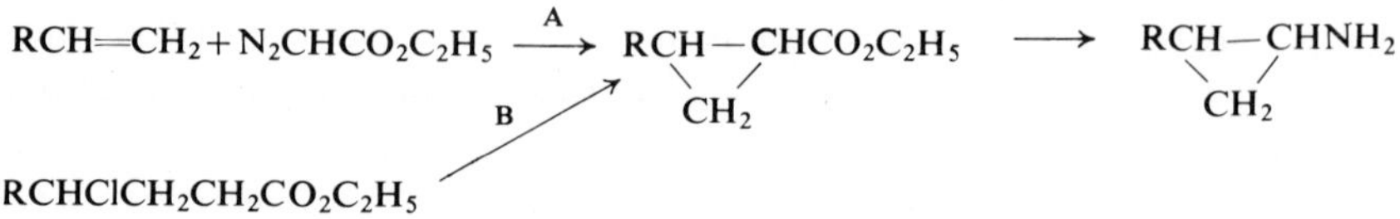

$$RCH\!=\!CH_2 + N_2CHCO_2C_2H_5 \xrightarrow{\text{A}} \underset{\underset{CH_2}{\diagup}}{RCH\!-\!CHCO_2C_2H_5} \longrightarrow \underset{\underset{CH_2}{\diagup}}{RCH\!-\!CHNH_2}$$

$$\text{B} \nearrow$$

$$RCHClCH_2CH_2CO_2C_2H_5 \nearrow$$

The intermediate ethyl cyclopropanecarboxylates were obtained by two general methods: condensation of ethyl diazoacetate with an olefin (Method A) (30) or cyclization of alkyl-4-aryl-4-chlorobutyrates (Method B) (84). Method A gave mixtures of *cis* and *trans* esters, whereas in method B only *trans* esters were isolated. The esters were hydrolyzed to the corresponding acids with aqueous–ethanolic potassium hydroxide. These 2-substituted cyclopropane-carboxylic acids were converted, via their azides, to corresponding amines by the Curtius procedure.

A homologous series of 2-phenylcycloalkylamines was also prepared and compared with 2-phenylcyclopropylamine. 2-Phenylcyclopentylamine (68, 145), and 2-phenylcycloheptylamine (31) had been prepared previously from the corresponding ketones via the Leuckart procedure. Conversion of similar ketones to amines by the Leuckart method gives predominantly the *cis* isomer, whereas reduction with sodium and ethanol of related oximes usually produces the *trans* isomer.

Examples of 1-substituted cyclopropylamines were also prepared by these authors. 1-Aminomethyl-1-phenylcyclopropane was made by a lithium aluminum hydride reduction of 1-phenylcyclopropanecarbonitrile. *N*-Methyl-1-phenylcyclopropylamine was prepared through the lithium aluminum hydride reduction of 1-phenylcyclopropyl isocyanate.

The MAO inhibitory activity of these compounds was measured *in vivo* by Zirkle *et al.* (159) by potentiation of tryptamine convulsions. An excellent structure–activity relationship was given by these authors. In general, substituents on the phenyl ring, whether electron-attracting or electron-donating, had little effect upon potency. The great degree of specificity of the cyclo-propane ring for MAO inhibition was demonstrated by the data on the higher ring homologs of 2-phenylcyclopropylamine. Of the cyclobutyl, cyclopentyl, cyclohexyl, and cycloheptylamines, only the *cis*-2-phenylcyclohexylamine (3) showed significant activity, and it was about 1/100th as potent as tranyl-cypromine.

Tranylcypromine was studied clinically and is now marketed solely as an antidepressant. A complete and excellent review of this compound has recently been published by Atkinson and Ditman (5). The pharmacology of this com-pound is complicated by the multiplicity of effects produced. The earliest report of effects on blood pressure appears to be that of Spencer *et al.* (136) who found it to produce an initial pressor response following intravenous injection in anesthetized dogs; subsequent injections resulted in a sustained hypotension which they associated with a central action. Oral doses in unanesthetized dogs produced only slight to moderate decreases in blood pressure. More recently (63), it was reported that tranylcypromine, in small doses, produced a rapid hypotensive effect of short duration, similar to that seen after administration of acetylcholine, in anesthetized rats. Larger doses produced a prolonged lowering of blood pressure. Although pretreatment with atropine decreased the hypotensive action of tranylcypromine, pretreatment with dibenzyline plus atropine resulted in a hypertensive response of short duration. Glavas *et al.* (63) attributed the hypotensive action of tranylcypromine to an action on cholinergic receptors and the hypertensive activity to a direct pressor action on blood vessels. The hypertensive effects noted in man can probably be attributed to the sympathomimetic action which this compound possesses.

E. PROPYNYLAMINES

N-Benzyl-*N*-methyl-2-propynylamine (pargyline) is the most recent MAO inhibitor to reach the market. It is unique in that it is the only member of this class of drugs that the Food and Drug Administration has permitted for use in the treatment of hypertension rather than depression. Its ability to elevate mood, however, has enhanced its usefulness since depression is frequently seen in hypertensive patients. The MAO inhibitory properties of this compound were first described by Taylor *et al.* (138).

Swett *et al.* (137) have reported on the structure–activity relationships taken from over a hundred compounds in this series. The preparation of pargyline shown in Scheme II illustrates the most general method of synthesis used in this work.

Scheme II

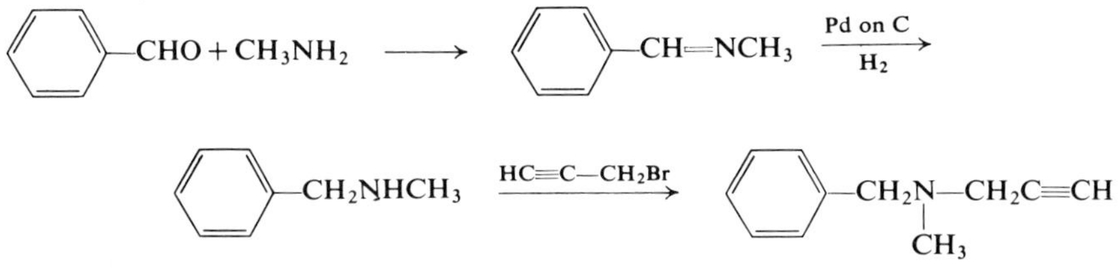

$$\bigcirc\text{—CHO} + CH_3NH_2 \longrightarrow \bigcirc\text{—CH}=NCH_3 \xrightarrow[H_2]{Pd\ on\ C}$$

$$\bigcirc\text{—CH}_2NHCH_3 \xrightarrow{HC\equiv C-CH_2Br} \bigcirc\text{—CH}_2N-CH_2C\equiv CH$$
$$\qquad\qquad\qquad\qquad\qquad\qquad\qquad\qquad\qquad\qquad\overset{|}{CH_3}$$

Further studies in animals (50) showed pargyline to be a long-acting irreversible MAO inhibitor with low toxicity and marked antidepressant activity. These compounds were tested *in vitro* in a system in which the MAO enzyme

Pargyline

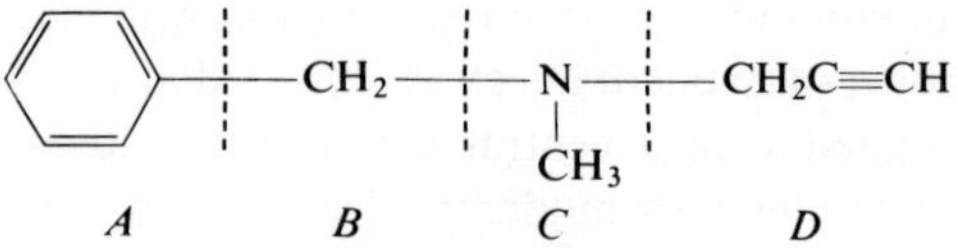

$$\text{⬡} \underset{A}{|} -CH_2- \underset{B}{|} -\underset{\underset{CH_3}{|}}{N}- \underset{C}{|} -CH_2C{\equiv}CH \quad \underset{D}{}$$

In vitro (conc., mole/liter)	*In vivo* i.p. (mg/kg/duration in hours)	Oral
9×10^{-7}	10/96	75/96

Fig. 1.

Table III

CHANGES IN GROUP A

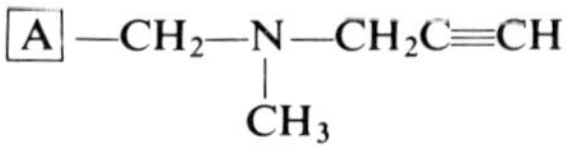

$$\boxed{A} -CH_2-\underset{\underset{CH_3}{|}}{N}-CH_2C{\equiv}CH$$

A	*In vitro* (conc., mole/liter)	*In vivo* i.p. (mg/kg/duration in hours)	Oral
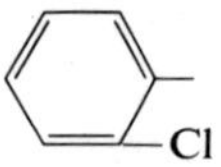 Cl-substituted phenyl	5×10^{-8}	5/24	25/96
 Br-substituted phenyl	6.5×10^{-8}	15/24	25/96
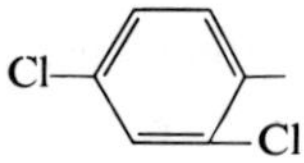 Cl-, Cl-substituted phenyl	7.5×10^{-8}	15/24	25/96
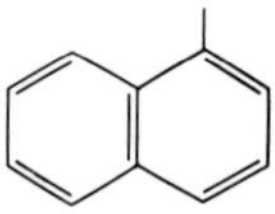 naphthyl	9×10^{-8}	10/24	20/24
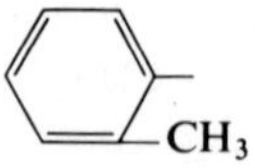 CH$_3$-substituted phenyl	1.7×10^{-7}	25/24	100/24
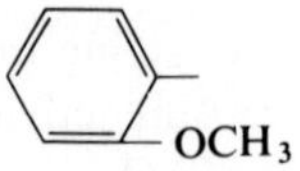 OCH$_3$-substituted phenyl	1.7×10^{-7}	100/24	100/24

acts on the substrate serotonin to develop a dark brown pigment. The method was reported by Wykes *et al.* (154). The *in vivo* method, reported by Everett and Wiegand (49), consists of observing a behavioral response in mice that were pretreated with the inhibitor and subsequently challenged with 200 mg per kilogram of DL-dihydroxyphenylalanine (DOPA).

Table IV

CHANGES IN GROUP B

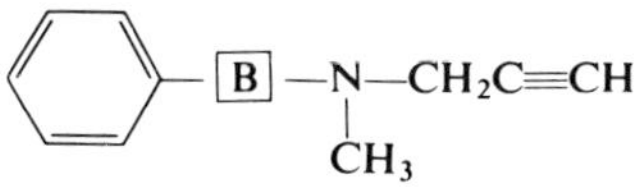

$$\text{[benzene ring]}-\boxed{B}-N-CH_2C\equiv CH$$
$$\qquad\qquad\qquad\quad |$$
$$\qquad\qquad\qquad\quad CH_3$$

B	In vitro (conc. mole/liter)	In vivo i.p. (mg/kg/duration in hours)	Oral
—CH$_2$CH$_2$—		20/72	75/72
—CH$_2$CH$_2$CH$_2$—		25/72	100/72

—CH—
   |
   CH$_3$
	7×10^{-7}	25/72	25/72

CH$_3$ | —C— | CH$_3$	7×10^{-6}	100/24	0

—CH$_2$CH—
    |
    CH$_3$
	1×10^{-4}	0	0

To investigate the structural changes and their effect on activity, the pargyline molecule was divided into four parts—A, B, C and D, as shown in Fig. 1. Also shown in Fig. 1 are the *in vitro* and *in vivo* data of pargyline. A 9×10^{-7} molar concentration was required to inhibit 50% of the enzyme in the *in vitro* test. An intraperitoneal (i.p.) dose of 10 mg per kilogram and an oral dose of 75 mg per kilogram gave a maximum behavioral response in the *in vivo* test and was of a 96-hour duration. These same data are given in the structure–activity tables.

As changes in the A portion of the molecule were made, it became apparent that an aromatic system was essential for activity. The effect of substitutions on the benzene ring can be seen in Table III. Halogen substitutions were particularly effective, especially in the *ortho* position. Lower alkyl and alkoxy substituents were less effective.

Group B was varied from a 1- to a 6-carbon chain, with and without branching. It is difficult to distinguish a change in activity up through the 3-carbon chain; however, beyond that the activity fell off quickly.

Table V

CHANGES IN GROUP C

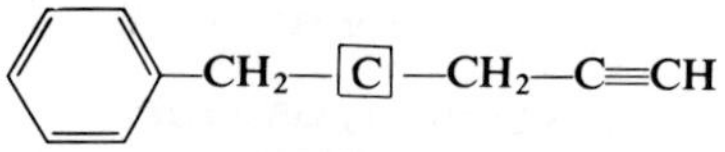

$$\text{C}_6\text{H}_5\text{—CH}_2\text{—}\boxed{\text{C}}\text{—CH}_2\text{—C}\equiv\text{CH}$$

C	In vitro (conc., mole/liter)	In vivo i.p. (mg/kg/duration in hours)	Oral
—N— | H	5×10^{-6}	25/24	50/24
—N— | CH_2CH_3	1.7×10^{-3}	0	0
—N— 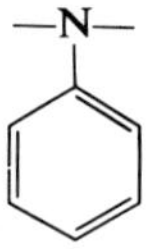 (phenyl)	$> 10^{-3}$	0	0
—N— | $COOC_2H_5$	1.7×10^{-3}	0	0

Table VI

CHANGES IN GROUP D

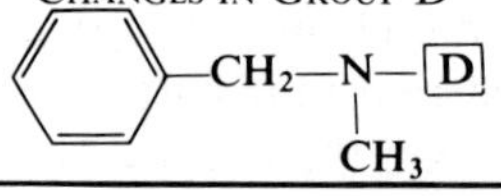

$$\text{C}_6\text{H}_5\text{—CH}_2\text{—N—}\boxed{\text{D}}$$
$$\underset{\text{CH}_3}{|}$$

D	In vitro (conc. mole/liter)	In vivo i.p. (mg/kg/duration in hours)	Oral
—$CH_2CH_2CH_3$	$> 10^{-3}$	0	0
—$CH_2CH{=}CH_2$	2×10^{-3}	0	0
—CH—C≡CH | CH_3	$> 10^{-3}$	0	0
—CH_2—C≡C—CH_3	1×10^{-5}	0	0

The limitations of group C were quite strict with —NH— and —NCH$_3$— comprising the only active amine portions found. Replacing the hydrogen or methyl group with higher alkyl, alkenyl, alkynyl, acyl, or aryl groups led to a reduction in activity.

Changes in group D were again quite stringent. The triple bond is essential and it must be β to the nitrogen for inhibition of the enzyme. Variations that were made in this group were: (1) moving the triple bond up and down the carbon chain; (2) branching at the α-carbon; (3) replacing the propynyl radical with alkyl, alkenyl, and haloalkenyl; and (4) making use of the active acetylenic site and preparing Mannich bases and alkylated products. The last compound shown in Table VI was the only alteration which maintained a desirable response.

In addition to pargyline, two other candidates from this work were evaluated clinically. These were N-benzyl-2-propynylamine (MO936) and ethyl-N-benzyl-N-cyclopropylcarbamate (MO1255).

MO936   MO1255

Everett *et al.* (50) reported that MO1255 is a potent MAO inhibitor *in vivo* but not *in vitro*. This led Martin *et al.* (100) to attempt to identify the metabolites of MO1255. Single oral doses of MO1255 labeled on the carbon adjacent to the benzene ring were given to rats and the metabolites in their urine identified via gas chromatography equipped with both mass and radioactivity detector. Total radioactivity extracted from urine and identified was 85% of the dose. Results are given in Table VII. The unknown metabolite listed in the table is possibly N-hydroxylbenzylamine. Cyclopropylbenzylamine is an MAO inhibitor *in vitro* and may thus contribute to the MAO activity of MO1255. It is of particular interest that MO1255 has not exhibited an antihypertensive effect in man (50) nor has MO936 (28).

As with most other MAO inhibitors, the hypotensive activity of pargyline was first noted during its early clinical trials as an antidepressant. The postural hypotensive effects appeared to be more pronounced than with other MAO inhibitors and clinical studies to delineate this activity were soon initiated. Horwitz and Sjoerdsma (81) were the first to report its clinical effectiveness as an antihypertensive agent. They believed that the decrease in blood pressure was the result of a selective decrease in sympathetic nerve activity. Subsequently, that year Ford (53) and Bryant *et al.* (27) reported effective lowering of blood pressure in significant numbers of hypertensive patients. Although the predominant effect was on standing blood pressure, decreases in recumbent

Table VII

Table VII

METABOLITES OF MO1255[a]

Metabolite identified in urine	Per cent
Unchanged MO1255	37.3
Benzylamine	13.0
Cyclopropylbenzylamine	38.3
Unknown component[b]	11.4
Total	100.00

[a] From Martin *et al.* (100).
[b] Conjectured to be *N*-hydroxylbenzylamine.

blood pressure were noted as well. Many other reports have since appeared in the literature attesting to the antihypertensive activity and relative safety of pargyline in man. In general, the therapeutic effect of pargyline develops slowly, sometimes taking several weeks to appear and it persists for some time after the drug is discontinued (7–9 days). When administered concomitantly with the diuretic, methyclothiazide, pargyline produced a greater reduction in blood pressure than seen with pargyline alone (28). This and subsequent studies by others established the clinical utility of this combination and its use by the medical profession has recently been allowed by the Food and Drug Administration. Bryant *et al.* also found that MO936, the demethylated derivative of pargyline, did not have antihypertensive activity in man. Since this compound was an MAO inhibitor (137), this finding cast doubt on the theory that reduction in blood pressure is causally related to MAO inhibition. This will be discussed more fully later in this chapter (Section IV).

The hemodynamic responses to pargyline were studied in man by Brest *et al.* (21) who found that pargyline reduced blood pressure primarily by decreasing peripheral vascular resistance without significantly affecting cardiac output. Since cardiac output was not decreased, they suggested that the antihypertensive mechanism of pargyline was neither by sympathetic nor ganglionic blockade. Similar hemodynamic responses had previously been observed following a different MAO inhibitor, 1-DL-seryl-2-isopropylhydrazide, RO4-1038 (104) as described in Section II of this chapter.

Pargyline hydrochloride, which does not have the hydrazine moiety in its structure, has not been associated with the type of side effects such as optic nerve atrophy, liver toxicity, and visual disturbances which have occurred with hydrazine-type compounds. Other side effects which seem to be associated with MAO inhibition are seen with pargyline and will be described in Section V of this chapter.

The cardiovascular effects of pargyline have also been studied in experimental animals. Intraperitoneal injections over a 4-day period produced a small but significant decrease in the mean systolic arterial blood pressure of unanesthetized normotensive rats (124). Although myocardial norepinephrine levels were elevated in these rats, it appeared unrelated to the hypotensive effect, since a smaller dose of pargyline which did not significantly lower blood pressure produced an almost identical increase in the concentration of myocardial norepinephrine.

Table VIII

EFFECT OF PARGYLINE ON BLOOD PRESSURE AND HEART RATE OF
UNANESTHETIZED HYPERTENSIVE DOGS

Dog number	Type of hypertension	Average blood pressure (mm Hg)		Average heart rate (beats/minute)	
		Before pargyline	After pargyline	Before pargyline	After pargyline
1	Neurogenic	183	205	112	134
2	Neurogenic	240	202	144	140
3	Neurogenic	158	150	120	102
4	Renal	149	153	92	116
5	Renal	170	175	104	98

Single and multiple (4 consecutive days) intraperitoneal injections of pargyline to anesthetized cats also resulted in a lowering of mean arterial blood pressure. In some of those cats given the drug over a 4-day period, an increase in pressure on the first (and occasionally, second) treatment day was observed before the depressor response was seen. In these cats, cardiac norepinephrine levels definitely declined, whereas increases (though less pronounced) were seen in the levels of norepinephrine in brain and superior cervical ganglia. There was no clear correlation between the amount of pressure fall and changes in norepinephrine levels among the individual cats.

In other pharmacological studies, pargyline has been found to reduce the pressor response to 1,1-dimethyl-4-phenylpiperazinium iodide (DMPP), a ganglion stimulant, in anesthetized cats. Other MAO inhibitors have also shown this activity. Also, the depressor response to 45° tilt was potentiated in most cases. Other autonomic variables such as the responses to bilateral carotid occlusion, epinephrine, norepinephrine, acetylcholine, histamine, serotonin, and dopamine were not consistently affected.

The effects of pargyline were also studied in three neurogenic and two renal hypertensive trained dogs given 20 mg per kilogram pargyline orally on each of 8 consecutive days. Pressures were taken by needle puncture of a femoral artery. Average mean pressures before and during treatment are summarized in Table VIII. Only dog number 2 experienced a significant decline in blood pressure. Since dogs with experimentally induced hypertension generally respond to most known antihypertensive agents, it is of considerable interest and challenge to investigators to try to explain why this compound is so effective in hypertensive man and so ineffective in hypertensive dogs. A discussion of attempts to determine the mechanism of the antihypertensive action of pargyline and other MAO inhibitors follows in Section IV of this chapter.

IV. Mechanism of action

The hypotensive properties of many of the MAO inhibitors were discovered mainly during the clinical use of the drugs. For a time it was believed that all MAO inhibitors had the ability to lower blood pressure, the differences between them being quantitative. Because of this, the term MAO inhibitors has been used in a broad sense, implying a pharmacological as well as a biochemical classification for this group of compounds. The belief was widespread that these compounds lowered blood pressure by a mechanism causally related to their MAO inhibitory activity. The enzyme is involved in the biological degradation of several monoamines, including norepinephrine (NE) and epinephrine (E) as depicted in Scheme III taken from a review by Mendlowitz et al. (107). Since it has been generally concluded that there is no excess production of norepinephrine in the usual hypertensive patient (128), it would seem paradoxical that a compound capable of inhibiting the degradation of pressor amines should produce a lowering of blood pressure in man. The same author concluded that there was no evidence for a deficiency of either MAO or catechol-o-methyl transferase in hypertensives. However, the evidence available at that time suggested that a hypotensive response paralleled demonstrable evidence of MAO inhibition with various MAO inhibitors, including pargyline (81, 139), which had a structure much different from MAO inhibitors known at that time. A causal relationship between MAO inhibition and lowering of blood pressure was thus postulated. However, a different point of view was expressed by Zbinden (155). After reviewing the experimental and clinical data on hundreds of MAO inhibitors, he concluded that all compounds which (1) inhibit MAO in vivo, (2) potentiate 5-hydroxytryptophan (5-HTP) and dihydroxyphenylalanine, and (3) block various reserpine effects, had a therapeutic action on blood pressure. Marked differences in potency were found among MAO inhibitors tested in man, indicating a lack of relationship between MAO inhibition in animals and effects on blood pressure in man.

Numerous attempts have been made to correlate the antihypertensive effects of various MAO inhibitors with MAO inhibition as measured by increased urinary excretion of tryptamine. This was proposed by Sjoerdsma *et al.* (129) as an index of MAO inhibition in man since tryptamine is more dependent on the MAO pathway than are serotonin and the catecholamines. Orvis *et al.* (113, 114) found that the antihypertensive effects of pargyline were positively correlated with enzyme levels using urinary tryptamine levels as an index. A gross correlation between dose, magnitude of antihypertensive response, and increase in urinary tryptamine levels was observed. They also observed that antihypertensive tolerance seen in some patients correlated with decreased urinary tryptamine levels.

Later, Levine and Sjoerdsma (97) measured MAO activity in specimens of human jejunal mucosa obtained by peroral biopsy. Oral doses of isocarboxazid and oral and intravenous pargyline produced maximal inhibition of MAO in this tissue. The results correlated with changes in urinary tryptamine levels. Unfortunately, blood pressure responses were not monitored concurrently, so no direct correlation between MAO activity and blood pressure could be made. In contrast to these reports, other investigators such as Maxwell (103) found a lack of correlation between increases in urinary tryptamine excretion and hypotensive responses in individual patients, suggesting that the hypotensive effect of MAO inhibitors is not related to inhibition of this enzyme. Likewise, Winsor (149) did not observe a consistent positive correlation between MAO inhibition, as reflected in increased urinary levels of tryptamine, and the antihypertensive effect in human subjects treated with pargyline. A better correlation appeared to exist between the loss of the digital inspiratory reflex and the antihypertensive effect of pargyline than between urinary excretion of tryptamine and the antihypertensive effect. It was postulated that the sympathetic blocking effect of the drug may be independent, at least in part, of enzyme inhibition.

Causal relationships between the antihypertensive effect of "MAO inhibitors" and direct measurement of MAO in the same species have thus not been conclusive. In addition, Everett *et al.* (50) reported that ethyl-*N*-benzyl-*N*-cyclopropylcarbamate, MO1255, is a highly effective MAO inhibitor *in vivo* in animals, yet failed to produce an antihypertensive effect in man even at high dose levels. Bryant *et al.* (28) also reported that demethylated pargyline HCl (MO936), a MAO inhibitor also, had no significant antihypertensive effects in human patients. These important findings lent further support to the hypothesis that the hypotensive action of MAO inhibitors may not be related to their MAO-inhibiting properties.

The present state of knowledge seems to indicate that the so-called MAO inhibitors often but do not uniformly produce hypotension in animals (33, 43) or man (50, 156) and that the mechanism of the hypotension is not definitely related, at least primarily, to inhibition of this enzyme system. The MAO inhibitors, like all drugs, have a multiplicity of pharmacological actions on the body, which differ quantitatively and qualitatively from one another, and which are independent or only related secondarily to inhibition of MAO.

Other pharmacological effects observed after administration of MAO inhibitors in animals and man have provided other hypotheses to account for the antihypertensive effects. Based on some early clinical observations in which side effects resembling those seen after ganglionic blocking agents (constipation, urinary retention, postural hypotension) were sometimes observed after administration of MAO inhibitors, some investigators (35, 78) suggested that MAO inhibitors functioned as slow-acting ganglion-blocking agents. Gertner *et al.* (59) and Gertner (60) demonstrated that various MAO inhibitors blocked transmission when perfused through the isolated superior cervical ganglion of the cat. The block was slow in onset, gradual and progressive with time, and was qualitatively different from that produced by known ganglion blockers. They suggested that either there was an interference with the normal functioning of the neuromediator at the ganglionic synapse or that an active amine was accumulating at the ganglionic synapse. Goldberg and DaCosta (64) demonstrated inhibition of transmission through sympathetic ganglia by intravenous administration of large doses of harmine and iproniazid. The inhibition was relatively weak and transitory. They also found that these agents exerted a selective inhibitory action on the sympathetic synapse without depressing parasympathetic ganglia. They did note, however, some dissociation of the hypotensive effect and the ganglionic action with iproniazid. Others had previously reported that MAO inhibitors exhibited little, if any, ganglionic blocking activity following intravenous administration. Marrazzi (99) demonstrated that norepinephrine and epinephrine cause inhibition of synaptic transmission in sympathetic ganglia which suggested to Costa and Brodie (39) that norepinephrine localized in ganglia may modify synaptic transmission. They speculated whether some forms of hypertension might be due to a defect in the mechanism by which norepinephrine modulates ganglionic transmission and questioned whether the hypotensive action of MAO inhibitors might be explained by elevated levels of norepinephrine in ganglia. Subsequently, Levine (96) studied the MAO activity in ganglia of cats after intravenous injections of pargyline and iproniazid and correlated these results with those of Goldberg and DaCosta. They found that doses of iproniazid which resulted in ganglionic blockade produced only 45% inhibition of MAO, whereas doses of pargyline producing 100% inhibition of MAO would not be capable of blocking ganglionic transmission. Also, complete recovery of ganglionic transmission occurred within 30 minutes after a dose of pargyline sufficient to produce complete inhibition of MAO activity lasting at least 24 hours. They concluded that pargyline and iproniazid depressed ganglionic transmission in the cat by some mechanism other than the inhibition of MAO activity.

Also, Urquiaga *et al.* (144) found no relation between ganglionic blockade and MAO inhibition and only a minimal activity in compounds which were not phenethylamine derivatives.

Davey *et al.* (43) tested nialamide and iproniazid for ganglionic blocking properties by measuring changes in ganglionic action potentials evoked by electrical stimulation of the preganglionic cervical sympathetic and recorded from the ganglion. They found no indication of an alteration of pre- or post-synaptic excitability and transmission. This and other experiments led them to exclude ganglion-blocking activity as a cause for the hypotension during MAO inhibitor treatment.

Other clinical studies (19, 76) indicated no parasympatholytic side reactions. Present opinion indicates little support for the hypothesis that ganglionic blockade plays any major role in the mechanism of the hypotensive effect of MAO inhibitors (21).

An adrenergic blocking mechanism has also been proposed as a contributing mechanism to the hypotensive action of MAO inhibitors. Griesemer *et al.* (72) showed that iproniazid competes with norepinephrine at the receptor site of smooth muscle in blood vessels. Adrenergic blocking activity was also demonstrated on the isolated uterus of the guinea pig and the seminal vesicle of the rat for iproniazid by Kamijo *et al.* (87). However, Zbinden *et al.* (156) reported that although certain other MAO inhibitors were found to be adrenergic blocking agents, other derivatives which clinically induce marked hypotension were inactive or only slightly active as adrenolytic agents. It appears, therefore, that adrenergic blockade, like ganglionic blockade, plays only a minor role, if any, in the hypotensive activity of MAO inhibitors.

As a consequence of inhibition of MAO, changes occur in levels of endogenous amines involved in the various metabolic pathways indicated in Scheme III and much speculation exists as to whether these secondary effects of altered amine levels contribute to the mechanism of the hypotensive effect. For example, most investigators (25, 69, 109, 117) have reported that the administration of various hydrazine and nonhydrazine MAO inhibitors results in an increase in the levels of endogenous norepinephrine in tissues of various species. In a few cases, no changes in the levels of endogenous norepinephrine were observed following certain MAO inhibitors (110, 135, 146). Also, some investigators have noted decreased levels of norepinephrine following MAO inhibitors (108, 147). Goldberg and Shideman (67) demonstrated that the MAO inhibitors tranylcypromine (SKF-385) and iproniazid caused a depletion of myocardial catecholamines in the cat and that tranylcypromine elevated catecholamines in the rat myocardium. Also, Schoepke and Wiegand (124) found that pargyline produced significant increases in the ventricular norepinephrine levels of rats. Concomitant decreases in systolic blood pressure were observed; however, the two findings did not necessarily appear to be

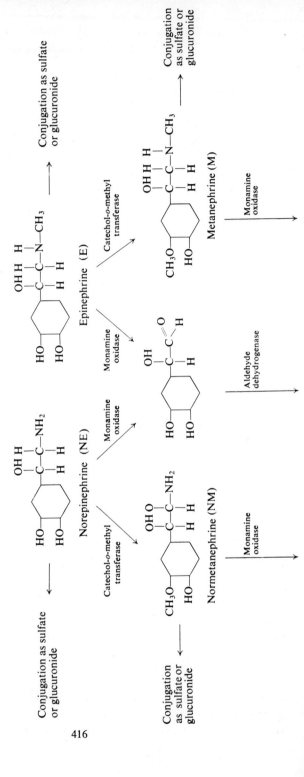

Scheme III

(from Mendlowitz *et al.* 107)

416

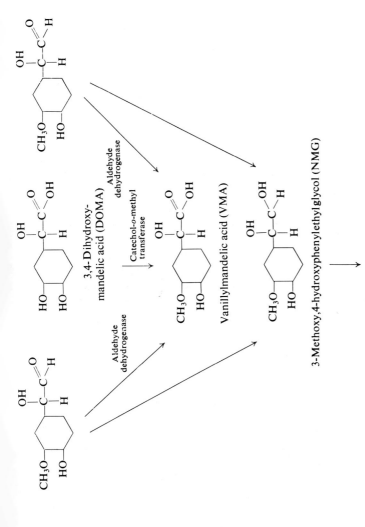

3,4-Dihydroxy-mandelic acid (DOMA)

Aldehyde dehydrogenase

Catechol-*o*-methyl transferase

Aldehyde dehydrogenase

Vanillylmandelic acid (VMA)

3-Methoxy,4-hydroxyphenylethylglycol (NMG)

Conjugation as sulfate or glucuronide

417

directly related. In cats, pargyline produced decreases in ventricular norepinephrine and either no changes or elevations in brain and superior cervical
ganglia norepinephrine, depending on dose and time. Blood pressure of cats
decreased and the authors concluded that no simple relationship existed
between norepinephrine levels in the heart and hypotensive effect. Previous
workers (94, 121) had also suggested that the effect of MAO inhibitors on
catecholamine concentrations will vary between tissues in the same species
and between species. This diversity could be due to the relative importance of
MAO in detoxification of catecholamines in individual tissues or to the interference by the agent with the enzyme-independent uptake, binding, storage,
or release of norepinephrine, thus producing an effect on norepinephrine levels
opposite to that produced by MAO inhibition.

Another hypothesis to explain the hypotensive activity of MAO inhibitors
is that the accumulation of catecholamines due to inhibition of the enzyme
may produce a decreased sensitivity of the tissues to the action of endogenously
released norepinephrine. For example, Bächtold and Pletscher (9) found that
iproniazid significantly decreased the norepinephrine-induced contractions of
isolated rabbit aortas. More specifically, Burn and Rand (32) and Sjoerdsma
(130) suggested that MAO inhibitors cause an accumulation of dopamine in
tissues and that in certain circumstances dopamine can compete with norepinephrine for the same receptors. Since dopamine has been found in sympathetic nerves and is a depressor agent in some species, Horwitz et al. (80)
studied the effects of several MAO inhibitors on the blood pressure responses
to norepinephrine and dopamine in hypertensive patients. They found that
dopamine produced a pressor effect in man and believed it due to an increased
cardiac output. The pressor effects of dopamine were potentiated by the MAO
inhibitors and this potentiation seemed to bear a direct relationship to the
degree of MAO inhibition as measured by urinary tryptamine levels. It seemed
paradoxical that any potentiation of dopamine could produce hypotension.
However, these investigators argued that a similar paradox exists in patients
with excess norepinephrine due to pheochromocytoma, who exhibit postural
hypotension as noted by Smithwick et al. (131). Horwitz et al. (80) did not feel
that the augmentation of norepinephrine by the MAO inhibitors was directly
related to inhibition of the enzyme.

In order to explain the multitudinous effects of neurohormones at sympathetic nervous system receptor sites, Brodie (26) proposed that all these sites
of drug action be considered as parts of an organized molecular unit responsible for the formation, storage, inactivation, and physiological release of a
neurohormone. Since these molecular units would transform one kind of
energy into another, he suggested the term "neurochemical transducer" to
describe it. Brodie et al. (24) viewed the function of MAO as a regulatory
mechanism to prevent the uncontrolled release of norepinephrine onto receptor

sites. Monoamine oxidase was thus considered important in regulating the amount of stored norepinephrine while catechol-*o*-methyl transferase functioned to inactivate circulating catecholamines (6). Monoamine oxidase also functions in the deamination of the *o*-methylated amines formed from administered catecholamines. Based on the model of a neurochemical transducer, Brodie and his colleagues offered a hypothesis to explain the mechanism whereby MAO inhibitors lowered blood pressure in man. Gessa *et al.* (61, 62) had presented evidence that MAO inhibitors of widely diverse structure exerted a bretyliumlike action by counteracting the decline in heart norepinephrine produced by guanethidine and the pressor response to the ganglionic stimulant 1,1-dimethyl-4-phenylpiperazinium iodide (DMPP) and by preventing sympathetic nerve impulses from releasing norepinephrine at sympathetic nerve endings. This bretyliumlike action of MAO inhibitors appeared to be independent of their action on MAO. The two actions could be separated by employing appropriate dose levels with most but not all inhibitors. These findings were in accord with those of Davey *et al.* (44) who found that nialamide reduced the quantity of norepinephrine released from splenic nerves by electrical stimulation. Since MAO inhibitors did not relax the nictitating membrane of cats nor block the contraction produced by stimulating the cervical sympathetic nerves, Brodie theorized that the free norepinephrine spared by MAO inhibition counteracts the bretyliumlike action. Thus the net effect of MAO inhibition would depend on the amount of norepinephrine released spontaneously on receptors.

Some of the available evidence seems to contradict the bretyliumlike action theory. For instance, the MAO inhibitor tranylcypromine potentiated rather than reduced the pressor effect of DMPP (62). Also, the hemodynamic response in man to bretylium and MAO inhibitors, such as pargyline, differs in several important respects. In particular, the effect of MAO inhibitors is predominantly on peripheral resistance rather than on cardiac output, in contrast to bretylium (21).

Perhaps the most recent theory concerning the mechanism of the hypotensive effect of MAO inhibitors centers around the formation of less active amines which displace norepinephrine at the sympathetic nerve endings. Kakimoto and Armstrong (86) found that administration of a MAO inhibitor resulted in the accumulation of octopamine and normetanephrine in rabbit tissues (brain, heart, lung, spleen, kidney, liver). As indicated earlier in this discussion, much speculation has centered around the possible significance of the accumulation in tissues of the various amines found after MAO inhibition. Day and Rand (46, 47) believed that the decreased response to sympathetic nerve stimulation following chronic MAO inhibition and the decreased release of norepinephrine might be the result of the replacement of norepinephrine in sympathetic nerve, endings by amines which are less active than norepinephrine. The formation

of other amines which would replace norepinephrine and act as "false neurochemical transmitters" was supported by the evidence of accumulation in
tissues of α-methylnorepinephrine (111) and metaraminol (41) which were
released by sympathetic nerve stimulation in the same ratio to norepinephrine
as found in tissues. Carlsson and Waldeck (34) and Fischer *et al.* (52) found
that administration of labeled tyramine resulted in the accumulation of
tyramine in sympathetic nerves. This work was extended by Kopin *et al.* (90)
who found that administration of tyramine-^{3}H or *m*-tyramine-^{3}H resulted in
the rapid formation of the β-hydroxylated derivatives of these amines, octo-
pamine-^{3}H and *m*-octopamine-^{3}H, in the heart and salivary glands of the rat.
Formation of these derivatives was enhanced by intact salivary gland by
the administration of the MAO inhibitor pheniprazine, but α-methyloctopa-
mine-^{3}H formation from α-methyltyramine-^{3}H was unchanged. Since α-methyl
amines are not substrates for MAO, the results suggested that the action of
pheniprazine on octopamine accumulation was mediated by inhibition of
MAO and not inhibition of amine release. They found that chronic administration of pheniprazine resulted in a marked increase in the endogenous octopamine content of the heart, spleen, and salivary glands of cats. Chronic
sympathetic denervation largely prevented the octopamine accumulation in
salivary gland. They believed, therefore, that octopamine formation and
storage occurs in sympathetic nerves and that more than one octopamine
analog may be present in sympathetic nerves after MAO inhibition. The
increase in β-hydroxylated amines after MAO inhibition was believed to be
due to inhibition of oxidation of the precursor amine as well as its β-hydroxylated product. Since it had previously been demonstrated (93) that octopamine
has only 1% of the activity of norepinephrine, Kopin *et al.* proposed the
hypothesis that the partial sympathetic blockade observed after chronic
inhibition of MAO may be the consequence of replacement of norepinephrine
by a false, inactive neurochemical transmitter. This interesting hypothesis will
require further critical investigation to determine whether this will adequately
explain the mechanism of action of this type of antihypertensive agent.

V. Side effects and toxic reactions

It has been pointed out that the group of compounds designated as MAO
inhibitors may differ qualitatively and even quantitatively from each other
as to their pharmacological actions. As with all drugs, differences between
species must always be recognized and the translation of experimental results
from lower animals to man must always be reviewed critically. Finally, it has
been pointed out, that although many interesting theories have been proposed,
the mechanism of the antihypertensive action still remains a mystery. Because
of all these differences, the side effects and toxic reactions produced by these

compounds are varied and numerous and for the purposes of this discussion can be divided into three broad categories.

A number of side effects of these compounds appear to be relatively non-specific or are related generally to the therapeutic response itself. This would include effects occasioned by the general disturbance of autonomic function produced by most of these compounds, such as constipation, difficulty in micturition, blurred vision, dryness of mouth, impotence, and delayed ejaculation. It should be pointed out that a number of these and subsequently described reactions are generally observed only with marked overdosage; however, the potential for these reactions at normal therapeutic doses in sensitive individuals cannot be overlooked. Muscle twitching with gross involuntary movement of the extremities due to increased neuromuscular activity has also been observed. Other effects such as fluid retention, a tendency to weight gain, skin alterations, sweating, nausea, and headache have been reported from time to time. As was pointed out earlier in this chapter (Section IV), not all MAO inhibitors lower blood pressure in man and/or animals. However, many of them do have this activity and in the case of pargyline, this has proved to be useful therapeutically. Since the response is primarily orthostatic in nature and can be severe with overdosage, it may be considered as a "side effect" in some cases. Orthostatic hypotension, if marked, can be potentially more of a problem with the other MAO inhibitors which are used clinically as antidepressants and where any lowering of blood pressure may pose a problem. In the elderly patient especially, a sharp drop in the systolic and diastolic blood pressure may result in decreased cardiac output with congestive failure and peripheral edema. This can usually be minimized by dosage adjustment. The ability of certain MAO inhibitors to evoke a sympathomimetic response as an intrinsic part of their pharmacodynamic activity has occasionally produced serious side effects. Tranylcypromine particularly and pheniprazine and phenelzine have produced marked central nervous system and cardiovascular stimulation similar to amphetamine. Hypertensive reactions with tachycardia and headache have occurred in patients in doses inadequate to inhibit MAO (38), indicating this toxic response to be independent of inhibition of the enzyme. Other MAO inhibitors such as isocarboxazid, pargyline, and nialamide have no amphetaminelike activity (66).

A second type of toxic reaction seems to be related to the chemical structure and not to MAO inhibition or the therapeutic action of the drugs involved. The most serious of these is toxic necrosis of the liver seen with many hydrazine derivatives. This occurred in a significant enough number of patients receiving iproniazid and pheniprazine to result in their removal from the market. The incidence of liver damage is reportedly greater with hydrazine derivatives than with nonhydrazines (66). For example, there have been no reports of liver damage which can be attributed to pargyline. The use of pheniprazine has resulted in optic nerve atrophy, accompanied by loss of vision and color blindness which appear to be unique for this particular structure.

Maling *et al.* (98) and Highman and Maling (75) reported that prolonged administration to dogs of large doses of the MAO inhibitors phenylisopropyl-hydrazine (pheniprazine, JB516) and phenylisobutylhydrazine (JB835) produced bilaterally symmetrical neuropathologic lesions involving the inferior olivary nucleus and less frequently, the pyriform lobe, particularly the amygdaloid nuclei. No such neuropathologic lesions were found in cats, rabbits, and squirrel monkeys given these two hydrazine inhibitors, and no such lesions were found in dogs following prolonged administration of other MAO inhibitors.

Although unexplained anemia, normochromic and normocytic, has occurred with the use of MAO inhibitors, blood disorders have been infrequent and have not been a serious problem except in the case of etryptamine where the development of a sufficient number of cases of agranulocytosis forced its withdrawal.

A third category of adverse reactions are those which appear to be directly related to or a direct consequence of MAO inhibition, including CNS effects such as excessive stimulation with accompanying agitation, mania, and increased anxiety. Other manifestations include a prolongation and potentiation of sympathomimetic amines ingested as such or which are contained in certain foodstuffs. Much of the recent data concerning this reaction has been reviewed by Goldberg (66). As early as 1955, Furchgott (54) reported that the action of tyramine on isolated rabbit aortic strips was intensified following iproniazid. Later Goldberg and Sjoerdsma (65) found that the actions of dopamine, tryptamine, and tyramine on heart contractile force and arterial pressure were significantly augmented by six MAO inhibitors of varied structural types and postulated that the potentiation was related to MAO inhibition. There were no significant changes in the actions of norepinephrine, and the effects of serotonin were generally diminished. The augmentation of the actions of dopamine, tryptamine, and tyramine was unrelated to the cardiovascular effects of the inhibitors. Other workers (88) later found similar results. These reports received renewed attention when reports appeared describing hypertension and severe headaches in patients ingesting quantities of aged cheese while on tranylcypromine medication. It was postulated that the reaction was related to the presence of amines such as tyramine in the cheeses. They demonstrated the presence of tyramine, β-phenethylamine, and tryptamine by chromatographic analysis in a variety of cheeses and found increased urinary excretion of *p*-hydroxyphenylacetic acid, the oxidation product of tyramine, in patients who had consumed cheese. Other reports followed, describing extreme hypertension accompanied by headache and cerebrovascular accidents, atrial and ventricular arrhythmias, and pulmonary edema (11, 12, 45, 105). These reactions were noted with various MAO inhibitors when certain aged cheeses were consumed, although the most severe reactions followed the use of MAO inhibitors with strong sympathomimetic properties such as tranylcypromine, phenelzine, and pheniprazine. Tranylcypromine, in the absence of cheese or other precipitating factors, has produced hypertension culminating in intracranial bleeding and death in some cases. This is well summarized by Atkinson and Ditman (5) in their review of this drug. Horwitz et al. (82) produced marked potentiation of the pressor effects of tyramine hydrochloride, given orally and intravenously, in patients receiving pargyline. Further analysis revealed large quantities of tyramine in certain cheeses, particularly those of the aged variety. Various other reports of patients experiencing adverse effects following consumption of cheeses while on MAO inhibitor therapy leads to the conclusion that the response may occur following any potent MAO inhibitor. That it occurs with relative infrequency considering that many people have apparently eaten cheese with impunity in the past while on MAO inhibitor therapy, has led to interesting investigation and speculation. One explanation has been offered by Blackwell and Mabbitt (13) who found that the tyramine content of cheese is related to maturation time, bacterial flora, and details of manufacture, and that individual samples of the same type of cheese differ widely in tyramine content. Foods other than cheese, such as certain beers, wines, and yogurt also contain tyramine (4). However, yeast extracts (14) and chocolate (91) have also been implicated in hypertensive reactions with MAO inhibitors. Although no tyramine is found in these foods, other amines present may be involved. Headache and hypertension have also been seen in patients on pargyline therapy who ate broad beans (77). The effect was apparently due to the amino acid, dl-dihydroxyphenylalanine found in pods and seeds of some legume plants. Another explanation to explain the lack of consistent adverse responses to cheese and MAO inhibitors could be the variability in sensitivity between individual patients to the MAO inhibitors themselves.

Toxic effects related to an intensification of the adrenergic nervous system or the presence of sympathomimetic metabolites may be relieved by the administration of α-adrenergic blocking agents such as phentolamine or chlorpromazine.

A number of sympathomimetic drugs have produced hypertensive reactions in patients on MAO inhibitor therapy. These include amphetamines, phenylephrine, phenylpropanolamine, mephentermine, metaraminol, methylphenidate, and phenmetrazine (112).

There are a number of other drugs that are not metabolized by MAO, yet are potentiated by prior administration of MAO inhibitors. These drugs include CNS stimulants such as imipramine, amitriptyline, and CNS depressants such as anesthetics, meperidine, morphine, barbiturates, codeine, and alcohol. A summary of these reactions and their possible explanation is given by Goldberg (66).

References

1. Aceves, J., Pulido, P., Mendez, R., *Cardiologia* **37**, Suppl. II, 29 (1960).
2. Anderson, F. E., Kaminsky, D., Dubnick, B., Klutchko, S. R., Cetenko, W. A., Gylys, J., and Hart, J. A., *J. Med. Pharm. Chem.* **5**, 221 (1962).
3. Arnold, R. T., and Richardson, P. N., *J. Am. Chem. Soc.* **76**, 3649 (1954).
4. Asatoor, A. M., Levi, A. J., and Milne, M. D., *Lancet* **II**, 733 (1963).
5. Atkinson, R. M., and Ditman, K. W. S., *Clin. Pharmacol. Therap.* **6**, 631 (1965).
6. Axelrod, J., *Physiol. Rev.* **39**, 751 (1959).
7. Axelrod, J., *Ciba Found. Symp. Adrenergic Mechanisms* p. 28 (1960).
8. Axelrod, J., Hertting, G., and Patrick, R. W., *J. Pharmacol. Exptl. Therap.* **134**, 325 (1961).
9. Bächtold, H. P., and Pletscher, A., *Experientia* **15**, 265 (1959).
10. Biel, J. H., Drukker, A. E., Mitchell, T. F., Sprengeler, E. P., Nuhfer, P. A., Conway, A. C., and Horita, A., *J. Am. Chem. Soc.* **81**, 2805 (1959).
11. Blackwell, B., *Lancet* **II**, 849 (1963).
12. Blackwell, B., and Marley, E., *Lancet* **I**, 530 (1964).
13. Blackwell, B., and Mabbitt, L. A., *Lancet* **I**, 938 (1965).
14. Blackwell, B., Marley, E., and Taylor, D., *Lancet* **I**, 1166 (1965).
15. Blaschko, H., *Pharmacol. Rev.* **4**, 415 (1952).
16. Blaschko, H., *Pharmacol. Rev.* **6**, 23 (1954).
17. Boura, A. L. A., Copp, F. C., Duncombe, W. G., Green, A. F., and McCoubrey, A., *Brit. J. Pharmacol.* **15**, 265 (1960).
18. Boura, A. L., Copp, F. C., Green, A. F., Hodson, H. F., Ruffell, G. K., Sim, M. F., Walton, A., and Grivsky, E. M., *Nature* **191**, 1312 (1961).
19. Brest, A. N., Kodama, R., Dreifus, L., Weber, A., and Moyer, J. H., *Am. J. Med. Sci.* **241**, 199 (1961).
20. Brest, A. N., Onesti, G., Sekine, G., Dreifus, L., and Moyer, J. H., *Current Therap. Res.* **3**, 313 (1961).
21. Brest, A. N., Onesti, G., Heider, C., and Moyer, J. H., *Ann. N.Y. Acad. Sci.* **107**, 1016 (1963).
22. Brodie, B. B., Shore, P. A., and Pletscher, A., *Science* **123**, 992 (1956).
23. Brodie, B. B., and Shore, P. A., *Ann. N.Y. Acad. Sci.* **66**, 631 (1957).
24. Brodie, B. B., Spector, S., and Shore, P. A., *Pharmacol. Rev.* **11**, 548 (1959).
25. Brodie, B. B., Spector, S., and Shore, P. A., *Ann. N.Y. Acad. Sci.* **80**, 609 (1959).
26. Brodie, B. B., *Circulation* **28**, 970 (1963).
27. Bryant, J. M., Torosdag, S., Schvartz, N., Fletcher, L., Jr., Fertig, H., Schwartz, M. S., and Quan, R. B. F., *J. Am. Med. Assoc.* **178**, 406 (1961).
28. Bryant, J. M., Schvartz, N., Torosdag, S., Fertig, H., Fletcher, L., Jr., Schwartz, M. S., and Quan, R. B. F., *Ann. N.Y. Acad. Sci.* **107**, 1023 (1963).
29. Bulbring, E., and Lin, R. C. Y., *J. Physiol. (London)* **140**, 381 (1958).
30. Burger, A., and Yost, W. L., *J. Am. Chem. Soc.* **70**, 2198 (1948).
31. Burger, A., Walter, C. R., Jr., Bennet, W. B., and Turnbull, L. B., *Science* **112**, 306 (1950).
32. Burn, J. H., and Rand, M. J., *Brit. J. Pharmacol.* **13**, 471 (1958).
33. Cahn, J., and Herold, M., *Chemotherapia* **4**, 262 (1962).
34. Carlsson, A., and Waldeck, B., *Acta Pharmacol. Toxicol.* **20**, 371 (1963).

35. Cesarman, T., *Ann. N. Y. Acad. Sci.* **80**, 988 (1959).
36. Chessin, M., Dubnick, B., Leeson, G., and Scott, C. C., *Ann. N. Y. Acad. Sci.* **80**, 597 (1959).
37. Clark, J. A., *Lancet* **I**, 618 (1961).
38. Cooper, A. J., Magnus, R. V., and Rose, M. J., *Lancet* **I**, 527 (1964).
39. Costa, E., and Brodie, B. B., *J. Am. Geriat. Soc.* **9**, 419 (1961).
40. Craver, B. N., Barrett, W., Cameron, A., and Yonkman, F. F., *J. Am. Pharm. Assoc., Sci. Ed.* **40**, 559 (1951).
41. Crout, J. R., and Shore, P. A., *Clin. Res.* **12**, 180 (1964).
42. Crumpton, C. W., *Am. J. Cardiol.* **6**, 1117 (1960).
43. Davey, M. J., Farmer, J. B., and Reinert, H., *Chemotherapia* **4**, 314 (1962).
44. Davey, M. J., Farmer, J. B., and Reinert, H., *Brit. J. Pharmacol.* **20**, 121 (1963).
45. Davies, E. B., *Lancet* **II**, 691 (1963).
46. Day, M. D., and Rand, M. J., *Brit. J. Pharmacol.* **21**, 84 (1963).
47. Day, M. D., and Rand, M. J., *J. Pharm. Pharmacol.* **15**, 221 (1963).
48. Drain, D. J., Howes, J. G. B., Lazare, R., Salaman, A. M., Shadbolt, R., and Williams, H. W. R., *J. Med. Chem.* **6**, 63 (1963).
49. Everett, G. M., and Wiegand, R. G., *Proc. 1st Intern. Pharmacol. Meeting, Stockholm, 1961* Vol. 8, p. 85. Pergamon Press, Oxford, 1962.
50. Everett, G. M., Wiegand, R. G., and Rinaldi, F. U., *Ann. N. Y. Acad. Sci.* **107**, 1068 (1963).
51. Fink, M. A., *Proc. Soc. Exptl. Biol. Med.* **92**, 673 (1956).
52. Fischer, J. E., Musacchio, J., Kopin, I. J., and Axelrod, J., *Life Sci.* **3**, 413 (1964).
53. Ford, R. V., *Current Therap. Res.* **3**, 378 (1961).
54. Furchgott, R. F., Weinstein, P., Huebl, H., Bozorgmehri, P., and Mensendick, R., *Federation Proc.* **14**, 341 (1955).
55. Gaddum, J. H., *Ciba Found. Symp. Hypertension-Humoral Neurogenic Factors* p. 75. (1955).
56. Gardner, T. S., Wenis, E., and Lee, J., *J. Med. Pharm. Chem.* **2**, 133 (1960).
57. Gardner, T. S., Wenis, E., and Lee, J., *J. Med. Pharm. Chem.* **3**, 241 (1961).
58. Gardner, T. S., Wenis, E., and Lee, J., *J. Med. Pharm. Chem.* **5**, 503 (1962).
59. Gertner, S. B., Paasonen, M. K., and Giarman, N. J., *Federation Proc.* **16**, 299 (1957).
60. Gertner, S. B., *J. Pharmacol. Exptl. Therap.* **131**, 223 (1961).
61. Gessa, G. L., Cuenca, E., and Costa, E., *Pharmacologist* **4**, No. 2, 179 (1962).
62. Gessa, G. L., Cuenca, E., and Costa, E., *Ann. N. Y. Acad. Sci.* **107**, 935 (1963).
63. Glavas, E., Stojanova, D., Trajkov, T., and Nikodijevic, B., *Arch. Intern. Pharmacodyn.* **155**, 381 (1965).
64. Goldberg, L. I., and DaCosta, F. M., *Proc. Soc. Exptl. Biol. Med.* **105**, 223 (1960).
65. Goldberg, L. I., and Sjoerdsma, A., *J. Pharmacol. Exptl. Therap.* **127**, 212 (1959).
66. Goldberg, L. I., *J. Am. Med. Assoc.* **190**, 456 (1964).
67. Goldberg, N. D., and Shideman, F. E., *J. Pharmacol. Exptl. Therap.* **136**, 142 (1962).
68. Govindachari, T. R., Nagarajan, K., Pai, B. R., and Arumugam, N., *J. Chem. Soc.* p. 4280 (1956).
69. Green, H., and Erickson, R. W., *J. Pharmacol. Exptl. Therap.* **129**, 237 (1960).
70. Greig, M. E., Walk, R. A., and Gibbons, A. J., *J. Pharmacol. Exptl. Therap.* **127**, 110 (1959).
71. Greig, M. E., Seay, P. H., and Freyburger, W. A., *J. Neuropsychiat.* Suppl. 1, p. 131 (1961).
72. Griesemer, E. C., Dragstedt, C. A., Wells, J., and Zeller, E. A., *Experientia* **11**, 182 (1955).
73. Gunn, J. A., *Arch. Intern. Pharmacodyn.* **50**, 379 (1935).

74. Heinzelman, R. V., Anthony, W. C., Lyttle, D. A., and Szmuszkovicz, J., *J. Org. Chem.* **25**, 1548 (1960).
75. Highman, B., and Maling, H. M., *J. Pharmacol. Exptl. Therap.* **137**, 344 (1962).
76. Hobbs, L. F., *Angiology* **11**, 86 (1960).
77. Hodge, J. V., Nye, E. R., and Emerson, G. W., *Lancet* **I**, 1108 (1964).
78. Hollander, W., and Wilkins, R. W., *in* "Hypertension: First Hahnemann Symposium on Hypertensive Disease" (J. Moyer, ed.), p. 399. Saunders, Philadelphia, Pennsylvania, 1959.
79. Holzbauer, M., and Vogt, M., *J. Neurochem.* **1**, 8 (1956).
80. Horwitz, D., Goldberg, L. I., and Sjoerdsma, A., *J. Lab. Clin. Med.* **56**, 747 (1960).
81. Horwitz, D., and Sjoerdsma, A., *Proc. Soc. Exptl. Biol. Med.* **106**, 118 (1961).
82. Horwitz, D., Lovenberg, W., Engelman, K., and Sjoerdsma, A., *J. Am. Med. Assoc.* **188**, 1108 (1964).
83. Johnson, R. L., Freis, E. D., and Schnaper, H. W., *Circulation* **5**, 833 (1952).
84. Julia, M., Julia, S., and Bemont, B., *Bull. Soc. Chim. France* p. 304 (1960).
85. Kaiser, C., Lester, B. M., Zirkle, C. L., Burger, A., Davis, C. S., Delia, T. J., and Zerngibl, L., *J. Med. Pharm. Chem.* **5**, 1243 (1962).
86. Kakimoto, Y., and Armstrong, M. D., *J. Biol. Chem.* **237**, 422 (1962).
87. Kamijo, K., Koelle, G. B., and Wagner, H. H., *J. Pharmacol. Exptl. Therap.* **117**, 213 (1956).
88. Kono, C., Kanda, Z., Sekiya, A., and Saji, E., *Nagoya J. Med. Sci.* **24**, 159 (1962).
89. Kopin, I. J., *Pharmacol. Rev.* **16**, 179 (1964).
90. Kopin, I. J., Fischer, J. E., Musacchio, J. M., Horst, W. D., and Weise, V. K., *J. Pharmacol. Exptl. Therap.* **147**, 186 (1965).
91. Krikler, D. M., and Lewis, B., *Lancet* **I**, 1166 (1965).
92. Kuntzman, R. G., and Jacobson, M. M., *J. Pharmacol. Exptl. Therap.* **141**, 166 (1963).
93. Lands, A. M., and Grant, J. I., *J. Pharmacol. Exptl. Therap.* **106**, 341 (1952).
94. Leeper, L. C., Weissbach, H., and Udenfriend, S., *Arch. Biochem. Biophys.* **77**, 417 (1958).
95. Lesse, S., *Intern. Rec. Med.* **173**, 632 (1960).
96. Levine, R. J., *Biochem. Pharmacol.* **11**, 395 (1962).
97. Levine, R. J., and Sjoerdsma, A., *Clin. Pharmacol. Therap.* **4**, 22 (1963).
98. Maling, H. M., Highman, B., and Spector, S., *J. Pharmacol. Exptl. Therap.* **137**, 334 (1962).
99. Marrazzi, A. S., *J. Pharmacol. Exptl. Therap.* **65**, 395 (1939).
100. Martin, Y. C., Cardinal, E., Miller, J. P., and Wiegand, R. G., unpublished observations (1966).
101. Matthews, R. J., *Arch. Intern. Pharmacodyn.* **142**, 90 (1963).
102. Matthews, R. J., Roberts, B. J., and Adkins, P. K., *J. Neuropsychiat.* Suppl. 1 p. 151 (1961).
103. Maxwell, M. H., *Ann. N. Y. Acad. Sci.* **107**, 993 (1963).
104. Maxwell, M. H., Gonick, H. C., Scaduto, L., Pearce, M. L., and Kleeman, C. R., *Circulation* **26**, 1279 (1962).
105. McClure, J. L., *Lancet* **I**, 1351 (1962).
106. McCoubrey, A., *J. Pharm. Pharmacol.* **14**, 727 (1962).
107. Mendlowitz, M., Gitlow, S. E., Wolf, R. L., and Tuckman, J., *Am. Heart J.* **70**, 677 (1965).
108. Miyahara, M., *Japan. Circulation J.* [*English Ed.*] **26**, 1 (1962).
109. Muscholl, E., *Experientia* **15**, 428 (1959).
110. Muscholl, E., *J. Soc. Cien. Med. Lisboa* **123**, 76 (1959).

111. Muscholl, E., and Maitre, L., *Experientia* **19**, 658 (1963).
112. Oates, J. A., and Doctor, R. B., *Postgrad. Med.* **37**, 58 (1965).
113. Orvis, H. H., Horwitz, D., Thomas, R., Tamagna, I., and Sjoerdsma, A., *Clin. Res.* **10**, 178 (1962).
114. Orvis, H. H., Tamagna, I., Horwitz, D., and Thomas, R., *Ann. N.Y. Acad. Sci.* **102**, 958 (1963).
115. Page, I. H., and McCubbin, J. W., *Circulation Res.* **1**, 354 (1953).
116. Pennes, H. H., and Hoch, P. H., *Am. J. Psychiat.* **113**, 887 (1957).
117. Pletscher, A., *Experientia* **14**, 73 (1958).
118. Pletscher, A., and Besendorf, H., *Experientia* **15**, 25 (1959).
119. Pletscher, A., Besendorf, H., Bächtold, H. P., and Gey, K. F., *Helv. Physiol. Pharmacol. Acta* **17**, 202 (1959).
120. Pletscher, A., Gey, K. F., and Zeller, P., *Fortschr. Arzneimittelforsch.* **2**, 417 (1960).
121. Pletscher, A., Göschke, H., Gey, K., and Thölen, H., *Med. Exptl.* **4**, 113 (1961).
122. Rooney, C. S., Cragoe, E. J., Jr., Porter, C. C., and Sprague, J. M., *J. Med. Pharm. Chem.* **5**, 155 (1962).
123. Rowe, R. P., *Diseases Nervous System* **20**, August Supp. 5 (1959).
124. Schoepke, H. G., and Wiegand, R. G., *Ann. N.Y. Acad. Sci.* **107**, 924 (1963).
125. Schroeder, H. A., *Circulation* **5**, 28 (1952).
126. Schuler, W., and Wyss, E., *Arch. Intern. Pharmacodyn.* **128**, 431 (1960).
127. Shore, P. A., Mead, J. A. R., Kuntzman, R. G., Spector, S., and Brodie, B. B., *Science* **126**, 1063 (1957).
128. Sjoerdsma, A., *Circulation Res.* **9**, 734 (1961).
129. Sjoerdsma, A., Oates, J. A., Zaltzman, P., and Udenfriend, S., *J. Pharmacol. Exptl. Therap.* **126**, 217 (1959).
130. Sjoerdsma, A., Gillespie, L., and Udenfriend, S., *Ann. N.Y. Acad. Sci.* **80**, 969 (1959).
131. Smithwick, R. H., Greer, W. E. R., Robertson, C. W., and Wilkins, R. W., *New Engl. J. Med.* **242**, 252 (1950).
132. Snyder, H. R., and Katz, L., *J. Am. Chem. Soc.* **69**, 3140 (1947).
133. Spector, W. G., and Willoughby, D. A., *Nature* **179**, 318 (1957).
134. Spector, S., Prockop, D., Shore, P. A., and Brodie, B. B., *Science* **127**, 704 (1958).
135. Spector, S., Shore, P. A., and Brodie, B. B., *J. Pharmacol. Exptl. Therap.* **128**, 15 (1960).
136. Spencer, J. N., Porter, M., Froehlich, H. L., and Wendel, H., *Federation Proc.* **19**, 277 (1960).
137. Swett, L. R., Martin, W. B., Taylor, J. D., Everett, G. M., Wykes, A. A., and Gladish, Y. C., *Ann. N.Y. Acad. Sci.* **107**, 891 (1963).
138. Taylor, J. D., Wykes, A. A., Gladish, Y. C., Martin, W. B., and Everett, G. M., *Federation Proc.* **19**, 278 (1960).
139. Taylor, J. D., Wykes, A. A., Gladish, Y. C., and Martin, W. B., *Nature* **187**, 941 (1960).
140. Tedeschi, D. H., Tedeschi, R. E., and Fellows, E. J., *J. Pharmacol. Exptl. Therap.* **126**, 223 (1959).
141. Tedeschi, R. E., Tedeschi, D. H., Ames, P. L., Cook, L., Mattis, P. A., and Fellows, E. J., *Proc. Soc. Exptl. Biol. Med.* **102**, 380 (1959).
142. Udenfriend, S., Shore, P. A., Bogdanski, D. F., Weissbach, H., and Brodie, B. B., *Recent Progr. Hormone Res.* **13**, 4 (1957).
143. Udenfriend, S., Witkop, B., Redfield, B. G., and Weissbach, H., *Biochem. Pharmacol.* **1**, 160 (1958).
144. Urquiaga, X., Villarreal, J., Alonso-de Florida, F., and Pardo, E. G., *Arch. Intern. Pharmacodyn.* **146**, 126 (1963).
145. Van Zoeren, G. J., U.S. Patent 2,520,516 (1950).

146. Vogt, M., *J. Physiol. (London)* **123**, 451 (1954).
147. Vogt, M., *Pharmacol. Rev.* **11**, 483 (1959).
148. Warner, R. R. P., *J. Mt. Sinai Hosp., N.Y.* **26**, 450 (1959).
149. Winsor, T., *Geriatrics* **19**, 598 (1964).
150. Woolley, D. W., *Science* **125**, 752 (1957).
151. Woolley, D. W., and Shaw, E., *Proc. Natl. Acad. Sci. U.S.* **40**, 228 (1954).
152. Woolley, D. W., and Shaw, E., *Science* **124**, 34 (1956).
153. Woolley, D. W., and Shaw, E. N., *Ann. N.Y. Acad. Sci.* **66**, 649 (1957).
154. Wykes, A. A., Gladish, Y. C., and Taylor, J. D., *Federation Proc.* **18**, 462 (1959).
155. Zbinden, G., *Am. J. Cardiol.* **6**, 1121 (1960).
156. Zbinden, G., Randall, L. O., and Moe, R. A., *Diseases Nervous System* **21**, March Suppl., 89 (1960).
157. Zeller, E. A., Barsky, J., Fouts, J. R., Kirchheimer, W. F., and Van Orden, L. S., *Experientia* **8**, 349 (1952).
158. Zeller, P., Pletscher, A., Gey, K. F., Gutmann, H., Hegedüs, B., and Straub, O., *Ann. N.Y. Acad. Sci.* **80**, 555 (1959).
159. Zirkle, C. L., Kaiser, C., Tedeschi, D. H., and Tedeschi, R. E., *J. Med. Pharm. Chem.* **5**, 1265 (1962).

CHAPTER XII

Hypotensive *Veratrum* Alkaloids

S. Morris Kupchan

Werner E. Flacke

I. Introduction, 429

II. Alkaloids and Taxonomy of *Veratrum* and Related Genera, 430

III. Chemical Classification of *Veratrum* Alkaloids, 430

IV. Chemistry and Relative Activity of the Hypotensive *Veratrum* Alkaloids, 430

V. Chemistry and Relative Hypotensive Activity of Semisynthetic Alkamine Esters, 436

VI. Pharmacological Actions and Methods Used for Comparative Evaluation, 439
    A. Site and Mode of Basic Action, 439
    B. Primary and Secondary Effects of *Veratrum* Alkaloids, 440
    C. Selectivity of Action, 442
    D. Hypotensive and Emetic Activity, 444
    E. Methods Used, 448

VII. *In Vivo* Distribution, 450

VIII. Clinical Uses, 451
    References, 453

I. Introduction

Veratrum and related plants have been used for medicinal purposes for hundreds of years. Galenical preparations were used in the Middle Ages for purposes of sorcery and in mystical rites. Subsequently, the crude extracts have been used in the treatment of fevers, as local counterirritants in neuralgia, as cardiac tonics, as emetics, as crow poisons, and as insecticides (46, 69). The use of veratrum in the control of hypertension, at least in the United States, dates from the report of Baker in 1859 (6). Several attempts were made to introduce the use of veratrum extracts into medical practice during the second half of the nineteenth century, but these attempts were unsuccessful. The treatments during this period continued to employ crude extracts containing many alkaloids. The results achieved with these crude extracts were erratic and the treatments fell into disrepute. Some 50 years later, during the late 1930's, purified alkaloidal preparations responsible for the hypotensive activity of veratrum became available for the first time. Poethke in Germany (128) and Craig and Jacobs in the United States (19) improved the extraction and purification procedures and made available the first crystalline powerfully hypotensive alkaloid preparation, protoveratrine. Careful pharmacological investigation of the crystalline preparations, spearheaded by Krayer and his associates, demonstrated that some drugs were suitable for clinical trials (70). These clinical trials were followed by introduction of protoveratrine and related preparations into clinical use in the treatment of certain types of hypertension (21, 56, 108, 108a). The basic pharmacology of the *Veratrum* ester alkaloids of both the organ system and at the cellular level is of great interest per se, and has made them very useful pharmacological tools. In addition, their hypotensive effect has several exceedingly desirable characteristics. However, the undesirable side effects which accompany the latter positive elements have limited their clinical usefulness.

II. Alkaloids and taxonomy of *Veratrum* and related genera

The *Veratrum* alkaloids occur in plants of the tribe Veratreae, which is part of the subfamily Melanthioideae of the family Liliaceae. The compounds which have received most attention have been obtained from various species of the genera *Veratrum* (e.g., *V. album* from Europe, *V. viride* from the United States and Canada), *Schoenocaulon* (e.g., *S. officinale* from Mexico) and *Zygadenus* (e.g., *Z. venenosus* and *Z. paniculatus* from the United States). The occurrence of alkaloids in plants of the Veratreae, the classical botanical taxonomy of the Veratreae, and the implications of alkaloid occurrence and structure to the taxonomy of the Veratreae have recently been discussed elsewhere (95).

III. Chemical classification of *Veratrum* alkaloids

The steroid C_{27} bases or alkamines obtainable from plants of the Veratreae, either by direct extraction or after hydrolysis, fall into two distinct chemical groups. The jerveratrum alkamines constitute a group (e.g., jervine, rubijervine, isorubijervine, veratramine) which contain only one to three atoms of oxygen and are found in unhydrolyzed plant extracts in part as free alkamines and in part in combination with one molecule of D-glucose as glucoalkaloids. The ceveratrum bases (i.e., zygadenine, zygadenilic acid δ-lactone, sabine, veracevine, germine, protoverine) are highly hydroxylic and contain seven to nine atoms of oxygen. The latter alkamines usually occur esterified with various acids as ester alkaloids, but are in some instances unconjugated; they have never been found as glycosides (28, 59, 83, 111, 118).

IV. Chemistry and relative activity of the hypotensive *Veratrum* alkaloids

The principal hypotensive principles of *Veratrum* extracts are known to be ester derivatives of the six highly hydroxylated ceveratrum alkamines whose structures are given in Fig. 1. The structure elucidation and chemistry of the latter alkamines have been summarized in detail elsewhere (28, 59, 82, 83, 111, 118). For present purposes, it is sufficient to note that all six contain the

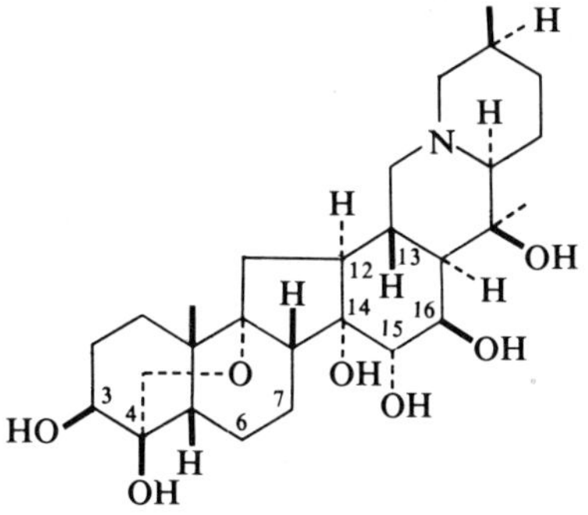

Zygadenine

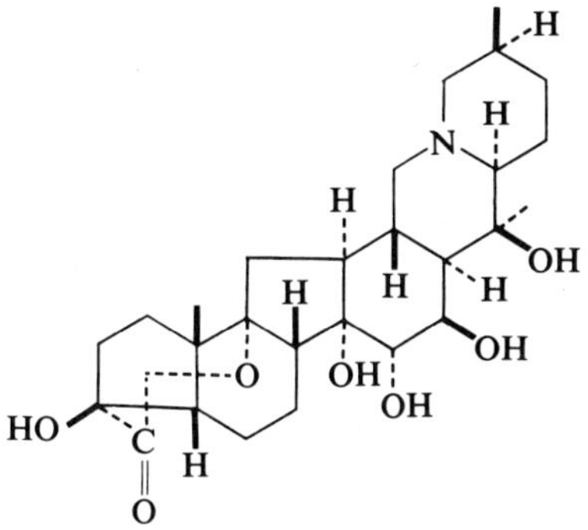

Zygadenilic acid δ-lactone

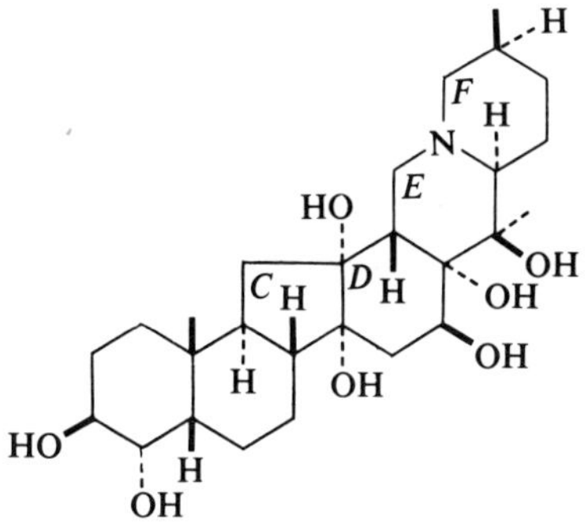

Sabine

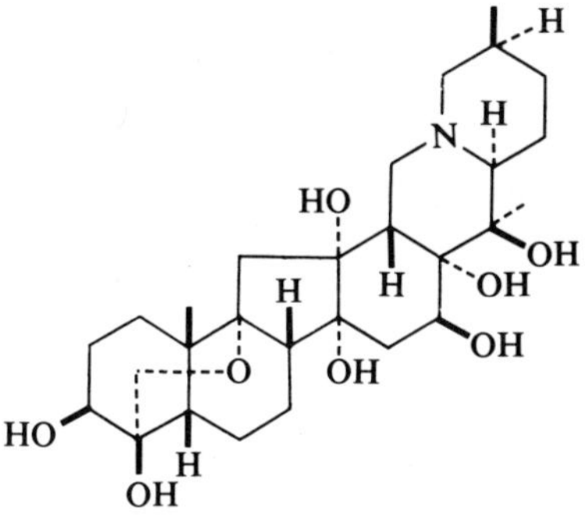

Veracevine

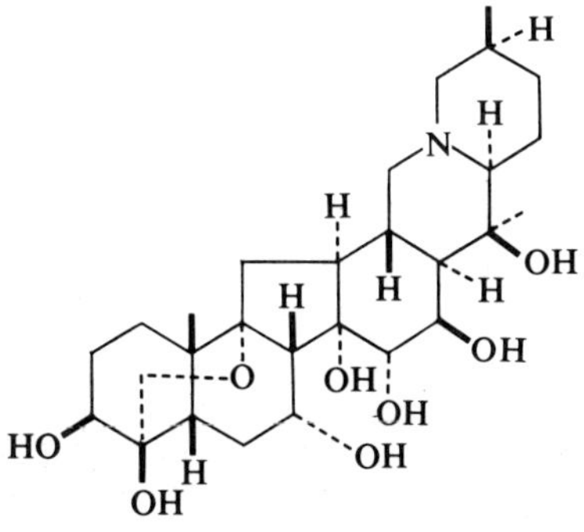

Germine

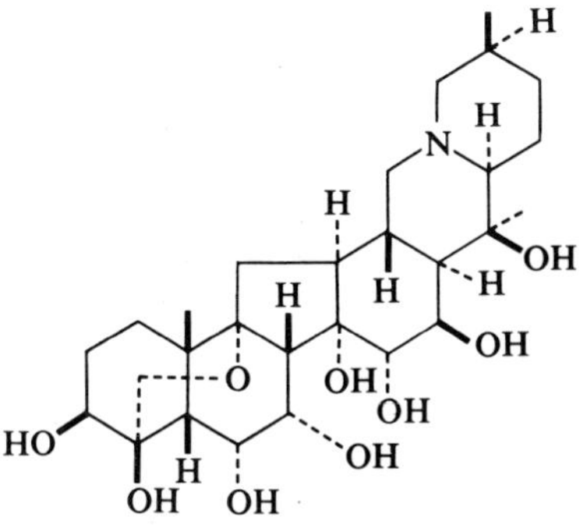

Protoverine

Fig. 1. The ceveratrum alkamines.

Table I
Structures of the Hypotensive *Veratrum* Ester Alkaloids

Compound	Formula	Acyl groups[a]				Reference
		C-3	C-6	C-7	C-15	
Esters of zygadenine						
Zygacine	$C_{29}H_{45}NO_8$	Ac				(74, 92)
Angeloylzygadenine	$C_{32}H_{49}NO_8$	An				(148)
3-(*l*-2-methylbutyryl) zygadenine	$C_{32}H_{51}NO_8$	MB				(170)
Veratroylzygadenine	$C_{36}H_{52}NO_{10}$	Ve				(84, 144)
Vanilloylzygadenine	$C_{35}H_{49}NO_{10}$	Va				(84)
Ester of zygadenilic acid δ-lactone						
Angeloylzygadenilic acid δ-lactone[b]	$C_{32}H_{47}NO_8$	Ac				(153, 171)
Ester of sabine						
Sabadine	$C_{29}H_{47}NO_8$	Ac				(89, 109, 110)
Esters of veracevine						
Cevacine	$C_{29}H_{45}NO_9$	Ac				(91, 155)
Cevadine	$C_{32}H_{49}NO_9$	An				(77, 125, 142)
Veratridine	$C_{36}H_{51}NO_{11}$	Ve				(91, 125, 142, 155)
Vanilloylveracevine[c]	$C_{35}H_{49}NO_{11}$	Va				(146)
Esters of germine						
Germitetrine	$C_{41}H_{63}NO_{14}$	HMAB		Ac	MB	(78, 83, 116, 118)
Germitrine	$C_{39}H_{61}NO_{12}$	MB		Ac	HMB	(38, 73)

						References
Neogermitrine	$C_{36}H_{55}NO_{11}$	Ac		Ac	MB	(37, 73)
Germanitrine	$C_{30}H_{59}NO_{11}$	An		Ac	MB	(62, 76)
Germinitrine[d]	$C_{39}H_{57}NO_{11}$					(62)
Germerine	$C_{37}H_{59}NO_{11}$	MB			HMB	(73, 127, 128)
Germidine	$C_{34}H_{53}NO_{10}$	Ac			MB	(37, 73)
Neogermidine[e]	$C_{34}H_{53}NO_{10}$			Ac	MB	(73, 85, 117)
Germbudine	$C_{37}H_{59}NO_{12}$	t-DMB			MB	(83, 88, 117)
Neogermbudine	$C_{37}H_{59}NO_{12}$	e-DMB			MB	(78, 116)
Protoveratridine	$C_{32}H_{51}NO_{9}$	MB			MB	(73, 127, 128)
Esters of Protoverine						
Protoveratrine A[f]	$C_{41}H_{63}NO_{14}$	HMB	Ac		MB	(61, 80, 116, 119, 143)
Protoveratrine B[g]	$C_{41}H_{63}NO_{15}$	t-DMB	Ac		MB	(61, 80, 83, 116, 119, 143)
Escholerine	$C_{41}H_{61}NO_{13}$	An	Ac		MB	(63, 79)
Desacetylprotoveratrine A	$C_{39}H_{61}NO_{13}$	HMB	Ac		MB	(81, 116)
Desacetylprotoveratrine B[h]	$C_{39}H_{61}NO_{14}$	t-DMB	Ac		MB	(64, 81, 83, 117)

[a] Ac = acetyl; An = angeloyl; Va = vanilloyl; Ve = veratroyl; HMAB = *erythro*-2-hydroxy-2-methyl-3-acetoxybutyryl; MB = (*l*)-2-methyl-butyryl; HMB = (*d*)-2-hydroxy-2-methylbutyryl; t-DMB = (*d*)-*threo*-2,3-dihydroxy-2-methylbutyryl; e-DMB = (*l*)-*erythro*-2,3-dihydroxy-2-methylbutyryl.

[b] This ester has been characterized as the 16-angelate (171).

[c] Also called vanilloylcevine.

[d] Germinitrine has been reported to be a triester of germine which yields acetic acid, tiglic acid, and angelic acid upon hydrolysis (62). The positions of the acyl groups have not been determined.

[e] Also called isogermidine.

[f] Also called protoveratrine.

[g] Also called neoprotoveratrine and veratetrine.

[h] Also called desacetylneoprotoveratrine.

modified steroid cevane nucleus. The latter skeletal structure is characterized by the C-nor-D-homo ring system (which may formally be regarded as having originated by migration of the C-13, C-14 bond of a normal steroid to the C-12, C-14 position) along with a folding of the normal cholesterol side chain around the nitrogen atom. A feature common to zygadenine, germine, veracevine, and protoverine is the α-ketol hemiketal system found in rings A and B. Sabine and veracevine have identical structures in rings D, E, and F. Likewise, zygadenine, zygadenilic acid δ-lactone, germine, and protoverine

Table II

RELATIVE HYPOTENSIVE ACTIVITY OF CERTAIN *Veratrum*
ESTER ALKALOIDS

Alkaloid	Relative hypotensive activity		Reference
	Maison[a]	Myers[b]	
Veratroylzygadenine	0.9		(62, 150)
Cevadine	0.18		(99)
Veratridine	0.5		(99)
Germitetrine		2.1	(116)
Germitrine	11.0		(99)
Neogermitrine	8.7		(99)
Germanitrine	8.3		(62)
Germinitrine	2.4		(62)
Germerine	5.3		(99)
Germidine	2.4		(99)
Neogermidine		0.1	(117)
Germbudine		0.8	(117)
Neogermbudine		1.0	(116)
Protoveratrine A	5.4		(61, 149)
Protoveratrine B	4.0	1.5	(61, 117, 149)
Escholerine	3.3		(63)
Desacetylprotoveratrine A		0.4	(116)
Desacetylprotoveratrine B	1.0	0.4	(64, 117)

[a] Activity relative to a mixed alkaloidal ester preparation (Veriloid, activity = 1.0) which produced a 30% fall in mean arterial pressure when administered at a dose of 1 μg per kilogram per minute by intravenous injection of 10 minutes' duration in anesthetized dogs (61–64, 99, 149, 150).
[b] Activity relative to a mixed alkaloidal ester preparation from *Veratrum viride* (Deravine, activity = 1.0) which produced a 30% fall in mean arterial pressure of the anesthetized dog at a dose of 2 μg per kilogram administered intravenously over a 10-minute period (116, 117).

have identical structures in rings *C*, *D*, *E*, and *F*. Protoverine has been degraded to a germine derivative and germine to a zygadenine derivative by suitable alteration of ring *B*. Veracevine and zygadenine have identical structures in rings *A* and *B*, and this resemblance may figure in the similar pattern of esterification in the naturally occurring ester derivatives of the latter alkamines.

The systematic chemical investigations of the hypotensive *Veratrum* ester alkaloids have recently been surveyed (75, 83), and the structural conclusions are summarized in Table I. The relative hypotensive activity of those *Veratrum* ester alkaloids for which comparative data are available is listed in Table II. The pharmacological data indicate that the number, the nature, and the positions of the esterifying acids are of importance in determining the degree of hypotensive activity. The structure–activity relationships which are apparent from the data in Table II follow:

(1) In the germine series, the 3,7,15-triesters are the most active compounds. Removal of the C-7 acetate group from a germine 3,7,15-triester is accompanied by a diminution in hypotensive potency [compare germitetrine *vs.* desacetylgermitetrine [relative "Myers" activity, 1.8 (116)]; neogermitrine *vs.* germidine; germitrine *vs.* germerine; germanitrine *vs.* germanidine [relative "Maison" activity, 1.3 (62)]].

(2) Among the germine 3,7,15-triesters, variations in the nature of the ester group affixed at C-3 are not accompanied by particularly marked changes in hypotensive potency [compare germitetrine *vs.* neogermitrine *vs.* germanitrine].

(3) Among the germine diesters, the 3,15-derivatives show a relatively high order of activity [compare germerine, germidine, germbudine, and neogermbudine *vs.* neogermidine].

(4) In the protoverine series, the 3,6,7,15-tetraesters are the most active compounds. Removal of the C-7 acetate group from a protoverine 3,6,7,15-tetraester is accompanied by a diminution in hypotensive potency [compare protoveratrine A *vs.* desacetylprotoveratrine A; protoveratrine B *vs.* desacetylprotoveratrine B].

(5) Among the protoverine 3,6,7,15-tetraesters, variations in the nature of the ester group affixed at C-3 are not accompanied by particularly marked changes in hypotensive potency [compare protoveratrine A *vs.* protoveratrine B *vs.* escholerine].

(6) In contrast to the many polyesters of germine that have been found in plant extracts, only monoesters of veracevine and zygadenine have been isolated. Among them the nature of the acid moiety at C-3 is a major factor in determining potency. The veratric acid esters, veratridine and veratroylzygadenine, are more potent than cevadine and vanilloylzygadenine. Veratroylzygadenine is more potent than veratridine. The potency of angeloylzygadenine and of vanilloylveracevine is not known.

(7) A comparison of the (C-3) monoacetates of the alkamines shows that only sabadine, the monoacetate of sabine, possesses weak hypotensive potency (89). The only difference between sabadine and cevacine is the absence of the oxide ring between C-4 and C-9 in sabadine.

V. Chemistry and relative hypotensive activity of semisynthetic alkamine esters

In a series of acetate esters of germine and of protoverine only the tetra- and pentaesters of germine were regularly hypotensive (30). In the protoverine series, the tri-, penta-, and hexacetate caused hyper- or hypotension depending upon the anaesthesia used (50). All acetate esters of germine and protoverine were found to induce repetitive electrical activity and induce an increase in duration and tension development after a single electrical stimulation in isolated frog muscles. The duration of repetitive activity corresponded with activity in the circulation. Esters causing only a brief prolongation of activity in the muscle were without hypotensive activity. Those that caused a greater prolongation in the muscle were hypotensive in the circulation (9, 30–32, 50, 51). The correlation can be extended to include cevadine and veratridine, which cause a still greater prolongation of the muscle twitch and are the more potent hypotensive agents. The correlation is pointed out here because it might be useful as a screening test.

The synthesis of a number of esters of high hypotensive activity by stepwise esterification of germine was reported by Weisenborn and co-workers (161). All of the monoesters showed a low order of activity; the diesters which carried a branched α-methyl group showed an order of activity comparable to the naturally occurring germine diesters. Several of the semisynthetic triesters were highly active, and showed roughly the same potency as the most active natural esters, germitrine and neogermitrine. The structures of the naturally occurring esters were unknown at that time, but the authors suggested, on the basis of comparisons of pharmacological activities and molecular rotations with those of the natural esters, that direct acylation of germine introduces the acid radicals on the same hydroxyl groups. This view was supported by synthesis of germidine and monoacetylneogermitrine from germine (162).

Attempts to prepare hypotensive esters by acylation of zygadenine and veracevine, and of the veracevine isomerization products cevagenine and cevine, met with less success (123, 139, 140, 155, 156). Nevertheless, biological evaluation of semisynthetic ester derivatives revealed: (a) Synthetic esters of naturally occurring alkamines (e.g., veracevine, zygadenine) are generally more active than esters of alkamine isomers (e.g., cevine, pseudozygadenine). (b) Toxicity and activity of the ester derivatives depend upon the nature of the alkamine and the nature and location of ester groups.

After elucidation of the structures of germine and its naturally occurring ester derivatives was completed (73, 76, 78, 88, 93), it became possible to assign structures to the synthetic germine esters as well. It then became apparent (90) that: (a) The 3,7,15,16-tetraesters derived from either germine or from a naturally occurring germine polyester were essentially inactive. (b) The 3,15-diesters showed relatively high activity. (c) The 3,15-diesters bearing branched-chain acid residues at position 15 were more active than those with straight-chain acid residues. (d) The ester grouping at position 3 need not be branched. (e) Position 7 need not be esterified. (f) Esterification at position 7 with a branched-chain acid may be disadvantageous.

Several studies aimed at elucidating structure–activity relationships among synthetic esters of protoverine have been reported. One report concerned synthetic 3,6,7,15-tetraesters which contain one, two, or three isobutyryl residues and in which the remaining acyl groups are acetyl (90). Pharmacologic evaluation of the semisynthetic esters revealed: (a) Esterification at position 16 is accompanied by a profound loss in activity. (b) Esterification at positions 3 and 15 is required for high activity. (c) Esterification at position 15 with a branched-chain acid is advantageous. (d) The ester group at position 3 need not be branched. (e) Positions 6 and 7 need not be esterified. (f) Esterification at position 7 with a branched-chain acid may be disadvantageous.

A second study supplemented and extended the structure–activity relationships among esters and other derivatives of protoverine (94). It was shown that: (a) Oxidation of the alcohol group at C-16 to a ketone group is accompanied by a loss in activity. (b) Acetonide formation at positions 14 and 15 is accompanied by a profound loss of activity. (c) Esterification at position 4 may be disadvantageous. (d) Esterification at C-16 with isobutyrate is as disadvantageous as the earlier-noted effect of acetylation at C-16.

Two developments stimulated studies involving the synthesis and pharmacological evaluation of analogs of the clinically useful alkaloids, protoveratrine A and protoveratrine B. On the clinical side, significant differences between protoveratrine A and protoveratrine B were noted when the substances were administered orally (163, 164, 169). Protoveratrine A is a potent hypotensive agent with a narrow therapeutic range. Protoveratrine B, on the other hand, is inactive orally in doses several times the hypotensive dose of protoveratrine A. However, studies of divided doses of more than 10 mg a day indicated that protoveratrine B has strong hypotensive activity, which may be prolonged and not accompanied by emetic effects. On the chemical side, intensive structural studies led to elucidation of the complete structures and configurations of protoveratrine A and protoveratrine B (80, 83). It is evident (see Fig. 2) that the structures of the two compounds are exceedingly similar, and, indeed, differ only in the nature of the acid moiety of the ester at C-3. In view of the pronounced apparent difference in activity between protoveratrine A and protoveratrine B, two series of analogs were prepared which differ from the protoveratrines solely in the nature of the acid residue (i.e., the "R" group in Fig. 2) affixed at C-3 (87). In one approach, the first step consisted of selective cleavage of the 2',3'-dihydroxy-2'-methylbutyrate residue from C-3 by sodium periodate treatment (80), to yield desatrine (from *des*acylprotover*atrine*). Acylation of desatrine under controlled conditions afforded one series of protoveratrine analogs. Direct partial acylation of protoveratrine B at the 2'-hydroxy group yielded a second series of protoveratrine analogs. Pharmacological evaluation indicated that considerable alterations can be made in the structure of the ester affixed at C-3 without greatly altering hypotensive activity.

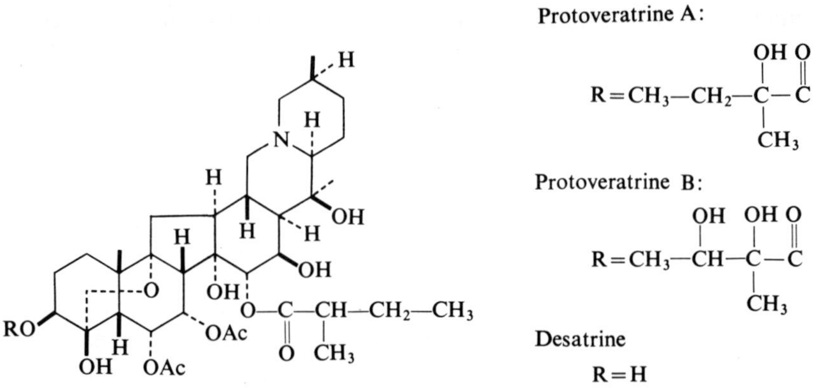

Protoveratrine A:

$$R = CH_3-CH_2-\overset{\overset{\displaystyle OH}{|}}{C}-\overset{\overset{\displaystyle O}{\|}}{C}$$
$$\overset{|}{CH_3}$$

Protoveratrine B:

$$R = CH_3-\overset{\overset{\displaystyle OH}{|}}{CH}-\overset{\overset{\displaystyle OH}{|}}{C}-\overset{\overset{\displaystyle O}{\|}}{C}$$
$$\overset{|}{CH_3}$$

Desatrine

$$R = H$$

Fig. 2. The protoveratrines and analogs.

On the other hand, a study of semisynthetic protoverine tetraesters, which differ from each other only in the nature of the acid residue affixed at C-15, indicated that alteration in the structure of the ester at C-15 profoundly affects hypotensive potency (86).

A recent report described an evaluation of active protoveratrine analogs in the unanesthetized dog, to seek possible differences in hypotensive–emetic ratios (160). Very preliminary data suggested that a partial dissociation of hypotensive and emetic activities may be observable in the unanesthetized dog. Thus, increased hypotensive–emetic ratios or margins of safety (relative to the protoveratrines) appeared to be indicated for desatrine 3-trichloroacetate and desatrine 3-tosylate. On the other hand, several of the semisynthetic tetraesters failed to show hypotensive activity at the doses tested, although emesis was evoked. Considerable additional investigation, which must necessarily include clinical study, will be required to evaluate definitively whether dissociation of hypotensive and emetic activities is demonstrable among analogs of the protoveratrines.

VI. Pharmacological actions and methods used for comparative evaluation

A. SITE AND MODE OF BASIC ACTION

The basic effect of all *Veratrum* alkaloids studied is an alteration of the permeabilities of membranes of excitable cells or tissues. While the whole complexity of the changes induced by the alkaloids is not fully understood, an increase in permeability to sodium ions is the most easily demonstrable effect (35, 154, 168). The interaction between alkaloid molecules and cell membrane components is probably physicochemical in nature. Gershfeld and Shanes (42, 138) have demonstrated that dissolution of one of the alkaloids in a monomolecular layer of stearic acid reduces the stability of such layers and decreases the "spreading force" exerted by them. Shanes (137) has proposed that a similar interaction takes place between the alkaloids and lipids in the cell membrane, thereby affecting the size of ionic channels and thus the permeability to ion fluxes. While our information of the structures and factors responsible for regulating specific permeabilities in cell membranes is still too scanty to permit the construction of a coherent theory, it seems likely that these experiments indicate the nature of the changes produced by the alkaloids. It should be pointed out that no specific "binding site" or "receptor" has been recognized for the veratrum alkaloids and there are no specific antagonists known (49).

The bioelectrical consequences of the induced permeability changes depend upon the nature of the tissue involved, upon the nature and the concentration of the alkaloid, and upon other factors such as the activity of the tissue. Basically, the electrophysiological effects may be one of four types: (a) an increased negative afterpotential (70, 136), as seen, for example, in nodes of Ranvier of certain medullated nerve fibers (154); (b) the induction of repetitive electrical activity following an elicited action potential, typically seen in skeletal muscle and in crustacean axons (26, 135, 166, 168); (c) depolarization or failure of repolarization, usually seen with higher drug concentrations (34, 145, 154); (d) an alteration in the shape of the action potential other than a typical negative afterpotential, as seen in cardiac fibers (97, 129). Concentrations of *Veratrum* causing a marked effect on active tissue (see above; types a, b, d) do not alter demonstrably the properties of resting cells (35, 154).

While it is justified to thus summarize the qualitative actions of all *Veratrum* alkaloids, it should be borne in mind that there are distinct quantitative differences between different pure alkaloids. Unfortunately, little electrophysiological work on comparative activities of different alkaloids has been done, but there is sufficient evidence to show that different alkaloids may exert distinctly different effects which cannot be accounted for by concentration differences. For example, the duration of the negative afterpotential of veratridine is greater than that of cevadine (136). The duration of the series of repetitive potentials elicited in frog muscle by a single stimulus is much shorter for the mono- and diacetates of germine than for the tetra- and pentaacetates, and these in turn induce a shorter duration of repetitive firing than does veratridine (32). Also, the ratio between a concentration of an alkaloid which induces one of the above changes without depolarization and consequent inexcitability of the cell, to the concentration which will depolarize differs among different alkaloids. With veratridine, a concentration that induces repetitive activity in all fibers of a frog muscle already depolarizes some fibers. The germine mono- and diacetates, on the other hand, do not depolarize any fibers in concentrations eliciting repetitive activity in all (51). With many of the naturally occurring esters of protoverine and germine, any concentration which will elicit an effect will, in time, render the muscle inexcitable (11, 72).

B. PRIMARY AND SECONDARY EFFECTS OF *Veratrum* ALKALOIDS

In principle, all excitable cells can be affected by the *Veratrum* alkaloids. However, the concentrations or doses required differ. Thus some actions can be observed in an intact animal, others only after measures have been taken to prevent manifestation of the drug effect upon more sensitive structures, or *in vitro*. It is convenient to distinguish among the actions of the alkaloids between those that are a direct manifestation of the presence of the drugs in the tissue itself and those that are secondary to an action of the alkaloids upon nerves or afferent receptors. Thus primary and secondary effects will be distinguished.

1. *Tissues Demonstrating Primary Effects*

a. Peripheral Nerves, Afferent and Efferent Nerve Endings. In the intact animal, effects of any of the alkaloids on nerve trunks will hardly occur because of the difficulty of access of the drugs. However, *in vitro* or after removal of the diffusion barriers, myelinated and unmyelinated nerve fibers are sensitive to the actions of *Veratrum* alkaloids (53). The main sites of action without such measures are afferent and efferent nerve endings where access of substances circulating in the blood is much easier. Several authors have reported repetitive activity in motor nerve endings (2, 24, 27), but the most important site of action of the alkaloids is upon afferent endings or receptor structures (22, 124, 134). The drug effects upon afferent receptors can again be classified as stimulating, that is, causing activity in the absence of a physiological stimulus, or sensitizing, that is, intensifying activity already present, or paralyzing at higher concentrations. It is this effect of the *Veratrum* alkaloids on afferent nerves that is responsible for most of the prominent drug effects seen in an intact animal. The same action is also apparent in the signs of sensory stimulation noted by the earliest observers, such as prickling and tingling, or gustatory and thermal sensations (70, 121). Electrophysiological evidence for a stimulant or sensitizing effect of veratrine upon sensory receptors has been presented by Witzleb (167).

b. Skeletal Muscle. Repetitive electrical activity was first shown by Hoffmann (55) to occur during the so-called "veratrine response," and this observation has been repeated by many investigators, usually in isolated frog muscles (70). In intact animals, the greater sensitivity of afferent structures leading to hypotension and bradycardia has made it difficult to observe the skeletal muscle effect *in vivo*, so that only few reports exist (27, 131a). The recent finding of alkaloids with no hypotensive activity has permitted closer study of this effect (32).

c. *Cardiac Muscle*. The most interesting effect of the *Veratrum* alkaloids on the heart is a positive inotropic effect that resembles pharmacologically that of the cardiac glycosides (8, 64a, 70, 97). Higher doses lead to conduction block and ventricular ectopic activity (8).

d. *Central Nervous System*. It is difficult to separate direct effects upon central nervous system structures from indirect ones that result from the change in afferent inflow which is caused by the action of the alkaloids upon afferent nerves and receptors. However, changes in sustained potentials and evoked potentials have been demonstrated after local application and do represent a local effect of the alkaloids upon CNS structures (44, 45).

e. *Autonomic Ganglia*. Facilitation of ganglionic transmission and an increased response to injection of ganglion-stimulating substances has been demonstrated by several investigators who used the response of an effector organ as indicator (33a, 67) as well as by electrophysiological observation (25, 66, 131a). A detailed analysis of this action has not been made yet, and it is not clear upon which intraganglionic structures the alkaloids act.

f. *Adrenal Glands*. A special case is the stimulation of catecholamine release by the adrenal medulla, which is elicited by large doses of the *Veratrum* alkaloids (3, 102). The effect seems to be analogous to the ganglionic effect since it was blocked by tetraethylammonium or azamethonium (102).

2. Secondary Effects

a. *Hypotension and Bradycardia*. The most important indirect effect is the well-known reflex hypotension and bradycardia (70). This effect is treated in more detail below. It is less well known that the same or slightly higher doses of hypotensive alkaloids will cause an increase in blood pressure (9, 52). This increase is observed also when the alkaloids are injected into an extremity which is connected to the experimental animal by nervous pathways only (32a, 52). It may be assumed, therefore, that the hypertension seen with intravenous injections in intact animals is due to a stimulant effect upon peripheral structures whose identity is not known. However, a central effect cannot be excluded.

b. *Respiration*. Respiratory change, usually an initial period of apnea followed by deeper and sometimes faster breathing, is also a classical effect of most *Veratrum* alkaloids (22, 70, 112). This effect is also the result of stimulation of afferents. In intact animals, the drug's action on baro- and chemoreceptors plays a part; after denervation of these structures and by perfusion and isolation techniques, an effect upon respiration by an action upon other peripheral nervous structures can be shown (32a, 52).

c. Glandular Secretions. Increased salivation is one of the oldest observations made with *Veratrum* alkaloids (11, 121). This effect is blocked by small doses of atropine and may thus be assumed to be elicited indirectly (30).

d. Renal Function. Little attention has been paid to the alteration of kidney function by *Veratrum* alkaloids. A transient fall in renal plasma flow and glomerular filtration rate during the period of marked hypotension has been observed, but the decrease in urine flow outlasted the duration of the hemodynamic changes (10, 122). Release of antidiuretic hormone has been suggested as the cause of this effect, but it is clear that the problem requires considerably more study. Such studies have become more important in view of the evidence that fluid volume and kidney function are regulated by a "sensing" system with afferent receptors in the low- and high-pressure vascular system (39). Since the *Veratrum* alkaloids have been shown to strongly affect the function of both types of receptors (96, 120), a careful analysis of the effect of the alkaloids upon volume of body fluids and renal function promises to be informative.

e. Smooth Muscle. Various smooth muscle preparations (isolated intestine of rabbits and seminal vesicles of guinea pigs) are stimulated by *Veratrum* alkaloids (48, 103). However, it has not been adequately demonstrated that this effect is due to an action on the smooth muscle proper and not to stimulation of nervous structures in the preparations. In the isolated frog stomach muscle, a preparation free of nerve structures, veratridine had no effect (32a).

C. SELECTIVITY OF ACTION

It is quite obvious that the interesting and potentially useful pharmacological actions of the *Veratrum* alkaloids are of no value unless they can be selectively induced. Selectivity of drug action is, of course, always relative. Absolute selectivity does not exist. The highest degree of selectivity is usually observed among biogenic agents such as hormones or autonomic transmitters. These agents are highly selective in terms of specificity of the receptors,* upon which they act, but usually the distribution of receptors in the organism is such that in practice selectivity is very poor. Acetylcholine reacts only with specific receptors but these receptors occur in smooth muscles, glands, autonomic gang-

---

* Unfortunately, the term receptor is used in biology and also in this review for two different concepts. The original physiological concept of a receptor is a macro- or microscopic nerve structure specialized to respond to a physical or chemical modality in this environment. Examples are the baroreceptors, chemoreceptors, touch receptors, etc. More recently, pharmacologists, enzymologists, immunologists, and molecular biologists have used the same word to denote a component of a biological unit, such as a cell or enzyme, of molecular dimensions, thought to interact with a chemical agent, e.g., a drug.

lia, and in muscle end plates. In the case of the *Veratrum* alkaloids, a different type of selectivity operates. There is little specificity at the "receptor" level (in principle, all excitable cells may respond), but there may be a high practical degree of specificity for other reasons.

(1) The first such reason for selectivity is a difference in affinity of the alkaloids for different membranous structures. This would seem to be the reason for the difference in sensitivity of different sensory nerve structures. Thus, the majority of naturally occurring alkaloids examined affect most strongly those receptors whose activation results in reflex hypotension, but, as described above, the same doses also affect receptors whose activation will cause hypertension. With most alkaloids the former effects vastly overshadow the latter (9, 15). On the other hand, alkaloids like the germine mono- and diacetates do not seem to affect hypotensive receptors at all but do cause a reflex hypertension (30).

(2) A second reason for differences in sensitivity, perhaps causally related to differences in affinity, may be the functional differences between various electrogenic membranes affected by the alkaloids. It has been mentioned above that some tissues display only an increased negative afterpotential which may be of little consequence for the function of the tissue, while others respond with repetitive electrical activity. Still others, such as smooth muscle (?), may possess membrane structures and functions where the presence of an alkaloid is of little or no consequence.

(3) Another reason for difference in sensitivity may be the difference in functional state of the target tissue. This may best be exemplified by the following extreme examples. It has been stated above that there is little evidence for a *Veratrum*-induced change in the resting tissue. Only the passing of an impulse, either induced by stimulation or occurring in the course of the normal physiological activity, will let the presence of the drug become manifest. On the other hand, if a tissue is already being activated at maximal rate, the addition of repetitive responses will make no difference. An example may be seen in the effect of some alkaloids upon skeletal muscle. The presence of repetitive activity after a single stimulation may cause the muscle to develop three to five times the tension which it would develop in the absence of the alkaloid (31). However, tension output during stimulation at tetanic frequencies is not affected since electrical activity and, therefore, the duration of the active state and tension development are already maximal. Of equal importance is the functional connection of the tissue affected. It is possible—although no exact data exist— that the basic effect of a given alkaloid upon hypotensive receptors and upon receptors whose activation will result in hypertension is identical. Nevertheless, the result of the drug-induced increase in "inflow" will be hypotension and bradycardia because the influence of the hypotensive afferents upon the vasomotor regulatory system is predominant.

(4) A final reason for selectivity that must be mentioned is the difference in access of the drug to the tissue. It has already been stated that the sensitivity of peripheral nerve fibers appears to be of the same order as that of receptors when the diffusion barrier of the nerve sheath is removed. However, in intact animals, the presence of these diffusion barriers, especially the nerve sheath, will prevent access of the alkaloid. It is possible that similar differences in accessibility of different receptor structures exist, which will result in greater apparent sensitivity of the more easily accessible structure. Unfortunately, there are almost no data available at present on the physicochemical properties of the *Veratrum* alkaloids and their distribution in an intact organism.

D. HYPOTENSIVE AND EMETIC ACTIVITY

These two types of activity are of major interest in the context of this discussion and will therefore be treated somewhat more extensively.

1. *Hypotensive Activity*

The basis for the hypotensive effect of all *Veratrum* alkaloids so far examined is the sensitization of receptors which results in a reflex lowering of blood pressure, heart rate, and sympathetic tone to the myocardium.

a. Afferent Receptors. The receptors implicated in this reflex have been studied perhaps more extensively than any other aspect of the pharmacology of the *Veratrum* alkaloids. Von Bezold and Hirt (157) correctly guessed the nature of the effect, although they left the proof largely to later investigators. Jarisch and his associates (58) deserve credit for establishing the reflex nature of the effect of the alkaloids. The receptors identified by them were located in the heart, and the hypotension and bradycardia elicited reflexly from cardiac receptors are therefore called the Bezold-Jarisch effect (68). Additional receptors have been identified since, and hypotensive receptors stimulated by *Veratrum* alkaloids are now recognized in the following areas: the left ventricle, both auricles, the pulmonary vascular system, and the baroceptors in the aortic arch and carotid sinus. Under proper circumstances, it is possible to elicit the drug effect from either the areas in the chest or from the carotid sinus alone (9). The physiological role of the baroreceptors in the aortic arch and in the carotid sinus is unquestioned; the role of the cardiac receptors whose existence was pointed out by the drug effect is less clear, but evidence is accumulating that the receptors involved are also stretch receptors and that the adequate stimulus for the cardiac receptors is also the blood pressure—intraventricular pressure in the case of ventricular receptors, venous pressure in the case of atrial receptors (5, 23, 133).

b. Central Components of the Reflex Arch. Several investigators have reported findings which they could explain only by a direct action of an alkaloid upon CNS structures (4, 54, 159). Both stimulant and depressant effects were observed and there were differences between different alkaloids.

While it is almost to be expected that substances with the type of pharmacological activity represented by the *Veratrum* alkaloids should exert actions upon structures of the CNS, it has to be emphasized that experimental proof or refutation of such an action is very difficult indeed. Obviously, it is impossible to separate the CNS from all afferent connections and, if it were possible, the value of such a preparation would be doubtful. It has been emphasized above that the effect of a given dose or concentration of an alkaloid may depend upon the functional state or activity of the target structure. Thus, by removal of the normal connections, entirely misleading effects may be observed. Furthermore, since the alkaloids are known to induce activity in so many afferent nervous structures and since vasomotor effects of such stimulation may be only incidental side effects, it has to be proved that the observed effect is germane to the hypotensive action of the drug under more normal experimental and especially under clinical conditions. It has been pointed out that both hypotensive and hypertensive effects can be elicited under conditions where access of the drug to the CNS is avoided and with doses in the normal range of hypotensive doses (32a, 52, 54).

It is also known that the hypotensive response to acute injection of *Veratrum* alkaloids can be blocked by barbiturates (9, 40, 41). Injection of pentobarbital during a sustained alkaloid-induced hypotension sometimes produces a return of the blood pressure to normal levels (9). These observations should not be interpreted as evidence for a central effect of the *Veratrum* alkaloids, but rather as pointing out the importance of the state of the central substrate for the "processing" of afferent input.

c. Efferent Mechanisms. The efferent pathways and mechanisms used in the hypotensive response to the *Veratrum* alkaloids are those which are normally in the employ of the pressure-homeostatic system. There is a general decrease in sympathetic vasoconstrictor tone which is manifest as decrease in peripheral resistance in the arterial bed (9, 33) and as increase in capacitance in the venous vascular bed (7). Heart rate is reduced by an increase in vagal activity (which can be blocked by atropine) and a simultaneous decrease in sympathetic accelerator tone (9). Sympathetic activity to the myocardium is equally reduced and results in a fall of sympathetic influences upon myocardial contractility (9, 131). Cardiac output may be reduced temporarily, to a variable extent (7, 131).

Thus, the result of the injection of a hypotensive *Veratrum* alkaloid is a coordinated activation of efferent mechanisms leading to a fall in blood pressure. Clear-cut differences in these mechanims between the effects of different alkaloids have not been found. It seems likely that the type of change produced depends more upon the state of the vascular system at the time of drug

446 S. Morris Kupchan and Werner E. Flacke

administration than upon differences between different alkaloids. The only difference in efferent effects produced by five different alkaloids were those in potency and duration of action (9).

d. *Time Course of Action.* There are very few systematic studies of the time course of the hypotensive and heart rate-lowering action of *Veratrum* alkaloids beyond the demonstration that there are marked differences between different alkaloids. In one study (9) a long duration of action was always coupled with a slow onset, and this seems to be the usual observation. In the absence of any attempt at analyzing the factors involved and since no data of physicochemical characteristics of different alkaloids, such as lipid solubility and pK_a, exist, it cannot be decided whether access of the alkaloids to their site of action, differences in rate of drug action, or still other factors are responsible. *In vitro* studies in a convenient model system would be very desirable to shed further light on these problems.

In spite of the fact that the picture of the mechanism of action of the *Veratrum* alkaloids presented appears to be fairly coherent, there are still unanswered questions which should prohibit undue confidence. For example, it has been repeatedly observed that the rise in arterial blood pressure, which is normally elicited in a vagotomized animal when carotid arteries are occluded simultaneously, is reduced or blocked after administration of a *Veratrum* alkaloid (1, 130, 132). That this block cannot be explained as the result of a central action of the alkaloids can be concluded from the observation that sectioning of the sinus nerves during the hypotensive period, when the occlusion response is absent, results in an immediate blood pressure rise to hypertensive levels (13, 152). The alternative explanation is that the receptors are already maximally activated by the drug so that reduction in intrasinus pressure cannot further increase receptor activity. The difficulty with this explanation is emphasized by the fact that the occlusion response is often reduced at a time when the level of blood pressure is not altered or very little affected (130). It would then have to be assumed that the hypotension is not related in a simple way to baroceptor activity, but experimental evidence is lacking.

2. *Emetic Activity*

The work of Borison and Fairbanks (12) has established that the emetic effect of the *Veratrum* alkaloids is also due to stimulation of afferent structures, located this time in or near the nodose ganglion of the vagus. Nerve section below the level of the ganglion did not affect the vomiting response, but sectioning above the ganglion blocked it. Emesis occurs after parenteral as well as after oral administration of *Veratrum* alkaloids, and Swiss (149) could find little evidence for a contributory effect from local action upon the intestines. Unfortunately, the sensitivity of the receptors responsible for the emetic effects appears to be very similar to that of the receptors responsible for the hypotensive effect. Thus Swiss (149) and Swiss and Mountain (151) found no significantly different ratios of hypotensive to emetic effects in a series of 21 alkaloids or alkaloid mixtures which differed in their absolute potency by a factor of 100. There has been some evidence in the work of Weaver *et al.* (160) that the ratio of hypotensive to emetic activity may be increased in a series of semisynthetic esters of protoverine. That emetic activity is not an obligatory property of all *Veratrum* alkaloids is apparent from the lack of emetic activity of the germine acetates and the protoverine acetates, but these alkaloids also lack hypotensive activity. The fact that emesis can be induced in animals in which hypotensive activity has been eliminated by interruption of afferent pathways from hypotensive receptor areas is further proof that the two actions can be separated. Efforts to control emesis by combination with other drugs have not been successful. There was some indication that sedative doses of *Rauwolfia* extracts reduced the emetic property of alkavervir while a dose of pentobarbital, inducing about the same degree of sedation, did not affect the emetic action (47, 100). However, even large doses of scopolamine, atropine, methanteline, dimenhydrinate, and chlorpromazine were ineffective (149). Only yohimbine has shown some effect (16). Thus, a strong, but not absolute correlation between hypotensive and emetic activity exists and all efforts at separation have not been very successful.

3. *Conclusions*

It is obvious that the most important practical question concerning the usefulness of the *Veratrum* alkaloids as antihypertensive agents is the question of whether or not hypotensive and emetic activity can be separated. The frustrating results of all efforts so far undertaken have created a pessimistic atmosphere. Yet, the fact that separation of emetic and hypotensive activity can be observed by selective surgical inactivation of receptor structures is proof that the connection between hypotension and emesis is not causal. It seems more likely that the connection is to be seen in a close similarity of the drug sensitivity of the respective receptor structures involved in these effects. The results obtained first with the germine acetates and now extended to the acetates of protoverine and of zygadenine and veracevine indicate that there are variations in the relative sensitivities of different affector organs to different *Veratrum* alkaloids. These two facts leave open the possibility that further search will eventually lead to more specific alkaloids and sufficient separation of hypotensive and emetic activity.

In this connection, a certain built-in bias in the experimental approach used so far may be pointed out. Emetic activity has usually been tested only in alkaloids with good hypotensive potency. Perhaps the direction of the search should be changed toward identification of the structural features which lead to an increased hypotensive–emetic potency ratio. The most important factor in the usefulness of any drug is not absolute potency but the ratio of desirable to undesirable activities. Morphine is one of the least potent narcotic analgetics if newer synthetic compounds are taken into consideration, but it is free of some of the undesirable effects of the more potent agents. Once the structural requirements of the desired ratio of activities are recognized, it may be possible to concentrate upon increase in potency.

E. METHODS USED

1. *Circulation*

a. Dose–Response Curves. Quantitative values of hypotensive potency of different alkaloids or alkaloid mixtures may be obtained by injection of single doses in anesthetized cats or dogs and measurement of maximal hypotensive and heart rate-decreasing activity. Successive injections may be given after return of the parameters to the baseline. A dose–response plot can be made and the ED_{50} can be read most easily from a probit plot. Mean ED_{50}'s can be obtained from a small number of animals and can be treated with standard statistical methods (9).

The advantage of the method is that values for maximal effect, duration of action, and the slope of the dose–response curve are obtained in addition to the ED_{50}. Thus, this method is useful for the initial pharmacological characterization of an alkaloid. The accuracy of the method depends upon the number of animals used. Comparisons can be made only between different animals or animal groups. With single injections equilibrium conditions are not achieved, but the method can easily be modified by using continuous infusion for the administration of the drug.

b. Bracketing Procedure. For purposes of comparing potency of a known standard with that of an unknown, Stutzman *et al.* (147) and Maison *et al.* (99) have used a "bracketing" procedure. Infusion of a known solution over a 10-minute period was followed after recovery by an infusion of the unknown. Infusion of the standard solution was repeated and the unknown thus bracketed. The known solutions were chosen to cause a fall in pressure of between 20 and 40% and the concentration of the unknown was adjusted to give about a 30% decrease in arterial pressure.

Although this method has been used for the determination of potency of most of the alkaloids described in Sections IV and V, it has been criticized because it is a single-point determination and thus does not give information about maximal effect, slope of the dose–response relation, or duration of action. A relatively large number of animals would be required for accuracy.

Richardson and co-workers (130) first used the depression of the carotid occlusion response for assessing the effect of *Veratrum* alkaloids. This method has been considerably refined by Rubin and Burke (132). Several cumulative doses can be given. The unknown is bracketed by two standards. The method is more accurate and does give information about dose–response relationships. Systematic errors can be expected if the standard and the unknown differ markedly in duration of action.

It goes without saying that information concerning site and mechanism of action should precede the use of quantitative methods. Alkaloids with an entirely different mechanism of hypotensive action, like veratramine, have been assayed in a series of ester alkaloids, without taking cognizance of the fundamental qualitative differences among the alkaloids.

2. *Emetic Activity*

Emesis can be easily produced in unanesthetized dogs after single doses, with continuous infusions of test alkaloids, or after oral administration. The incidence of positive response after a given dose is recorded and the results are analyzed according to the method of Litchfield and Wilcoxon (98). The method has worked well in the hands of Swiss (149) who demonstrated the remarkable constancy of the ratio between hypotensive and emetic potency among alkaloids of widely differing absolute potency. The disadvantage is the relatively large quantity of alkaloid required. Considerably less material is required for an essentially similar method in which pigeons are used. This method was pioneered by Christensen (17, 60). Swiss and Mountain (151) compared the dog assay with the pigeon assay and found good correlation. Gujral (50) used the method to distinguish between protoveratrine A and B and inactive protoverine acetates.

With both methods care must be exercised against conditioning of the animals with repeated drug administration. Sufficient time intervals between administration of the drug and control injection of saline are used to guard against this possibility, but it should be realized that the subjective sensations, other than emesis, of the animal after administration of a ceveratrum alkaloid and after saline are probably quite different.

3. *Skeletal Muscle*

It has been stated above that there was a good correlation between the duration of the veratrinic response in isolated frog muscle and the quality of the effect on the circulation. Thus, this simple test (71) may be utilized to screen alkaloids of which only small quantities are available. Additional information is obtained if the magnitude of tetanic output under the influence of the drug is observed (31). A decrease of tetanic tension indicates loss of excitability, probably by depolarization, of a fraction of fibers of the muscle. The ratio between the concentration eliciting an effect upon the twitch and the concentration depressing tetanic tension is a measure of the "therapeutic range," i.e., the range between the concentration which causes a pharmacological effect and the concentration which produces loss of function.

4. *Electrophysiology*

A simple electrophysiological method for the screening of *Veratrum* alkaloids is still not available. Such a method would be very desirable in order to characterize comparatively the basic effects of an alkaloid. The method should be simple enough for screening purposes and distinguish not only quantitatively but also qualitatively between different alkaloids. Thus, the method should not only give concentration-dependent effects but also allow differentiation of the type of effect, such as duration of negative afterpotential or duration of repetitive activity. It is, of course, hoped that empirical correlations with cardiovascular activity will be recognized, for this would facilitate screening programs.

VII. *In vivo* distribution

There is an almost total lack of specific information concerning absorption, distribution, metabolic fate, and excretion of the *Veratrum* alkaloids. It is to be assumed, though, that the alkaloids behave like other lipid-soluble compounds. Thus, they are absorbed from the gastrointestinal tract and distributed at equilibrium in at least total body water. No information concerning specific binding is available. The one study in which radioactively labeled germidine was given to rats showed that rapid metabolism occurred mainly in liver. Eighty-three per cent of the radioactivity was secreted during the first 24 hours, mainly as water-soluble metabolites in the feces. Four different metabolites were separated but not identified (126).

The existing data concerning ratio of oral to parenteral, and rapid to slow parenteral administration fit this general scheme. The ratio of equipotent parenteral to oral doses is about 10 to 15. The ratio of equipotent doses in terms of peak fall in blood pressure with acute (10–30 seconds) injection and continuous infusion is about 10. If it is assumed that the blood-pressure response indicates the drug concentration at the site of action (presumably the afferent receptors), and if diffusion of the drug to the site of action is rapid, a much higher blood and receptor concentration will be achieved with the same dose when this dose is injected into a small volume of passing blood than when it is permitted to distribute equally in the total volume of circulating blood. Loss of alkaloid into the extracellular and finally intracellular fluid accentuates the difference.

It has recently been found (108) that addition of veratridine to the perfusion fluid of a perfused squid axon differs from addition to the external fluid in the rapid reversibility of the drug's effect on the electrical behavior of the axon, after removal of the alkaloid. "Washing-out" of a drug effect from an isolated nerve or muscle when the drug has been added to the bathing solution is extremely slow if the alkaloid has been in contact with the tissue for any length of time. It seems likely that the difference is due to penetration of the alkaloid into the cell plasma and a consequent "depot" effect. These observations are reported here to demonstrate the entrance of the alkaloids into the cells.

VIII. Clinical uses

It has been stated in Section I that the early use of plant extracts of *Veratrum* in the treatment of hypertension entailed the disadvantages which resulted from the differences in composition of different preparations. Since pure alkaloids differ markedly in quality and potency of their pharmacological actions (see above), a mixture of alkaloids of unknown and variable composition could not be expected to produce reliable and reproducible clinical results. This was emphasized by Krayer and his co-workers (70, 108a). The clinical preparations used today are either mixtures of alkaloids which are standardized biologically or else pure alkaloids. Unfortunately, no pure alkaloid has yet been found with a sufficient ratio of hypotensive to emetic potency.

The fact that the *Veratrum* alkaloids are stubbornly maintaining a place among the clinically employed antihypertensive agents (14) indicates that they possess, to compensate for their emetic side effects, some very desirable features. Clinical use of the *Veratrum* alkaloids today is largely restricted to two classes of patients (113): First, there are a number of individuals who do not experience nausea and vomiting, and these patients seem to demonstrate the potential of the alkaloids: control of blood pressure without distressing or dangerous side effects and without limitation of normal function (65, 169). The second group encompasses hypertensive emergencies of limited duration, where the emetic effect is tolerated because of the reliable antihypertensive power of the alkaloids (107, 113, 114).

It is assumed that the mechanism of the antihypertensive action of the *Veratrum* alkaloids in patients is the same as the mechanism of hypotensive action in experimental animals (107). Thus the alkaloids are presumed to affect afferent receptor structures, especially those with baroceptor function, and to increase their sensitivity to their adequate stimulus, i.e., blood pressure. The afferent input to the central regulatory system is increased and leads to a decrease of vasomotor and cardiac stimulant efferent output and an increase in vagal activity. Since the homeostatic arch is not interrupted or its function depressed, pressure homeostasis is maintained but at a lower absolute level. This explains the rarity of orthostatic hypotension during veratrum therapy.

Although the exact role of the baroceptor system in the pathogenesis of hypertension is not fully understood, it is generally recognized that homeostatic control of blood pressure is not absent in hypertensive disease but only fixed at a higher level. The "barostat" has been reset. If such an adjustment of the system did not occur, one would have to see evidence of increased efforts of the baroceptor system to reduce blood pressure to its normal level, but such evidence has not been found. The *Veratrum* alkaloids accomplish a lowering of the pressure setpoint of the homeostatic system not by an action upon the central mechanisms but rather by increasing the sensitivity of the peripheral "sensors." This discussion is not intended to conceal the fact that we do not completely understand the functioning of the central control system. This type of drug action explains why the efferent mechanisms of the circulatory control system, i.e., the sympathetic outflow to the vascular bed and sympathetic and parasympathetic outflow to the heart, appear to be well coordinated in the presence of the alkaloids. Vasodilatation, decrease in heart rate, and sometimes a decrease in cardiac output are observed (21, 36, 57, 115). Renal plasma flow, glomerular filtration rate, and urine flow may be temporarily decreased (36, 43, 57, 104, 105, 106, 158), but fluid and electrolyte retention is not a feature of veratrum therapy (107).

The rapid onset of action and the relatively short duration of the *Veratrum* alkaloids has to be appreciated. Therapy should always begin slowly and the desired dose level should be maintained evenly (20, 108a, 141). Thus the best control is obtained when the alkaloids are given by infusion. Oral administration should be in frequent, divided doses (141).

The alkaloids used clinically are those distinguished by a relatively slow onset and long duration of action. Yet, even these preparations are rapid and brief of action in comparison with other antihypertensive agents such as reserpine and the saluretics. A better-sustained effect could, of course, be achieved if higher drug doses could be given. This is a common means of increasing the duration of action of a drug, but it cannot be used here, because of the narrow range between hypotensive dose and doses causing side effects.

Frequently, combinations of *Veratrum* alkaloids with other antihypertensive agents are recommended (158). There is no experimental evidence for an additive or potentiating effect of any of the combinations (113). The dose–response relationship of the *Veratrum* alkaloids is steep and small doses are most likely without effect.

Side Effects and Toxicity

As with all drugs, one has to distinguish between effects that are simply extensions of the therapeutic effects and true side effects which occur independently of therapeutic effects. Excessive vagal activity on the heart is an extension of the desired therapeutic effect (20). In emergencies it can be combatted by small doses of atropine (101, 106) but, in the main, such effects should be avoided by adjustment of dosage (20, 169).

The most frequent and most bothersome side effect encountered is the emetic effect. The frequency of its occurrence varies in different reports (20, 165, 169). It is highest with intravenous administration, that is, under conditions when a high blood level may temporarily occur (29). On the other hand, it has been observed that the incidence of nausea and vomiting increases with time during prolonged treatment. The dose–response curve of emetic activity is steep and, with sufficiently high doses, vomiting can be induced in all individuals. The dose required in clinical use is dictated by the desired therapeutic effect, but once this therapeutic dose level has been reached it should not be surpassed (164). Efforts to combat emesis with other agents, especially *Rauwolfia* alkaloids and chlorpromazine (18), have failed.

The emetic side effect forces discontinuation of veratrum medication in a high percentage of patients. However, there are marked differences in susceptibility and some patients tolerate effective hypotensive doses without difficulty. In these patients the dose may be increased to levels where side effects upon the neuromuscular system may be seen, especially with protoveratrine. The symptoms range from cramps of differing severity to a myotonialike syndrome. Attacks seem to be precipitated by exercise and are fully reversible when the drug is withdrawn or the dosage reduced (65, 163).

As a final group of side effects, symptoms attributable to stimulation of sensory receptors must be mentioned. Such symptoms are substernal burning, tingling, gustatory, and thermal sensations. Occasionally, sensations resembling angina pectoris are described. Again, these symptoms occur mainly with high doses but also in an occasional unusually susceptible patient.

In view of these frequently distressing side effects of the *Veratrum* alkaloids, one must emphasize that the incidence of serious side effects is very low. Meilman states that he knows of no fatal outcome of veratrum administration (107). In this statement he repeats the assertions which Norwood made as early as 1856 (121). This early and fervent advocate of extract of *V. viride* used truly heroic doses but assures us that in 12 years of use he has "not observed a single case where any ultimate ill-effects were sustained whatever."

References

1. Abreu, B. E., Richards, A. B., Alexander, W. M., and Weaver, L. C., *J. Pharmacol Exptl. Therap.* **112**, 73 (1954).
2. Acheson, G. H., and Rosenblueth, A., *Am. J. Physiol.* **133**, 736 (1941).
3. Aronow, L., Ph.D., Dissertation, Cambridge, Massachusetts (1956).
4. Aviado, D. M., Jr., Cerletti, A., Li, T. H., and Schmidt, C. F., *J. Pharmacol. Exptl. Therap.* **115**, 329 (1955).
5. Aviado, D. M., Jr., and Schmidt, C. F., *Am. J. Physiol.* **196**, 726 (1959).
6. Baker, P. D., *Southern Med. Surg.* **15**, 579 (1859).

7. Barer, G. R., and Nüsser, E., *Brit. J. Pharmacol.* **13**, 372 (1958).
8. Benforado, J. M., *J. Pharmacol. Exptl. Therap.* **120**, 412 (1957).
9. Benforado, J. M., Flacke, W., Swaine, C. R., and Mosimann, W., *J. Pharmacol. Exptl. Therap.* **130**, 311 (1960).
10. Blackmore, W. P., *J. Pharmacol. Exptl. Therap.* **114**, 87 (1955).
11. Boehm, R., *Handbuch Exptl. Pharmakol.* **2**, Part 1, 249 (1920).
12. Borison, H. L., and Fairbanks, V. F., *J. Pharmacol. Exptl. Therap.* **105**, 317 (1952).
13. Borison, H. L., Fairbanks, V. F., and White, C. A., *Arch. Intern. Pharmacodyn.* **101**, 189 (1955).
14. Brest, A. N., and Moyer, J. H., *Angiology* **14**, 64 (1963).
15. Calliauw, L., *Arch. Intern. Pharmacodyn.* **107**, 75 (1956).
16. Cheymol, J., and Quniquaud, A., *J. Physiol.* (*Paris*) **44**, 240 (1952).
17. Christensen, B. V., and McLean, A. B., *J. Am. Pharm. Assoc.* **25**, 414 (1936).
18. Conner, P. K., McConn, R. G., and Moyer, J. H., *Am. Practitioner Dig. Treat.* **7**, 1127 (1956).
19. Craig, L. C., and Jacobs, W. A., *J. Biol. Chem.* **143**, 427 (1942).
20. Currens, J. H., Myers, G. S., and McGinty, J. S., *J. Clin. Invest.* **31**, 623 (1952).
21. Currens, J. H., Myers, G. S., and White, P. D., *Am. Heart J.* **46**, 576 (1953).
22. Dawes, G. S., and Comroe, J. H., Jr., *Physiol. Rev.* **34**, 167 (1954).
23. Doutheil, U., and Kramer, K., *Arch. Ges. Physiol.* **269**, 114 (1959).
24. Dun, F. T., and Feng, T. P., *Chinese J. Physiol.* **15**, 405 (1940).
25. Eccles, J. R., *J. Physiol.* (*London*) **103**, 27 (1944).
26. Falk, G., in "Biophysics of Physiological and Pharmacological Actions," Publ. No. 69, pp. 259–279. Am. Assoc. Advance. Sci., Washington, D.C., 1961.
27. Feng, T. P., and Li, T. H., *Chinese J. Physiol.* **16**, 139 (1941).
28. Fieser, L. F., and Fieser, M., "Steroids," pp. 867–895. Reinhold, New York, 1959.
29. Finnerty, F. A., *Proc. Soc. Exptl. Biol. Med.* **84**, 379 (1953).
30. Flacke, W., *Arch. Exptl. Pathol. Pharmakol.* **240**, 369 (1961).
31. Flacke, W., *J. Pharmacol. Exptl. Therap.* **137**, 62 (1962).
32. Flacke, W., *J. Pharmacol. Exptl. Therap.* **141**, 230 (1963).
32a. Flacke, W., unpublished observations.
33. Flacke, W., Benforado, J. M., Swaine, C. R., and Mosimann, W., *J. Pharmacol. Exptl. Therap.* **130**, 321 (1960).
33a. Flacke, W., and Gillis, R. A., unpublished observations.
34. Fleckenstein, A., *Arch. Exptl. Pathol. Pharmakol.* **212**, 416 (1951).
35. Frank, G. B., *J. Neurophysiol.* **21**, 263 (1958).
36. Fries, E. D., Stanton, J. R., Culbertson, J. W., Litter, J., Halperin, M. H., Burnett, C. H., and Wilkins, R. W., *J. Clin. Invest.* **28**, 353 (1949).
37. Fried, J., Numerof, P., and Coy, N. H., *J. Am. Chem. Soc.* **74**, 3041 (1952).
38. Fried, J., White, H. L., and Wintersteiner, O., *J. Am. Chem. Soc.* **72**, 4621 (1950).
39. Gauer, O. H., and Henry, J. P., *Physiol. Rev.* **43**, 423 (1963).
40. Gellhorn, E., *Arch. Intern. Pharmacodyn.* **93**, 434 (1953).
41. Gellhorn, E., *Proc. Soc. Exptl. Biol. Med.* **97**, 400 (1957).
42. Gershfeld, N. L., and Shanes, A. M., *Science* **129**, 1427 (1959).
43. Goldman, R., and Frierson, H. R., *Am. J. Med.* **14**, 169 (1953).
44. Goldring, S., and O'Leary, G. L., *Electroencephalog. Clin. Neurophysiol.* **6**, 189 (1954).
45. Goldring, S., and O'Leary, G. L., *Electroencephalog. Clin. Neurophysiol.* **6**, 201 (1954).
46. Goodman, L. S., and Gilman, A., "The Pharmacological Basis of Therapeutics," 2nd ed., pp. 747–754. Macmillan, New York, 1955.
47. Gourzis, J. T., *Proc. Soc. Exptl. Biol. Med.* **89**, 57 (1955).

48. Gourzis, J. T., and Bauer, R. O., *J. Pharmacol. Exptl. Therap.* **103**, 471 (1951).
49. Grundfest, H., *Ann. Rev. Pharmacol.* **4**, 341 (1964).
50. Gujral, P. K., Ph.D., Dissertation, Harvard University, Cambridge, Massachusetts (1965).
51. Gujral, P. K., and Flacke, W., *J. Pharmacol. Exptl. Therap.* **152**, 95 (1966).
52. Hashimoto, K., Kumakura, S., and Taira, N., *Japan. J. Physiol.* **14**, 299 (1964).
53. Herr, F., and Akcasu, A., *J. Pharmacol. Exptl. Therap.* **130**, 328 (1960).
54. Heymans, C., and DeVleeschhouver, G., *Arch. Intern. Pharmacodyn.* **84**, 409 (1950).
55. Hoffmann, P., *Z. Biol.* **58**, 55 (1912).
56. Hoobler, S. W., Corley, R. W., Kabza, T. G., and Loyke, H. F., *Ann. Internal Med.* [N.S.] **37**, 465 (1952).
57. Hoobler, S. W., Kabza, T. G., and Corley, R. W., *J. Clin. Invest.* **34**, 559 (1955).
58. Jarisch, A., and Richter, H., *Arch. Exptl. Pathol. Pharmakol.* **193**, 355 (1939).
59. Jeger, O., and Prelog, V., *Alkaloids* 7, 363–417 (1960).
60. Jenkins, H. J., and Christensen, B. V., *J. Am. Pharm. Assoc.* **41**, 239 (1952).
61. Klohs, M. W., Arons, R., Draper, M. D., Keller, F., Koster, S., Malesh, W., and Petracek, F. J., *J. Am. Chem. Soc.* **74**, 5107 (1952).
62. Klohs, M. W., Draper, M. D., Keller, F., Koster, S., Malesh, W., and Petracek, F. J., *J. Am. Chem. Soc.* **75**, 4925 (1953).
63. Klohs, M. W., Draper, M. D., Keller, F., Koster, S., Malesh, W., and Petracek, F. J., *J. Am. Chem. Soc.* **76**, 1152 (1954).
64. Klohs, M. W., Draper, M. D., Keller, F., Malesh, W., and Petracek, F. J., *J. Am. Chem. Soc.* **75**, 3595 (1953).
64a. Koch-Weser, J., *Abstr. 3rd Intern. Pharmacol. Congr., Sao Paulo, 1966* p. 198.
65. Kolb, E. J., and Korein, J., *Neurology* **11**, 159 (1961).
66. Komalahiranya, A., and Volle, R. L., *J. Pharmacol. Exptl. Therap.* **138**, 57 (1962).
67. Konzett, H., and Rothlin, E., *Arch. Exptl. Pathol. Pharmakol.* **225**, 101 (1955).
68. Krayer, O., *Arch. Exptl. Pathol. Pharmakol.* **240**, 361 (1961).
69. Krayer, O., *in* "Pharmacology in Medicine" (V. A. Drill, ed.), 2nd ed., pp. 515–524. McGraw-Hill, New York, 1958.
70. Krayer, O., and Acheson, G. H., *Physiol. Rev.* **26**, 383 (1946).
71. Krayer, O., and George, H. W., *J. Pharmacol. Exptl. Therap.* **103**, 249 (1951).
72. Krayer, O., Kupchan, S. M., Deliwala, C. V., and Rogers, B. H., *Arch. Exptl. Pathol. Pharmakol.* **219**, 371 (1953).
73. Kupchan, S. M., *J. Am. Chem. Soc.* **81**, 1921 (1959).
74. Kupchan, S. M., *J. Am. Chem. Soc.* **81**, 1925 (1959).
75. Kupchan, S. M., *J. Pharm. Sci.* **50**, 273 (1961).
76. Kupchan, S. M., and Afonso, A., *J. Am. Pharm. Assoc.* **48**, 731 (1959).
77. Kupchan, S. M., and Afonso, A., *J. Am. Pharm. Assoc.* **49**, 242 (1960).
78. Kupchan, S. M., and Ayres, C. I., *J. Am. Pharm. Assoc.* **48**, 440 (1959).
79. Kupchan, S. M., and Ayres, C. I., *J. Am. Pharm. Assoc.* **48**, 735 (1959).
80. Kupchan, S. M., and Ayres, C. I., *J. Am. Chem. Soc.* **82**, 2252 (1960).
81. Kupchan, S. M., Ayres, C. I., and Hensler, R. H., *J. Am. Chem. Soc.* **82**, 2616 (1960).
82. Kupchan, S. M., Ayres, C. I., Neeman, M., Hensler, R. H., Masamune, T., and Rajagopalan, S., *J. Am. Chem. Soc.* **82**, 2242 (1960).
83. Kupchan, S. M., and By, A. W., *Alkaloids* 10, (1967) in press.
84. Kupchan, S. M., and Deliwala, C. V., *J. Am. Chem. Soc.* **75**, 1025 (1953).
85. Kupchan, S. M., and Deliwala, C. V., *J. Am. Chem. Soc.* **76**, 5545 (1954).
86. Kupchan, S. M., Fujita, E., Grivas, J. C., and Weaver, L. C., *J. Pharm. Sci.* **51**, 1140 (1962).

87. Kupchan, S. M., Grivas, J. C., Ayres, C. I., Pandya, L. J., and Weaver, L. C., *J. Pharm. Sci.* **50**, 396 (1961).
88. Kupchan, S. M., and Gruenfeld, N., *J. Am. Pharm. Assoc.* **48**, 737 (1959).
89. Kupchan, S. M., Gruenfeld, N., and Katsui, N., *J. Med. Pharm. Chem.* **5**, 690 (1962).
90. Kupchan, S. M., Hensler, R. H., and Weaver, L. C., *J. Med. Pharm. Chem.* **3**, 129 (1961).
91. Kupchan, S. M., Lavie, D., Deliwala, C. V., and Andoh, B. Y. A., *J. Am. Chem. Soc.* **75**, 5519 (1953).
92. Kupchan, S. M., Lavie, D., and Zonis, R. D., *J. Am. Chem. Soc.* **77**, 689 (1955).
93. Kupchan, S. M., and Narayanan, C. R., *J. Am. Chem. Soc.* **81**, 1913 (1959).
94. Kupchan, S. M., Weaver, L. C., Ayres, C. I., and Hensler, R. H., *J. Pharm. Sci.* **50**, 52 (1961).
95. Kupchan, S. M., Zimmerman, J. H., and Afonso, A., *Lloydia* **24**, 1 (1961).
96. Langrehr, D., *Arch. Ges. Physiol.* **271**, 257 (1960).
97. Leonard, E., and Hajdu, S., *in* "Handbook of Physiology" (W. F. Hamilton and P. Dow, eds.), Vol. 1, Sect. 2, pp. 151–198. Am. Physiol. Soc., Washington, D.C., 1962.
98. Litchfield, J. T., Jr., and Wilcoxon, F., *J. Pharmacol. Exptl. Therap.* **96**, 99 (1949).
99. Maison, G. L., Gotz, E., and Stutzman, J. W., *J. Pharmacol. Exptl. Therap.* **103**, 74 (1951).
100. Malhotra, C. L., and Sidhu, R. K., *J. Pharmacol. Exptl. Therap.* **116**, 123 (1956).
101. Margolin, E. G., Levine, H. D., and Merrill, J. P., *Am. Heart J.* **52**, 257 (1956).
102. Martini, L., and Calliauw, L., *Arch. Intern. Pharmacodyn.* **51**, 49 (1955).
103. Meier, R., Tripod, J., and Bruni, T., *Arch. Exptl. Pathol. Pharmakol.* **226**, 319 (1955).
104. Meilman, E., *J. Pharmacol. Exptl. Therap.* **101**, 27 (1951).
105. Meilman, E., *J. Clin. Invest.* **32**, 80 (1953).
106. Meilman, E., *J. Am. Med. Assoc.* **153**, 540 (1953).
107. Meilman, E., *in* "Hypertension: First Hahnemann Symposium on Hypertensive Disease" (J. H. Moyer, ed.), pp. 395–399. Saunders, Philadelphia, Pennsylvania, 1959.
108. Meves, H., *Arch. Ges. Physiol.* **290**, 211 (1966).
108a. Meilman, E., and Krayer, O., *Circulation* **6**, 212 (1952).
109. Mitchner, H., and Parks, L. M., *J. Am. Pharm. Assoc.* **48**, 303 (1959).
110. Möhrle, H., and Auterhoff, H., *Arch. Pharm.* **292**, 337 (1959).
111. Morgan, K. J., and Barltrop, J. A., *Quart. Rev. (London)* **12**, 34 (1958).
112. Mosey, L., and Kaplan, A., *J. Pharmacol. Exptl. Therap.* **104**, 67 (1952).
113. Moyer, J. H., and Brest, A. N., *in* "Hypertension: Second Hahnemann Symposium on Hypertensive Disease" (A. N. Brest and J. H. Moyer, eds.), pp. 296–301 and 516–537. Lea & Febiger, Philadelphia, Pennsylvania, 1961.
114. Moyer, J. H., Miller, S. I., Tashnek, A. B., Snyder, H., and Bowman, R. O., *Am. J. Med.* **14**, 175 (1953).
115. Myers, G. S., Friedlich, A. L., Scannel, J. G., O'Neill, J. R., and Currens, J. H., *Proc. New Engl. Cardiovascular Soc.*, *10*, **4**, (1951–52).
116. Myers, G. S., Glen, W. L., Morozovitch, P., Barber, R., Papineau-Couture, G., and Grant, G. A., *J. Am. Chem. Soc.* **78**, 1621 (1956).
117. Myers, G. S., Morozovitch, P., Glen, W. L., Barber, R., Papineau-Couture, G., and Grant, G. A., *J. Am. Chem. Soc.* **77**, 3348 (1955).
118. Narayanan, C. R., *in* "Progress in the Chemistry of Organic Natural Products" (L. Zechmeister, ed.), Vol. 20, p. 298. Springer, Vienna, 1962.
119. Nash, H. A., and Brooker, R. M., *J. Am. Chem. Soc.* **75**, 1942 (1953).
120. Neil, E., and Joels, N., *Arch. Exptl. Pathol. Pharmakol.* **240**, 453 (1961).

121. Norwood, W. C., "The Therapeutic Powers and Properties of Veratrum Viride," 2nd ed. Bedford, New York, 1856.
122. Nungesser, W. C., and Hiatt, E. P., *J. Pharmacol. Exptl. Therap.* **110**, 68 (1954).
123. Oda, T., *Osaka City Med. J.* **9**, 31 (1963).
124. Paintal, A. S., *Pharmacol. Rev.* **16**, 341 (1964).
125. Pelletier, S. W., and Jacobs, W. A., *J. Am. Chem. Soc.* **75**, 3248 (1953).
126. Pircio, A., and Geiling, E. M. K., *J. Am. Pharm. Assoc.* **41**, 552 (1952).
127. Poethke, W., *Arch. Pharm.* **275**, 357 (1937).
128. Poethke, W., *Arch. Pharm.* **275**, 571 (1937).
129. Reiter, M., *Arch. Exptl. Pathol. Pharmakol.* **246**, 45 (1964).
130. Richardson, A. P., Walker, H. A., Farrar, C. B., Griffith, W., Pound, E., and Davidson, J. R., *Proc. Soc. Exptl. Biol. Med.* **79**, 79 (1952).
131. Rose, J. C., and Lazaro, E. J., *J. Pharmacol. Exptl. Therap.* **117**, 461 (1956).
131a. Rosenblueth, A., and Del Pozo, E. C., *Am. J. Physiol.* **136**, 699 (1942).
132. Rubin, B., and Burke, J. C., *J. Pharmacol. Exptl. Therap.* **105**, 409 (1952).
133. Salisbury, P. F., Cross, C. E., and Rieben, P. A., *Circulation Res.* **8**, 530 (1960).
134. Schafer, H., *Ergeb. Physiol., Biol. Chem. Exptl. Pharmakol.* **46**, 71 (1950).
135. Shanes, A. M., *J. Cellular Comp. Physiol.* **38**, 17 (1951).
136. Shanes, A. M., *J. Pharmacol. Exptl. Therap.* **105**, 216 (1952).
137. Shanes, A. M., *Pharmacol. Rev.* **10**, 165 (1958).
138. Shanes, A. M., and Gershfeld, N. L., *J. Gen. Physiol.* **44**, 345 (1960).
139. Shimizu, B., *J. Pharm. Soc. Japan* **80**, 32 (1960).
140. Shimizu, B., *Takamine Kenkyusho Nempo* **13**, 62 (1961).
141. Spuhler, O., and Wyss, S., *Schweiz. Med. Wochschr.* **84**, 925 (1954).
142. Stoll, A., and Seebeck, E., *Helv. Chim. Acta* **35**, 1270 (1952).
143. Stoll, A., and Seebeck, E., *Helv. Chim. Acta* **36**, 718 (1953).
144. Stoll, A., and Seebeck, E., *Helv. Chim. Acta* **36**, 1570 (1953).
145. Straub, R., *Helv. Physiol. Pharmacol. Acta* **14**, 1 (1956).
146. Stuart, D. M., and Parks, L. M., *J. Am. Pharm. Assoc.* **45**, 252 (1956).
147. Stutzman, J. W., Simon, H., and Maison, G. L., *J. Pharmacol. Exptl. Therap.* **101**, 310 (1951).
148. Suzuki, M., Murase, Y., Hayashi, R., and Sanpei, N., *J. Pharm. Soc. Japan* **79**, 619 (1959).
149. Swiss, E. D., *J. Pharmacol. Exptl. Therap.* **104**, 76 (1952).
150. Swiss, E. D., and Maison, G. L., *Federation Proc.* **11**, 395 (1952).
151. Swiss, E. D., and Mountain, C. F., *Proc. Soc. Exptl. Biol. Med.* **88**, 19 (1955).
152. Tanaka, K., and Kanno, T., *Yonago Acta Med.* **2**, 8 (1956).
153. Tsukamoto, T., and Yagi, A., *J. Pharm. Soc. Japan* **79**, 1102 (1959).
154. Ulbricht, W., and Flacke, W., *J. Gen. Physiol.* **48**, 1035 (1965).
155. Vejdělek, Z. J., Macek, K., and Buděšinský, B., *Collection Czech. Chem. Commun.* **22**, 98 (1957).
156. Vejdělek, Z. J., and Trčka, V., *Pharmazie* **12**, 582 (1957).
157. von Bezold, A., and Hirt, L., *Untersuch. Physiol. Lab. Wurzburg* **1**, 73 (1867).
158. Voskian, J., Assali, N. S., and Noll, L., *Surg., Gynecol. Obstet.* **102**, 37 (1956).
159. Wang, S. C., Ngai, S. H., and Grossman, R. G., *J. Pharmacol. Exptl. Therap.* **113**, 100 (1955).
160. Weaver, L. C., Jones, W. R., and Kupchan, S. M., *J. Pharm. Sci.* **51**, 1144 (1962).
161. Weisenborn, F. L., Bolger, J. W., Rosen, D. B., Mann, L. T., Johnson, L., and Holmes, H. L., *J. Am. Chem. Soc.* **76**, 1792 (1954).
162. Weisenborn, F. L., and Bolger, J. W., *J. Am. Chem. Soc.* **76**, 5543 (1954).

163. Winer, B. M., *New Engl. J. Med.* **255**, 1173 (1956).
164. Winer, B. M., *Circulation* **14**, 1019 (1956); **16**, 953 (1957).
165. Winkler, E. G., and Cangello, V. W., *Am. J. Obstet. Gynecol.* **75**, 433 (1958).
166. Witt, P. N., and Swaine, C. R., *J. Pharmacol. Exptl. Therap.* **120**, 63 (1957).
167. Witzleb, E., *Arch. Ges. Physiol.* **269**, 439 (1959).
168. Wright, E. B., and Tadao, T., *J. Cellular Comp. Physiol.* **67**, 181 (1966).
169. Wyss, S., and Spühler, O., *Acta Med. Scand.* **153**, 221 (1956).
170. Yagi, A., and Kawasaki, T., *J. Pharm. Soc. Japan* **82**, 210 (1962).
171. Yagi, A., and Kawasaki, T., *Chem. & Pharm. Bull.* (*Tokyo*) **10**, 519 (1962).

CHAPTER XIII

Use of Antihypertensive Drugs in Combinations

F. O. Simpson

J. V. Hodge

I. Introduction, 459
II. Combinations of Antihypertensive Drugs, 462
    A. Combinations Involving *Rauwolfia* Alkaloids, 462
    B. Combinations Involving Diuretics, 464
    C. Combinations Involving Ganglion-Blocking Drugs, 468
    D. Combinations Involving Sympatholytic Drugs, 469
    E. Combinations Involving Monoamine Oxidase Inhibitors, 471
    F. Combinations Involving Adrenolytic (α-Receptor Blocking) Drugs, 473
    G. Comment, 474
III. Antihypertensive Drugs Combined with Other Drugs, 475
    A. Amphetaminelike Drugs and Antihypertensive Therapy, 475
    B. Bronchodilator Drugs and Antihypertensive Therapy, 475
    C. "Common Cold Tablets," Nasal Decongestants and Compound Cough Linctuses and Antihypertensive Therapy, 475
    D. Antihistamines and Antihypertensive Therapy, 476
    E. Tranquilizers, Sedatives, and Antihypertensive Therapy, 476
    F. Antidepressants and Antihypertensive Therapy, 477
    G. Phenylbutazone and Antihypertensive Therapy, 479
    H. Drugs Used in the Treatment of Gout, and Antihypertensive Therapy, 479
    I. Antianginal Drugs and Antihypertensive Therapy, 479
    J. Antiarrhythmic Drugs and Antihypertensive Therapy, 480
    K. Cardiac Glycosides and Antihypertensive Therapy, 480
    L. Cholesterol-lowering Agents and Antihypertensive Therapy, 480
    M. Comment, 480
IV. Conclusion, 481
    References, 482

I. Introduction

Successful management of severe hypertension is seldom possible with one drug alone, usually because of troublesome side effects, sometimes because of inadequate response to the drug. It has long been recognized that the desirable action of antihypertensive drugs could be augmented and undesirable actions minimized by the use of two or more drugs in appropriate combinations (12, 57, 78, 126, 183) and this certainly accords with our own experience in the Dunedin hypertension clinic (145, 149, 152) where our policy of all-day blood pressure recording has allowed detailed comparison of different treatment regimens.

The practical advantages of combined treatment are: effective treatment of patients previously resistant to the action of a single drug, smoother control of blood pressure, lower doses of individual drugs and thus less troublesome side effects, and the possibility of cancellation of side effects by judicious selection of drugs. However, multiple drug regimens have their disadvantages—patients with limited intelligence find them difficult to manage, so that errors may occur, and, while some side effects are less troublesome, each additional drug introduces the possibility of new ones.

Since many combinations of antihypertensive drugs are now in general use, one might expect to find readily available explanations of the pharmacological mechanisms involved. However, this is often far from the case, and current knowledge in the field remains to a large extent empirical. Just as the usefulness of an individual drug is often known long before its mode of action is clarified, so the clinical usage of drug combinations has in many instances outstripped the study of their pharmacology. From what is known of the actions of individual antihypertensive agents, predictions can often be made as to the probable effect of combining these agents or of giving them with other drugs. Such predictions may not always be valid for man and several examples are given in later sections of apparently successful drug combinations to which objections may be raised on theoretical grounds. This may be due to basic differences between species, or to such other factors as lower dosages in man. Due consideration must certainly be given to all the evidence available before drugs are combined in novel ways and caution used if adverse results are anticipated, but data derived from animal pharmacology are not always directly relevant clinically. The physician who treats hypertensive patients should not be led by the complexity and possible danger of drug interactions to condemn multiple drug therapy outright; he should rather use all information available to him in a search for logical ways in which drugs may be combined with maximum benefit to the patient.

An attempt to classify this information is fraught with difficulty, but we would tentatively group the various possible interactions of antihypertensive drugs as follows:

(1) Interactions which affect the absorption, distribution, breakdown or excretion of one or other member of a drug combination. An example of this is the increase in plasma levels of pempidine which occurs when chlorothiazide

is given concomitantly (41). The current interest in the effects of drugs on the degree of binding of other drugs to plasma proteins (18) and on detoxication mechanisms in the liver (22, 132) may direct attention to further examples relevant to the field of antihypertensive therapy.

(2) Interactions between two drugs acting at the same point, e.g., the sympathetic nerve terminal. The action of one drug may in some way be complementary to that of the other, and there will thus be enhancement of the desired effect; examples of this include combinations of methyldopa and guanethidine, or methyldopa and reserpine, and these are discussed later (Sections II, F, 3; II, A, 5). Less desirable interactions are, in theory at least, also possible, though the evidence of such interactions in animal experiments does not appear always to be relevant for man. For instance, the drugs may compete for binding sites, so that one drug is rendered less effective than it would be if given by itself; thus reserpine has been shown to displace guanethidine from binding sites at the sympathetic nerve terminal in the experimental animal (18) but so far there is no evidence of such an effect in man (Section II, A, 3). Again, the action of one drug may be theoretically opposed to the action of another—for instance, bretylium and bethanidine (which interfere with the release of norepinephrine at the sympathetic nerve terminal (10)) have been found to delay the catecholamine-depleting effect of guanethidine (10, 33) and reserpine (10); yet the net effect of such combinations in man may be satisfactory (Sections II, A, 4; II, D. 2). Examples of clinically proved interference with the action of a hypotensive drug by another drug (amphetamine, imipramine, or amitriptyline) will be discussed later (Section III, A and F).

(3) Interactions between drugs acting at different sites. An example of this is the effect of an oral diuretic in rendering the maintenance of the blood pressure more dependent on neurogenic mechanisms and thus more vulnerable to the effects of drugs such as ganglion blockers or sympatholytics.

It must be admitted that such a grouping is speculative and probably oversimplified. The basic actions or sites of action of individual antihypertensive drugs are often not entirely clear. It may be incorrect to assume, for instance, that the sympatholytic drugs act only at the sympathetic nerve terminal; they may also have a direct action on smooth muscle (185).

The majority of patients who are treated for hypertension are over the age of forty, and many of them show other related or unrelated conditions requiring drug treatment. It is therefore common for antihypertensive regimens to be further complicated by the simultaneous use of drugs of other types, for example cardiac glycosides, coronary vasodilators, cholesterol and uric acid lowering agents, antiarryhthmics, oral hypoglycemic agents, anesthetics, sedatives and tranquilizers, to mention only a few. The modern therapeutic situation leaves few symptoms and abnormal findings beyond the reach of treatment and it is by no means uncommon to find patients who are regularly taking eight or more different drugs daily, often acquired from different sources. While such complicated drug treatment may be perfectly justified, it is necessary to be certain that the addition of a new drug to a patient's regimen is really desirable in terms of his life expectancy and comfort, and that the latest addition is compatible with the previous drugs.

It is natural, therefore, that the contents of this chapter should fall into two main subdivisions, one dealing with combinations involving only antihypertensive drugs, and the other with combinations of antihypertensives with other drugs. It will be readily apparent that the information available on some of the combinations is scanty and that we have in these cases included some initial personal experiences which are far from complete. This has been done in the full knowledge that these experiences may well not represent the whole truth about a given combination, but we hope that our account may help to direct attention to the problems and to stimulate further studies.

II. Combinations of antihypertensive drugs

The proliferation of drugs for treating hypertension is continually increasing the number of ways in which such drugs may be combined, although not all such combinations are of great practical value. The emphasis in this section is on drugs in common use, and reference to drugs with more limited application (e.g., protoveratrine, hydralazine) has been omitted, although these have been used in combination with other antihypertensives for many years (177, 179).

A. COMBINATIONS INVOLVING *Rauwolfia* ALKALOIDS

1. *Rauwolfia and Ganglion Blocking Drugs*

It was well recognized in the earlier days of hypotensive therapy that the combination of reserpine and ganglion-blocking drugs was more effective and satisfactory than ganglion-blocking drugs alone (47, 56, 154) mainly because the dose of the latter could be smaller and the side effects thereby reduced. The side effects of the combination remained fairly considerable, however, and included parasympatholytic effects, depression due to the large doses of reserpine used, and a tendency to fluid retention. Some augmentation of the hypotensive effect of ganglion-blocking drugs was also achieved by the use of other *Rauwolfia* alkaloids, e.g., rescinnamine (156) with less likelihood of drug-induced depression. However, these combinations are now seldom used without the inclusion of a thiazide-type diuretic in the regimen (Sections II, B; II, C, 1).

2. *Reserpine (or Other Rauwolfia Drug) and an Oral Diuretic*

This combination has achieved widespread popularity for the treatment of the milder grades of hypertension (52, 53, 57, 79, 95, 150, 159). The reduction of blood pressure occurs smoothly without diurnal fluctuations and although the blood pressure levels are usually lower in the standing than in the lying posture, the difference is insufficient to cause postural giddiness. Unfortunately, the antihypertensive effect is insufficient for the treatment of more severe cases; however, when a potent drug is needed, it is better to retain one or both of the milder antihypertensives as "background therapy" with the addition of either a ganglion-blocking or a sympatholytic drug (12, 60, 78, 150).

3. Reserpine and Guanethidine

Experimentally it has been shown that reserpine displaces guanethidine from specific binding sites at sympathetic nerve terminals (25), an observation which suggests that the action of guanethidine in man may be reduced rather than enhanced by reserpine. However, we have found no clinical evidence which would support this, and the combination has been used effectively in over forty patients at the Dunedin clinic without adverse effects or difficulty in blood pressure control being noted. In most cases we have used this combination in the sequence of reserpine first and guanethidine second, so that the effect of reserpine on the dose requirements of guanethidine has been difficult to assess.

4. Reserpine and Bethanidine

Bethanidine is stated to interfere with the norepinephrine-depleting effect of reserpine in animal studies (10), so that this combination might also be considered unsatisfactory on theoretical grounds. However, in our experience the addition of reserpine (0.25 mg daily) or other *Rauwolfia* preparation to a regimen containing bethanidine has a definite hypotensive effect, sometimes persisting indefinitely and at other times lessening to some extent after 2–4 weeks. The value of the combination used in the reverse sequence (i.e., bethanidine added to a *Rauwolfia* regimen) should be shown as an unusually small effective dose of bethanidine, but in practice the effect seems to be too variable to allow firm conclusions. No adverse results from combining these two drugs have been seen, however, and because an additional effect has been definite in some cases we believe that it is justifiable to add reserpine to bethanidine if the patient's response to the latter is unsatisfactory.

5. Reserpine and Methyldopa

Both of these drugs may cause mental depression and clearly the combination should not be used without awareness of this risk. However, in appropriate cases we have found it to be of surprising value. Some patients show a poor hypotensive response to methyldopa even if the dose is large (over 2 g daily) and even if an oral diuretic is being given. A proportion of such patients will show quite a dramatic hypotensive response when reserpine is added to the regimen, and sometimes the dose of methyldopa can be substantially reduced.

We have had experience of this combination in 28 patients, half of whom were being treated with reserpine at the time methyldopa was started. This group showed no side effects other than temporary sedation as seen with methyldopa alone, and blood pressure control was in most cases good. In the other cases, reserpine (0.125 mg or 0.25 mg daily) was added to a regimen of methyldopa and side effects in the initial period were sufficiently prominent to warrant abandoning the combination in four of these. The side effects were in one case depression, in another nightmares, in a third agitation, tremor, and diarrhea, and in the fourth, considerable fluid retention. A fifth patient showed temporary fluid retention with ankle swelling for the first few days only. Seven of the remaining ten patients showed lower blood pressures after the addition of reserpine, and three of these needed reduction in the aldomet dosage.

It is not easy to interpret this apparent synergism of reserpine and methyldopa in the light of animal experiments. Methyldopa is known to antagonize the sedative effect of reserpine in animals (38, 68) and to restore the pressor response to tyramine after this had been reduced by reserpine (125, 169); these points would tend to indicate some degree of antagonism between the two drugs. On the other hand, there is evidence that reserpine (at least in large doses) can cause depletion of α-methyl norepinephrine in the hearts of animals treated with methyldopa (99). α-Methyl norepinephrine is itself a pressor amine and may act as neurotransmitter in place of norepinephrine (37), thus providing a possible explanation of the development of resistance to methyldopa in man. If reserpine interferes also in man with the accumulation of α-methyl norepinephrine in sympathetic nerve terminals, then this may explain the additional hypotensive effect obtained when reserpine is combined with methyldopa.

B. Combinations Involving Diuretics

1. *General Considerations*

The oral diuretics occupy a unique place in the treatment of hypertension. Regardless of some uncertainty as to their mode of action on the blood pressure (see deStevens, Chapter VII) the net effect in patients appears to be to make the maintenance of their blood pressure more dependent on neurogenic mechanisms and therefore more vulnerable to the effects of drugs which interrupt these mechanisms at any point. Thus the diuretics are very widely used in combination with every conceivable type of hypotensive agent and in general they have greatly simplified the management of hypertensive patients. In our clinic 76% of the patients currently attending are taking an oral diuretic, 12% have taken a diuretic in the past and have changed to other therapy for various reasons, and 12% have never had a diuretic. We use mainly cyclopenthiazide (76), hydrochlorothiazide (157), trichloromethiazide or bendrofluazide, but we have experience also of chlorexolone (142), chlorthalidone and clopamide, all of which resemble the thiazides in most respects, triamterene (146), spirono-lactone, ethacrynic acid and furosemide. The latter four drugs have, of course, some special characteristics and will be commented on separately; the remainder will be classed together as "thiazide-type drugs."

In mild cases a diuretic alone, or with a small dose of a *Rauwolfia* preparation, has sufficient hypotensive effect to make the use of a more powerful agent unnecessary; in other cases, where a more powerful agent is also needed, the use of a diuretic usually leads to a smoother control of the blood pressure, a reduction in the dose requirement of the more powerful drug, and hence a diminution in side effects from it. An additional advantage comes from the diuretic effect itself; some hypertensive patients have dyspnoea on effort, or mild fluid retention (sometimes partly due to sympatholytic drugs) and these features are usually relieved by the administration of an oral diuretic.

2. Drawbacks

However, the benefits of the oral diuretics are not obtained without some cost, as the drug regimen is made more complicated, and there can be potentially serious side effects, three of which may necessitate the administration of yet another drug, i.e., hypokalemia, hyperuricemia, and impairment of carbo-hydrate tolerance. These will be discussed in some detail.

a. Hypokalemia. The effects of the various thiazide-type drugs on serum potassium levels are very similar, in our experience. The reduction in serum potassium usually averages about 0.3–0.6 mEq per liter, but individual patients vary greatly, and a particularly big drop may be an indication of a preexisting hyperaldosteronism (29, 48, 144). Long-standing hypokalemia is associated with deterioration in renal function (80, 131), and it seems wise to make sure that any severe degree of it is avoided by giving routine potassium supplements, preferably in the form of potassium chloride (87). When a diuretic and potassium chloride are being administered together, the two substances can be satisfactorily combined in one tablet, provided that this is done in such a way that the availability of the diuretic is not interfered with and the potassium chloride is present in a form which does not involve any danger of inducing ulceration of the small bowel. (98, 111).

Another approach to the problem of potassium depletion is to use a potassium-sparing diuretic such as spironolactone or triamterene (71, 77, 79, 86, 146), along with the thiazide-type diuretic (Section II, B, 4). Finally, it has been reported that methyldopa may also counteract the hypokalemic effect of a thiazide (27).

b. Hyperuricemia. This is quite commonly seen in patients on thiazide-type drugs (109), and gout is occasionally precipitated. If the degree of hyperuricemia is very considerable, e.g., serum uric acid levels over 9 mg %, or if an attack of gout should occur, then there are two courses open. If the diuretic is not considered to be an essential part of the patient's treatment, then it is best to stop the drug. On the other hand, there are patients in whom the diuretic plays an important part in the regimen, either because of threatened cardiac failure or because of difficulties in the control of the blood pressure; in such patients the correct decision is probably to continue the diuretic agent and to deal with the hyperuricemia by other means (Section III, H).

c. *Impairment of Carbohydrate Tolerance.* Finally, there is the question of the diabetogenic action of the thiazide-type diuretics (66, 140) which is not uncommonly seen, though seldom really serious. If diabetes develops during long-term diuretic therapy, the diuretic should, if possible, be stopped. However, as was the case with hyperuricemia, we feel that if the general condition of the patient—either from the point of view of the control of his blood pressure, or because of his cardiac state—seems to warrant the use of a diuretic, then the diuretic should be given without too much hesitation; the impaired glucose tolerance then has to be treated in the usual way with dietary restriction of carbohydrates and the use of insulin or an oral hypoglycemic agent.

3. *Ethacrynic Acid and Furosemide*

The place of these powerful shorter acting diuretics in the treatment of hypertension has not yet been fully established. Satisfactory reduction of blood pressure has been reported with ethacrynic acid (30, 42) at a dosage of 100–150 mg daily; in our hands, and using a rather smaller dosage of 50–100 mg daily, the hypotensive effect has been very variable, and less reliable than that of the thiazide-type drugs. Furosemide causes a slight decrease in blood pressure in most cases when used as a diuretic (5), and a satisfactory hypotensive effect in conjunction with reserpine has been reported (50). It is debatable whether the rapid diuretic action of these drugs is an advantage or a disadvantage for long-term routine use in hypertension; on the whole we would consider it a disadvantage. Both these drugs produce an additional diuresis and natriuresis when given with a thiazide-type drug (42, 134), and their place may prove to be mainly as an addition to other regimens, used like mersalyl once or twice a week when extra diuresis is needed. However, there is evidence that ethacrynic acid (30, 104, 143, 160) and furosemide (5, 124) may be less troublesome than the older thiazide-type diuretics in their effects on serum potassium and carbohydrate tolerance, and if this is confirmed, it would justify their more widespread use in hypertension.

4. *Combinations of Diuretic Agents*

The use of furosemide or ethacrynic acid once or twice weekly when an additional diuretic effect is required in a patient on a thiazide-type drug has already been mentioned (Section II, B, 3), and we have found this to be of value.

A combination of ethacrynic acid with a thiazide has been reported to give a greater hypotensive effect than either drug alone (30), though at the cost of considerable hypokalemia; this regimen plus restriction of dietary sodium gave a particularly good reduction of blood pressure (30), but the safety of such a powerful combination of sodium- and potassium-depleting agents remains to be proved.

The combination of a potassium-sparing diuretic with a thiazide-type drug has been mentioned (Section II, B, 2, a), spironolactone having been shown to cause some further fall in blood pressure and an improvement in serum potassium values (77, 79, 86), though at the cost of some increase in blood urea (86). Triamterene by itself has comparatively little antihypertensive effect (146), and has been reported not to cause any additional reduction of blood pressure when added to a regimen of chlorthalidone (35). However, we feel that the main point of a combination of triamterene and a thiazide-type drug is not to hope for an increased antihypertensive effect from the triamterene, but rather that part of the thiazide dosage might be replaced, as it were, by a dose of triamterene in such a way that the effect on blood pressure remains the same, while hypokalemia is avoided. For this purpose, a combined preparation of triamterene and a thiazide has been tried and found satisfactory in edematous patients (168), and in our hands in hypertensive patients. We have found that this combined preparation of 25 mg benzthiazide and 50 mg triamterene twice daily has, if anything, a slightly superior effect on blood pressure compared to that of 50 mg benzthiazide twice daily, while serum potassium levels were more satisfactory (mean 4.2 mEq per liter) on the combined preparation than on benzthiazide alone (mean 3.7 mEq per liter). These results were obtained in ten patients, selected because of hypokalemia on previous diuretic therapy; potassium chloride supplements, usually 1 g daily, were given throughout the trial.

5. Undesirable Interactions Between Diuretic Agents and Other Hypotensive Drugs

Such reactions seem to be comparatively unusual. However, the combination of a thiazide diuretic with the nondiuretic thiazide drug diazoxide seems to have a particularly potent diabetogenic effect (43, 115), and although diazoxide may be useful when acute reduction of blood pressure is required (52, 79), the combination of this drug with a thiazide diuretic should probably be avoided.

The only other unusual reaction of a diuretic with another antihypertensive drug of which we are aware has occurred in our hands with clopamide (55) which apart from the usual sulfonamide structure has a side chain which includes a hydrazinelike linkage. It has proved to be a satisfactory diuretic agent (14, 121), and also to have a satisfactory hypotensive effect in our hands when given alone or with reserpine or bethanidine. However, in five patients who were taking methyldopa we encountered side effects, including night-mares and minor hallucinations (one case), headaches and an unconscious episode (one case) diarrhea (three cases) with abdominal pain and hemolytic anemia in one of these and fever in two of them; the only other patient who took methyldopa and clopamide had a marked deterioration in her diabetic state during clopamide therapy. The degree to which clopamide was respon-sible for the reactions in the first five patients is, of course, debatable, but such difficulties have, in our experience, been uncommon when methyldopa is used with other thiazide or thiazide-type diuretics.

An undesirable reaction in the form of severe hypotension can, of course, occur if a diuretic agent is added abruptly to a regimen of powerful hypotensive agents. It will not occur if the diuretic is started in very small doses, or if the dose of the more powerful agent is first reduced.

6. *Multiple Drug Tablets*

Because of the frequent use of diuretics in conjunction with other hypo-tensive agents, various preparations are available containing such combinations of drugs in one tablet. We feel that such multiple drug tablets are probably useful when both the drugs in the tablet are "fixed dose drugs," i.e., they are given at a certain dosage and if the effect is not satisfactory then the dose is not increased but yet another drug is added. Thus, combinations of a diuretic with a small dose of reserpine (53), or of a thiazide and triamterene (71, 168) are probably useful; on the other hand, combinations of a diuretic with drugs such as guanethidine or methyldopa, the doses of which have to be tailored to the patient's needs, seem much less satisfactory. If one of these more powerful drugs is needed, it is usually much better to give the diuretic by itself, or in a preparation combined with potassium chloride, and then to add the sym-patholytic drug in a separate tablet.

C. Combinations Involving Ganglion-Blocking Drugs

1. *Ganglion-Blocking Drugs with Reserpine and/or a Diuretic*

The use of ganglion blockers with reserpine and ganglion blockers with diuretics has already been mentioned. These combinations, and also the triple combination of a ganglion blocker, reserpine and a diuretic, have largely been supplanted by regimens which include one of the sympatholytic drugs. The triple combination was, however, very effective—control of the blood pressure was reliable and the side effects, though fairly troublesome, were predictable. It is our impression that blood pressure control with the sympatholytic drugs is in some patients less consistent than with the ganglion blockers. However, at present the ganglion blockers are usually only used as an adjunct to other drugs in long-term therapy and as parenteral therapy when rapid reduction of blood pressure is required. For long-term use, pempidine is probably the most satisfactory of the ganglion blockers.

2. *Pempidine and Guanethidine*

When uncontrollable diarrhea limits the dosage of guanethidine, the practice in our clinic as in others (69, 101) has been to combine it with pempidine. The constipating effect of the pempidine will often allow a return to normal bowel habits and, as with bethanidine (Section II, D, 2), the times of pempidine administration can be adjusted to give better 24-hour blood pressure control. Usually the dose of pempidine required is insufficient for other side effects of ganglion blockade to be troublesome, and in our own experience with 29 patients this has been a very successful combination of posturally acting drugs, particularly in resistant cases. The greatest effect on blood pressure is often achieved if the individual doses are weighted toward the ganglion-blocking rather than the sympatholytic effect. Side effects from parasympathetic blockade may then become more prominent but are never as great as with pempidine alone.

D. Combinations Involving Sympatholytic Drugs

1. *General Considerations*

The sympatholytic drugs are the mainstay of treatment for moderate and severe hypertension. This section deals mainly with guanethidine, methyldopa and bethanidine, all well established and widely used drugs, but sympatholytic activity is of course possessed also by reserpine (Section II, A) and by the monoamine oxidase inhibitor, pargyline (Section II, E, 2). In addition, new sympatholytic drugs are being introduced with increasing frequency (e.g., guanoxan, isocaramidine; see chapter III) while others have been superseded (e.g., bretylium). Together, all these drugs demonstrate a fascinating spectrum of modes of action—a paradise for the experimental pharmacologist but a rather impenetrable jungle for the clinician. Fortunately, the use of these drugs in practice is less difficult than a complete understanding of their pharmacology.

Apart from their many valuable characteristics, the sympatholytic drugs have several features which are less desirable—they all cause postural hypotension, they all cause impairment of sexual function in man, they may cause fluid retention, they tend (with the exception of guanoxan) to heighten the pressor response to norepinephrine, they have individual side effects which may limit the doses used, and they are not effective in tolerable doses in 100% of patients. Therefore, while some patients can undoubtedly be comfortably maintained on a sympatholytic drug alone, in most cases the addition of one or more other drugs will improve the control of the blood pressure and the patient's well-being. The use together of a sympatholytic drug and a thiazide-type diuretic (Section II, B) forms perhaps the most reliable and widely used of all antihypertensive drug combinations; with the addition of the diuretic, the dose of sympatholytic drug can usually be reduced while the tendency to fluid retention is overcome.

There are a number of patients in whom a combination of a diuretic and a sympatholytic drug in full doses fails to give adequate control of the blood pressure or in whom a diuretic is contraindicated (Section II, B). Some of these patients respond well to the addition of a ganglion blocker (Section II, C) and the constipating effect of the ganglion blocker may be welcomed by patients in whom large doses of guanethidine are causing diarrhea.

It has also seemed logical and reasonable to try the effect of combining various types of sympatholytic drugs with the aim of obtaining a more nearly perfect control of the blood pressure. The literature on this subject is scanty, but favorable reports have appeared on combinations of guanethidine and methyldopa (70, 96), and bethanidine and methyldopa (11). We have used these combinations in our clinic, and also a number of others including guanethidine and bethanidine (155).

2. Guanethidine Plus Bethanidine

Because of the prolonged action of guanethidine, morning hypotension is often a problem whatever time the daily dose is given. This is probably associated with the reduction in plasma volume in the mornings (34). If troublesome faintness at this time is to be avoided, the dose must be kept to one which often gives an unsatisfactory degree of control of the blood pressure in the later part of the day. To overcome this disadvantage of treatment with guanethidine, a shorter acting drug (e.g., bethanidine) may be added to the regimen, and this should be given at times which provide a supplementary hypotensive effect in the afternoon and evening. We have used this combination quite widely at the Dunedin clinic (155) and we feel that smoother blood pressure levels can usually be achieved by a judicious combination of these drugs. However, while the initial effects are often good, control may later become less satisfactory, probably because of tolerance to bethanidine, and an increase in dose may be necessary to overcome this. Occasionally severe hypertension may prove unresponsive to both these drugs, used either singly or in combination.

Drugs such as bethanidine which have a bretyliumlike action may retard the depletion of norepinephrine stores by guanethidine (33) but this does not seem to interfere with the clinical use of such combinations—indeed, the relevance of norepinephrine depletion to the hypotensive action of guanethidine is still not clear (26).

3. *Guanethidine Plus Methyldopa*

A similar improvement in diurnal fluctuation of the blood pressure can be achieved by the addition of methyldopa to the regimen of guanethidine (60, 70, 96). We have used these drugs together for the treatment of 13 patients, most of whom have been comfortably and effectively managed in this way. The usual sequence has been a resistance to the effect of increasing doses of methyldopa followed by the addition of guanethidine. It may be argued that in such cases the use of methyldopa is of doubtful value and that the drug should, therefore, be discontinued when guanethidine is started. However, it does seem possible that the combination of methyldopa and an amine-depleting drug may have a special advantage (Section II, A, 5) and we feel that the combination of methyldopa and guanethidine is well worth further trial.

4. *Bethanidine and Methyldopa*

We have used this combination in 12 patients, usually with a diuretic and usually in the sequence of methyldopa first and bethanidine added later because of poor control. These patients were therefore a selected group in that blood pressure control was not particularly easy. The bethanidine caused some further fall in blood pressure, but doses up to 30 mg t.d.s. had to be used, and over-all control of the blood pressure continued to be rather unsatisfactory in most cases. No particular side effects occurred but it appears that the combination is not as useful as the combination of methyldopa with an amine-depleting drug such as reserpine or guanethidine. Others have reported more favorably on this combination (11), adding bethanidine in an average dose of 25.5 mg daily to the treatment of ten severe hyptertensives who were proving resistant to methyldopa (average dose 2.5 g daily); all showed a fall of blood pressure which was less dependent on posture than that produced by bethanidine alone.

E. COMBINATIONS INVOLVING MONOAMINE OXIDASE INHIBITORS

1. *General Considerations*

The dramatic side effects which can occur in patients on monoamine oxidase (MAO) inhibitors have given a tremendous fillip to the whole subject of drug interactions but have seriously limited the usefulness of this group of drugs in antihypertensive therapy (16, 63, 65, 147). Pressor amines in cheese (2, 7), wine (84) and yeast extracts (8), dihydroxyphenylalanine (dopa) in broad beans (75), pressor drugs (7, 83,107, 162), meperidine (120, 130, 171), antidepressants (63), barbiturates (44), methyldopa (122)—all these can interact with MAO inhibitors to cause hypertensive crises or other serious side effects. The pressor reactions may be controlled by the prompt use of an adrenolytic drug, e.g., phentolamine, but as they frequently occur without any associated symptoms

(75) and may not receive medical attention, the risk is by no means negligible. The rise of blood pressure may be very considerable, and death from cerebral hemorrhage has been reported (107).

2. *Pargyline*

These side effects are the more regrettable in view of the powerful antihypertensive effect of some MAO inhibitors, especially pargyline (13, 106, 114, 118, 166, 182). We have used this drug in the treatment of 24 patients, and 15 of these showed a useful blood pressure fall attributable to pargyline. Six patients showed no effect in doses from 50–225 mg daily and the effect in three cases was uncertain. Three patients had hypertensive reactions after eating broad beans (75). Two patients noted persistent headaches when on pargyline, while elation, insomnia, and hypomania were each observed in different individuals.

Our experience has thus been similar to that of others (51) who have found the side effects to be troublesome, and we came to the conclusion that the use of pargyline in the routine treatment of hypertension was not warranted in spite of the good blood pressure control in some cases. There is one clinical situation, however, in which difficulty may arise in the selection of suitable antihypertensive treatment: this is the depressed hypertensive patient. In such a patient reserpine and methyldopa should be avoided, and the hypotensive effect of other sympatholytic drugs may be lost if an imipramine-type antidepressant drug has to be given simultaneously (Section III, F, 2). In this type of patient, the effects of pargyline on both blood pressure and mood are sometimes most gratifying. There is also a small group of patients in whom side effects and inadequate blood pressure control prove to be major problems with all other drug regimens, and in such patients again the careful use of a MAO inhibitor may be justifiable.

The possibility arises of using other antihypertensive drugs in combination with pargyline in order to try to achieve better results with a smaller dosage. Diuretics have been used for this purpose (see next paragraph) but there is a definite need for careful testing of other combinations also. Our own experience is small but the literature is so meagre that the description of our findings in even a few cases may be of interest.

3. *Pargyline Combined with Thiazide Diuretics*

As with other antihypertensive drugs, the effect of pargyline is enhanced by thiazide diuretics, with improvement in blood pressure control, and lessening of side effects (21, 24, 127). Nine patients at the Dunedin clinic have been given pargyline together with a thiazide (hydrochlorothiazide or cyclopenthiazide), and the results were in general satisfactory.

4. *Pargyline Combined with Reserpine*

Although it has been reported (106) that the addition of reserpine (0.5 mg daily) does not increase the antihypertensive effect of a steady dose of pargyline, some of our best results were seen in three patients who were on reserpine before and during the period of pargyline treatment. All these patients felt very well during this combined therapy—one patient gave the impression of being unusually elated. Mania has been reported in a patient given large oral doses of reserpine in addition to a MAO inhibitor (67). Clearly, at present not enough is known of the interactions of these two drugs in man to permit any speculation about the value of their combined use.

5. *Pargyline Combined with Methyldopa*

Strong excitatory effects may result from the administration of methyldopa to mice on treatment with MAO inhibitors (136) and undesirable interactions in man have been predicted (112, 135). Hallucinosis has recently been reported in a patient on treatment with pargyline and methyldopa (122) but in other patients the combination has been used without difficulty for short periods (62, 73, 88). We used the combination in one patient who was resistant to large doses of methyldopa; the addition of pargyline in doses up to 225 mg daily did not reduce his blood pressure but equally did not cause any untoward side effects. However, the choice of drug combinations is sufficiently wide for this particular one to be unnecessary, and it may be better to avoid using it.

6. *Pargyline Combined with Guanethidine or Bethanidine*

Intravenous guanethidine may produce an initial sympathomimetic action in man (26) and should probably not be used in patients receiving pargyline. Oral guanethidine is not followed by a pressor phase, and may be used in combination with pargyline but we have found no reports of this combination of drugs in man and have not used it ourselves.

Bethanidine has some similarities to pargyline pharmacologically, and shows appreciable MAO inhibiting activity *in vitro* (91). We have had seven patients on treatment with these two drugs in combination but in only two was a clear benefit shown. No untoward reactions were observed, however. Postural hypertension is, of course, not lessened by such a combination, although there may be a reduction in severity of side effects peculiar to one or the other drug.

F. COMBINATIONS INVOLVING ADRENOLYTIC (α-RECEPTOR BLOCKING) DRUGS

The combination of an adrenolytic and a MAO inhibitor is logical and deserves clinical study. As mentioned earlier (Section II, E, 1), the short-acting adrenolytic phentolamine has been used in the treatment of pressor episodes occurring in patients receiving MAO inhibitors. An adrenolytic with a longer duration of action, such as phenoxybenzamine, may provide at least partial protection against pressor epidoses from sympatholytic drugs or amine-containing foods.

The addition of an α-receptor blocking drug to a regimen of sympatholytic drugs should also, in theory, be useful (126) because of the tendency of the sympatholytics to cause an increased α-receptor sensitivity (1).

Phenoxybenzamine has hitherto been the only α-receptor blocker suitable for long-term use. It has been combined with reserpine with some success (126) and with reserpine and protoveratrine (61) but it has not achieved widespread use as a hypotensive agent. Although its clinical use with sympatholytic drugs is an interesting possibility, experimental work (167) has indicated that it may partly block the action of guanethidine; the effect of such a combination in man is therefore not easy to predict.

A combination of sympatholytic and α-receptor blocking activities in a single drug has been achieved in guanoxan (74, 110, 123) but although it is an effective and useful hypotensive agent, it is not clear whether its α-receptor blocking properties confer any particular advantage.

G. Comment

As stated in the introduction, we believe that hypertensive patients can often be most effectively and comfortably treated by means of combinations of anti-hypertensive drugs. Until recently, the use of these drugs in various combinations has been on a largely empirical basis and many valuable combinations have been discovered and used. The increasing number of antihypertensive drugs is now making the empirical approach much less satisfactory, and there is also now an increasing awareness of the complexity of drug interactions (17, 92, 103).

The present review has emphasized the need (39) to study closely the various combinations of drugs in the human subject. As stated in the introduction, predictions based on theoretical considerations or animal pharmacology should certainly be heeded but they are not necessarily applicable directly to man—indeed there is often a difference between the predicted and actual results of a new drug combination. This may be due only to a difference in dosage of the drugs used; however, it is more probable that species differences play an important part. Workers in the field of human pharmacology, who have previously been concerned mainly with the actions of single drugs, are beginning to study the basic mechanisms and therapeutic applications of combined treatment also, and this should eventually lead to a more rational use of drugs in combination.

III. Antihypertensive drugs combined with other drugs

A. AMPHETAMINELIKE DRUGS AND ANTIHYPERTENSIVE THERAPY

There is evidence that amphetaminelike drugs can counteract the antihypertensive effect of guanethidine (72, 93, 155) and bretylium (180). The interaction of amphetamine and guanethidine has been investigated in the experimental animal and is thought to be a form of competitive antagonism (36), probably a displacement of guanethidine from the adrenergic neuron (18). There seem to be no reports of interactions in man between amphetamine and bethanidine or methyldopa, but in the experimental animal amphetamine may block the action of bethanidine (9) or interact with methyldopa to cause an unusually great central stimulation (158). The pressor response of amphetamine is increased by ganglion blockers (119), and the combination of amphetamine and a MAO inhibitor is well known to be dangerous (7, 97, 107). The newer appetite-suppressing compounds all appear to have sympathomimetic properties (15, 139), with the possible exception of fenfluramine (46), and they all probably in theory are capable of antagonizing the effects of sympatholytic drugs. It seems wisest to avoid using any amphetaminelike drug in combination with antihypertensive agents.

B. BRONCHODILATOR DRUGS AND ANTIHYPERTENSIVE THERAPY

The sympathomimetic drugs used in the treatment of asthma are those which possess significant β-adrenergic receptor stimulating properties—epinephrine, ephedrine, isoprenaline, orciprenaline. In theory, any pressor (α-adrenergic) effect which they possess should be increased by the simultaneous administration of sympatholytic drugs, because in the presence of the latter the blood vessels are more sensitive to circulating α-adrenergic agents (1). There seems to be no definite evidence on this point but one of our patients died of a cerebral hemorrhage after using an adrenaline inhaler vigorously. In our experience with a small study of six treated hypertensives, the inhalation of an isoprenaline spray had no effect on blood pressure levels. We have seen one patient on a diuretic and guanethidine in whom the addition of ephedrine (30 mg t.d.s.) seemed to make blood pressure control more erratic.

It is probably wise, when bronchodilators have to be combined with hypotensive drugs, to use as small doses as possible of the bronchodilators and to be on the alert for possible interactions.

C. "COMMON COLD TABLETS," NASAL DECONGESTANTS AND COMPOUND COUGH LINCTUSES, AND ANTIHYPERTENSIVE THERAPY

Many of these preparations contain an α-receptor stimulating drug as a vasoconstrictor. It is to be expected, therefore, that such medications will have some pressor effect and also that the pressor effect will be greater in patients whose α-receptors are sensitized to pressor substances by previous administration of sympatholytic drugs (1). We have experience of a bethanidine-treated patient who developed quite severe sinus tachycardia and a dangerously high blood pressure after taking a tablet containing the sympathomimetic, phenylpropanolamine, and two antihistamines. The antihistamines may also have played a part in this reaction (see Section III, D for other examples).

D. Antihistamines and Antihypertensive Therapy

Interactions between antihistamines and antihypertensive drugs do not seem to have been reported in man but we have had experience of one patient who seemed highly resistant to large doses of bethanidine and guanethidine until it was realized that she was on the antihistamine chlorpheniramine; when this drug was stopped, blood pressure control became very easy on small doses of antihypertensive agents. Another patient whose blood pressure became temporarily difficult to control was also found to be taking chlorpheniramine.

It is not clear at present whether other antihistamines have similar pressor effects in man in the presence of sympatholytic drugs, but the antihistamines tripellennamine and mepyramine have been reported to antagonize some effects of guanethidine in the experimental animal (64, 163).

E. Tranquilizers, Sedatives, and Antihypertensive Therapy

The widespread use of tranquilizers and sedatives makes it inevitable that they will at times be given to hypertensive patients. These drugs are of various types—barbiturates, phenothiazines, benzodiazepines, or analogs of meprobamate. When they are used in conjunction with hypotensive drugs, two questions are posed: first, do they contribute to the reduction of blood pressure? and, secondly, do they interfere in any way with specific antihypertensive therapy?

1. *Antihypertensive Effect*

Reduction of blood pressure is most prominent with the phenothiazines, particularly when these are used in high dosage or by a parenteral route (175), due perhaps partly to central effects and partly to the peripheral α-receptor blocking properties which they possess (141, 174). However, the phenothiazines are not in general use as antihypertensive agents, probably because their effects on the blood pressure are relatively minor compared with their effects on the central nervous system (155).

Of the nonphenothiazine drugs, the meprobamate analog mebutamate has been the most widely tested as an antihypertensive agent. Although some reports of its use, either alone or in combination with a diuretic, have been favorable (31, 54), other reports have been less so (20, 85, 128) and drowsiness is a common side effect. Barbiturates in small doses and benzodiazepines do not, in our experience, have any significant effect on the blood pressure of hypertensive patients when given either alone or in combination with antihypertensive drugs.

In general, therefore, the hypotensive effect of all these groups of drugs in hypertensive patients is small, although patients with labile, nervously mediated hypertension may show some response to them. The place of these drugs in the management of hypertension is not primarily to reduce blood pressure but to promote tranquility when this appears to be needed.

2. *Interference with Antihypertensive Therapy by Tranquilizers and Sedatives*

Direct interference with antihypertensive drug action does not seem to have been reported, and we have not encountered any specific episodes in our clinic. With regard to side effects, the phenothiazines probably have the greatest potential for causing difficulties because they share a number of side effects with reserpine and methyldopa, e.g., sedation, Parkinsonism, weight gain and lactation, and occasionally fever and hepatotoxicity. When one of these drugs and a phenothiazine are administered simultaneously, such side effects might be anticipated to be more troublesome. We have little experience of this combination, but it may be worth noting that a patient who was reported (58) to develop a severe puerperal depression and hallucinations following a total of only 7 g of methyldopa had been taking chlorpromazine and promethazine also.

The phenothiazines in high dosage may also cause independent side effects which are highly relevant to the management of patients with hypertension, e.g., ECG changes (3), ventricular arrhythmias, and possibly even sudden death (81, 133).

These considerations do not mean that phenothiazines are contraindicated in hypertension, only that they may complicate the clinical picture in patients who are taking hypotensive drugs. Other sedatives and tranquilizers do not appear to interfere with hypotensive therapy.

F. ANTIDEPRESSANTS AND ANTIHYPERTENSIVE THERAPY

1. *Depression in Hypertensive Patients*

Mental depression is well recognized as a side effect of some antihypertensive drugs, e.g., *Rauwolfia* alkaloids (45, 178), methyldopa (61, 151), and occasionally even guanethidine (40, 59, 155) and bethanidine (155). Combinations of these drugs might be expected to carry a higher risk of causing depression, but the only example which we have encountered was in a patient on methyldopa and reserpine (Section II, A, 5) and there seems to be no other evidence on this point.

The development of depression by a patient on treatment with any of these agents is a clear indication for changing to some other form of antihypertensive therapy. There are two reasons for making such a change. First, it is obviously unwise to continue treatment with a drug which is, or might be, causing the depression—provided that some suitable alternative mode of treatment exists. Second, although many cases of depression are satisfactorily treated with antidepressive drugs, the combination of such drugs with antihypertensive treatment may lead to grave difficulties.

2. *Simultaneous Treatment with Antidepressive and Antihypertensive Drugs*

We are concerned here not with the actual treatment of the depression but with the effects that such treatment may have on simultaneous antihypertensive treatment. Of the three main groups of antidepressive drugs (89), none can be given with impunity to patients on sympatholytic drugs. Amphetaminelike compounds and MAO inhibitors have already been discussed (Sections III, A; II, E), and the tricyclic drugs such as imipramine and amitriptyline remain to be considered.

Imipramine has been reported to antagonize both the hypotensive effects and the side effects of guanethidine (94). A reaction has also been reported to occur when amitriptyline was added to a regimen of methyldopa (176); 10 days after the antidepressant drug was started, the patient became agitated and developed a fine tremor, tachycardia, and an increase in blood pressure.

In our clinic, we have seen several examples of patients who were highly resistant to sympatholytic agents until it was realized that they were taking antidepressant drugs; when these were stopped, blood pressure control became dramatically easier.

3. *Pharmacology of Interactions Between Tricyclic Antidepressants and Sympatholytic Drugs*

In general, these antidepressants act by a central adrenergic effect (89). They potentiate many of the effects of norepinephrine (23, 63, 141, 165, 170), and, in fact, their antidepressant activity appears to be correlated with the potentiation of the norepinephrine responses (141). They block or delay some effects of reserpine, such as hypothermia (170) and norepinephrine depletion in the experimental animal (32, 105), and they also block the norepinephrine releasing effects of guanethidine (23, 63).

There is thus a good deal of experimental evidence to support the clinical observations of adverse interactions with sympatholytic drugs. In the light of present knowledge, the simultaneous administration of a sympatholytic drug and a tricyclic antidepressant should be avoided. As the antidepressants are in widespread use, this is a matter of considerable importance.

G. PHENYLBUTAZONE AND ANTIHYPERTENSIVE THERAPY

The tendency for phenylbutazone to cause fluid retention (19, 164) is of some importance when the drug is used in hypertensive patients and it can lead to ankle edema, increased shortness of breath, and left ventricular failure, to some extent even in patients on a thiazide diuretic (155). Blood pressure control can also occasionally be adversely affected (155).

H. DRUGS USED IN THE TREATMENT OF GOUT, AND ANTIHYPERTENSIVE THERAPY

A uricosuric agent such as probenecid or zoxazolamine (161) or a xanthine oxidase inhibitor, such as allopurinol (90, 137, 172, 184) may have to be given in conjunction with hypotensive therapy in patients with gout or hyperuricemia. In our experience hyperuricemia can usually be overcome by one or other of these agents, even though a thiazide diuretic is given concurrently (172). Blood pressure control is not adversely affected by allopurinol (172). Probenecid is, in theory, capable of antagonizing the diuretic effect of a thiazide (6) and it has been reported recently (82) to block also the effect of furosemide in the experimental animal. However, this phenomenon does not seem to have been reported in man (148) and in our clinic we have no evidence of any such effect although we have not specifically tested the point.

I. ANTIANGINAL DRUGS AND ANTIHYPERTENSIVE THERAPY

Glyceryl trinitrate does not, in our experience, have any unusual effects in patients on hypotensive therapy. It has, of course, some short-lived hypotensive effect in a proportion of patients, and if swallowed rather than sucked it can produce a longer-lasting and more useful fall in blood pressure in patients who are almost entirely resistant to other drugs, even intravenous hexamethonium (153).

The long-acting nitrates occasionally have a minor hypotensive effect (113) but they do not, in practice, appear to have any effect on blood pressure control by sympatholytic or other drugs.

Prenylamine is an antianginal agent which might be expected to affect the blood pressure by virtue of its depleting effect on catecholamine stores (102, 138) but an effect on blood pressure is not always detectable clinically (4). However, when the drug is given in conjunction with antihypertensive agents, the catecholamine-depleting effect may become more important and some lowering of the blood pressure may occur (143).

J. Antiarrhythmic Drugs and Antihypertensive Therapy

1. Quinidine and Procainamide

These drugs are well known (108) to have a hypotensive effect which has to be borne in mind when one of them is added to a regimen of antihypertensive drugs. The extent of blood pressure fall is very variable.

2. Propranolol

This β-receptor blocking drug has a hypotensive effect (129) which varies greatly from one individual to the next but can be quite useful (173). The fall in blood pressure is fully as great in the lying as in the standing posture, and it does not seem to depend on dose—so long as this is above 10 mg t.d.s. (173)—or on whether another antihypertensive agent is being given concomitantly. The dose of such an agent may have to be reduced when propranolol is added.

K. Cardiac Glycosides and Antihypertensive Therapy

The effects of cardiac glycosides can be modified in two ways by hypotensive drugs. The hypokalemia which may occur with oral diuretic therapy renders the heart more susceptible to digitalis-induced arrhythmias (117); such hypokalemia must therefore be avoided if possible. There is also evidence that *Rauwolfia* alkaloids can predispose to digitalis-induced arrhythmias (100), or can themselves cause ventricular ectopic beats (181).

L. Cholesterol-lowering Agents and Antihypertensive Therapy

1. Nicotinic Acid

The addition of nicotinic acid in oral doses up to 3 g daily to a regime of hypotensive drugs does not seem to affect blood pressure significantly (155). However, falls in blood pressure of up to 20% or more occur in some hypertensive patients after intravenous injections of nicotinic acid (28).

2. Clofibrate

Clofibrate in doses up to 1500 mg daily in hypercholesterolemic patients does not appear to have any effect on blood pressure (155). Some interaction with hypotensive drugs is theoretically possible, because of the tendency for clofibrate to displace other drugs from carrier sites on plasma proteins (49, 116). Such an effect would be most marked when a patient first starts clofibrate therapy; so far there have been no unusual occurrences at these times (155).

M. Comment

This survey of the effects of other drugs on antihypertensive therapy, by no means complete, draws attention to a number of interactions which can effect the control of the blood pressure. An antagonism to the antihypertensive drugs is, of course, particularly undesirable, and this seems to occur mainly with sympathomimetic drugs, antidepressants and some antihistamines. An increased antihypertensive effect, such as may occur with antiarrhythmic or antianginal drugs and occasionally with sedatives or tranquilizers, can be useful provided that the possibility of a fall in blood pressure is recognized and appropriate observations and adjustments to antihypertensive drug dosages are made.

The importance of these interactions is still a little difficult to assess. For instance, at present little is known of the susceptibility of individual patients to drug interactions. Because the effect of sympatholytic drugs seems to be blocked in some patients by antidepressant and sympathomimetic drugs, does this mean that all patients would be similarly affected? At present, all that can be said is that antagonistic interactions between certain drugs occur in some individuals. If these combinations of drugs are used clinically, the possibility of adverse effects must be kept in mind.

IV. Conclusion

This review has indicated the practical advantages which may result from the use of antihypertensive drugs in many different combinations. Pharmacological studies of these drugs in animals are not necessarily applicable directly to man, and worthwhile results may be achieved clinically with several combinations to which theoretical objections can be raised. The simultaneous administration of antihypertensive agents with powerful drugs given for other purposes is an increasing cause for concern; adverse effects, including loss of blood pressure control may result from such combinations.

However, the study of drug interactions is so new that any conclusions must be tentative at this stage. The drugs now available for the treatment of hypertension and associated conditions can be used in a great many possible combinations, and for most of these the documentation is still sketchy and deductions rather speculative.

We have presented a number of preliminary observations drawn from personal experience, and these may well require modification in the light of wider clinical studies. If some of the adverse interactions mentioned prove to have been coincidental, so much the better; if some of the more favorable combinations mentioned turn out to cause unsuspected side effects, it will be a pity. What is important is that everyone who has dealings with an antihypertensive drug, from the stage of development and basic experimentation in animals to the actual treatment of patients, should have in mind the possibility of both favorable and unfavorable interactions with other antihypertensive drugs and with drugs given for quite different reasons.

The drugs with which we are dealing are powerful, the patients taking them are numerous, and the duration of treatment is usually the patient's lifetime. We have an obligation to select our combinations of antihypertensive drugs in such a way that the greatest possible value is obtained from them, and we must ensure that our knowledge of interactions between antihypertensive and other drugs is sufficient to protect the patients we treat from possible hazard.

References

1. Abrams, W. B., Pocelinko, R., Moe, R. A., Bates, H., Hanauer, L., and Camacho, S., *Diseases Chest* **48**, 178 (1965).
2. Asatoor, A. M., Levi, A. J., and Milne, M. D., *Lancet* **II**, 733 (1963).
3. Ban, T. A., and St. Jean, A., *Am. Heart J.* **70**, 575 (1965).
4. Baumgarten, A., *Med. J. Australia* **49**, 429 (1962).
5. Bencomo, L., Fyvolent, J., Kahana, S., and Kahana, L., *Current Therap. Res.* **7**, 336 (1965).
6. Beyer, K. H., and Baer, J. E., *Pharmacol. Rev.* **13**, 517 (1961).
7. Blackwell, B., *Lancet* **II**, 849 (1963).
8. Blackwell, B., and Marley, E., *Brit. J. Pharmacol.* **26**, 142 (1966).
9. Boura, A. L. A., and Green, A. F., *Brit. J. Pharmacol.* **20**, 36 (1963).
10. Boura, A. L. A., and Green, A. F., *Ann. Rev. Pharmacol.* **5**, 183 (1965).
11. Breckenridge, A., and Dollery, C. T., *Lancet* **I**, 1074 (1966).
12. Brest, A. N., and Moyer, J. H., *Diseases Chest* **45**, 345 (1964).
13. Brest, A. N., Onesti, G., Heider, C., Sellar, R. H., and Moyer, J. H., *Am. Heart J.* **68**, 621 (1964).
14. Briggs, J. D., McSween, R. N. M., and Kennedy, A. C., *Postgrad. Med. J.* **41**, 193 (1965).
15. *Brit. Med. J.* (Editorial) **II**, 853 (1963).
16. *Brit. Med. J.* (Editorial) **I**, 578 (1964).
17. *Brit. Med. J.* (Editorial) **I**, 811 (1966).
18. Brodie, B. B., *Proc. Roy. Soc. Med.* **58**, 946 (1965).
19. Brodie, B. B., Lowman, E. W., Burns, J. J., Lee, P. R., Chenkin, T., Goldman, A., Weiner, M., and Steele, J. M., *Am. J. Med.* **16**, 181 (1954).
20. Bryant, J. M., *J. Am. Med. Assoc.* **182**, 67 (1962).
21. Bryant, J. M., Schvartz, N., Torosdag, S., Fertig, H., Fletcher, L., Jr., Schwartz, M. S., and Quan, R. B. F., *Ann. N.Y. Acad. Sci.* **107**, 1023 (1963).
22. Burns, J. J., Cucinell, S. A., Koster, R., and Conney, A. H., *Ann. N.Y. Acad. Sci.* **123**, 273 (1965).
23. Cairncross, K. D., McCulloch, M. W., and Mitchelson, F., *J. Pharmacol. Exptl. Therap.* **149**, 365 (1965).
24. Campione, K. M., *J. Am. Geriat. Soc.* **14**, 490 (1966).
25. Chang, C. C., Costa, E., and Brodie, B. B., *J. Pharmacol. Exptl. Therap.* **147**, 303 (1965).
26. Cohn, J. N., Liptak, T. E., and Freis, E. D., *Circulation Res.* **12**, 298 (1963).
27. Colwill, J. M., Dutton, A. M., Morrissey, J., and Yu, P. N., *New Engl. J. Med.* **271**, 696 (1964).
28. Condorelli, L., *in* "Niacin in Vascular Disorders and Hyperlipemia" (R. Altschul, ed.), pp. 156–207. Thomas, Springfield, Illinois, 1964.
29. Conn, J. W., Knopf, R. F., and Nesbit, R. M., *Am. J. Surg.* **107**, 159 (1964).
30. Conway, J., and Leonetti, G., *Circulation* **31**, 661 (1965).

31. Corcoran, A. C., and Loyke, H. F., *J. Am. Med. Assoc.* **181**, 1043 (1962).
32. Costa, E., Garattini, S., and Valzelli, L., *Experientia* **16**, 461 (1960).
33. Costa, E., Kuntzman, R., Gessa, G. L., and Brodie, B. B., *Life Sci.* **1**, 75 (1962).
34. Cranston, W. I., and Brown, W., *Clin. Sci.* **25**, 107 (1963).
35. Cranston, W. I., Semmence, A. M., Richardson, D. W., and Barnett, C. F., *Am. Heart J.* **70**, 455 (1965).
36. Day, M. D., and Rand, M. J., *Brit. J. Pharmacol.* **20**, 17 (1963).
37. Day, M. D., and Rand, M. J., *J. Pharm. Pharmacol.* **15**, 221 (1963).
38. Day, M. D., and Rand, M. J., *J. Pharm. Pharmacol.* **15**, 631 (1963).
39. Dollery, C. T., *Proc. Roy. Soc. Med.* **58**, 983 (1965).
40. Dollery, C. T., Emslie-Smith, D., and Milne, M. D., *Lancet* **II**, 381 (1960).
41. Dollery, C. T., Emslie-Smith, D., and Muggleton, D. F., *Brit. J. Pharmacol.* **17**, 488 (1961).
42. Dollery, C. T., Parry, E. H. O., and Young, D. S., *Lancet* **I**, 947 (1964).
43. Dollery, C. T., Pentecost, B. L., and Samaan, N. A., *Lancet* **II**, 735 (1962).
44. Domino, E. F., Sullivan, T. S., and Luby, E. D., *Am. J. Psychiat.* **118**, 941 (1962).
45. Doyle, A. E., and Smirk, F. H., *Lancet* **I**, 1096 (1954).
46. Duncan, E. H., Regan, N. A., Hyde, C. A., and Sweetman, B., *Brit. J. Clin. Pract.* **19**, 451 (1965).
47. Dustan, H. P., Taylor, R. D., Corcoran, A. C., and Page, I. H., *Ann. N.Y. Acad. Sci.* **59**, 136 (1954).
48. Edmonds, C. J., and Wilson, G. M., *Lancet* **I**, 505 (1960).
49. Engel, G. B., and Melville, J. A., *Proc. Univ. Otago Med. School* **44**, 1 (1966).
50. Engelmann, G., *Muench. Med. Wochschr.* **107**, 1060 (1965).
51. Esbenshade, J. G., Fewell, J. W., Frankl, W. S., Sutnick, A. I., and Turner, L. W., *Am. J. Med. Sci.* **251**, 81 (1966).
52. Finnerty, F. A., *Med. Clin. N. Am.* **48**, 329 (1964).
53. Finnerty, F. A., Kakaviatos, N., and Chupkovich, V., *Circulation* **32**, 13 (1965).
54. Fishback, D. B., and Castor, L. H., *J. Am. Geriat. Soc.* **11**, 432 (1963).
55. Flückiger, E., Schalch, W., and Taeschler, M., *Schweiz. Med. Wochschr.* **93**, 1232 (1963).
56. Ford, R. V., and Moyer, J. H., *Am. Heart J.* **46**, 754 (1953).
57. Freis, E. D., *New Engl. J. Med.* **266**, 607 (1962).
58. Fullerton, A. G., and Morton-Jenkins, D., *Brit. Med. J.* **I**, 538 (1963).
59. Galskov, Å., Clausen, E., Hilden, T., and Krogsgaard, A. R., *Acta Med. Scand.* **170**, 31 (1961).
60. Gifford, R. W., Jr., and Humphrey, D. C., *in* "Cardiovascular Drug Therapy: Eleventh Hahnemann Symposium" (A. N. Brest and J. H. Moyer, eds.), pp. 52–65. Grune & Stratton, New York, 1965.
61. Gilhespy, R. O., *Brit. Med. J.* **I**, 556 (1959).
62. Gillespie, L., Jr., Oates, J. A., Crout, J. R., and Sjoerdsma, A., *Circulation* **25**, 281 (1962).
63. Gillette, J. R., *Ann. N.Y. Acad. Sci.* **123**, 42 (1965).
64. Gokhale, S. D., Gulati, O. D., and Udwadia, B. P., *Arch. Intern. Pharmacodyn.* **160**, 321 (1966).
65. Goldberg, L. I., *J. Am. Med. Assoc.* **190**, 456 (1964).
66. Goldner, M. G., Zarowitz, H., and Akgun, S., *New Engl. J. Med.* **262**, 403 (1960).
67. Gradwell, B. G., *Brit. Med. J.* **II**, 1018 (1960).
68. Gunne, L. M., and Jonsson, J., *J. Pharm. Pharmacol.* **15**, 774 (1963).
69. Hallwright, G. P., *New Zealand Med. J.* **61**, 322 (1962).

70. Hamilton, M., and Kopelman, H., *Brit. Med. J.* **I**, 151 (1963).
71. Heath, W. C., and Freis, E. D., *J. Am. Med. Assoc.* **186**, 119 (1963).
72. Heine, B. E., and Turner, P., *Brit. J. Clin. Pract.* **17**, 529 (1963).
73. Herting, R. L., *Lancet* **I**, 1324 (1963).
74. Hodge, J. V., unpublished observations (1966).
75. Hodge, J. V., Nye, E. R., and Emerson, G. W., *Lancet* **I**, 1108 (1964).
76. Hodge, J. V., Simpson, F. O., and Spears, G. F., *New Zealand Med. J.* **61**, 258 (1962).
77. Hollander, W., Chobanian, A. V., and Wilkins, R. W., *Ann. N.Y. Acad. Sci.* **88**, 975 (1960).
78. Hollander, W., and Wilkins, R. W., *Am. J. Surg.* **107**, 204 (1964).
79. Hollander, W., and Wilkins, R. W., *Progr. Cardiovascular Diseases* **8**, 291 (1966).
80. Hollander, W., Winters, R. W., Williams, T. F., Bradley, J., Oliver, J., and Welt, L. G., *Am. J. Physiol.* **189**, 557 (1957).
81. Hollister, L. E., *J. Am. Med. Assoc.* **192**, 1035 (1965).
82. Hook, J. B., and Williamson, H. E., *J. Pharmacol. Exptl. Therap.* **149**, 404 (1965).
83. Horler, A. R., and Wynne, N. A., *Brit. Med. J.* **II**, 460 (1965).
84. Horwitz, D., Lovenberg, W., Engelman, K., and Sjoerdsma, A., *J. Am. Med. Assoc.* **188**, 1108 (1964).
85. Janney, J. G., Jr., Pierre, G. D., Thurmann, M., Utley, J. H., Aykent, Y., and Castro, J., *Clin. Pharmacol. Therap.* **4**, 720 (1963).
86. Johnston, L. C., Grieble, H. C., Schoenberger, J. A., and Fuller, J. B., *Am. J. Med. Sci.* **247**, 164 (1964).
87. Kassirer, J. P., Berkman, P. M., Lawrenz, D. R., and Schwartz, W. B., *Am. J. Med.* **38**, 172 (1965).
88. Kinross-Wright, J., and Charalampous, K. D., *Clin. Res.* **11**, 177 (1963).
89. Klerman, G. L., and Cole, J. O., *Pharmacol. Rev.* **17**, 101 (1965).
90. Klinenberg, J. R., Goldfinger, S., Miller, J., and Seegmiller, J. E., *Arthritis Rheumat.* **6**, 779 (1963).
91. Kuntzman, R., and Jacobson, M. M., *J. Pharmacol. Exptl. Therap.* **141**, 166 (1963).
92. *Lancet* (Editorial) **I**, 82 (1966).
93. Laurence, D. R., and Rosenheim, M. L., *Ciba Found. Symp., Adrenergic Mechanisms* pp. 201–208 (1960).
94. Leishman, A. W. D., Matthews, H. L., and Smith, A. J., *Lancet* **I**, 112 (1963).
95. Leon, A. S., Belle, M. S., and Halpern, M., *Diseases Chest* **42**, 626 (1962).
96. Leonard, J. W., Gifford, R. W., Jr., and Humphrey, D. C., *Am. Heart J.* **69**, 610 (1965).
97. Lewis, E., *Brit. Med. J.* **I**, 1671 (1965).
98. Lindholmer, B., Nyman, E., and Räf, L., *Acta Chir. Scand.* **128**, 310 (1964).
99. Lindmar, R., and Muscholl, E., *Arch. Exptl. Pathol. Pharmakol.* **249**, 529 (1965).
100. Lown, B., Ehrlich, L., Lipschultz, B., and Blake, J., *Circulation* **24**, 1185 (1961).
101. Lowther, C. P., and Turner, R. W. D., *Brit. Med. J.* **II**, 776 (1963).
102. Lundborg, P., *Experientia* **22**, 59 (1966).
103. Macgregor, A. G., *Proc. Roy. Soc. Med.* **58**, 943 (1965).
104. Maher, J. F., and Schreiner, G. E., *Ann. Internal Med.* **62**, 15 (1965).
105. Manara, L., Sestini, M. G., Algeri, S., and Garattini, S., *J. Pharm. Pharmacol.* **18**, 194 (1966).
106. Maronde, R. F., and Haywood, L. J., *Ann. N.Y. Acad. Sci.* **107**, 975 (1963).
107. Mason, A., *Lancet* **I**, 1073 (1962).
108. Moe, G. K., and Abildskov, J. A., *in* "The Pharmacological Basis of Therapeutics" (L. S. Goodman and A. Gilman, eds.), 3rd ed., pp. 699–715. Macmillan, New York, 1965.

109. Monroe, K. E., Grant, L. H., Sasahara, A. A., and Littman, D., *New Engl. J. Med.* **261**, 290 (1959).
110. Montuschi, E., and Lovel, T. W. I., *Lancet* **II**, 1339 (1964).
111. Morgenstern, L., Freilich, M., and Panish, J. F., *J. Am. Med. Assoc.* **191**, 637 (1965).
112. Natarajan, S., *Lancet* **I**, 1330 (1964).
113. Neumann, M., and Luisada, A. A., *Am. J. Med. Sci.* **247**, 156 (1964).
114. Oates, J. A., Seligmann, A. W., Clark, M. A., Rousseau, P., and Lee, R. E., *New Engl. J. Med.* **273**, 729 (1965).
115. Okun, R., Russell, R. P., and Wilson, W. R., *Arch. Internal Med.* **112**, 882 (1963).
116. Oliver, M. F., Roberts, S. D., Hayes, D., Pantridge, J. F., Suzman, M. M., and Bersohn, I., *Lancet* **I**, 143 (1963).
117. Oram, S., Resnekov, L., and Davies, P., *Brit. Med. J.* **II**, 1402 (1960).
118. Orvis, H. H., Tamagna, I. G., Horwitz, D., and Thomas, R., *Ann. N.Y. Acad. Sci.* **107**, 958 (1963).
119. Page, I. H., and McCubbin, J. W., *Arch. Intern. Pharmacodyn.* **157**, 152 (1965).
120. Palmer, H., *Brit. Med. J.* **II**, 944 (1960).
121. Parsons, V., and Kemball-Price, R., *Practitioner* **195**, 648 (1965).
122. Paykel, E. S., *Brit. Med. J.* **I**, 803 (1966).
123. Peart, W. S., and MacMahon, M. T., *Brit. Med. J.* **I**, 398 (1964).
124. Peltola, P., *Acta Med. Scand.* **177**, 777 (1965).
125. Pettinger, W., Horwitz, D., Spector, S., and Sjoerdsma, A., *Nature* **200**, 1107 (1963).
126. Pickering, G. W., Cranston, W. I., and Pears, M. A., "The Treatment of Hypertension." Thomas, Springfield, Illinois, 1961.
127. Pollack, P. J., *Current Therap. Res.* **7**, 10 (1965).
128. Porter, G. A., Baird, M. D., and Griswold, H. E., *Am. Heart J.* **63**, 754 (1962).
129. Prichard, B. N. C., and Gillam, P. M. S., *Brit. Med. J.* **II**, 725 (1964).
130. Reid, N. C. R. W., and Jones, D., *Brit. Med. J.* **I**, 408 (1962).
131. Relman, A. S., and Schwartz, W. B., *J. Clin. Invest.* **34**, 959 (1955).
132. Remmer, H., and Merker, H. J., *Ann. N.Y. Acad. Sci.* **123**, 79 (165).
133. Richardson, H. L., Graupner, K. I., and Murphree, O. D., *Circulation* **32**, II, 179 (1965).
134. Robson, A. O., Kerr, D. N. S., Ashcroft, R., and Teasdale, G., *Lancet* **II**, 1085 (1964).
135. Rossum, J. M. van, *Lancet* **I**, 950 (1963).
136. Rossum, J. M. van, and Hurkmans, J. A. T. M., *J. Pharm. Pharmacol.* **15**, 493 (1963).
137. Rundles, R. W., Wyngaarden, J. B., Hitchings, G. H., Elion, G. B., and Silberman, H. R., *Trans. Assoc. Am. Physicians* **76**, 126 (1963).
138. Schoene, H. H., and Lindner, E., *Arzneimittel-Forsch.* **10**, 583 (1960).
139. Seaton, D. A., and Duncan, L. J. P., *Brit. J. Clin. Pract.* **19**, 89 (1965).
140. Shapiro, A. P., Benedek, T. G., and Small, J. L., *New Engl. J. Med.* **265**, 1028 (1961).
141. Sigg, E. B., Soffer, L., and Gyermek, L., *J. Pharmacol. Exptl. Therap.* **142**, 13 (1963).
142. Simpson, F. O., *Current Therap. Res.* **6**, 21 (1964).
143. Simpson, F. O., unpublished observations (1966).
144. Simpson, F. O., and Barnett, A. J., *Med. J. Australia* **48**, 729 (1961).
145. Simpson, F. O., and Smirk, F. H., *Am. J. Cardiol.* **9**, 868 (1962).
146. Simpson, F. O., and Waal, H. J., *New Zealand Med. J.* **63**, 199 (1964).
147. Sjöqvist, F., *Proc. Roy. Soc. Med.* **58**, 967 (1965).
148. Smilo, R. P., Beisel, W. R., and Forsham, P. H., *New Engl. J. Med.* **267**, 1225 (1962).
149. Smirk, F. H., "High Arterial Pressure." Blackwell, Oxford, 1957.
150. Smirk, F. H., *Am. Heart J.* **61**, 272 (1961).
151. Smirk, F. H., *Brit. Med. J.* **I**, 146 (1963).
152. Smirk, F. H., *Lancet* **I**, 743 (1963).

153. Smirk, F. H., unpublished observations (1966).
154. Smirk, F. H., Doyle, A. E., and McQueen, E. G., *Lancet* **II**, 159 (1954).
155. Smirk, F. H., Hodge, J. V., Macmillan, B. M., Simpson, F. O., and Waal, H. J., unpublished observations (1966).
156. Smirk, F. H., and McQueen, E. G., *Proc. Univ. Otago Med. School* **33**, 10 (1955).
157. Smirk, F. H., McQueen, E. G., and Morrison, R. B. I., *Brit. Med. J.* **I**, 515 (1960).
158. Smith, C. B., *J. Pharmacol. Exptl. Therap.* **142**, 343 (1963).
159. Smith, W. M., Damoto, A. N., Galluzzi, N. J., Garfield, C. F., Hanowell, E. G. Stimson, W. H., Thurm, R. H., Walsh, J. J., and Bromer, L., *Ann. Internal Med.* **61**, 829 (1964).
160. Sperber, R. J., DeGraff, A. C., and Lyon, A. F., *Am. Heart J.* **69**, 281 (1965).
161. Sperber, R. J., Fisch, S., DeGraff, A. C., and Freudenthal, R. R., *Am. J. Med. Sci.* **249**, 269 (1965).
162. Stark, D. C. C., *Lancet* **I**, 1405 (1962).
163. Stone, C. A., Porter, C. C., Stavorski, J. M., Ludden, C. T., and Totaro, J. A., *J. Pharmacol. Exptl. Therap.* **144**, 196 (1964).
164. Strandberg, B., *Acta Rheumatol. Scand.* Suppl. 10, p. 1 (1965).
165. Sulser, F., Watts, J., and Brodie, B. B., *Ann. N.Y. Acad. Sci.* **96**, 279 (1962).
166. Sutnik, A. U., Fewell, J. W., Esbenshade, J. H., and Soloff, L. A., *Clin. Pharmacol. Therap.* **5**, 167 (1964).
167. Thoenen H., Huerlimann, A., and Haefely, W., *J. Pharmacol. Exptl. Therap.* **151**, 189 (1966).
168. Thompson, R. A., and Crowley, M. F., *Postgrad. Med. J.* **41**, 706 (1965).
169. Varma, D. R., and Benfey, B. G., *J. Pharmacol. Exptl. Therap.* **141**, 310 (1963).
170. Vernier, V. G., Hanson, H. M., and Stone, C. A., *in* "Psychosomatic Medicine" (J. H. Nodine and J. H. Moyer, eds.), pp. 683–690. Lea & Febiger, Philadelphia, Pennsylvania, 1962.
171. Vigran, I. M., *J. Am. Med. Assoc.* **187**, 953 (1964).
172. Waal, H. J., unpublished observations (1966).
173. Waal, H. J., *Clin. Pharmacol. Therap.* **7**, 588 (1966).
174. Webster, R. A., *Brit. J. Pharmacol.* **25**, 566 (1965).
175. Welsh, A. L., *Med. Clin. N. Am.* **48**, 459 (1964).
176. White, A. G., *Lancet* **II**, 441 (1965).
177. Wilkins, R. W., *Ann. Internal Med.* **37**, 1144 (1952).
178. Wilkins, R. W., *Ann. N.Y. Acad. Sci.* **59**, 36 (1954).
179. Wilkins, R. W., and Judson, W. E., *New Engl. J. Med.* **248**, 48 (1953).
180. Wilson, R., and Long, C., *Lancet* **II**, 262 (1960).
181. Wilson, B. N., and Wimberley, N. A., Jr., *J. Am. Med. Assoc.* **159**, 1363 (1955).
182. Winsor, T., *Geriatrics* **19**, 598 (1964).
183. Wolf, R. L., Mendlowitz, M., Naftchi, N. E., and Gitlow, S. E., *Am. Heart J.* **66**, 414 (1963).
184. Wyngaarden, J. B., Rundles, R. W., and Metz, E. N., *Ann. Internal Med.* **62**, 842 (1965).
185. Zaimis, E., *Proc. Roy. Soc. Med.* **58**, 1067 (1965).

Acknowledgment

We are indebted for financial support to the Medical Research Council of New Zealand.

Author Index

Numbers in parentheses are reference numbers and indicate that an author's work is referred to although his name is not cited in the text. Numbers in italics show the page on which the complete reference is listed.

A

Abaffy, F., 235(201), *262*
Abe, S. I., 129(107), *148*
Abels, J. C., 21(50), *59*
Abildskov, J. A., 480(108), *484*
Ablad, B., 70(1), 71(1), 73(1), 86(1), 91(1) 98(1), 104(1), 105(1), *109*
Abrams, W. B., 137(1), *145*, 474(1), 475(1), 476(1), *482*
Abreu, B. E., 446(1), *453*
Aceves, J., 395(1), 409(1), 412(1), *424*
Acheson, G. H., 430(70), 439(70), 440(2, 70), 441(70), 451(70), *453*, *455*
Achor, R. W. P., 266(47), *277*
Ackerman, J. F., 349(42), *385*
Adam, H. M., 193(1), 207(1), *215*
Adams, J. Q., 224(1), 255(1), *257*
Adamson, D. W., 286, *293*
Adank, K., 361(1), *384*
Adkins, P. K., 403(102), *426*
Adlerova, E., 200(139, 140), 203(140), *219*
Afonso, A., 430(95), 432(77), 432(76), 437(76), *455*, *456*
Agarwal, S. L., 371, *384*
Ahlquist, R. P., 116(78), *147*, 332, 348(3) 371(5), 374(4, 6), 375, 379, *384*, *388*
Akawie, R. I., 152(41), 158(41), 166(41), 167(41), 168(41), 169(41), 170(41), 171(41), 172(41), 173(41), 174(41), 175(41), *187*
Akcasu, A., 440(53), *455*
Akgun, S., 466(66), *483*
Alam, G. M., 13, 15(4), 38, 39, 51, 56, *58*
Alarcon-Segoria, D., 224(2), 225(2), 255(2), *257*
Albrecht, W., 193(2), 207(2), *215*, 237, 248(102), 249(174), 253, *257*, *260*, *261*
Alcala, R., 250(51), *258*
Alexander, F., 8(70), *60*
Alexander, J. A., 255(4), *257*
Alexander, J. K., 57(6), *58*
Alexander, N., 46, *58*

Alexander, W. M., 446(1), *453*
Algeri, S., 478(105), *484*
Allais, A., 197(119, 197), *218*, *220*
Allanby, K. D., 325, 327(2), *328*
Allen, F. M., 263, 274(1), *276*
Allen, M. J., 285(2), *293*
Alleyne, C. A. O., 383(7), *384*
Almirante, L., 199(96, 97), 200(96), *218*
Alonso-de Florida, F., 290(3, 36), *293*, *294*, 415(144), *427*
Alpert, E., 276(36), *277*
Alstad, K. S., 8(255), 9(255), 13(262), 14(262), 15(262), *64*
Alvarado, F. H., 341(152), *389*
Amad, K. H., 57(6), *58*
Ambache, N., 290(4), *293*
Ambard, L., 263, 274(2), *276*
Amenta, J. S., 256(5), *257*
Ames, P. L., 403(141), *427*
Ames, R. P., 74(104), *112*, 274(9), *276*
Amory, D. W., 380, *392*
Anchini, M., 70(2), 71(2), 73(2), 81, 86(2) 91(2), 98(2), 105(2), *109*
Anderson, F. F., 70(3), 86(3), 91(3), 98(3), 99, *109*
Anderson, F. E., 398(2), 409(2), 412(2), *424*
Anderson, F. S., 246(202), *262*
Andoh, B. Y. A., 432(91), *456*
Angers, M., 30(149), 31(149), *62*, 182(13), *187*
Anthony, W. C., 402(74), *426*
Antonchak, N., 9(90), *60*, 87(49), 91(48), 103(49), 104(49), *110*
Antonis, A., 383(193), *390*
Aoki, K., 19(199), *63*
Archer, S., 355(8, 256), 356(8), *384*, *392*
Armstrong, H. G., 39, *58*
Armstrong, M. D., 419, *426*
Arnold, A., 355(8), 356(8), *384*
Arnold, H., 298(60), 299(64), 302(64), 326(60), *329*
Arnold, R. T., 404(3), 409(3), 412(3), *424*

Aronow, L., 371(40), 375(39), *385*, 440(2), 441(3), *453*
Arons, R., 433(61), 434(61), *455*
Aroyan, A. A., 137(2), *145*
Arumugam, N., 404(68), *425*
Asatoor, A. M., 409(4), 423(4), *424*, 471(2), *482*
Ashcroft, R., 466(134), *485*
Ashford, A., 193(3), 213(3), *215*
Asma, W. J., 201(89), 203(89, 90), *218*
Assali, N. S., 252(127), *260*, 452(158), *457*
Assenmacher, I., 193(4), 213(4), *215*
Asteroth, H., 51, *58*
Astrom, A., 365, *384*
Atkins, E. C., 250(197), *262*
Atkinson, R. M., 404, 423, *424*
Augstein, J., 138(5), 139(3), 144(3, 4), *145*, 342(10), *384*
Aurell, M., 215(72), *217*
Auterhoff, H., 432(110), *456*
Avakian, S., 335(134), *388*
Aviado, D. M., Jr., 293, 374(11), *384*, 444(5), 445(4), *453*
Axelrod, J., 117(63), *147*, 208(76), 209(5, 68), 210(51, 68), *215*, *216*, *217*, 371(40), 375(39), *385*, 393, 399, 419(6), 420(52), *424*, *425*
Ayers, C. R., 74(26), 88(26), 89(26), *110*
Aykent, Y., 477(85), *484*
Ayman, D., 39, 41, *58*
Ayres, C. I., 431(82), 432(78), 433(78–81), 437(78, 80, 94), 438(80), *455*, *456*
Azaryan, A. S., 137(2), *145*

B

Bach, F. L., Jr., 353, *385*
Bader, F. E., 193(206, 207), *221*
Bächtold, H. P., 398(119), 418, *424*, *427*
Baer, J. E., 273, 274(3, 4), *276*, 296(3), 324(3), *328*, 479(6), *482*
Bärwald, L., 159(38), *187*
Baget, J., 308(20), *328*
Bagwell, E. E., 212(6, 7), *215*
Baines, M. W., 138(6), *145*, 344(13), 345, *385*
Baird, M. D., 477(128), *485*
Baker, P. D., 429, *453*
Baldwin, E. de F., 40(96), *61*
Ball, C. O. T., 91(128), *112*, *113*
Baltzly, R., 129, *148*

Balzer, H., 153(117), 184(117), *189*, 207(8, 9), *215*
Ban, T. A., 185(80), *188*, 477(3), *482*
Banziger, R., 117(90), 118(90), 120(90), 137(90), *147*
Barany, F. R., 33, 40, *58*
Barath, E., 42, *58*
Barbaras, G. K., 305(10, 11), *328*
Barbeau, A., 185(1), *186*
Barber, H. J., 126(7), *145*, 282, *293*, 310(30), *328*
Barber, J. K., 32(16), *59*
Barber, R., 432(116), 433(116, 117), 434(116, 117), 435(116), *456*
Barbour, B., 271(38), *277*
Barchas, J., 168(47), 169(47), *187*
Barcroft, H., 377, 378, *385*
Bardhanabaedya, S., 369(57), 376(57), *386*
Barer, G. R., 445(7), *454*
Bargeton, D., 230(6), 257
Barlow, R. B., 68, 70(4), 86(4), 91(4), *109*, 280, *293*
Barltrop, J. A., 430(111), 431(111), *456*
Barnett, A. J., 9(14, 15), *58*, *59*, 383(15), *385*, 465(144), *485*
Barnett, C. F., 273(12), *276*, 467(35), *483*
Barraclough, C. A., 207(52), *216*
Barrett, W., 73(5), 86(5, 6), 91(5, 6), 100, 104(152), 105, *109*, *113*, 141(8), *145*, 197(149), 209(134), *219*, 246(7), *257*, 296(51), 298(51), *329*, 374(15a), *385*, 394(40), *425*
Barrnett, R. J., 214, *217*
Barron, D. I., 143(9), *145*
Barsky, J., 394(157), *428*
Bartter, F. C., 32, *59*
Barzaghi, F., 144(11), *145*
Basu, B. D., 192, *217*
Bates, H., 137(1), *145*, 474(1), 475(1), 476(1), *482*
Bates, H. M., 117(90), 118(90), 120(90), 137(90), *147*
Bauer, G. E., 327(13), *328*
Bauer, J., 42, *59*
Bauer, L., 125(10), *145*
Bauer, R. O., 442(48), *455*
Baum, T., 212, *215*
Baumgarten, A., 479(4), *482*
Bavin, P. M. G., 143(9), *145*

Baylé, J. D., 193(4), 213(4), *215*
Bayliss, R. I. S., 182(2), 185(2), *186*
Bayliss, W. M., 80, *109*
Beaujard, E., 263, 274(2), *276*
Beaven, M. A., 208, *216*
Becache, A., 213(79), *217*
Bech, V., 8(229), *64*
Bechgaard, P., 8(18), *59*, 363(16), *385*
Beck, J. L., 186(10), *187*
Beguin, M., 341(81), *387*
Beiler, J. M., 152(51, 52), *188*
Bein, H. J., 100(10), 103(131), 104(11, 12), 105(125), *109*, *112*, *113*, 192(117), 206(11, 13), 207, 208(11, 14), 209, 210(11a), 211, 212, *215*, *216*, *218*, 239(10), 241(10, 114), 244(12, 113), 245(11, 13), 246(8, 10, 114), 248, 249, 250(10), 251(113), *257*, *260*, *262*, 282, 292, *293*
Beisel, W. R., 479(148), *485*
Bell, C. L., 125, *145*
Bell, D. M., 373(62), *386*
Bell, M. R., 355(8), 356(8), *384*
Belle, M. S., 462(95), *484*
Belleau, B., 349, 352, 377(21), *385*
Bellville, T. P., 354(123), *388*
Bemont, B., 404(84), *426*
Bencomo, L., 466(5), *482*
Benedek, T. G., 466(140), *485*
Benfey, B. G., 214(17), *216*, 381, *385*, 464(169), *486*
Benforado, J. M., 436(9), 441(8, 9), 443(9), 444(9), 445(9, 33), 446(9), 448(9), *454*
Bennet, G., 323, *328*
Bennett, M. V. L., *293*
Bennet, W. B., 404(31), *424*
Bennett, A., 29(84, 190), *60*, *63*
Benoit, G., 342, 343(23), *385*
Berdahl, J. M., 367(87), *387*
Bergman, P. G., 49, *65*, 67, 71, *114*
Berkman, P. M., 465(87), *484*
Berneis, H. L., 305(10), *328*
Bernier, M., 354(174), 355(174), 356(174), *390*
Bersohn, I., 480(116), *485*
Berthaux, P., 197(18), *216*
Bertler, A., 207(34), 208(34), *216*
Besendorf, H., 398(119), *427*
Best, C. H., 92, *111*
Besterman, E. M., 383, *385*

Beyer, K. H., 183(105), *189*, 273(3), 274(3, 4), *276*, 296(3, 62), 317(62), 318(62), 323(62), 324(3), 326(61, 62), *328*, *329*, 479(6), *482*
Beyerholm, O., 20(19), *59*
Bhargava, K. P., 245(85), *259*
Bhatia, B. B., 192(19), *216*
Bhattacharya, B. K., 207(20), *216*
Bianchi, M., 144(11), *145*, 209, *216*
Bickel, G., 254, *258*
Bickel, H., 193(206, 207), *221*
Bickerton, R. K., 30(34), *59*, 362(25, 26), *385*
Bicking, J. B., 273(45), *277*
Biel, J. H., 132(122), *148*, 165(3), *186*, 398(10), *424*
Bienfet, V., 355(172), 372(172), *390*
Biermacher, U., 134(131), *148*
Bilecki, G., 285(9), *293*
Billinghurst, J. W., (1), *293*
Binet, L., 250, *258*
Biniecki, S., 225(18), 227(19, 20), 228(17), 229, 233(16), *258*, *259*
Binion, J., *114*
Binkley, S. B., 349(254), *392*
Binnion, P. F., 382(51), *386*
Bircher, R., 379(46), *386*
Bird, R. B., 73(199), *114*
Biron, P., 26(92), 31(92), *60*
Bizzi, L., 198(126), *218*
Björk, S., 215(72), *217*
Black, H., 40, *60*
Black, J. W., 366, 379, 383, *385*
Blacket, R. B., 23, *59*
Blackmore, W. P., 442(10), *454*
Blackwell, B., 422(11, 12), 423(14), *424*, 471(7, 8), 475(7), *482*
Blake, J., 480(100), *484*
Blalock, A., 23(21), *59*
Blanshard, G., 271, *276*
Blaquier, P. C., 25(273), 26(273), 27, 29(41), *59*, *65*, 79, *109*
Blaschko, H., 152(4), 168(5), *186*, 393, *424*
Blessing, J. A., 184(107), *189*
Bloom, B. M., 357(118), *388*
Bock, K. D., 211(22), *216*, 254, *258*
Bock, M., 305(28), *328*
Boehm, R., 440(11), 442(11), *454*
Boehme, W. R., 349(218), *391*
Boey, J., 342(248), *392*
Bogdanski, D. F., 402(142), *427*

Bohr, D. F., 26(22), 27(22), 29(41), *59*, 79(162), *113*

Boissier, J. R., 353(29, 201), 355(201), 356(201), *385*, *390*

Bojs, G., 182(81), *188*

Bolen, C. H., 349(117), *388*

Bolger, J. W., 128(12), *145*, 436(161, 162), *457*

Bolhofer, W. A., 273(45), *277*

Bolliger, A., 21(111), *61*

Bollinger, F. W., 161(92), 162(7), 163(6, 92), 175(92), 181(92), 184(92), *189*

Bollinghurst, J. W., 286(1), *293*

Bongiovanni, A. M., 23, *62*, 85, *112*

Bonner, W. H., 305(10), *328*

Bonnet, V., 374(113), *388*

Booher, K. D., 117(128), 118(128), 121(128), 137(127, 128), *148*

Bookman, J. J., 264(40), *277*

Boren, M. M., 338(162), 340(162), 353(163), *389*

Borison, H. L., 446(13), *454*

Borowicka, M., 284, *293*

Bose, B. C., 192(38, 163), *216*, *220*

Bose, K. C., 192(163), *229*

Botha, P. W. A., 327(5), *328*

Botton, I., 132, *145*

Boucher, R., 25(290), 26(92), 31(92), *60*, *65*, 76, 81, *109*

Bouckaert, J. J., 46, *59*, 84, *111*

Boullin, D. J., 207(23), *216*

Boura, A. L. A., 84, 99, 101(51), *109*, *110*, 117(14), 118(14, 21), 119(22), 121(22), 123(20, 23), 124(14, 15, 18), 128(16), 140, 141(19), *145*, *146*, 288, *293*, 399, *424*, 461(10), 463(10), 475(9), *482*

Bovet, D., 280, *293*, 333, 334(34, 70, 72), 337, 338(33, 150), 339(30, 33, 150), 340(35, 80, 149), 341(80, 152, 166), 342(36, 71), 343(23, 71), 353, 361(151), 368(70), 372, *385*, *386*, *387*, *389*

Bovet-Nitti, F., 334(34), 338(33), 339(33), 342(36), 353(32), *385*

Bowlus, W. E., 272, *276*

Bowman, R. O., 451(114), *456*

Bozorgmehri, P., 422(54), *425*

Brabander, H. J., 353(12), *385*

Bradley, J., 465(80), *484*

Bragina, L. N., 235(161), *261*

Brahm, C. A., 228(208), *262*

Bramanti, G., 202(179), *216*, *220*

Brammell, H., 380(249), *392*

Brandstater, M. E., 383(15), *385*

Braun, L., 85, *110*

Braun-Menéndez, E., 25(127), 47(26), 48, *59*, *61*, 69, 71, 72, 76, *110*

Braunwald, E., 211(37, 107), *216*, *218*

Braverman, I. M., 255(30), *258*

Bravo, R. R., 361(37), *385*

Brazeau, P., 378(38), *385*

Breckenridge, A., 470(11), 471(11), *482*

Brendel, R., 152(52), *188*

Brennan, B. B., 73(199), *114*

Brest, A. N., 182(8), 183(65), *187*, *188*, 224, 254, *258*, *260*, 270, *276*, 398(20), 410, 415(19, 21), 419(21), *424*, 451(113), 452(113), *454*, *456*, 460(12), 463(12), 472(13), *482*

Bretherick, L., 312, 315(6, 8), 319, *328*

Bridges, W. C., 86(62), *111*

Briggs, J. D., 467(14), *482*

Briggs, J. F., 39, *59*

Bright, R., 69, *110*

Brodie, B. B., 119(31), *146*, 184(9), *187*, 205(130), 207, 208, 209(175), *216*, *219*, *220*, 325, *328*, 371(40), 375(39), *385*, 402(22, 23, 127, 134, 142), 414, 415(25, 135), 418, *424*, *425*, *427*, 451(14), *454*, 461(18, 33), 463(25), 470(33), 475(18), 478(165), 479(19), *482*, *483*, *486*

Bromer, L., 462(159), *486*

Brondyk, H. D., 145(125), *148*

Bronner, H. A., 153(103), 161(103), *189*

Brooker, R. M., 433(119), *456*

Brooks, B., 82(133), *113*

Brooks, P. W., 10, *60*, 249(70, 71), *259*

Brooks, R. H., 382(102), *387*

Brooks, V. B., 290(13), *293*

Brown, G. E., 38, 39, 40(109), *61*

Brown, G. M., 45, 46, *59*

Brown, H. C., 305(10, 11), *328*

Brown, H. O., 371(181), *390*

Brown, J. J., 25, 26(51), 28, 31, *59*

Brown, J. P., 129(24), *146*

Brown, L. T., 46(198), *63*

Brown, W., 470(34), *483*

Brown, W. T., 185(102), *189*

Brüni, C., 241(119), 253(118), *260*

Bruening, C. H., 204, *216*

Bruger, M., 39, *63*

Bruni, T., 442(103), *456*
Brunner, H., 25(107), 26(108), 27(108, 224), *61*, *64*, 78(73), *111*, 212(67), *216*, *217*, 246(8), 248, 251(111), *257*, *258*, *260*
Bryant, J. M., 137(25), *146*, 271, *276*, 409(28), 410(28), 413, *424*, 472(21), 477(20), *482*
Bucher, K., 252, *258*
Buchholz, J. H., 267(17), *276*
Buck, J. S., 349(117), 362(115), *388*
Buckley, J. P., 30(34), *59*, 85, *111*, 132(13, 26), *145*, *146*, 228(57), 232(57), *259*, 362(122), 367, *388*
Buděšinský, B., 235(89), *259*, 432(155), 436(155), *457*
Buhlmann, A., 29(292), *65*
Buhs, R. P., 186(10), *187*
Bulbring, E., 402(29), *424*
Buller, R. H., 362(26), *385*
Bullock, A. C., 268(20), *276*
Bumpus, F. M., 71(143), 72(166), 76(143, 144), *113*
Burch, G. E., 33(35, 191), 34(35, 191), *59*, *63*
Burcin, A., 184(76), *188*
Burger, A., 403(85), 404(30, 31), *424*, *426*
Burkard, W. P., 175(12), 177(71), 179, 182(11), *187*, *188*
Burke, J. C., 446(132), 448, *457*
Burn, J. H., 245(34), *258*, 280, *293*, 418, *424*
Burnett, C. F., Jr., 8(36), *59*
Burnett, C. H., 29(86), *60*, 452(36), *454*
Burns, J. J., 368, *385*, 461(22), 479(19), *482*
Burstein, M., 250, *258*
Burnstock, G., 206, *216*
Buting, W. E., 338(162), 340(162), *389*
Buzas, A., 199, *216*
By, A. W., 430(83), 431(83), 432(83), 433(83), 435(83), 437(83), *455*
Byer, S. S., 175(78), 177(78), 178(78), 179(78), 181(78), *188*
Bygdeman, M., 237, *258*
Byrom, F. B., 9, 22, *59*, *65*, 68, 77, 78(23), 80, *110*, *114*

C

Cahill, J., 90(27), *110*
Cahn, J., 413(33), *424*
Cairncross, K. D., 478(23), *482*
Cairoli, V. J., 212(30), *216*
Calliauw, L., 441(102), 443(15), *454*, *456*

Camacho, S., 474(1), 475(1), 476(1), *482*
Cameron, A., 394(40), *425*
Cameron, W. B., 224(1), 255(1), *257*
Campbell, A., 8(38), *59*, 128(28), 143(27, 32), *146*
Campbell, A. J. M., 9(39), *59*
Campbell, B. K., 349(42), *385*
Campbell, K. N., 349(42), *385*
Campione, K. M., 472(24), *482*
Cangello, V. W., 453(165), *458*
Cannon, P. J., 74(104), *112*, 182(13), 186(10), *187*, 274, *276*
Cannon, W. B., 98, *110*
Cannon, W. N., 338(162), 340(162), *389*
Caplovitz, C., 326(41), *329*, 373(172a), *389*
Caprio, L., 199(96, 97), 200(96), *218*
Carbon, J. A., 129(29), *146*
Cardinal, E., 409(100), 410(100), *426*
Carlsson, A., 119(30), *146*, 184, 186(14), *187*, 205, 207(34, 161), 208(33, 34), 209(33), 210, *216*, *219*, 420, *424*
Carpenter, C. C. J., 74, 88(26), 89, *110*
Carraro, A., 214(35), *216*
Cartier, P., 26(92), 31(92), *60*
Cass, R., 119(31), *146*
Castor, L. H., 477(54), *483*
Castro, J., 477(85), *484*
Cato, J., 290(3, 36), *293*, *294*
Cavalla, J. F., 361(43), *385*
Cavallini, G., 357, *385*
Cavallito, C. J., 287(15), *293*
Ceglowski, M. J., 196(98, 99), *218*
Century, B., 375, *386*
Cerletti, A., 288(45, 52), *294*, 379, *386*, 445(4), *453*
Cesarman, T., 414(35), *425*
Cetenko, W. A., 398(2), 409(2), 412(2), *424*
Chabrier, P., 358(175), *390*
Chaigneau, M., 235(40), *258*
Chang, C. C., 463(25), *482*
Chang, C. S., 130(33), *146*
Chapuis, G., 28(30), *59*
Chappel, C. I., 90(27), *110*
Charalampous, K. D., 473(88), *484*
Charest, M. P., 90(27), *110*
Chart, J. J., 89(50), 90, 91(50), 103(28), 105(158), *110*, *113*, 212(53a, 54), 213(53a, 54), 214(53), *216*, *217*
Chatterjee, A., 192(36), *216*
Chavez, B., 184(101), *189*

Chavez-Lara, B., 173(100), 185(100), 186 (100), *189*
Chemerda, H. M., 161(92), 163(92), 175(92), 181(92), 184(92), *189*
Chen, G., 143(32), *146*
Chen, H. Y., 130, *146*
Cheney, L. C., 349(254), *386*, *392*
Cheng, Y. H., 130(33), *146*
Chenkin, T., 479(19), *482*
Chernyaeva, A. T., 225(184), *262*
Chesley, E. R., 39, 59
Chesley, L. C., 39, *59*
Chess, D., 357(49), 375(48, 258), *386*, *392*
Chessin, M., 398(36), *425*
Cheymol, J., 447(16), *454*
Chiavarelli, S., 361(1), 361(50, 151), *384*, *386*, *389*
Chidsey, C. A., 211(37), *216*
Child, C. G., 24(94), *60*, 70(29), *110*
Chimoskey, J. E., 29, *59*
Chinery, E., 349(218), *391*
Chiong, M. A., 382, *386*
Chittum, J. R., 223(77), *259*
Chobanian, A. V., 105(87), *111*, 264(30), 265(30), 266(30), 268(31), *277*, 465(77), 467(77), *484*
Chopra, I. C., 192(38), *216*
Chopra, R. N., 192, *216*
Chou, T. C., 282(16), *293*
Chretien, M., 26(92), 31(92), *60*
Christensen, B. V., 449, *454*, *455*
Christianssen, J., 284(17), *293*
Chupkovich, V., 137(67), *147*, 462(53), 468(53), *483*
Cibrario, N., 335(75), 338(76), 339(76), *386*, *387*
Clampit, J. M., 86(61), *111*
Clark, C. W., Jr., 375(247), *392*
Clark, E. G., 18(91, 242), *60*, *64*
Clark, J. A., 403(37), *425*
Clark, M. A., 472(114), *485*
Clark, W. G., 151(15), 152(15, 16, 41), 158(41), 166(41), 167(41), 168(41), 169(41, 89), 170(41), 171(41), 172(41), 173(15, 16, 41), 174(41), 175(41), 176(15), 177(39, 40), 178(39), 179(73), 185(49), *187*, *188*
Clausen, E., 477(59), *483*
Cobb, D. B., 138(6), *145*, 343(13), 344(13), *385*

Cochrane, C. M., 184(54), *188*
Coda, S., 132, *146*
Coffee, K., 105, *114*
Cohen, R. D., 32, *62*, 80, *112*
Cohn, A. E., 33(35, 191), 34(35, 191), *59*
Cohn, J. N., 470(26), 473(26), *482*
Cohn, V. H., Jr., 236, *258*
Coker, G. G., 123(36), *146*
Cole, J. O., 478(89), *484*
Cole, V. W., 57(6), *58*
Colo, V. A., 132(34), *146*
Colwill, J. M., 465(27), *482*
Combes, G., 204, *219*
Comens, P., 238(145), 239(141), 255(145), *261*
Comroe, J. H., Jr., 440(22), 441(22), *454*
Condorelli, L., 480(28), *482*
Conn, E. S., 88, *110*
Conn, J. W., 30, *59*, 88, *110*, 465(29), *482*
Connamacher, R., 184(110), 185(110), *189*
Conner, P. K., 453(18), *454*
Conney, A. H., 461(22), *482*
Constantine, J. W., 117(128), 118(128), 121(128), 137(128), *148*
Contratto, A. W., 8(44), *59*
Conway, A. C., 165(3), *186*, 398(10), *424*
Conway, J., 45, *59*, 274, *276*, 466(30), 467(30), *482*
Cook, D. L., 362(52), *386*
Cook, L., 403(141), *427*
Cook, W. F., 74, *110*
Coon, J. M., 375(45), *386*
Cooper, A. J., 421(38), *425*
Cooper, P., 349(20), *385*
Cooper, S. R., 8(70), *60*
Coopp, F. C., 101(15), *109*
Copp, F. C., 117(14), 118(14), 123(15, 35, 36), 124(14, 15), 128(16), 140(17), *145*, *146*, 399(17, 18), *424*
Corbin, A., 214(35), *216*
Corcoran, A. C., 9(172), 14(66), 45(173), 46(173), 49(171), *60*, *62*, 86(114), 90(115), 104(113, 116), *112*, 145(37), *146*, 248(106), *260*, 266, *276*, 462(47), 477(31), *483*
Corley, R. W., 430(56), 452(57), *455*
Corne, S. J., 132(76), *147*, 296(31), 299(17), 300(17), 301(17), 302(17), 307(31), 324, *328*
Corry, D. C., 21(46), *59*

Costa, E., 184(9), *187*, 399(61), 414, 419(61, 62), *425*, 461(33), 463(25), 470(33), 478(32), *482*, *483*
Cottier, P., 254, *258*
Coy, N. H., 433(37), *454*
Cragoe, E. J., Jr., 273(45), *277*, 398(122), *427*
Craig, L. C., 430, *454*
Cranston, W. I., 254(149), *261*, 273, *276*, 460(126), 467(35), 470(34), 474(126), *483*, *485*
Craver, B. N., 223, *258*, 357(160), 372(160), *389*, 394(40), *425*
Crawford, M. A., 326(39), *329*
Cretti, A., 255(48), *258*
Creveling, C. R., 184(17), *187*
Croll, F. J. T., 327, *328*
Cross, C. E., 444(133), *457*
Crout, J. R., 182(34), *187*, 420(41), *425*, 473(62), *483*
Crowley, M. F., 467(168), 468(168), *486*
Crowther, A. F., 144(38), *146*, 366(28), 379(28), *385*
Croxatto, H., 25, *64*
Crumpton, C. W., 394, *425*
Cucchi, J. N., 25(72), *60*
Cucinell, S. A., 461(22), *482*
Cuenca, E., 399(61), 419(61, 62), *425*
Culbertson, J. W., 29(86), 40(134), *60, 61*, 378(74), *386*, 452(36), *454*
Culp, D. A., 373(131), *388*
Currens, J. H., 430(21), 452(20, 21, 115), 453(20), *454*, *456*
Cushman, P., 213(39), *216*
Cusic, J. W., 362(52), *386*
Czyba, J. C., 213(79), *217*

D

DaCosta, F. M., 106(52), *110*, 414, *425*
Dahl, L. K., 20, *59*, 92, *110*
Dailey, R. F., 362(26), *385*
Dale, H. H., 244(49), *258*, 280, *293*, 333, 377, *386*
Dale, N., 383, 384(233), *391*
Dalessio, D. J., 182(33), 183(33), *187*
D'Alo, G., 128(39), *146*
Daly, J. de B., 244(50), 245(50), *258*
Daly, J. J., 33, *59*
Damoto, A. N., 462(159), *486*
Daniel, A. I., 100(120), 101(119), *112*, 117(87), 118(87), 127(86), *147*

Daniel, P. M., 23, *59*
Daniels, E. G., 82(133), *113*
Dapero, M. R., 126(100), 127(100, 102), 130(98, 100, 101), 131(98), 134(101), *148*, 227(131b), *260*, 354(174), 355(174), 356(174), *390*
Davenport, E., 375(167), *389*
Davey, M. J., 117(40), 118(40), 121(40), 139(40), *146*, 413(43), 415(43), 419, *425*
David, J. Q., 74(26), 88(26), 89(26), *110*
Davidson, J. R., 446(130), 448(130), *457*
Davies, D. L., 25(31, 32, 33), 31(32), *59*
Davies, E. B., 422(45), *425*
Davies, J. P. H., 381(243), *392*
Davies, P., 480(117), *485*
Davis, C. S., 403(85), *426*
Davis, J. O., 88(26), 75, *110*
Davis, R. A., 182(18), *187*
Dawes, G. S., 440(22), 441(22), *454*
Day, M. D., 184(20, 21), 185(19), *187*, 419, *425*, 464(37, 38), 475(36), *483*
Deal, C. P., Jr., 376, *386*
Dean, A. L., 21(50), *59*
DeBeer, E. J., 362(115), *388*
Deberdt, R., 372(55), *386*
de Bono, E., 26(51), *59*
de Champlain, J., 25(290), 26(92), 31(92), *60, 65*, 76(14), 81(14), *109*
Decker, J. L., 255(205), *262*
De Costa, F. M., 183(35), *187*
De Elio, F. J., 282(16), *293*
De Gennaro, A., 375, *387*
Degering, E. F., 129(41), *146*
de Graaf, W., 35(78), *60*
De Graff, A. C., 466(160), 479(161), *486*
de Groot, S., 200, *216*
Deicke, E., 40, *59*
de Jongh, D. K., 78, 100(155), 102(155), *113*
de la Barreda, P., 250(51), *258*
Delay, J., 372(56), *368*
Delea, C., 32(16), *59*
de Lestrange, Y., 334(72), *386*
Del Greco, F., 49(171), *62*
Delia, T. J., 403(85), *426*
Deliwala, C. V., 432(84, 91), 433(85), 440(72), *455, 456*
Del Pozo, E. C., 441(131a), *457*
De Marchi, F., 341(166), *389*
Deming, Q. B., 88(103), 89(103), *112*
Demis, D. J., 186(22), *187*

De Moura, R. S., 76, *110*

Dengler, H., 117(42), *146*, 153(23), 184(23), *187*

Deniker, P., 372(56), *386*

Denison, A. B., Jr., 369(57, 230), 376, *386*, *387*, *391*

Dennis, E., 326(42), 326(41, 42, 43), *329*

Dennis, E. G., 238(172), *261*

Deodhar, S. D., 32, *59*, 74, *110*

Depierre, F., 280(12), *293*

Dermenghem, J. F., 372(216), *391*

Desaulles, P. A., 248(9), 252(115), *257*, *260*

Desclin, L., 213(41), *216*

deStevens, G., 264(13), *276*, 349, 354(174), 355(174), 356(174), *386*, *390*

de Vito, E., 25(72), *60*, 73(41), *110*

DeVleeschhouver, G., 445(54), *455*

Dewar, H. A., 383(231), *391*

Dexter, L., 48, 49, *61*, 104(79), *111*

Diaz, J., 250, *258*

Dickinson, C. J., 28, 54, *59*, 383(7), *384*

Didier, J. T., 139(68), *147*

Dieckmann, W. J., 39, *59*

Diehl, H. S., 11(57), *60*

Dietrich, E. V., 362(257), *392*

Dillaha, C. J., 237(52), *258*

Dillaha, J., 237(52), *258*

di Paco, G., 202(24, 179), *216*, *220*

Di Pierro, F., 132(122), *148*

Distler, A., 30, *60*

Distler, M. H. W., 182(98), 185(102), *189*

Ditman, K. W. S., 404, 423, *424*

Dixon, W. E., 85, *110*

Doctor, R. B., 423(112), *427*

Dóda, M., 124, *146*

Dodson, L. F., 22, *59*, 80, *110*

Doebelin, R., 103(71), *111*, 246(83), *259*

Dollery, C. T., 122(45, 46), 125(45, 46), *146*, 173(24), 182(24), 183(24), *186*, 274, *276*, 325(15), 326(14), *328*, 461(41), 466(42), 467(43), 470(11), 471(11), 474(39), 477(40), *482*, *483*

Doluisio, J. T., 202, *220*

Dominguez, A. M., 256(5), *257*

Domino, E. F., 471(44), *483*

Donald, K. W., 373(240), 374(240), *391*

Donald, M. W., 185(80), *188*

Donnet, J. L., 372(56), *386*

Dontas, A. S., 210, *216*

Dorfman, L., 195(159), *219*

Dornhorst, A. C., 366(28), 379(28), 383(7, 58a), *384*, *385*, *386*

Doub, H. P., 21(111), *61*

Douglas, R. M., 9(59), *60*

Douglass, C. D., 229, 237(52), 238, *258*

Doutheil, U., 444(23), *454*

Doyle, A. E., 8(60), 9(257), 15, 29, 33(62, 64), 34, 40, *60*, *64*, 326(16), *328*, 462(154), 477(45), *483*, *486*

Doyne, T., 193(129), *219*

Dragstedt, C. A., 415(72), *425*

Drain, D. J., 177(25), 178(25), 182(18), *187*, 398(48), *425*

Draper, M. D., 433(61–64), 434(61–64), 435(62), *455*

Drcifus, L., 398(20), 415(19), *424*

Drell, W., 179(73), *188*

Dresel, P. E., 371(59), *386*

Drewes, P. A., 207(52), *216*

Druey, J., 128(124), 130(124), *148*, 223(82), 224(55), 225(54, 165), 226(54, 55, 82), 227(54, 55), 228(54, 55), 229(54, 55), 230(54, 82), 231(54, 166), 233(54), 239 (82), *259*, *261*, 284(47), *294*, 333(31), *385*

Drukker, A. E., 165(3), *186*, 398(10), *424*

Drury, D. E., 46, *65*

Drury, D. R., 46(7), *58*

Dubnick, B., 398(2, 36), 409(2), 412(2), *424*, *425*

Dubois, E. L., 255(56), *259*

Duff, R. S., 33, *59*, *60*

Dumont, C., 353(29, 201), 355(201), 356(201), *385*, *390*

Dun, F. T., 440(24), *454*

Dunant, Y., 335(242), *392*

Duncan, E. H., 475(46), *483*

Duncan, L. E., Jr., 32(16), *59*

Duncan, L. J. P., 475(139), *485*

Duncombe, W. G., 117(14), 118(14), 124(14, 18), 141(19), *145*, *146*, 399(17), *424*

Dungan, K. W., 365(232), 366, *386*, *391*

Dunlop, D., 102(189), *114*, 305(59), 319(59), 324(59), *329*

Dunnigan, D. A., 134(131), *148*

Durant, G. J., 143(9), *145*

Durst, G. G., 212(6), *215*

Dustan, H. P., 14(66), *60*, 100, 104(116), *112*, *113*, 122(65), 127(110), 131(110),

147, *148*, 215, *216*, 248(106), *260*, 462(47), *483*
Dutta, A. T., 192(61), *217*
Dutton, A. M., 465(27), *482*
Dziemian, R. L., 194(148), 196(98), 197 (148, 150), *218*, *219*

E

Earl, A. E., 104(152), *113*, 209(134), *219*, 285(41), *294*
Easton, N. R., 353(163), *389*
Eccles, J. C., *293*
Eccles, J. R., 441(25), *454*
Eden, R. J., 138(6), *145*, 343(13), 344(13), *385*
Edge, N. D., 132(76), *147*, 296(31), 299, 300, 301, 302(17), 307(31), 312(7), 319(7), 324, *328*
Edlin, A. I., 228(57), 232(57), *259*
Edmonds, C. J., 465(48), *483*
Edmunds, V., 8(266), *64*
Edwards, K. D. G., 183, 186(119), *189*
Egbert, M. E., 126(100), 127(100), 130(98, 100, 101), 134(101), *148*
Ehrhart, G., 357(61), *386*
Éhrlich, L., 480(100), *484*
Ehrreich, S., 381(205), *391*
Eichenberger, K., 232(167), *261*
Eiduson, S., 173(120), *189*
Eisleb, O., 344(182), *390*
Elaut, L., 46(23), *59*
Elion, G. B., 479(137), *485*
Ellinwood, L. E., 375(45), *386*
Elliot, A. H., 40, *60*
Elliott, D. F., 72, *110*
Ellison, T. E., 164(26), *187*
Elming, N., 301(54), 302(54), *329*
Eloy, F., 126(47), *146*
Emerson, G. W., 423(77), *426*, 471(75), 472(75), *484*
Emlet, J. R., 373(62), *386*
Emslie-Smith, D., 122(45, 46), 125(45, 46), *146*, 326(14), *328*, 461(41), 477(40), *483*
Engel, G. B., 480(49), *483*
Engelman, K., 423(82), *426*, 471(84), *484*
Engelmann, G., 273, *276*, 466(50), *483*
Ensor, C. R., 143(32), *146*
Eppinger, H., 42, *60*
Epstein, F. H., 40(135), *61*
Erickson, R. W., 415(69), *425*

Erlenmeyer, E., 129, *146*, 160(27, 28), *187*
Erlenmeyer, H., 236(61), 237(62), *259*
Ernest, I., 196(46), 197(45, 48, 49), *216*
Erspamer, V., 250, *259*
Eryetishir, I., 43(211), 44(211), 45(211), *63*
Esbenshade, J. H., 472(51, 166), *483*, *486*
Escousse, A., 139(68), 141(138), *147*, *149*
Essigman, W., 271, *276*
Evans, J. A., 8(36), *59*
Evelyn, K. A., 8(70), *60*
Everett, G. M., 209(50), *216*, 405(50, 137, 138), 407, 409, 410(137), 413, *425*, *427*
Exley, K. A., 117(49, 50), *146*

F

Fain, J., 374(154), *389*
Fairbanks, V. F., 446(13), *454*
Fakstorp, J., 284, *293*, 301(54), 302(54), *329*
Falco, M. R., 361(151), *389*
Falk, G., 439(26), *454*
Falkheden, T., 215(72), *217*
Fallab, S., 236, 237(62), *259*, *262*
Fallis, N., 271(49), *277*
Fargier, M. C., 209, *216*
Farmer, J. B., 413(43), 415(43), 419(44), *425*
Farrar, C. B., 446(130), 448(130), *457*
Farrelly, R. O., 274(41), *277*
Farrington, J. A., 102(189), *114*, 305(59), 319(59), 324(59), *329*
Farris, E. J., 23, *60*
Fasciolo, J. C., 24(126), 25, 47(73), *60*, *61*, 69(20), 71(19), 72(19), 73, *110*, *111*
Fassett, D. W., 362(115), *388*
Fastier, F. N., 35, *60*, 126, *146*
Faust, J. A., 357, *386*
Fehér, O., 124(43), *146*
Feigl, E. O., 75(92), *112*
Feinstein, M., 213(66), *217*
Feldberg, W., 30, *60*
Feldkamp, R. F., 367(87), *387*
Fel'dman, I. K., 131, *146*
Feldt, R. H., 38, 39, 41, 42, *60*
Fellman, J. H., 167(29), *187*
Fellows, E. J., 348(129), 349(64, 129), 351(129), *386*, *388*, 403(140, 141), *427*
Feltham, L. A. W., 25(146), *62*
Feng, T. P., 440(24, 27), 441(27), *454*
Fenton, G. W., 13(226), *64*
Fenton, H., 342(65), *386*

Ferguson, F. G., 352, *386*
Ferrini, P. G., 138, *146*
Fertig, H., 137(25), *146*, 271(8), *276*, 409(27, 28), 410(28), 413(28), *424*, 472(21), *482*
Fewell, J. W., 472(51, 166), *483, 486*
Field, L. W., 35, *60*
Fielden, R., 137, 138(6), *145, 146*, 343(13), 344(13), *385*
Fiene, T. J., 383(67), *386*
Fieser, L. F., 430(28), 431(28), *454*
Fieser, M., 430(28), 431(28), *454*
Figueroa, J. E., 50(144), *62*
Fink, M. A., 402(51), *425*
Finlayson, J. K., 29(301), *65*
Finnerty, F. A., 462(52, 53), 467(52), 468(53), *483*
Finnerty, F. A., Jr., 137(56, 67), *146, 147*, 223, *259*, 267, *276*, 453(29), *454*
Finocchio, D., 104(152), *113*
Fisch, S., 479(161), *486*
Fischer, E., 160(30), *187*
Fischer, J. E., 210(51), *216*, 420(90), *425, 426*
Fishback, D. B., 477(54), *483*
Fishman, J., 375(68, 69), *386*
Fishman, R. A., 255(152), *261*
Fitzgibbon, W. E., 349(254), *392*
Flacke, W., 436(9, 30, 31, 32, 51), 439(154), 440(32, 51), 441(9, 32, 32a, 33a), 442(30, 32a), 443(9, 30, 31), 444(9), 445(9, 32a, 33), 446(9), 448(9), 449(31), *454, 455, 457*
Fleckenstein, A., 439(34), *454*
Fleming, H. A., 23, *60*
Fleming, R. M., 177(40), *187*
Fletcher, J., Jr., 271(8), *276*
Fletcher, L., Jr., 137(25), *146*, 409(27, 28), 410(28), 413(28), *424*, 472(21), *482*
Flock, E. V., 373(211), *391*
Floyer, M. A., 22, 48, *60*, 80, 81, *110*
Flückiger, E., 467(55), *483*
Foggie, P., 244(50), 245(50), *258*
Folkers, K., 151(31), *187*
Folty, E. S., 274(16), *276*
Ford, R. V., 8(83, 186), *60, 63*, 266(18), 268, 271, *276*, 326(18, 41, 42), *328*, 409, *425*, 462(56), *483*
Forman, S., 29(84), *60*
Forsham, P. H., 479(148), *485*
Foster, R., 383(193), *390*

Fourneau, E., 334, 342, 343(71), 368(70), *386*
Fouts, J. R., 251(132), *260*, 394(157), *428*
Fowler, P. B. S., 8(265, 266), *64*
Franc, B., 139(68), *147*
Frank, G. B., 439(35), *454*
Frank, M. H., 73(199), *114*
Frank, N., 375(73), *386*
Frankl, W. S., 472(51), *483*
Fraschetti, F., 341(152), *389*
Fraschini, F., 214(35), *216*
Fraser, J. R. E., 9(15), 33(62, 63), 34(62, 63), *59, 60*
Frediani, H. A., 361(151), *389*
Freeman, H., 214(146), *219*
Fregly, M. J., 105, *110*
Freifelder, M., 199(169), *220*
Freilich, M., 465(111), *485*
Freis, E. D., 8(139), 14(85), 29(86), *60, 62*, 131(57), *146*, 223, 254, *259, 260*, 264, *276*, 326(19), *328*, 378, *386*, 394(83), *426*, 452(36), *454*, 460(57), 462(57), 465(71), 468(71), 470(26), 473(26), *482, 483, 484*
Freudenthal, R. R., 479(161), *486*
Frey, A. J., 193(206, 207), *221*
Freyburger, W. A., *293*, 371(168), *389*, 403(71), *425*
Fried, J., 432(38), 433(37), *454*
Friedberg, L., 46(137), *61*
Friedewald, W. T., 182(33), 183(33), *187*
Friedhoff, A. J., 355(109), *387*
Friedland, C. K., 46(136), *61*
Friedlander, D. H., 383(24), *385*
Friedlich, A. L., 452(115), *456*
Friedman, C. L., 86, 91(45), 105(46), *110*
Friedman, H., 255(65), *259*
Friedman, M., 47(138), *61*
Friedman, S. M., 86, 91(45), 105, *110*
Frierson, H. R., 452(43), *454*
Froeb, H. F., 8(293), *65*
Froehlich, H. L., 405(136), *427*
Frohlich, E. D., 131(57), *146*
Fuentes, J., 209(91, 92), *218*
Fujii, K., 233(66), *259*
Fujita, E., 438(86), *455*
Fuller, J. B., 465(86), 467(86), *484*
Fullerton, A. G., 477(58), *483*
Fulton, R. M., 383(7), *384*
Funke, A., 335(77), 338, 339(76), *386, 387*

Furchgott, R. F., 244(68), *259*, 365, 369(78), *387*, 422, *425*
Fyvolent, J., 466(5), *482*

G

Gaddum, J. H., 402(55), *425*
Gaillot, P., 308, *328*
Gaimster, K., 282, *293*
Gaines, W., 298(60), 326(60), *329*
Gaines, W. A., 299(64), 302(64), *329*
Gal, E. M., 207(52), *216*
Galambos, E., 184(69), *188*
Galluzzi, N. J., 462(159), *486*
Galskov, Å., 477(59), *483*
Gamo, T., 253(163), *261*
Ganong, W. F., 30, *63*
Garattini, S., 478(32, 105), *483*, *484*
Gardiner, J. E., 324, *328*
Gardner, D. L., 9, 10, *60*, 104, *110*, 249(69, 70, 71), *259*
Gardner, J. N., 138(6), *145*, 343(13), 344(13), *385*
Gardner, T. S., 398(56–58), *425*
Garfield, C. F., 462(159), *486*
Garfield, C. I., 10(174), 11(174), *62*
Garrett, H. E., 250(197), *262*
Gatti, G. L., 340, 341(80, 81), *387*
Gaudry, R., 159(32), *187*
Gauer, O. H., 442(39), *454*
Gaunt, R., 9, 60, 87, 89, 90(28), 91, 103(28, 49), 104, 105(158), *110*, *113*, 212, 213(54), 214, *216*, *217*
Gearien, J. E., 203, *218*, *220*
Gearing, F. R., 18(242), *64*
Geigy, A. G., 343(82), 344(82), *387*
Geiling, E. M. K., 450(126), *457*
Gelfman, N. A., 182(33), 183(33), *187*
Geller, E., 173(120), *189*
Gellhorn, E., 445(40, 41), *454*
Genas, M., 131, *146*
Genest, J., 25(290), 26, 30, 31(92), *60*, *65*, 76(14), 81(14), *109*, 255(150), *261*
George, H. W., 449(71), *455*
Gershfeld, N. L., 439, *454*, *457*
Gertner, S. B., 252(72), *259*, 414, *425*
Geschickter, C. F., 287(35), *294*
Gessa, G. L., 399, 419, *425*, 461(33), 470(33), *483*

Gessler, U., 254, *259*
Gey, K. F., 175(12), 177(71, 72), 178(72), 179(12), 182(11), *187*, *188*, 393(120), 398(119, 158), 418(121), *427*, *428*
Ghosh, S., 192(61), *217*
Giarman, N. J., 414(59), *425*
Gibbons, A. J., 403(70), *425*
Gifford, R. W., Jr., 123(59), *146*, 266(47), 267(22), *276*, *277*, 373(83), *387*, 463(60), 470(96), 471(60, 96), *484*
Gijon, E., 290(36), *294*
Giletti, B. J., 206(167), *220*
Gilhespy, R. O., 474(61), 477(61), *483*
Gill, E. W., 380(84), *387*
Gillam, P. M. S., 382(196), 383(85), 384, *387*, *390*, 480(129), *485*
Gillespie, L., 106(135), *113*, 153(64), 173(64), 182(34, 64), *187*, *188*, 398(130), 418(130), *427*, 473(62), *483*
Gillette, J. R., 471(63), 478(63), *483*
Gillis, C. N., 211(55, 56, 57), *217*, 253, *259*
Gillis, R. A., 441(33a), *454*
Gilman, A., 429(46), *454*
Gilman, M., 91(48), *110*
Ginn, W. M., Jr., 381, 383(86), *387*
Giordano, C., 47(180), *63*
Girod, C., 213(58), *217*
Giroud, C. J. P., 90(51), *110*
Gitlow, S. E., 33(176, 178), 34(179), *62*, 412(107), 416(107), *426*, 460(183), *486*
Giudicelli, R., 132(103), 135(60, 105, 106), 139(104), *146*, *148*, 201(121), *218*, 358(175), *390*
Gladish, Y. C., 405(137, 138), 407(154), 410(137), 412(139), *427*, *428*
Glaesser, A., 132(34), *146*
Glavas, E., 405, *425*
Glen, W. L., 432(116), 433(116, 117), 434(116, 117), 435(116), *456*
Glenn, F., 24(94), *60*
Gloss, J., 132(26), *146*
Glowinski, J., 208(76), *217*
Göschke, H., 418(121), *427*
Gösswald, R., 319(25), 321(25), *328*
Gokhale, S. D., 476(64), *483*
Goldberg, L. I., 106, *110*, 183(35), *187*, 414, 418(80), 421(66), 422, 424, *425*, *426*, 471(65), *483*

Goldberg, N. D., 415, *425*

Goldblatt, H., 21, 32(53), *59*, *60*, 68, 69, 70, 71(53, 58, 59), 74(38), 82, *110*, *111*

Goldenberg, M., 40, *61*

Goldfinger, S., 479(90), *484*

Goldman, A., 479(19), *482*

Goldman, R., 452(43), *454*

Goldner, M. G., 466(66), *483*

Goldnick, R. B., 327(13), *328*

Goldring, S., 441(44, 45), *454*

Goldshine, A. D., 39, 41, *58*

Goldstein, M., 154(36), 156(36), *187*

Goldstein, S., 246, *259*

Gombert, R., 335(77), *387*

Gomi, Y., 132(109), *148*

Gonick, H. C., 395(104), 398(104), 410(104), *426*

Gonnard, P., 152(74), *188*

Goodman, L. S., 344, *390*, 429(46), *454*

Goormaghtigh, N., 26, *61*

Gordon, D. B., 82, *111*

Gordon, E. K., 208(88), *218*

Gordon, W., 40, *61*

Gornall, A. G., 25(146), *62*

Gotz, E., 106(112), *112*, 434(99), 448(99), *456*

Gould, A. B., 77, *111*

Gould, R. G., Jr., 363, *388*

Gould, W. A., 367, *387*

Gourzis, J. T., 442(48), 447(47), *454*, *455*

Govaerts, P., 49, *61*

Govindachari, T. R., 404(68), *425*

Gowenlock, A. H., 31(100), *61*

Grabner, G., 360, *387*

Gradwell, B. G., 473(67), *483*

Graeme, M. L., 349(218), *391*

Graham, J. D. P., 332(88), 369, *387*

Graham, J. G., 9(39), *59*

Grandjean, T., 383(100), *387*

Grant, G. A., 90(27), *110*, 432(116), 433(116, 117), 434(116, 117), 435(116), *456*

Grant, J. I., 420(93), *426*

Grant, L. H., 465(109), *485*

Grassi-Bertazzi, C., 375, *387*

Graubner, W., 360(91a), *387*

Graupner, K. I., 477(133), *485*

Grayson, J., 381, *390*

Grayson, M., 305(10), *328*

Greaney, J. F., 185(59), *188*

Green, A. F., 84, 99, 101(15), *109*, *110*, 117(14, 61), 118(14, 21), 119(22), 121(22), 123(15, 20, 23), 124(14, 15), 128(16), 140(17), 141, *145*, *146*, 286(1), *293*, 399(17, 18), *424*, 461(10), 463(10), 475(9), *482*

Green, D. M., 86(61, 62), *111*

Green, H., 415(69), *425*

Green, H. D., 369(57, 92, 230), 373(125, 204), 375(125, 169), 376(57, 125), *386*, *387*, *388*, *389*, *390*, *391*

Green, H. O., 341(200), *390*

Green, J. H., 51(160), *62*, 73(121), 79(121), 84(121), *112*

Green, K. G., 383(7), *384*

Green, P. N., 342(65), *386*

Green, S. M., 138(5), 139(3), 144(3, 4), *145*, 342(10), *384*

Greene, D. G., 40(96), *61*

Greer, W. E. R., 418(131), *427*

Gregoriadis, G., 154(57), *188*

Gregory, R., 29(84, 190), *60*, *63*

Greig, M. E., 403(70, 71), *425*

Greisman, S. E., 33, *61*

Gren, A. F., 288(11), *293*

Greshoff, M., 192(60), *217*

Grieble, H. C., 465(86), 467(86), *484*

Griesemer, E. C., 415, *425*

Griffin, J. R., 383(67), *386*, *387*

Griffith, R. S., 86(80), *111*

Griffith, W., 446(130), 448(130), *457*

Grimson, K. S., 46, *61*, 84, 103, *111*, 223, *259*, 373(62, 96), 374(95), 375(95), *386*, *387*

Griswold, H. E., 477(128), *484*

Grivas, J. C., 438(86), *455*, *456*

Grivsky, E. M., 140(17), *145*, 399(18), *424*

Groden, B. M., 185(37), *187*

Grogan, C. H., 285, *293*, *294*

Grollman, A., 47(105), 48(103, 104), *61*, 78, 82, 92, 103(65), 104(65), *111*, *114*, 246(204), *262*, 263, 264(25), *276*

Gross, F., 25(107), 26, 27(224), *61*, *64*, 70(2), 71(2), 73(2), 75, 78, 81(164), 86(2), 87, 89(50), 91(2, 50, 69), 98(2), 103, 104(12), 105(2, 125), *109*, *110*, *111*, *112*, *113*, 223, 226(82), 230, 234(84), 236(84), 239(10, 82), 241(10, 114), 245(11), 246(10, 78, 80, 83, 114), 248)79, 80, 81),

250(10), 253(84), *257, 259, 260,* 357 (160), 372(160), *389*
Gross, J., 71(59), *111*
Grossman, R. G., 445(159), *457*
Grün, A., 335(97), *387*
Gruenfeld, N., 432(89), 433(88), 436(89), 437(88), *456*
Grumelli, E., 357(44), *385*
Grundfest, H., 439(49), *455*
Gubitz, F. W., 349(117), *388*
Guillebeau, J., 90(178), *114*
Gujral, P. K., 436(50, 51), 440(51), 449, *455*
Gulati, O. D., 476(64), *483*
Gump, W. S., 344, 345(183), 347, 349(183), 350(183), 351(183), 352, 369(183), *390*
Gunn, C. G., 341, *387*
Gunn, J. A., 398, 399(73), *425*
Gunne, L. M., 464(68), *483*
Gupta, J. C., 192(38, 61), *216, 217*
Gupta, K. P., 245(85), *259*
Gutkowska, B., 233(16), *258*
Gutman, A. B., 8(293), *65*
Gutmann, H., 398(158), *428*
Gyermek, L., 281(20, 31), 282(20, 31), 288, *293, 294,* 306, *328,* 476(141), 478(141), *485*
Gylys, J., 398(2), 409(2), 412(2), *424*
György, L., 124(43, 44), *146*

H

Haack, E., 195(62, 136), 196(136), *217, 219*
Haas, E., 32(53), *59,* 74(38), *110*
Haase, A., 227(17), 228(17), 229(17), *258*
Hach, V., 200(140), 203(140), *219*
Hachova, E., 200(139), *219*
Haefely, W., 474(167), *486*
Häfliger, F., 357(217), *391*
Häggendal, J., 207, *217*
Haensel, A., 199(65), *217*
Hagedorn, C. W., 274(27, 28), *276*
Hagen, P., 214, *217*
Hahn, G., 159(38), *187,* 199(65), *217*
Haimovici, H., 371(99), *387*
Hajdu, S., 439(97), 441(97), *456*
Haley, T. J., 206(103), *218*
Halkerston, I. D. K., 213(66), *217*
Hall, C. E., 68(171), 86(75, 171), *111*
Hall, G. C., 348(64, 129), 349(64, 129), 351(129), *386, 388*
Hall, O., 86(75), *111*

Hall, W. H., 12, 18(256), *64,* 92, 94, *114*
Halliday, R. P., 362(25), *385*
Halliwell, G., 214(142), *219*
Hallwright, G. P., 469(69), *483*
Halperin, M. H., 29(86), *60,* 378(74), *386,* 452(36), *454*
Halpern, M., 462(95), *484*
Hamer, J., 383(100), *387*
Hamilton, J. G., 82, *111*
Hamilton, M., 9(257), 13(287), 18(287), *64,* 65, 470(70), 471(70), *484*
Hammarström, S., 8(18), *59*
Hanauer, L., 474(1), 475(1), 476(1), *482*
Handley, C. A., 376, *387*
Handley, P., 355(109), *387*
Hanke, M. E., 186(48), *187*
Hanowell, E. G., 462(159), *486*
Hanson, H. M., 478(170), *486*
Hanson, L. C. F., 207(162), *220*
Hansson, E., 177(39, 40), 178(39), *187*
Hanzal, R. F., 21(95), *60,* 68(57), 70(58), 71(58, 59), *111*
Hardgrove, M., 40, *61*
Hardley, C. A., 326(42), *329*
Harington, M., 8(110), *61,* 173(24), 182(24), 183(24), *187,* 327(23), *328*
Harris, L. S., 355(8), 356(8), *384*
Harris, W. S., 382, *387*
Harrison, D. C., 383(67), *386, 387*
Harrison, T. R., 246(204), *262, 263, 264, 276*
Hart, J. A., 398(2), 409(2), 412(2), *424*
Hartman, F. W., 21(111), *61*
Hartman, W. J., 152(41), 158(41), 166(41), 167(41), 168, 169(41), 170(41), 171(41), 172, 173, 174, 175(41), *187*
Hartmann, M., 357, 360(105), *387*
Hartroft, P. M., 74, *111*
Hartroft, W. S., 92, *111*
Hartung, G., 236(200), 237(200), *262*
Hartwich, A., 47(112), *61*
Harvey, S. C., 371, 379(106), *384, 387*
Harvey-Smith, E. A., 182(2), 185(2), *186*
Hasek, R. H., 318(50), *329*
Hashimoto, K., 441(52), 442(52), 445(52), *455*
Hatch, F. T., 8(293), *65*
Hatcher, J. D., 382(51), *386*
Hayao, S., 354, *387*
Hayashi, R., 432(148), *457*
Hayes, D., 480(116), *485*

Hayes, D. W., 377(108), *387*
Haynes, F. W., 104(79), *111*
Haywood, L. J., 271(38), *277*, 472(106), 473(106), *484*
Hazard, J. B., 9(172), *62*
Heath, W. C., 465(71), 468(71), *484*
Hebb, C., 244(50), 245(50), *258*
Hechter, O., 213(66), *217*
Hedwall, P., 212(67), *217*, 251(31, 32, 111), *258, 260*
Heetderks, D. R., 47(180), *63*
Hefferman, J. F., 91(94), *112*
Hegedüs, B., 398(158), *428*
Heider, C., 326(43), *329*, 410(21), 415(21), 419(21), *424*, 472(13), *482*
Heine, B. E., 475(72), *484*
Heine, M., 20(47), *59*, 92(33, 34, 35), *110*
Heine, W. I., 255(65), *259*
Heinzelman, R. V., 402, *426*
Heise, R., 151(42), *187*
Hejtmancik, M. R., 266(29), *277*
Hekimian, L., 355(109), *387*
Heller, H., 85, *110*
Helmer, O. M., 25(115), 28(113), 29, 49, *61, 63*, 71(95), 72, 73, 76, 86(80), *111, 112*
Helps, E. P. W., 373(110), *387*
Helsper, J. T., 375(73), *386*
Henatsch, H. D., 340, *388*
Hendrix, J. P., 374(95), 375(95), *387, 388*
Heneage, P., 168(99), *189*
Hennemann, H. H., 255(86), *259*
Hennessey, M. A., 298(40), *329*
Henning, M., 70(1), 71(1), 73(1), 86(1), 91(1), 98(1), 104(1), 105(1), *109*
Henry, J. P., 442(39), *454*
Hensler, R. H., 431(82), 433(81), 437(90, 94), *455, 456*
Herman, J., 374(113), *388*
Hermans, B., 342(248), *392*
Hermansen, K., 137(62), *147*
Herold, M., 413(33), *424*
Herr, F., 440(53), *455*
Herring, A. B., 384(114), *388*
Herrmann, G. R., 266(29), *277*
Herting, R. L., 473(73), *484*
Hertting, G., 117(63), *147*, 209(68), 210, *217*, 399(8), *424*
Herzberg, J. J., 255(87), *259*
Hesdorffer, M. B., 11(57), *60*
Hess, F. O., 40, *61*

Hess, R., 27(224), *64*, 212(69), *217*
Hess, S. M., 184(110), 185(110), *189*, 208(127), *218*
Hetényi, S., 40, *61*
Heuer, G. J., 24(94), *60*
Heymans, C., 46(23), *59*, 68, 83, 84, *111*, 373(250), *392*, 445(54), *455*
Hiatt, E. P., 442(122), *457*
Hickler, R. B., 73, 82(108), *111, 112*
Higgins, J., 127(102), *148*, 227(131b), *260*
Higgins, T. F., 8(139), *62*
Highman, B., 422(98), *426*
Hilden, T., 477(59), *483*
Hill, I. D., 383(7), *384*
Hillarp, N.-A., 205, 208(33), 209(33), *216*
Hilliard, J., 213(77), *217*
Hillman, F., 327(47), *329*
Hiltmann, R., 134(144), *149*, 319, 321, *328*
Hilton, J. G., 213(39), *216*
Hines, E. A., Jr., 11(120), 38, 39(297), 41, *61, 65*
Hinman, J. W., 82(133), *113*
Hirakawa, A., 145(37), *146*
Hirsch, C. W., 184(9), *187*
Hirt, L., 444, *457*
Hitchings, G. H., 479(137), *485*
Hjort, A. H., 362, *388*
Hobbs, L. F., 415(76), *426*
Hobolth, N., 327(26), *328*
Hoch, P. H., 399(116), *427*
Hodge, J. V., 8(123), 9(123), 10, 20(258), 37, *61, 62, 64*, 103(123), *112*, 317, 327, *329*, 423(77), *426*, 464(76), 470(155), 471(75), 472(75), 474(74), 475(155), 476(155), 477(155), 479(155), 480(155), *484, 486*
Hodson, H. F., 140(17), *145*, 399(18), *424*
Hoech, H. H., 201(89), 203(89), *218*
Hoefke, W., 359, *388*
Hoffman, C., 199(29), *216*
Hoffmann, P., 441(55), *455*
Hofmann, A., 362(235), 364(234, 235), 377, *388, 391*
Hogan, R., 229, 238, *258*
Hollander, W., 93, 105, *111*, 264, 265(30), 266, 268, *277*, 414(78), *426*, 460(78), 462(79), 463(78), 465(77, 79, 80), 467(77, 79), *484*
Holley, H. L., 255(88), *259*
Hollister, L. E., 477(81), *484*

Holman, D. V., 71(89), 111
Holmes, H. L., 436(161), *457*
Holtz, P., 151, *187*, 207(8), *215*
Holzbauer, M., 205, *217*, 402(79), *426*
Holze, E. A., 33(155), *62*
Hong, E., 355(206), *391*
Honkomp, L. J., 367, *388*
Honour, A. J., 13(226), *64*
Hoobler, S. W., 26(22), 27(22), 56, *59*, *61*, 215, *217*, 430(56), 452(57), *455*
Hood, B., 215, *217*
Hook, J. B., 479(82), *484*
Horita, A., 165(3), *186*, 214, *217*, 398(10), *424*
Horler, A. R., 471(83), *484*
Horlington, M., 177(25), 178(25), 182(18), *187*
Horst, W. D., 420(90), *426*
Horton, B. T., 377(108), *387*
Horwitz, D., 184(68), *188*, 409, 412(81), 413(113, 414), 418, 423, *426*, *427*, 464(125), 471(84), 472(118), *484*, *485*
Hosansky, N., 195(73), *217*
Houssay, B. A., 24(126), 47(73), 48, 49, *60*, *61*, 71, *111*
Howard, B. E., 271, *277*
Howes, J. G. B., 398(48), *425*
Howie, N., 90(28), 103(28), *110*
Howitt, G., 383(214), 384(214), *391*
Hsu, I., 194(148), 197(148, 150), *219*
Hubert, M., 235(40), *258*
Hudak, W. J., 85, *111*
Huebl, H., 422(54), *425*
Huebner, C. F., 194(101)
Hückel, W., 299, 309, *328*
Hülse, W., 40, *59*
Huerlimann, A., 474(167), *486*
Huggins, R. A., 374(4), 375(4), *384*
Huidobro, F., 25(127), *61*
Hull, L. D., 214, *217*
Humphrey, D. C., 463(60), 470(96), 471(60, 96), *483*, *484*
Hunt, R., 195(159), *219*
Hunter, A., 11(128), *61*
Hunter, W. T., 349(117), *388*
Hurkmans, J. A. T. M., 473(136), *485*
Hurley, R. E., 122(65), *147*
Hurst, P., 383(7), *384*
Huston, M. J., 253(125), *260*
Hutcheon, D. E., 357(118), *388*

Hutter, O. F., 291(21), *293*
Hyde, C. A., 475(46), *483*
Hye, H. K. A., 193(1), 207(1), *215*

I

Iggo, A., 209, *217*
Iliev, V., 376(198), *390*
Ing, H. R., 68, 70(4), 86(4), 91(4), *109*, 280, *293*
Inscoe, J. K., 209(5), *215*
Iradyan, M. A., 137(2), *145*
Irons, G. V., Jr., 381(86), 383(86), *387*
Irvine, R. O. H., 13(287), 18(287), *65*, 182(43), *187*
Iselin, B., 72(160), *113*
Isler, H., 357, 360(120), *387*, *388*
Iversen, L. L., 117(66), *147*, 208, *217*
Izdebski, J., 225(18), 227(17), 228(17), 229(17), *258*

J

Jackson, W. B., 33(130), *61*
Jacob, J., 338(76), 339(76), *387*
Jacobs, W. A., 363, *388*, 430, 432(125), *454*, *457*
Jacobs, W. M., 255(4), *257*
Jacobson, M. M., 401, 402, *426*, 473(91), *484*
Jacquier, R., 231(100), *260*
Jageneau, A. H. M., 245(164), *261*, 342(215), *391*
Jakovleva, A. J., 253(105), *260*
James, P., 33, 40, *58*
Jančik, F., 235(89), *259*
Jandhyala, B. S., 362(122), *388*
Janecek, J., 27(283), *65*, 354(123), *388*
Janney, J. G., Jr., 477(85), *484*
Jansen, W. H., 40, *61*
Janssen, P. A. J., 342(185, 215, 248), 372, *390*, *391*, *392*
Januszewicz, V., 88(103), 89(103), *112*
Jaques, R., 236(92), 237(90), 252, *259*
Jaret, R. S., 196(172), *220*
Jarisch, A., 444, *455*
Jeger, O., 430(59), 431(59), *455*
Jen, H. C., 130(33), *146*
Jenkins, H. J., 449(60), *455*
Jenne, J. W., 237, *259*

Jequier, R., 197(198), *220*
Jilek, J. O., 196(46), 200(139, 140), 201(141), 203(140), *216, 219*
Joels, N., 442(120), *456*
Johannesen, R. B., 305(10), *328*
Johnson, A. D., 86(62), *111*
Johnson, C. A., 32, *61*
Johnson, H. D., 373(125), 375, 376, *388*
Johnson, L., 436(161), *457*
Johnson, P. C., 22(133), *61*
Johnson, R. L., 394(83), *426*
Johnsson, G., 70(1), 71(1), 73(1), 86(1), 91(1), 98(1), 104(1), 105(1), *109*
Johnston, L. C., 465(86), 467(86), *484*
Johnstone, C. I., 383(239), *391*
Johnstone, M., 383(126), *388*
Jones, A. W., 75, *112*
Jones, D., 471(130), *485*
Jones, F., 82(132), *113*
Jones, P. O., 287(29), *294*
Jones, P. S., 374(203), *390*
Jones, R. T., 162, *187*
Jones, W. R., 438(160), 447(160), *457*
Jonsson, H., 464(68), *483*
Jose, A. D., 383(239), *391*
Jourdon, F., 374(113), *388*
Jucker, E., 288(50, 51), *294*
Judson, W. E., 40, *61*, 73, 76, *111*, 462(179), *486*
Julia, M., 404(84), *426*
Julia, S., 404(84), *426*

K

Kabza, T. G., 430(56), 452(57), *455*
Kaese, H. J., 340(111), *388*
Kahali, B. S., 192(61), *217*
Kahana, L., 466(5), *482*
Kahana, S., 466(5), *482*
Kahn, J. R., 72(174, 175), 77(74), *111, 114*
Kaindl, F., 365(127), *388*
Kaiser, C., 403, 404(159), *426, 428*
Kaiser, F., 195(62), *217*
Kakaviatos, N., 137(67), *147*, 462(53), 468(53), *483*
Kakimoto, Y., 253(163), *261*, 419, *426*
Kamijo, K., 415, *426*
Kamin, D. L., 209(83), *217*
Kaminsky, D., 398(2), 409(2), 412(2), *424*

Kanai, T., 210(202), *220*
Kanda, M., 227(109), 228(109), 229, 235, *260*
Kanda, Z., 422(88), *426*
Kanematsu, S., 213(77, 78), *217*
Kanno, T., 446(152), *457*
Kaplan, A. A., 274(27, 28), *276*, 441(112), *456*
Kapp, F., 46, *61*
Kappeler, H., 72(160), *113*
Kashii, C., 79(117), *112*
Kassirer, J. P., 465(87), *484*
Katritzky, A. R., 144(4), *145*
Katsui, N., 432(89), 436(89), *456*
Kattus, A. A., 383(148), *389*
Katz, L., 430, *427*
Katz, L. N., 46(137), 47(138), *61*, 91(109), *112*
Katz, R., 362(257), *392*
Kawanishi, M., 201(124), *218*
Kawasaki, T., 432(170, 171), 433(171), *458*
Keasling, H. H., 144(83), *147*
Keelan, P., 383(128), *388*
Keen, H., 26(51), *59*
Kehl, R., 213(79), *217*
Keller, F., 195(85, 86), *217*, 433(61–64), 434(61–64), 435(62), *455*
Kelley, R. T., 8(139), *62*
Kelly, W. G., 30(149), 31(149), *62*, 87(102), 88(102, 103), 89(103), *112*
Kemball-Price, R., 467(121), *485*
Kempf, G. F., 78, *112*
Kempner, W., 8(140), *62*, 263, *277*
Kennedy, A. C., 467(14), *482*
Kern, R., 131, *146*
Kernodle, C. E., 373(96), *387*
Kerr, D. N. S., 466(134), *485*
Kerwin, J. F., 344, 348(64, 129), 349(64), 351(129), 369, *386, 388, 392*
Kesler, E., 227(17, 94), 228(17), 229(17), *258, 259*
Kezdi, P., 51, *62*
Kiefer, B., 199, *219*
Kierstad, R. W., 193(206, 207), *221*
Kiesel, R. J., 194(148), 196(99), 197(148, 150), *218, 219*
Kilpatrick, J. A., 13, *62*
Kimura, N., 7(143), *62*
Kincaid-Smith, P., 327(23, 24), *328*

Kinnard, W. J., 132(13, 26), *145*, *146*, 228(57), 232(57), *259*
Kinross-Wright, J., 473(88), *484*
Kircher, F., 305(28), *328*
Kirchheimer, W. F., 394(157), *428*
Kirchhoff, H., 237(95), 255(95), *259*
Kirkendall, W. M., 373(131), *388*
Kirpekar, S. M., 211(81), *217*, 236, 238, 251, *259*
Kirshner, N., 208(82), 209(83), *217*
Kirtikar, R. K., 192, *217*
Kisch, F., 42, *60*
Kissin, M., 38, 39, 40, *63*
Kitter, J., 29(86), *60*
Klages, F., 305(28, 29), *328*
Klapper, M. S., 271, *277*
Klarer, W., 360, *388*
Kleeman, C. R., 395(104), 398(104), 410(104), *426*
Klepping, J., 139(68), 141(138), *147*, *149*
Klerman, G. L., 185(59), *188*, 478(89), *484*
Klinenberg, J. R., 479(90), *484*
Klohs, M. W., 195(85, 86), *217*, 433(61–64), 434(61–64), 435(62), *455*
Klupp, H., 340, *388*
Klutchko, S. R., 398(2), 409(2), 412(2), *424*
Knell, J., 153(117), 184(117), *189*
Knopf, R. F., 30(43), *59*, 465(29), *482*
Knowlton, A. I., 91(94), *112*
Kobayashi, M., 29(84, 190), *60*, *63*
Kobayashi, T., 246(202), *262*
Kobinger, W., 359, *388*
Koch, R. C., 117(128), 118(128), 121(128), 137(127, 128), *148*
Kodama, R., 415(19), *424*
Koelle, G. B., 415(87), *426*
Körbl, J., 235(89), *259*
Kohli, J. D., 375(45), *386*
Kohlstaedt, K. G., 28(116), *61*, 71(95), *112*
Koiw, E., 30(93), *60*
Kolb, E. J., 451(65), 453(65), *455*
Koletsky, S., 79, 91, *112*
Kolff, W. J., 48, 50, *62*
Komalahiranya, A., 441(66), *455*
Kondratas, B., 105(169), *114*
Kono, C., 422(88), *426*
Konzett, H., 288(45, 52), *294*, 377(14), 378(14), *385*, 441(67), *455*
Koo, J., 335(134), *388*

Kopelman, H., 470(70), 471(70), *484*
Kopin, I. J., 208(88), 210(51), *216*, *218*, 393, 420(52), *425*, *426*
Koppelman, R., 186(48), *187*
Kordik, P., 245(98), 251(98), *260*
Korein, J., 451(65), 453(65), *455*
Korol, B., 105(169), *114*
Korotkov, N. S., 69, *112*
Kosinski, M., 82(133), *113*
Koster, R., 461(22), *482*
Koster, S., 433(61–63), 434(61–63), 435(62), *455*
Kostial, K., 291(21), *293*
Koštiř, J. V., 131(69), *147*
Kountz, S. L., 237(52), *258*
Kralt, T., 201, 203, *218*
Kramer, D. W., 375(135), *388*
Kramer, K., 444(23), *454*
Kramsch, D. M., 93(88), *111*
Krapcho, J., 342(136), *388*
Krause, F. W., 207(105), 212(104), *218*
Krayer, O., 209(91, 92, 125), *218*, 429(69), 430(70, 108a), 439(70), 440(70, 72), 441(70), 444(68), 449(71), 451, 452 (108a), *455*, *456*
Kremen, S., 73(199), *114*
Kremer, M., 84, *112*
Kreunziger, H., 51, *58*
Krieger, E. M., 84, *112*
Krieger, H., 139(70), *147*
Krieger, K. H., 162(44), *187*
Krikler, D. M., 423(91), *426*
Krogsgaard, A. R., 477(59), *483*
Kroneberg, G., 134(144), *149*, 182(45), *187*, 214(93), *218*
Krus, D., 214(146), *219*
Kuehne, M. E., 196(98), *218*
Kühns, K., 285(22), *293*
Kündig, H., 246(83), *259*
Küng, H. L., 357(137), *388*
Kullnig, R. K., 355(8), 356(8), *384*
Kumada, S., 226(99), 227(99), 232(99), 233(99), *260*
Kumakura, S., 441(52), 442(52), 445(52), *455*
Kumar, D., 25(146), *62*
Kuna, S., 318(50), *329*
Kundiz, H., 103(71), *111*
Kuntzman, R. G., 119(31), *146*, 184(9), *187*, 209(175), *220*, 401, 402(127), *426*, *427*, 461(33), 470(33), 473(91), *483*, *484*

Kuntzman, R. G., 402(127), *427*
Kupchan, S. M., 430(83, 95), 431(82, 83), 432(73, 74, 77, 78, 83, 84, 89, 91, 92), 433(73, 76, 78, 79, 80, 81, 83, 85, 88), 435(75), 436(89), 437(73, 76, 78, 80, 88, 90, 93, 94), 438(80, 86, 160), 440(72), 447(160), *455, 456, 457*
Kuperman, I., 73(199), *114*
Kuroda, A., 129, *147*
Kuschinsky, G., 367(138), *388*
Kushner, S., 353(12), *385*
Kusserow, G. W., 195(85, 86), *217*
Kuz'micheva, T. P., 225(184), *262*
Kvale, W. F., 373(83, 139, 211), *387, 388, 391*
Kylin, E., 40, *62*

L

Lagerlof, H., 29(294), *65*
Lago, J., 162(44), *187*
Lampen, H., 51, *62*
Landau, S. J., 182(33), 183(33), *187*
Landis, E. M., 46(136), *61*
Landi-Vittory, R., 338(150), 339(150), 340(140, 149), 341(81, 152), 342(36), 361(50, 151), 362, *385, 386, 387, 388, 389*
Lands, A. M., 420(93), *426*
Langford, H. G., 86(101), 272, *112, 276*
Langrehr, D., 340(111), *388*, 442(96), *456*
Lanier, J. T., 373(125), 375(125), 376(125), *388*
Laragh, J. H., 30, 31, *62*, 74, 87(102), 88, 89, *112*, 182(13), 186(10), *187*, 274(9), *276*
Lasslo, A., 202, *219*
Laurence, D. R., 123(23), *146*, 383(7), *384*, 475(93), *484*
Lauwers, P., 215, *217*
Laverty, R., 24(152), 29, 30, 35, 37(152), *60, 62*, 92(105), *112*
Lavie, D., 432(91, 92), *456*
Lawler, C. A., 362(52), *386*
Lawrason, F. D., 276(36), *277*
Lawrence, J. R., 28, *59*
Lawrenz, D. R., 465(87), *484*
Lawrie, T. D. V., 117(75), 118(75), 121(75), 144(75), *147*
Lazare, R., 177(25), 178(25), 182(18), *187*, 398(48), *425*

Lazaro, E. J., 445(131), *457*
Leach, W. J., 255, *260*
Ledingham, J. M., 32, 48, *62*, 80, *112*
Leditschke, H., 357(61), *386*
Lee, G. de J., 26(51), *59*
Lee, G. E., 132(76), *147*, 296, 299(17), 300(17, 32), 301(17), 302(17), 307, 309(33), 310(30), 312(7), 319(7), *328, 329*
Lee, J., 398(56–58), *425*
Lee, J. B., 82, *112*
Lee, P. R., 479(19), *482*
Lee, R. E., 33(155), *62*, 472(114), *485*
Leeper, L. C., 418(94), *426*
Leeson, G., 398(36), *425*
Lefevre, F., 135(60), *146*
Leff, W. A., 327(47), *329*
Lehman, J. H., 86(62), *111*
Lehmann, G., 287(42), *294*
Leiby, C. M., 168(77), 176(77), 177(77), 178(77), 184(77), 185(77), *188*
Leishman, A. W. D., 478(94), *484*
Leloir, L. F., 69(20), 71(19), 72(19), *110*
Lemberger, L., 368, *385*
Lenaers, R., 126(47), *146*
Lenel, R., 91, *112*
Lenke, D., 284(23), *293*
Lennox, J. A., 327(34), *329*
Lentz, K., 72(175), *114*
Leo, S. D., 71(153), *113*
Leon, A. S., 462(95), *484*
Leonard, E., 439(97), 441(97), *456*
Leonard, J. W., 470(96), 471(96), *484*
Leonard, N. J., 132, *147*
Leonetti, G., 274, *276*, 466(30), 467(30), *482*
Lerner, O. M., 131, *146*
Lesage, M. A., 382(251), *392*
Lesse, S., 403(95), *426*
Lester, B. M., 403(85), *426*
Lestrange, Y., 280(12), *293*
Leth, T. D., 134(131), *148*
Lettenbauer, G., 195(136), 196(136, 138), 197(137), *219*
Lever, A. F., 25(31, 32, 33), 31(32), *59, 62*, 76(111), 81, *112*
Levi, A. J., 409(4), 423(4), *424*, 471(2), *482*
Levine, H. D., 453(101), *456*
Le Vine, P. B., 203, *218*
Levine, R. J., 184(46), *187*, 413, 414, *426*
Levitt, B., 381(205), *391*

Levitt, G., 40, *61*
Levy, B., 116(78), *147*, 332(142), 371(5), *384*, *388*
Levy, J. V., 212(95), *218*, 380, 381, 384, *388*
Levy, S. E., 23(21), *59*
Lewis, B., 423(91), *426*
Lewis, E., 475(97), *484*
Lewis, G. P., 30, *60*, *62*, 207(20), *216*
Lewis, H. A., 71(153), 86(114), *112*, *113*
Lewis, J. J., 211(56, 57, 81), *217*, 236, 238, 251, 253, *259*
Lewis, T. R., 355(8), 356(8), *384*
Leyrie, J., 372(56), *386*
Li, T. H., 440(27), 441(27), 445(4), *453*, *454*
Libermann, D., 230(101), 231(101), 231(100, 101), *260*
Libman, D. D., 284, *294*
Lichtlen, P., 29(292), *65*, 182(86), *188*
Liddle, G. W., 32(16), *59*
Liebau, H., 30(58), *60*
Lieberman, S., 30(149), 31(149), *62*, 88(103), 89(103), *112*
Liebeskind, H., 285(22), *293*
Liechty, R. D., 373(131), *388*
Lin, R. C. Y., 402(29), *424*
Lindholmer, B., 465(98), *484*
Lindenmann, A., 288(51), *294*
Lindmar, R., 119(79), *147*, 464(99), *484*
Lindner, E., 479(138), *485*
Lindqvist, M., 184, 186(14), *187*, 207, *217*
Ling, J. S., 357(118), *388*
Linker, R. P., 212(7), *215*
Lippmann, H. I., 375(146), *389*
Lipschultz, B., 480(100), *484*
Liptak, T. E., 470(26), 473(26), *482*
Lipton, M. A., 184(54), *188*
Lish, P. M., 365(232), 366, 367(87), *386*, *387*, *391*
Litchfield, J. T., Jr., 449, *456*
Litter, J., 40(134), *61*, 378(74), *386*, 452(36), *454*
Littman, D., 465(109), *485*
Lloyd, K., 154(57), *188*
Lobeck, W. G., Jr., 367(87), *387*
Locket, S., 287(25), *294*
Loeb, E. N., 91(94), *112*
Logemann, W., 199(96, 97), 200, *218*
Loiseau, J., 201(121), *218*
Long, C., 475(180), *486*
Longino, F. H., 373(96), *387*

Lorimer, A. R., 117(75), 118(75), 121(75), 144(75), *147*
Lott, W. A., 342(136), *388*
Loustalot, P., 87(72), 89(72), *111*, 248(9), *257*, *260*
Lovel, T. W. I., 139(93), *147*, 474(110), *485*
Lovenberg, W., 168, 169(47), 186(114), *187*, *189*, 423(82), *426*, 471(84), *484*
Lowe, R. D., 383(192, 193), *390*
Lowell, F. M., 193(129), *219*
Lowman, E. W., 479(19), *482*
Lown, B., 480(100), *484*
Lowther, C. P., 469(101), *484*
Loyke, H. F., 145(37), *146*, 430(56), *455*, 477(31), *483*
Luby, E. D., 471(44), *483*
Lucas, R. A., 104(152), *113*, 194(148), 196(98, 99), 197(148, 149, 150, 166), 206(168), *218*, *219*, *220*
Lucchesi, B. R., 381, *389*
Ludden, C. T., 184(107), *189*, 476(163), *486*
Ludwig, W., 40, *62*
Lüdtke, K., 151(42), *187*
Luisada, A. A., 479(113), *485*
Luk'jančikova, G. I., 235(103), *260*
Luna, C., 287(34), *294*
Lundborg, P., 479(102), *484*
Lunsford, C. D., 202, *218*
Lunt, E., 310(30), 312(7), 319(7), *328*
Luria, M. N., 29(301), *65*
Luskin, L. S., 144(80), *147*
Luxton, R. W., 21(159), *62*
Lynch, J., 21(95), *60*, 68(57), 70(58), 71(58), *111*
Lynn, R. B., 375, *389*
Lyon, A. F., 466(160), *486*
Lyttle, D. A., 402(74), *426*

M

Mabbitt, L. A., 423, *424*
MacAlpin, R. N., 383(148), *389*
McAlpine, S. G., 117(75), 118(75), 121(75), 144(75), *147*
McCann, S. McD., 23(300), *65*
McCarthy, D. A., 143(32), *146*
McClure, J. L., 422(105), *426*
McConn, R. G., 453(18), *454*
McCormack, L. J., 104(116), *112*, 248(106), *260*

McCoubrey, A., 117(14), 118(14), 123(23), 124(14, 18), 141(19), *145*, *146*, 288(11), *293*, 399(7), *424*, *426*

McCoy, F. W., 255, *260*

McCubbin, J. W., 49, 51, *62*, 73, 75(179, 180), 76(37, 122), 79, 84, 88, 104(141), *110*, *112*, *113*, *114*, 210, *218*, 402(115), *427*, 475(119), *485*

McCulloch, M. W., 478(23), *482*

McCurdy, R. L., 184(54), *188*

McDonough, F. J., 86(61), *111*

Macek, K., 201(141), *219*, 432(155), 436(155), *457*

McFadyen, I. R., 255(108), *260*

McGinty, J. S., 452(20), 453(20), *454*

Macgregor, A. G., 474(103), *484*

McGregor, D. D., 35, 36, 37, *62*

Mach, R. S., 255, *260*

MacIntosh, F. C., 129(81), *147*

McIntosh, H. D., 381(253), *392*

McIsaac, R. J., 323(36), *329*

McIsaac, W. M., 227(109), 228(109), 229, 235, *260*

McIvor, R. A., 159(32), *187*

McKendrick, C. S., 287(29), *294*

McKennis, H., Jr., 235(110), *260*

MacKenzie, G. J., 373(240), 374(240), *391*

Macko, E., 348(64, 129), 349(64, 129), 351(129), *386*, *388*

McLean, A. B., 449(17), *454*

McLean, J. R., 143(32), *146*

McLean, K., 383(226), *391*

McLean, R. A., 348(64, 129), 349(64, 129), 351(129), *386*, *388*

McMahon, F. G., 276(36), *277*

MacMahon, M. T., 123(114), 139(114), *148*, 474(123), *485*

McMichael, J., 8(164), *62*, 122(45), 125(45), *146*

Macmillan, B. M., 470(155), 475(155), 476(155), 477(155), 479(155), 480(155), *486*

MacPhillamy, H. B., 194(101, 148), 196(98), 197(148, 149, 150), *218*, *219*

McNeill, R. S., 384(155), *389*

McQueen, E. G., 8(123, 170), 9(123, 257), 10, 36, 37(167, 168), 48, *61*, *62*, 103(123), *112*, 326(56), *329*, 462(154, 156), 464(157), *486*

McShane, W. K., 117(128), 118(128), 121(128), 137(128), *148*

McSween, R. N. M., 467(14), *482*

McVaugh, R. B., 79(162), *113*

Maderni, P., 334(72), 342(71), 343(71), *386*

Madison, J. C., 326(18), *328*

Madoff, I. M., 93(88), *111*

Maegraith, G. G., 45, 46, *59*

Maggiolo, C., 206(103), *218*

Magnus, R. V., 421(38), *425*

Magus, R. D., 207(105), 212(104), *218*

Maher, J. F., 274(37), *277*, 466(104), *484*

Mahoney, L. E., 238(172), *261*

Maison, G. L., 106, *112*, 434(99, 150), 448(147), *457*

Maitre, L., 184(63), 185(62), *188*, 420(111), *427*

Majumdar, D. N., 202, *218*

Malesh, W., 433(61–64), 434(61–64), 435(62), *455*

Malhotra, C. L., 447(100), *456*

Maling, H. M., 422, *426*

Malton, S. D., 371(168), *389*

Manara, L., 478(105), *484*

Mandeles, S., 186, *187*

Manger, W. M., 373(139), *388*

Mann, L. T., 436(161), *457*

Maramba, L. R., 285(48), *294*

Marcus, St. M., 210(176), 212(176), *220*

Margerison, R. B., 131, *147*

Margolin, E. G., 453(101), *456*

Marini-Bettolo, G. B., 338, 339(150), 340, 341(152), 361(43, 50, 151), 362, *385*, *386*, *388*, *389*

Markee, S., 210(202), *220*

Markham, C. H., 185(49), *187*

Markman, P., 383(214), 384(214), *391*

Marley, E., 422(12), 423(14), *424*, 471(8), *482*

Maronde, R. F., 271, *277*, 472(106), 473(106), *484*

Marrazzi, A. S., 414, *426*

Marsden, C. D., 384(187), *390*

Marsh, D. O., 173(50), 185(50), *188*

Marsh, W. H., 72(174), *114*

Marshall, J., 173(50), 185(50), *188*

Marshall, R. J., 33(63), 34(63), *59*

Martin, D. G., 144(83), *147*

Martin, G. J., 152(51, 52), *188*, 335(134), *388*

Martin, J. C., 318(50), *329*

Martin, W. B., 405(137, 138), 410(137), 412(139), *427*

Martin, Y. C., 409, 410, *426*

Martinez, M. P., 158(53), *188*

Martini, L., 214(35), *216*, 441(102), *456*

Marxer, A., 128(124), 130(124), *148*, 225(54, 165), 226(54), 227(54), 228(54), 229 (54), 230(54), 231(54), 233(54), *259, 261*, 282, 284(47), *294*, 340(161), 357 (245), 358(245), 360(245), *389, 392*

Marzoni, F. A., 374(95), 375(95, 112), *387, 388*

Masamune, T., 431(82), *455*

Maškovskij, M. D., 253(105), *260*

Mason, A., 471(107), 472(107), 475(107), *258*

Mason, D. F. J., 284, *294*

Mason, D. T., 211(37, 107), *216, 218*

Massarani, E., 357(44), *385*

Masson, G. M. C., 9, 45, 46, 49, *62*, 79, 86(114), 90, 104, *112*, 248, *260*

Master, A. M., 10, 11(174), *62*

Mathisen, H. S., 327, *329*

Matthews, H. L., 478(94), *484*

Matthews, R. J., 403(101, 102), *426*

Mattia, V. D., 327(47), *329*

Mattis, P. A., 403(141), *427*

Maxwell, M. H., 395(104), 398, 410(104), 413, *426*

Maxwell, R. A., 100, 101(119), 102, 104(152), *112, 113*, 116(84), 117(87), 118(87), 126(99), 127(88), 130, *147, 148*, 209(108, 109), *218*, 227(131a), 260, 270(39), *277*, 285(41), *294*, 376(153), *389*

Maxwell, R. D. H., 9(39), *59*

May, L. G., 29(84, 190), *60, 63*

Mayer, S., 374(154), *389*

Mazzadro, M., 361(50), *386*

Mead, J. A. R., 402(127), *427*

Meaney, T. F., 215(44), *216*

Mechelke, K., 357(156), *389*

Meckelnberg, K. L., 299(64), 302(64), 323(63), *329*

Medoff, H. S., 23(71), *60, 62*, 85, *112*

Megibow, R. S., 264, *277*

Meier, M., 251(31, 32), *258, 260*

Meier, R., 87(72), 89(72), 104(11, 12), 105(125), *109, 111, 112*, 211(185), 212(67, 185), *217, 220*, 223(82), 226(82), 230(82), 234(84), 236(84, 92, 116), 237(90), 239(10, 82), 241(10, 114, 119), 244(12, 113, 192, 194), 245(11, 13, 194), 246(10, 114), 250(10, 117), 251(113, 195), 252(90, 115), 253(84, 175), *257, 259, 260, 261, 262, 282*, 292(8), *293*, 357(158, 159), 372, 374(157, 158), *389*, 442(103), *456*

Meilman, E., 252, *260*, 430(108a), 451(107), 452(104–107, 108a), 453(106, 107), *456*

Meites, J., 213(110, 111, 112, 115), 214(110), *218, 219*

Melendez, L., 383(100), *387*

Meli, A., 199(96, 97), 200(96), *218*

Melville, J. A., 480(49), *483*

Melvin, K. E. W., 274(41), *277*

Mendez, R., 395(1), 409(1), 412(1), *424*

Mendlowitz, J., 271(42), *277*

Mendlowitz, M., 33(176, 177, 178), 34, 47(138), *61, 62*, 412, 416, *426*, 460(183), *486*

Meneeley, G. R., 91, *112, 113*

Menhard, E. M., 45(200), 46(200), *63*

Menin, J., 201(121), *218*

Mennin, J., 135(106), *168*

Menon, G. N., 185(55), *188*

Mensendick, R., 422(54), *425*

Menziani, E., 227, 228(121), *260*

Merker, H. J., 461(132), *485*

Merrill, J. P., 47, *63*, 453(101), *456*

Merrillees, N. C. R., 206, *216*

Metcalf, B. H., 223(77), *259*

Metz, E. N., 479(184), *486*

Meves, H., 430(108), 450(108), 451(108), *456*

Meyer, R., 374(157), *389*

Meyerson, B. J., 214(113), *218*

Miasnikov, A. L., 20, *63*

Michaelson, J. K., 273(3), 274(3, 4), *276*

Michajlyszyn, V., 200(140), 203(140), *219*

Michalek, R., 360(87a), *387*

Michel, H. L., 39, *59*

Michel, R., 141(138), *149*

Miescher, K., 280(30), 282, *294*, 340(161), 357(245), 358(245), 360(245), *389, 392*

Miknius, S., 117(128), 118(128), 121(128), 137(128), *148*

Milani, C., 341(152), *389*

Mille, E., 357(44), *385*

Miller, C. E., 341(222), *391*
Miller, D. L., 228(208), *262*
Miller, F. M., 198, *218*
Miller, G. J., 9(90), *60*, 87(49), 91(48), 103(49), 104(49), *110*
Miller, J., 479(90), *426*
Miller, J. H., 39, *63*
Miller, J. P., 409(100), 410(100), *426*
Miller, S. I., 8(186), *63*, 451(114), *456*
Millerschoen, N. R., 323(36), *329*
Mills, E. J., 237, *261*
Mills, J., 335, 338(165), 340(162), 353, *389*
Milne, M. D., 122(46), 125(46), *146*, 325, 326, 327(24), *328*, *329*, 409(4), 423(4), *424*, 471(2), 477(40), *482*, *483*
Milnes, F. J., 348(64), 349(64), *386*
Misiti, D., 341(166), *389*
Missala, K., 154(57), *188*
Mitchell, R. H., 375(167), *389*
Mitchell, T. F., 165(3), *186*, 398(10), *424*
Mitchelson, F., 478(23), *482*
Mitchner, H., 432(109), *456*
Miyahara, M., 415(108), *426*
Mizgala, H., 271, *277*
Mizuno, H., 213(115), *218*
Mizzoni, R. H., 126(100), 127(100), 130(100, 101), 134(101), 140(89), *147*, *148*, 298(40), *329*
Moe, G. K., *293*, 371(168), *389*, 408(108), *484*
Moe, R. A., 117(90), 118(90), 120(90), 137(1, 90), *145*, *147*, 395(156), 397(156), 413(156), 415(156), *428*, 474(1), 475(1), 476(1), *482*
Moed, H. D., 201(89, 90), 203(89), *218*
Möhrle, H., 432(110), *456*
Moeschlin, S., 254, *260*
Moger, J. H., 264(43), *277*
Mohler, E. R., 254, *260*
Mohr, F. L., 276(36), *277*
Moister, F. C., 378(74), *386*
Molina, A. F., 250(51), *258*
Moll, M., 227(19), *258*
Monro, A. M., 138(5), 139(91), 144(4), *145*, *147*
Monroe, K. E., 465(109), *485*
Montanari, R., 213(116), *218*
Montuschi, E., 139(93), 141(92), *147*, 474(110), *485*

Moore, K. E., 253, *260*
Moore, P. E., 375, *389*
Moore-Jones, D., 239, *260*
Morales-Aguilera, A., 380, 381, *390*
Moran, J. F., 180, 182(98), *188*, *189*
Moran, N. C., 365, 370(171), 374(154), 379, *389*, *390*, *392*
Morgan, K. J., 430(111), 431(111), *456*
Morgenstern, L., 465(111), *485*
Morozovitch, P., 432(116), 433(116, 117), 434(116, 117), 435(116), *456*
Morren, H. G., 355, 372(172), *390*
Morris, J. A., 252(127), *260*
Morris, J. J., Jr., 381(253), *392*
Morris, M. J., 194(148), 197(148), *219*
Morris, R. C., 182(13), *187*
Morris, R. E., 73, *113*
Morris, R. E., Jr., 31, *63*
Morrison, A. S., 122(129), *148*
Morrison, B., 8(184), 9(184), *63*
Morrison, D. E., 353(224), *391*
Morrison, R. B. I., 464(157), *486*
Morrissey, J., 465(27), *482*
Morrow, A. G., 211(37), *216*
Morrow, J. D., 238(146), *261*
Morton-Jenkins, D., 477(58), *483*
Mosey, L., 441(112), *456*
Mosher, L. R., 185(59), *188*
Mosimann, W., 436(9), 441(9), 443(9), 444(9), 445(9, 33), 446(9), 448(9), *454*
Mottram, F. R., 26(51), *59*
Moulton, R., 33, *63*, 123(23), *146*
Mountain, C. F., 447, 449, *457*
Moyer, J. H., 8(186), *63*, 182(8), 183(65), *187*, *188*, 224, 254, *258*, *260*, 270, *276*, 326(18, 41, 42, 43), *328*, *329*, 373(172a), 376, *387*, *390*, 398(20), 410(21), 415(19, 21), 419(21), *424*, 451(14, 113, 114), 452(113), 453(18), *454*, *456*, 460(12), 462(56), 463(12), 472(13), *482*, *483*
Muehrcke, R. C., 325(37), 326(39), *329*
Mueller, F., 375(173), *390*
Müller, H., 211(22), *216*
Mueller, J. M., 103(131), *113*, 192(117), 194(118), 195(118), *218*
Müller, W., 285(22), *293*
Muggleton, D. F., 325(44), 326(14), *328*, *329*, 461(41), *483*
Muirhead, E. E., 47(105), *61*, 82(67), 111, 82(132, 133), *113*

Mull, R. P., 126(99, 100), 127(100, 102), 129(97a), 130(85), 131, 132(94, 97), 134(94, 97), 137(96), 139(95), 140(89), 141(8), *145, 147, 148,* 227(131a, 131b), *260,* 270(39), *277,* 354, 355, 356, *390*
Mullen, J. O., 251(132), *260*
Muller, G., 197(119), *218, 220*
Muller, R., 357(158, 159), 374(158), *389*
Mulrow, P. J., 30, 31, *63,* 182(33), 183(33), *187*
Munoz, J. M., 69(20), 71(19), 72(19), *110*
Murase, Y., 432(148), *457*
Murphey, R. S., 202(100), *218*
Murphree, O. D., 477(133), *485*
Murphy, E. A., 9(189), *63,* 326(16), *328*
Murphy, G. F., 173(100), 180, 182(98), 184(101), 185(1, 100, 102), 186(60, 100), *186, 188, 189*
Murray, J. R., 253(125), *260*
Musacchio, J., 420(52, 90), *425, 426*
Muscholl, E., 119(79), *147,* 184(63), 185, *188,* 208(120), *218,* 415(109, 110), 420(111), *426, 427,* 464(99), *484*
Myers, G. S., 430(21), 432(116), 433(116, 117), 434(116, 117), 435(116), 452(20, 21, 115), 453(20), *454, 456*

N

Nádor, K., 124(43, 44), *146,* 281(20, 31), 282(20, 31), 288, *293, 294,* 306, *328*
Naftchi, N. E., 460(183), *486*
Naftchi, N. N., 33(176, 177, 178), 34(179), *62*
Nagarajan, K., 404(68), *425*
Nagatsu, T., 156(112), *189*
Nager, F., 182(86), *188,* 254, *260*
Najer, H., 132(103), 135(60, 106), 139(104), *146, 148,* 201, *218,* 358, *390*
Nakagawa, K., 20, *64*
Nakamoto, S., 50(144), *62*
Nakashima, M., 91(45), 105(46), *110*
Nakazawa, F., 129(107), *148*
Nambury, C. N. V., 125(10), *145*
Napoli, M. D., 287(34), *294*
Narayanan, C. R., 430(118), 431(118), 432(118), 437(93), *456*
Nardi, D., 357(44), *385*
Nash, H. A., 433(119), *456*
Natarajan, S., 473(112), *485*

Natoff, I. L., 143(9), *145*
Nauta, W. T., 199, *219*
Navarro, A., 296(62), 317(62), 318(62), 323(62), 326(62), *329*
Neeman, M., 431(82), *455*
Neil, E., 442(120), *456*
Neilson, G. H., 326(16), *328*
Nelson, K. L. R., 305(10), *328*
Nelson, R. A., 29(190), *63*
Nerdel, F., 299, 309, *328*
Nesbit, R. M., 30(43), *59,* 465(29), *482*
Neuburger, F., 42, *59*
Neumann, C., 33(35, 191), 34(35, 191), *59, 63*
Neumann, F. W., 126(132), *148*
Neumann, M., 479(113), *485*
Newell, D. J., 383(231), *391*
Newman, M., 197(18), *216*
Newton, M., 255(134), *260*
Ngai, S. H., 445(159), *457*
Nichols, J., 90(178), *114*
Nickerson, M., 116(108), *148,* 344, 345(183), 347, 349, 350(183), 351(183), 352, 368(176), 369(178, 180, 183), 370(176), 371(179, 181, 184), 373(176), 376(180), 377(176), 379(106), *387, 390*
Nicoll, C. S., 213(112), *218*
Niemegeers, C. J. E., 342(185), *390*
Nieschulz, O., 357, *390*
Nikodijevic, B., 405(63), *425*
Nillson, J., 207(34), 208(34), *216*
Nober, G., 305(28), *328*
Nobles, W. L., 204, *216*
Noelpp, B., 103(71), *111,* 246(83), *259*
Nogradi, T., 199, 201, *218*
Noll, L., 452(158), *457*
Nolla-Panades, J., 27, 31, 37, *63,* 93(134), *113*
Nomaguchi, G. M., 369(177), 371(184), *390*
Nommensen, E. W., 132, *147*
Norris, A. H., 42, *63*
North, J. D. K., 182(43), *187,* 274(41), *277*
Norton, S., 296, 297, *329*
Norwood, W. C., 440(121), 442(121), 453(121), *457*
Nouvel, G., 139(68), *147*
Novack, P., 183(65), *188*
Novak, L., 200(139), *219*
Nowaczynski, W., 30(93), *60*
Nüsser, E., 445(7), *454*

Nugent, R. H., 194(188), *220*
Nuhfer, P. A., 165(3), *186*, 398(10), *424*
Numerof, P., 433(37), *454*
Nungesser, W. C., 442(122), *457*
Nussbaum, H. E., 327(47), *329*
Nusser, E., 357(156), *389*
Nuzum, F. R., 40, *60*
Nye, E. R., 20, *63*, 423(77), *426*, 471(75), 472(75), *484*
Nyman, E., 465(98), *484*

O

Oates, J. A., 106, *113*, 153(64), 173(64), 182(34, 64), *187*, *188*, 413(129), 423 (112), *427*, 472(114), 473(62), *483*, *485*
O'Brien, K. P., 182(43), *187*
Ocampo, J., 285(2), *293*
O'Connor, J. M., 194(151), *219*
Oda, T., 436(123), *457*
O'Dell, T. B., 287(15), *293*, *294*
O'Donovan, D. G., 129(126), *148*
Oerting, H., 39, *59*
Ogden, E., 24, 46, *63*, 79(113)
Ogg, J., 373(211), *391*
Ohtsuki, I., 132(109), *148*
Okamoto, K., 19(199), *63*
Okaya, Y., 193(129), *219*
Okun, R., 271(49), *277*, 467(115), *485*
O'Leary, G. L., 441(44, 45), *454*
Oliver, J., 465(80), *484*
Oliver, M. F., 480(116), *485*
Olmsted, F., 76(37), *110*
Olsen, N. S., 45, 46, *63*
O'Malley, W. E., 287, *294*
Onda, M., 201, *218*
O'Neill, G. Q., 326(61), *329*
O'Neill, J. R., 452(115), *456*
Onesti, G., 183(65), *188*, 254(28), *258*, 398(20), 410(21), 415(21), 419(21), *424*, 472(13), *482*
Oram, S., 381(243), *392*, 480(117), *485*
O'Rear, H. B., 373(96), *387*
Orgain, E. S., 373(62), 381(86), 383(86), *386*, *387*
Orser, M., 237, *259*
Orsingher, O., 342(36), *385*
Orvis, H. H., 413(113, 114), *427*, 472(118), *485*

Osborne, M. W., 102(118), *112*, 209(108, 109), *218*, 285(28), *294*
Overy, H., 380(249), *392*
Owen, D. A. L., 384(184), *390*
Ozaki, M., 106(52), *110*, 183(35), *187*
Ozawa, H., 132(109), *148*

P

Paasonen, M. K., 209(125), *218*, 414(59), *425*
Pádr, Z., 131(69), *147*
Page, E. W., 46(198), *63*
Page, I. H., 9(172), 14(66), 21(201), 28(116), 45(173), 46(173), 48, 49(171), 51(160), *60*, *61*, *62*, *63*, 68(137), 71(89, 95), 72 (166), 73(121), 75(137, 179, 180), 76 (122), 78, 79(121), 84(121), 85, 86(114), 88, 90(115), 93, 100, 104(113, 141), *111*, *112*, *113*, *114*, 122(65), 127(110), 131(110), *147*, *148*, 210, 215(44), *216*, *218*, 223, 250, 254, *260*, *261*, 380(249), *392*, 402(115), *427*, 462(47), 475(119), *483*, *485*
Pai, B. R., 404(68), *425*
Pain, D. L., 284(24), *294*
Paintal, A. S., 440(124), *457*
Paladini, A. C., 25(205), *59*, *63*, 73, *113*
Palazzo, G., 198(126), *218*, 361(50), *386*
Palkoski, Z. M., 117(90), 118(90), 120(90), 137(90), *147*
Palm, D., 207(8, 9), *215*
Palmer, A. J., 8(206), 9(206), *63*
Palmer, H., 471(120), *485*
P'An, S. Y., 105(169), *114*, 357(118), *388*
Pandow, M. L., 195(159), 196(187), *219*, *220*
Pandya, K. C., 158(66), *188*
Pandya, L. J., *456*
Panish, J. F., 465(111), *485*
Panisset, J. C., 79(117), *112*
Pantridge, J. F., 480(116), *485*
Papineau-Couture, G., 432(116), 433(116, 117), 434(116, 117), 435(116), *456*
Paquette, L. A., 144(111), *148*
Parcell, R. F., 353, *390*
Pardo, E. G., 290(3, 36), *293*, *294*, 355(206), *391*, 415(144), *427*
Parkinson, J., 324, *329*
Parks, L. M., 432(109, 146), *456*, *457*

Parratt, J. R., 381, 382(189), *390*
Parry, E. H. O., 274(14), *276*, 466(42), *483*
Parsons, V., 467(121), *485*
Pasini, C., 132(34), *146*
Paton, B., 380(249), *392*
Paton, W. D. M., 68, *113*, 129(81, 112, 113), *147*, *148*, 280, 289, *293*, *294*
Patrick, R. W., 399(8), *424*
Paul, B., 202, *218*
Paulsen, A., 335(75, 77), *386*, *387*
Paulsen, E. C., 208(127), *218*
Paulsen, L., 363(16), *385*
Paulson, S. F., 296(3), 324(3), *328*
Paykel, E. S., 471(122), 473(122), *485*
Payne, J. P., 324, *329*, 383(191), *390*
Pearce, M. L., 395(104), 398(104), 410(104), *426*
Pears, M. A., 254(149), *261*, 460(126), 474(126), *485*
Peart, W. S., 21(207), 26(51), *59*, *63*, 72, 76, *110*, *113*, 123(114), 139(114), *148*, 474(123), *485*
Peaston, M. J. T., 185(67), *188*
Pedersen, J. G. A., 284(17), *293*, 301(54), 302(54), *329*
Peets, E. A., 206(167), *220*
Pelikan, E. W., 285(48), *294*
Pelletier, S. W., 432(125), *457*
Peltola, P., 466(124), *485*
Penn, R. G., 212(128), *219*
Pennes, H. H., 399(116), *427*
Pentecost, B. L., 467(43), *483*
Peoples, S. A., 130(122a), *148*
Pepinski, R., 193(129), *219*
Percori-Giraldi, J., 341(81), *387*
Pereira, J. N., 117(128), 118(128), 121(128), 137(127, 128), *148*
Perera, G. A., 18(91, 242), *60*, *64*
Perkins, M. E., 370(171), 379, *390*
Perry, H. M., 235(137, 138), 236(138, 143, 147), 237(143, 144, 147), 238(138, 139, 143, 145, 146, 172), 239(141), 255(140, 145), *260*, *261*
Perry, W. L. M., 290, 291(39), *293*, *294*
Persch, W., 231(148), *261*
Peterfalvi, M., 197(198), *220*
Peters, G., 26(108), 27(108, 224), *61*, *64*, 78(73), *111*
Peters, G. A., 377(108), *387*
Peterson, L. H., 31, *63*, 75(92), *112*

Peterson, W. G., 287(42), *294*
Petracek, F. J., 433(61–64), 434(61–64), 435(62), *455*
Petrovanu, M., 128(145), *149*, 226(210), *262*
Pettinger, W., 464(125), *485*
Pfeifer, A. K., 184(69), *188*
Pfeiffer, J. B., 34, 63
Pfister, K., III, 153(103), 161(103), *189*, 298 (60), 299(64), 302(64), *329*
Phelan, E. L., 9, 16(260), 18(259), 19(259), 263), 43, 44(211), 45, *63*, *64*
Philippu, A., 185, *188*
Philips, A. P., 129, *148*
Philips, N. V., 137(115), *148*
Phillips, A. P., 296, 297, *329*
Pickens, P. T., 141(92), *147*
Pickering, G., 13(226), 17, 23, 26(51), 38, 39, 40, 46, 49, 53(212–214), *59*, *63*, *64*, 69, 74, 77(147), 81, 92, *110*, *113*, 254, *261*, 460(126), 474(126), *485*
Pierre, G. D., 477(85), *484*
Pigeon, G., 255(150), *261*
Pilkington, T. R. E., 383(7), 384, *390*
Pines, K. L., 40(96), *61*
Pinner, A., 126, *148*
Pircio, A., 450(126), *457*
Pircio, A. W., 318, *329*
Pirelli, A. M., 361(1), *384*
Pittinger, W. A., 184(68), *188*
Pivnicki, D., 185(102), *189*
Platt, R., 8(218), 9(217), 17, 63
Pletscher, A., 175(12), 177(71, 72), 178(72), 179(12), 182(11), *187*, *188*, 205, *219*, 393, 398(158), 402(22), 415(117), 418 (121), *424*, *427*, *428*
Plieninger, H., 199, *219*
Plummer, A. J., 100(120), 101(119), 102 (118), 103(151), 104(152), 105(7), *112*, *113*, 117(87), 118(87), 126(99), 127 (86, 88), 130(85), 141(8), *145*, *147*, *148*, 192, 193(158), 196, 197(149, 157), 198 (132), 199, 206(135, 167, 168), 209 (108, 109), 210, 211, *218*, *219*, *220*, 227 (131a), 246, 248(151), *260*, *261*, 270 (39), *277*, 285(28, 41), *294*, 296, 298 (51), *329*
Pocelinko, R., 137(1), *145*, 474(1), 475(1), 476(1), *482*
Poethke, W., 430, 433(127, 128), *457*

Pogrund, R. S., 152(16), 173(16), 179(73), *187, 188*
Pokorny, D., 360(87a), *387*
Pollack, P. J., 472(127), *485*
Pollak, H., 264(40), *277*
Pollard, C. B., 353, *390*
Polonovski, M., 152(74), *188*
Popelak, A., 195(62, 136), 196(136 138), 197(137), *217, 219*
Popendiker, K., 357(186), *390*
Porter, C. C., 106(191), *114*, 168(77), 173(75), 175(78), 176(77), 177(77, 78), 178(77, 78), 179, 181, 184(77, 107), 185(77), 186(75), *188, 189*, 398(122), *427*, 476(163), *486*
Porter, G. A., 477(128), *485*
Porter, M., 405(136), *427*
Potter, G. W. H., 138(5), *145*
Potter, L. T., 209(68), 210(68), *217*
Poulsen, E., 284(18), *293*
Poulter, G. A., 177(25), *178*(25), *187*
Pound, E., 446(130), 448(130), *457*
Poutasse, E. F., 50(144), *62*
Povalski, H., 100(120), *112*, 117(87), 118(87), 127(86), *147*, 246(7), *257*
Powell, C. E., 365, 379, *390*
Pozzati, C., 198(126), *218*
Prance, A. J., Jr., 184(54), *188*
Prelog, V., 430(59), 431(59), *455*
Prichard, B. N. C., 382, 383(7, 85), *384, 387, 390*, 480(129), *485*
Prichard, M. M. L., 23(49), *59*
Priestley, J. T., 373(139), *388*
Prinzmetal, M., 71, 77, 81, *113*
Pritchard, W. H., 79, *112*
Prockop, D., 402(134), *427*
Proosdij-Hartzema, E. G. van, 78, 100(155), 102(155), *113*
Protiva, M., 196(46), 197(48, 49), 200(196), 201, 203, *216, 219, 220*, 284(10), *293*, 317, *329*
Przic, R., 185(104), *189*
Pulewka, P., 323, *329*
Pulido, P., 395(1), 409(1), 412(1), *424*

Q

Quan, R. B. F., 137(25), *146*, 409(27, 28), 410(28), 413(28), *424*, 472(21), *482*

Quan, R. G., 271(8), *276*
Quinn, L., 90(28), 103(28), *110*
Quinton, R. M., 214(142), *219*
Quniquaud, A., 447(16), *454*

R

Raab, W., 39(219, 220), 40, 41, *63*
Räf, L., 465(98), *484*
Rafferty, J. A., 39, *58*
Raftos, J., 327(13), *328*
Rahier, J. P., 20, *63*
Rahn, K. H., 367(138), *388*
Rajagopalan, S., 431(82), *455*
Rajsner, M., 317(52), *329*
Ramirez, L., 290(3), *293*
Rand, M. J., 184(20, 21), 185(19), *187*, 418, 419, *424, 425*, 464(37, 38), 475(36), *483*
Randall, L. O., 287(42), *294*, 362(115), 375, 376(198), *388, 390*, 395(156), 397(156), 413(156), 415(156), *428*
Rapela, C. E., 341(200), *390*
Rapoport, C., 252(120), *260*
Raskin, M., 214(146), *219*
Raskin, N. H., 255(152), *261*
Rathbun, R. C., 335, 338(165), *389*
Rathke, B., 129, *148*
Raths, O., 354(123), *388*
Ratner, A., 213, *219*
Ratouis, R., 204, *219*, 353(29), 355(201), 356, *385, 390*
Rau, G. C., 21(223), *63*
Reading, H. W., 132(76), *147*, 296(31), 307(31), 325(44), *328, 329*
Reardon, M. J., 374(95), 375(95, 112), *387, 388*
Redfield, B. G., 398(143), *427*
Redleaf, P. D., 80, 105(156), *113, 114*
Redlich, F. K., 40, 41, *63*
Reedy, W. J., 375(202), *390*
Regan, N. A., 475(46), *483*
Regnier, G., 199(29), *216*
Regoli, D., 27, *64*, 81(164), *113*
Reichel, G., 153(23), 184(23), *187*
Reid, J. D., 175(79), 185(79), *188*
Reid, N. C. R. W., 471(130), *485*
Reilly, J., 129(126), *148*
Reilly, J. F., 212(30), *216*

Reinert, H., 117(40, 75), 118(40, 75), 121(40, 75), 139(40), 144(75), *146, 147,* 208(145), *219,* 291(39), *294,* 413(43), 415(43), 419(44), *425*
Reinhold, D., 162(108), *189,* 298(60), 299(64), 302(64), 326(60), *329*
Reit, E., 30, *62*
Reiter, M., 439(129), *457*
Relman, A. S., 465(131), *485*
Remmer, H., 461(132), *485*
Rennick, B. R., 371(168), *389*
Renzi, A. A., 9(90), *60,* 87(49), 89(50), 91(48, 50), 103(49), 104(49), 105, *110, 113,* 212(53a, 54), 213(53a, 54), 214(53), *216, 217*
Renzi, L., 338(150), 339(150), 341(152), *389*
Resnekov, L., 480(117), *485*
Resnick, O., 214, *219*
Restall, P. A., 9(225), *64*
Reubi, F., 104(159), *113,* 223, 254, 255, *261*
Reynolds, G. A., 229, *261*
Reyntjens, A. M., 355(172), 372(172), *390*
Ribbens, C., 199, *219*
Rice, L. M., 285, 287(35), *293, 294*
Richard, L., 271, *277*
Richards, A. B., 446(1), *453*
Richards, A. N., 244(49), *258*
Richards, V., 212(95), *218,* 380, 381, 384, *388*
Richardson, A. P., 250(197), *262,* 373(250), 374, *390, 392,* 446(130), 448, *457*
Richardson, A. W., 373(204), 375(169), *389, 390*
Richardson, D. W., 13, *64,* 131(120), *148,* 273(12), *276,* 467(35), *483*
Richardson, H. L., 477(133), *483*
Richardson, P. N., 404(3), 409(3), 412(3), *424*
Richter, H., 444(58), *455*
Richter, W., 284(18), *293*
Rieben, P. A., 444(133), *457*
Riedel, B. E., 207(105), 212(104), *218*
Rigby, B., 25(227), *64*
Rinaldi, F. U., 405(50), 409(50), 413(50), *425*
Ringier, B. H., 224(55), 226(55), 227(55), 228(55), 229(55), *259*
Riniker, B., 72(160), *113*
Rinsler, M. G., 25(227), *64*

Rittel, W., 72, *113*
Roberts, B. J., 403(102), *426*
Roberts, G., 373(204), *390*
Roberts, J., 212(30), *216,* 381, *391*
Roberts, S. D., 480(116), *485*
Robertson, C. W., 39, *64,* 418(131), *427*
Robertson, E., 8(38), *59*
Robertson, J. E., 132(121), *148*
Robertson, J. I. S., 25(31, 32, 33, 156), 28(30), 31(32), *59, 62,* 76(111), 81(111), *112*
Robinson, B. F., 383(7, 58a, 192, 193), *384, 386, 390*
Robinson, J. S., 383(226), *391*
Robinson, K. C., 373(110), *387*
Robinson, P. R., 31(183), *63,* 73(130), *113*
Robinson, S. C., 11(228), *64*
Robison, M. M., 194(148), 197(148, 149, 150), *219*
Robson, A. O., 466(134), *485*
Robson, R. D., 141(19), *146*
Rochelle, J. B., 268(20), *276*
Rockhold, W. T., 362(25, 26), *385*
Rodbard, S., 91(109), *112, 113*
Rodriguez, R., 355(206), *391*
Roe, A. M., 137(55), 138(6), *145, 146,* 343(13), 344(13), *385*
Roe, M. D., 376(198), *390*
Roetz, F. W., 266(29), *277*
Rogers, B. H., 440(72), *455*
Rogers, M. B., 8(44), *59*
Rogers, M. P., 375(207), *391*
Rogers, S. T., 255(4), *257*
Roh, C. E., 40(96), *61*
Romano, A., 252(72), *259*
Romero, J. C., 25(72), *60,* 73(41), *110*
Rondell, P. A., 79, *113*
Rønnov-Jessen, V., 8(229), *64*
Rooney, C. S., 398(122), *427*
Roquet, J., 230(6), *257*
Rorie, M., 209(83), *217*
Rorig, K. J., 362(208), *391*
Rosas, R. B., 25, *64*
Rose, E. K., 202(100), *218*
Rose, J. C., 445(131), *457*
Rose, M. J., 421(38), *425*
Rosen, D. B., 436(161), *457*
Rosen, W. E., 194(151), *219,* 285(44), *294*
Rosenblueth, A., 98(25), *110,* 440(2), 441(131a), *453, 457*

Rosenblum, W., 211(152), *219*
Rosengren, E., 207(34), 208(34), *216*
Rosenheim, M. L., 8(110, 232, 233), *61*, *64*, 123(23), *146*, 288(11), *293*, 383(7), *384*, 475(93), *484*
Rosenthal, M. E., 340(209), *391*
Rosnati, V., 341(166), *389*
Ross, C. A., 106(191), *114*, 184(107), *189*
Ross, E. J., 373(110), *387*
Ross, S. D., 101(119), 102(118), *112*, 127(88), *147*, 209(108, 109), *218*
Rossi, E., 255, *261*
Rossi, G. V., 246(76), *259*, 340, *391*
Rossum, J. M. van, 473(135, 136), *485*
Roston, E. H., 264(40), *277*
Roth, G. J., 373(211), *391*
Roth, G. M., 39(297), 40(109), 41, *61*, *65*, 373(83, 139), *387*, *388*
Roth, H. R., 367(87), *387*
Roth, L. W., 353, *391*
Rothballer, A. B., 23(300), *65*
Rothlin, E., 288(45), *294*, 376(212, 213), 377(212), 379(46, 213), *386*, *391*, 441(67), *455*
Rothman, S., 45(*64*
Rouaix, A., 230(101), 231(101), 232(101), *260*
Rousseau, P., 472(114), *485*
Rowe, G. G., 324, 325(37), 326(39), *329*
Rowe, R. P., 394, *427*
Rowlands, D. J., 383, 384(214), *391*
Rowley, E. M., 68(171), 86(171), *114*
Roy, P., 26(92), 31(92), *60*
Rubin, B., 446(132), 448, *457*
Rubinstein, K., 301, 302(54), *329*
Rucinschi, E., 128(145), *149*, 226(210), *262*
Ruffell, G. K., 140(17), 141(140), *145*, *149*, 399(18), *424*
Ruggieri, R., 227(159), 235, *261*
Rule, C., 48, *61*, 82, *111*
Rundles, R. W., 479(137, 184), *485*, *486*
Russek, H. I., 38, 39, *64*
Russell, R. P., 467(115), *485*
Russo, H. F., 273(3), 274(3, 4), *276*, 296(3), 324(3), *328*
Rutledge, A. H., 375(167), *389*
Rutledge, R., 105(7), *109*, 246(7), *257*
Ruyle, W. V., 299(64), 302(64), *329*
Ruzhentseva, A. K., 235(161), *261*

Rylski, L., 227(17, 19, 20), 228(17), 229(17), *258*

S

Sachnazazova, N. G., 253(105), *260*
Saffran, M., 213(153), *219*
Sah, H. J., 130, *148*
Sah, P. P. T., 130(122a), *148*
Sahyun, M., 357, *386*
Saint Cyr, S., 182(98), 185(102), *189*
Saint Jean, A., 185(80), *188*
Saji, E., 422(88), *426*
Salaman, A. M., 398(48), *425*
Salisbury, P. F., 444(133), *457*
Samaan, N. A., 467(43), *483*
Samet, B., 85, *110*
Samuels, S. S., 365(127), *388*
Sancetta, S. M., 29(237), *64*
Sanderson, P. H., 26(51), *59*
Sandor, T., 30(93), *60*
Sandri, G. C., 235(162), *261*
Sankoff, I., 185(102), *189*
Sannerstedt, R., 182(81), 183(82), *188*
Sano, I., 253(163), *261*
Sanpei, N., 432(148), *457*
Sapirstein, L. A., 91(163), *113*
Saravis, C. A., 82(108), *112*
Sarret, P., 308(20), *328*
Sasahara, A. A., 465(109), *485*
Sasamoto, M., 201(124), *218*
Sassa, K., 7(238), *64*
Sastry, B. V. R., 202, *219*
Sato, S., 233(66), *259*
Saunders, F. J., 86(61), *111*
Saunders, J. P., 256(5), *257*
Saville, S., 8(239), *64*
Sawyer, C. H., 213(77, 78, 155), *217*, *219*
Scaduto, L., 395(104), 398(104), 410(104), *426*
Scannel, J. G., 452(115), *456*
Scarff, R. W., 84(99), *112*
Schaechtelin, G., 26(108), 27(108), *61*, 78(73), 81, *111*, *113*
Schaer, H., 182(86), 184(83), *188*
Schafer, H., 440(134), *457*
Schalch, W., 467(55), *483*
Schales, O., 152, *188*
Schales, S. S., 152, *188*
Schaper, W. K. A., 245(164), *261*, 342(215), *391*

Schapira, G., 152(74, 85), 173(85), *188*
Schaub, F., 29(292), *65*, 182(86), *188*
Schauer, A., 236(200), 237(200), *262*
Schayer, R. W., 173(87), 185(87), *188*
Scheele, G. A., 31(183), *63*, 73(130), *113*
Schellenberg, H., 360(120), *388*
Schenker, K., 139(123), *148*
Scherrer, P., 372(216), *391*
Scheu, H., 285(46), *294*
Scheuermann, R., 357(186), *390*
Schiele, B. C., 354(123), *388*
Schilling, M., 284(18), *293*
Schindler, W., 357(137, 217), *388, 391*
Schipper, E., 349, *391*
Schlittler, E., 103(131), *113*, 128, 130, *148*,
    191(156), 192(117, 157), 193(158, 205),
    194(101), 195(159), 197(156, 157), *199*,
    218, 219, 220, 225(165), *261*, 284(47),
    294
Schmidt, C. F., 444(5), 445(4), *453*
Schmidt, G., 335, 338, 340(219), *391*
Schmidt, J. L., 145(125), *148*
Schmidt, P., 127(102), 148, 227(131b),
    231(166), 232(167), *260, 261*
Schmitt, H., 230(168), *261*
Schmitt, Hélène, 230(168), *261*
Schmutz, J., 362, *391*
Schnaper, H. W., 394(83), *426*
Schneckloth, R., 14(66), *60*
Schneider, F., 100(120), 101(119), *112*, 117
    (87), 118(87), 127(86), *147*
Schneider, J. A., 105(169), *114*, 193(158,
    205), 209(134), *219, 221*, 285(41), *294*,
    296(51), 298(51), *329*
Schnieden, H., 173(50), 185(50, 88), *188*
Schoenberger, J. A., 465(86), 467(86), *484*
Schoene, H. H., 479(138), *485*
Schoenfeld, C. D., 382(102), *387*
Schoepke, H. G., 107, *113*, 145(125), *148*,
    411(124), 415, *427*
Scholz, C. R., 298(40), *329*
Schott, H. F., 169(89), *188*
Schreibman, M., 341(222), *391*
Schreiner, G. E., 466(104), *484*
Schroeder, H. A., 8(240), 23, 45(200),
    46(200), *63, 64*, 223, 236(143), 237(143,
    144), 238(143, 145, 146, 171, 172),
    255(145), *261*, 263(44), 264(44), *277*,
    394(125), *427*
Schümann, H. J., 185, *188*

Schulenberg, J. W., 355(8), 356(8), *384*
Schuler, W., 234(84), 236(84, 116, 173), 237,
    248(102), 249(174), 253(84, 175), *259*,
    260, 261, 395, *427*
Schulert, A. R., 206(135, 167), *219, 220*,
    230(177), 233(177), 235, 238, 239, *261*
Schulman, L. E., 255(178), *261*
Schultz, E. M., 273, *277*
Schultz, F. B., 270, *277*
Schumann, E. L., 144(83), *147*
Schut, R. N., 354, *387*
Schvartz, N., 137(25), *146*, 409(27, 28),
    410(28), 413(28), *424*, 472(21), *482*
Schwartz, P. L., 236(147), 237(147), *261*
Schwartz, M. S., 271(8), *276*, 409(27, 28),
    410(28), 413(28), *424*, 472(21), *482*
Schwartz, N., 271(8), *276*
Schwartz, W. B., 465(87, 131), *484, 485*
Schwarz, H., 42, *60*, 72, *113*
Schweitzer, M. D., 18(91), *60, 64*
Schwyzer, R., 72(160), *73, 113*
Scornik, O. A., 25(205), *63, 73, 113*
Scott, C. C., 398(36), *425*
Scott, F. L., 129(126), *148*
Scriabine, A., 105, *114*, 117(128), 118(128),
    121(128), 137(127), *148*, 357(118), *388*
Seaton, D. A., 475(139), *485*
Seay, P. H., 403(71), *425*
Sédivy, Z., 284(10), *293*.
Sedvall, G., 210(160), *219*
Seebeck, E., 432(142, 144), 433(143), *457*
Seegmiller, J. E., 479(90), *484*
Sehales, O., 159(38), *187*
Seiden, L. S., 207(161, 162), *219, 220*
Sekine, G., 398(20), *424*
Sekiya, A., 380, *391*, 422(88), *426*
Self, A. D., 126(7), *145*
Seligmann, A. W., 472(114), *485*
Sellar, R. H., 472(13), *482*
Sellers, A. L., 23, *59*
Selman, D., 365(127), *388*
Selye, H., 68, 79, 85, 86, 91, *114*
Semmence, A. M., 273(12), *276*, 467(35), *483*
Sen, G., 192(163), *220*
Senfield, R. M., 383(191), *390*
Sestini, M. G., 478(105), *484*
Sestokas, E., 173(87), 185(87), *188*
Sette, J., 132(103), 135(105), 139(104), *148*
Shabica, A. C., 131, *147*, 285(44), *294*
Shadbolt, R., 398(48), *425*

Shaftel, H., 365(127), *388*
Shalit, I. E., 255(205), *262*
Shamma, M., 196(164, 165, 172), *220*
Shanes, A. M., 439(135, 136), *454*, *457*
Shanker, L. S., 122(129), *148*
Shanks, R. G., 366(28), 379(28), *385*
Shanor, S., 132(26), *146*
Shapero, M., 193(3), 213(3), *215*, 342(65), *386*
Shapiro, A. P., 466(140), *485*
Sharman, D. F., 173(90), 184(90), *188*
Shaw, E., 402(151, 152), 403(153), *428*
Shaw, G., 373(223), *391*
Shchukina, M. N., 225(184, 185), 227, *262*
Shelver, W. H., 341(222), *391*
Shenkin, H. A., 23(300), *65*
Shepard, E. R., 353(224), *391*
Shepherd, D. M., 175(79), 185(79), *188*
Sheppard, H., 105(7), *109*, 119(130), *148*, 197(166), 206(135, 167, 168), *219*, *220*
Sherrill, W. J., 263, 274(1), *276*
Shideman, F. E., 415, *425*
Shimada, A., 193(129), *219*
Shimizu, B., 436(139, 140), *457*
Shine, R. J., 196(165, 172), *220*
Shock, N. W., 42(195), *63*
Shore, P. A., 205(130), 207, 209(175), *216*, *219*, *220*, 236, *258*, 402(22, 23, 134, 142), 415(25, 135), 418(24), 420(41), *424*, *425*, *427*
Short, J. H., 134(131), 144(80), *147*, *148*, 199, *220*
Shriner, R. L., 126(132), *148*
Shulman, L. E., 255(178), *261*
Shumway, N. P., 72(174, 175), *114*
Siddiqui, R. H., 192, *220*
Siddiqui, S., 192, *220*
Sidhu, R. K., 447(100), *456*
Siegmund, E., 349(218), *391*
Sigg, E. B., 206(168), *220*, 476(141), 478(141), *485*
Silberman, H. R., 479(137), *485*
Sim, M. F., 140(17), *145*, 399(18), *424*
Simon, A., 333(31), 337, 339(30), 372, *385*
Simon, H., 448(147), *457*
Simonson, E., 20, *64*
Simpson, F. O., 13(261), 27, *63*, *64*, 460(145), 464(76, 142), 465(144, 146), 466(143), 467(146), 470(155), 475(155), 476(155),

477(155), 479(143, 155), 480(155), *484*, *485*, *486*
Sinclair, K., 327, *329*
Sinn, W., 244(203), *262*
Siphar, S. A., 367(225), *391*
Sitz, H., 305(29), *328*
Sjoerdsma, A., 106(135), *113*, 153(64), 173(64), 182(34, 64), 184(46, 68), *187*, *188*, 398, 409, 412(81, 128), 413(113), 418(80), 422, 423(82), *425*, *426*, *427*, 464(125), 471(84), 473(62), *483*, *484*, *485*
Sjöqvist, F., 471(147), *485*
Skeggs, L. T., 72, 77(74), *111*, *114*
Skelton, F. R., 36(244), *64*, 89, 90(178), *114*
Skinner, S. L., 75, *114*, 211, 221
Skom, J. H., 73(199), *114*
Slack, R., 284(24), *294*
Slater, I. H., 338(165), 365, 379, *389*, *390*
Sletzinger, M., 161(92), 162(7, 108), 163(6, 92), 175(92), 181(92), 184(92), *186*, *189*, 298(60), 299(64), 302(64), 326(60), *329*
Slimane-Taleb, S., 213(58), *217*
Sloman, G., 383(226), *391*
Small, J. L., 466(140), *485*
Smilo, R. P., 479(148), *485*
Smirk, F. H., 6, 7(252), 8(123, 248, 249, 251, 255), 9(123, 225, 248, 249, 255), 10(246, 247, 249), 11(249), 12, 13(251, 254, 261, 262, 264, 287), 14(245, 249), 15(4, 262), 16(254, 260), 17, 18(249, 256, 259, 287), 19(247, 249, 250, 259, 263), 20(254, 258), 21(254), 23(247), 24(152, 254), 29, 33(64), 35, 36, 37(152), 38, 39(249), 41(249), 43(211), 44(211, 254), 45(211), 47(254), 50(249, 254), 51, 53(246, 247, 249), 56, *58*, *60*, *61*, *62*, *63*, *64*, *65*, 69, 74, 82, 85, 92(105), 93(134, 185), 94, 109, *112*, *113*, *114*, 141(133), *148*, 254, *262*, 326(56), 317, 326(56), 327, *329*, 460 (145, 149, 152), 462(150, 154, 156), 463 (150), 464(157), 470(155), 475(155), 476 (155), 477(45, 151, 155), 479(153, 155), 480(155), *483*, *485*, *486*
Smith, A. H., 209(50), *216*
Smith, A. J., 478(94), *484*
Smith, C. B., 475(158), *486*
Smith, C. M., 285, *294*
Smith, E., 195(73), 196(172), *217*, *220*
Smith, J. L., 186(10), *187*
Smith, K. S., 8(265, 266), *64*

Smith, L. H., 366(28), 379(28), *385*
Smith, R. W., 252(127), *260*
Smith, S. E., 173(90), 183, 184(90), *188*, *189*
Smith, T. H., 375, *390*
Smith, T. H. F., 340(209), *391*
Smith, W. M., 462(159), *486*
Smithwick, R. H., 8(268), 39, *64*, *65*, 95, 97, *114*, 418, *427*
Snavely, J. R., 86(101), *112*
Snow, P. J. D., 383, *391*
Snyder, H., 451(114), *456*
Snyder, H. R., 403, *427*
Soffer, L., 476(141), 478(141), *485*
Sogo, Y., 193(129), *219*
Sokabe, H., 82, *114*
Soloff, L. A., 472(166), *486*
Somers, K., 325(37), 326(39), *329*
Sonn, A., 357, *391*
Sonnenschein, R. R., 371(229), *391*
Soper, Q. F., 338(162), 340(162), *389*
Sors, C., 48(285), *65*
Sourkes, T. L., 106, *114*, 151, 152(95), 154(57), 156(97), 166(95), 167(95), 168(95, 96, 99), 169(95, 96), 171(95), 173(100), 174, 180, 181(91), 182(98), 184(101), 185(1, 91, 100, 102), *186*(60, 100), *188*, *189*
Sowton, G. E., 383(100), *387*
Spears, G. F., 464(76), *484*
Spector, S., 184(68), *188*, 402(127), 415(25, 135), 418(24), 422(98), *424*, *426*, *427*, 464(125), *485*
Spector, W. G., 402(133), *427*
Spencer, A. G., 33(185), *63*
Spencer, J. N., 405, *427*
Spencer, M. P., 369(230), *391*
Sperber, R. J., 466(160), 479(161), *486*
Speth, O. C., 186(10), *187*
Spickett, R. G. W., 143(9), *145*
Spiegel, H. E., 117(42), *146*
Spingler, A., 195(62, 136), 196(136), *217*, *219*
Spink, W. W., 252(196), *262*
Spinks, A., 102(189), *114*, 132(134), *148*, 296, 305, 319, 324, *329*
Spittel, J. A., Jr., 266(47), *277*
Sprague, J. M., 273(45), *277*, 398(122), *427*
Sprengeler, E. P., 165(3), *186*, 398(10), *424*
Spühler, O., 285(46), *294*, 437(169), 451 (169), 452(141), 453(169), *457*, *458*

Spurr, C. L., 8(83), *60*
Srivastava, S. C., 383, *391*
Stachenko, J., 90(51), *110*
Stämpfli, R., 290(49), *294*
Stamey, T. A., 22, *65*
Stanbury, S. W., 8(218), *63*
Stanfield, C. A., 29(301), *65*
Stanton, H. C., 100, 105, 106, *141*, 365, *391*
Stanton, J. R., 29(86), *60*, 378(74), *386*, 452(36), *454*
Stark, D. C. C., 471(162), *486*
Stark, I., 137(1), *145*
Starke, H., 225(180), *262*
Staub, H., 254, *262*
Staunton, H. P., 373(240), 374(240), *391*
Stavorski, J., 299(64), 302(64), *329*
Stavorski, J. M., 476(163), *486*
Steele, J. M., 479(19), *482*
Steenhauer, A. J., 192(192), *220*
Stein, G. A., 153(103), 161, *189*, 298(60), 299(64), 302(64), 326, *329*
Stephenson, J. S., 366, 379, 383, *385*
Stern, P., 185(104), *189*
Stimson, W. H., 462(159), *486*
Stirman, J. A., 82(132), *113*
Stjärne, L., 208, 210, 220, 237, *258*
St. Jean, A., 477(3), *482*
Stock, J. P. P., 383, 384(233), *391*
Stockham, M. A., 213(116), *218*
Stoepel, K., 182(45), *187*, 214(93), *218*
Stoerck, H. C., 91(94), *112*
Stojanova, D., 405(63), *425*
Stoll, A., 288(51), *294*, 362, 364(235), 377, *391*, 432(142, 144), 433(143), *457*
Stollerman, G. H., 264(40), *277*
Stone, C. A., 106, *114*, 183(105), 184(107), 185(106), *189*, 296(62), 299, 302, 317, 318, 323(62), 326, *329*, 476(163), 478(170), *486*
Stone, G. R., 199(169), *220*
Stone, H., 79, 91, *114*
Stopel, K., 134(144), *149*
Stott, F. H., 13(226), *64*
Straffon, R. A., 50(144), *62*
Strandberg, B., 479(164), *486*
Strang, R. R., 384(237), *391*
Strating, J., 200, *216*
Straub, O., 398(158), *428*
Straub, R., 439(145), *457*
Strazza, J. A., Jr., 375(73), *386*

Strecker, A., 126, 129, *148*
Streller, I., 340, *388*
Stuart, D. M., 432(146), *457*
Studer, A., 211(185), 212(185), *220*, 244(192), 245, 251(182), *262*
Studer, S., 357, 360(105), *387*
Sturtevant, F. M., 86, *114*
Stutzman, J. W., 106(112), *112*, 434(99), 448(99), *456*, *457*
Sümegi, S., 40, *61*
Sullivan, B., 90(28), 103(28), *110*
Sullivan, T. S., 471(44), *483*
Sulser, F., 103(71), *111*, 246(83, 183), *259*, *262*, 478(165), *486*
Summerville, W. E., 68(57), 71(58), *111*
Summerville, W. W., 21(95), *60*, 70(58), *111*
Sutherland, G. R., 373(240), 374(240), *391*
Sutnick, A. I., 472(51), *483*
Sutnik, A. U., 472(166), *486*
Sutter, M. C., 371(59), *386*
Suzman, M. M., 480(116), *485*
Suzuki, M., 432(148), *457*
Swain, A. P., 341, *391*
Swaine, C. R., 436(9), 439(166), 441(9), 443(9), 444(9), 445(9, 33), 446(9), 448(9), *454*, *458*
Swan, H. J. C., 377(14), 378(14), *385*
Sweetman, B., 475(46), *483*
Swett, L. R., 405, 410(137), *427*
Swiss, E. D., 434(149, 150), 446, 447, 448, 449, *457*
Sycheva, T. P., 225, 227, *262*
Symonds, B., 11(271), *65*
Syrneva, In. I., 306, *329*
Szmuszkovicz, J., 402(74), *426*

T

Tadao, T., 439(168), *458*
Taeschler, M., 288, *294*, 467(55), *483*
Taggart, J., 46, *65*
Taira, N., 441(52), 442(52), 445(52), *455*
Takesada, M., 253(163), *261*
Taketomo, Y., 209(175), *220*
Talwalker, P. K., 213(115), *218*
Tamagna, I., 413(113, 114), *427*
Tamagna, I. G., 472(118), *485*
Tanaka, K., 446(152), *457*
Taniguchi, K., 253(163), *261*

Tannenbaum, C., 354(174), 355(174), 356(174), *390*
Tanz, R. D., 210(176), 212(176), *220*
Taquini, A. C., 25, 26, 47(73), *60*, *65*, 69(20), *110*
Taquini, A. C., Jr., 25(273), 26(22, 273), 27(22), *59*, *65*
Tashnek, A. B., 451(114), *456*
Tassinari, L., 20(47), *59*, 92(33, 34, 35), *110*
Tauro, C. S., 202(24), *216*, *220*
Taylor, D., 423(14), *424*
Taylor, J. D., 405(137), 407(154), 410(137), 412(139), *427*, *428*
Taylor, R. D., 45, *63*, 85, *114*, 462(47), *483*
Taylor, R. R., 383(239), *391*
Taylor, S. H., 373, 374(240), *391*
Taylor, W. I., 194(188, 190), *220*
Teasdale, G., 466(134), *485*
Tedeschi, D. H., 403(140, 141), 404(159), *427*, *428*
Tedeschi, R. E., 403(140, 141), 404(159), *427*, *428*
Teitlebaum, S., 236(147), 237(147), *261*
ten Broeke, J., 162(108), *189*
Tertiuk, W., 138(6), *145*, 343(13), 344(13), *385*
Tetreault, T., 271(49), *277*
Thacker, E. A., 39, 42, *65*
Thölen, H., 418(121), *427*
Thoenen, H., 474(167), *486*
Thoman, J. E. P., 209(50), *216*
Thomas, C. B., 39, 46, *65*
Thomas, R., 413(113, 114), *427*, 472(118), *485*
Thompson, H. K., Jr., 381(253), *392*
Thompson, J., 27(283), *65*
Thompson, J. E., 8(268), *65*
Thompson, R. A., 467(168), 468(168), *486*
Thorn, G. W., 82(108), *112*
Thorson, J., 210(160), *219*
Thurm, R. H., 462(159), *486*
Thurmann, M., 477(85), *484*
Tibbs, W. J., 46(7), *58*
Tiemann, F., 125, *149*
Tigerstedt, R., 67, 71, *114*
Tigerstedt, T., 49, *65*
Tindal, J. S., 213(180), *220*
Tinker, J. F., 229(157), *261*
Tinsley, C. M., 40(134), *61*
Titterington, E., 383(192), *390*

Titus, D. C., 173(75), 175(78), 177(78), 178(78), 179(78), 181(78), 186(75), *188*
Titus, E. O., 117(42), *146*
Tobian, L., 74, 75, 80, 105(156), *113*, *114*
Tobian, L., Jr., 26, 27(283), 31, 47(279), *65*
Todd, R. L., 39, *65*
Tomich, E. G., 209(175), *220*
Toohey, V. P., 285(44), *294*
Torchiana, M. L., 296(62), 299(64), 302(64), 317(62), 318(62), 323(62, 63), 326(61, 62), *329*
Torosdag, S., 271(8), *276*, 409(27, 28), 410(28), 413(28), *424*, 472(21), *482*
Totaro, J. A., 168(77), 175(78), 176(77), 177(77, 78), 178(77, 78), 179(78), 181(78), 184(76, 77, 107), 185(77), *188*, *189*, 476(163), *486*
Trajkov, T., 405(63), *425*
Trano, Y., 168(99), *189*
Trapold, J., 209(134), *219*, 285(41), *294*
Trapold, J. H., 374(241), *392*
Trčka, V., 198(195), 200(196), *220*, 317(52), 319, 320, *329*, 436(156), *457*
Tree, M., 25(156), *62*, 76(111), 81(111), *112*
Trefouel, J., 335(242), *392*
Tremblay, G., 26(92), 31(92), *60*
Trendelenburg U. 208(181), 210, *220*, *293*
Trenner, N. R., 186(10), *187*
Trewin, E., 8(170), *62*
Triggle, D. J., 333(241a), 352(17), *385*, *392*
Tripod, J., 104(11, 12), 105(125), *109*, *112*, 211(185), 212, *220*, 234(84), 236(84, 92), 239(10), 241(10, 114, 119), 244(186, 193, 194), 245(11, 13), 246(10, 114), 249, 250(10, 117), 251(182, 195), 253(84, 118), 257(187), *257*, *259*, *260*, *262*, 442(103), *456*
Tristram, E. W., 162, *189*
Tron-Loisel, H., 141(138), *149*
Trounce, J. R., 325, *328*
Troxler, F., 364(234), *391*
Troyer, W. G., 382(251), *392*
Truchot, R., 141(138), *149*
Trupp, T. Kh., 225(184), *262*
Tsien, W. H., 197(166), 206(167, 168), *220*
Tsolakas, T. C., 381(243), *392*
Tsukamoto, T., 432(153), *457*
Tubina, I. S., 235(161), *261*
Tuchmann-Duplessis, H., 105(125), *112*

Tuckman, J., 137(67), *147*, 267(17), *276*, 412(107), 416(107), *426*
Tuffanelli, D. L., 255(56), *259*
Turiaf, J., 48, *65*
Turley, J. W., 193(129), *219*
Turnbull, L. B., 404(31), *424*
Turner, D. M., 86(101), *112*
Turner, F. A., 203, *220*
Turner, L. W., 472(51), *483*
Turner, P., 475(72), *484*
Turner, R. W. D., 469(101), *484*
Twedt, R., 27(283), *65*
Tyler, C., 323(4), *328*

U

Udenfriend, S., 106(135), *113*, 153(64), 156(109, 112), 168(47), 169(47), 173(64), 182(64, 111), 184(17, 110, 111), 185(110, 111), 186(114), *187*, *188*, *189*, 325, *328*, 398(130), 402(142), 413(129), 418(94, 130), *426*, *427*
Udwadia, B. P., 476(64), *483*
Ueda, H., 7(286), *65*
Ulbricht, W., 439(154), *457*
Ulick, S., 88(103), 89(103), *112*
Ullyot, G. E., 344, 348(64, 129), 349(64, 129), 351(129), 369, *386*, *388*, *392*
Ulsamer, G., 90(28), 103(28), *110*
Ulshafer, P. R., 194(101, 188, 189, 190), 195(159), 196(187), *218*, *219*, *220*
Unna, K. R., 285(48), *294*
Urbanska, A., 182(18), *187*
Urech, E., 137(139), *149*, 359, 357, 360(120), *388*, *392*
Urivetzky, M., 252(120), *260*
Urquiaga, X., 415, *427*
Utley, J. H., 477(85), *484*

V

Vacik, J. H., 341(222), *391*
Vakidy, T. A., 158(66), *188*
Vakil, R. J., 192(191), *220*
Vallance, D. K., 143(9), *145*
Valzelli, L., 478(32), *483*
Van Allan, J. A., 229(157), *261*
Vanatta, J., 47(105), *61*, 82(67), *111*
Vand, V., 193(129), *219*
Van Daele, P., 342(248), *392*

Van der Eycken, C., 342(248), *392*
Van Deripe, D. R., 365, *392*
Van der Schoot, J. B., 184(17), *187*
Van de Westeringh, C., 342(248), *392*
Vanacek, M., 317(52), *329*
van Itallie, L., 192(192), *220*
Van Itallie, T. B., 375, *392*
Van Nueten, J. M., 342(185), *390*
Van Orden, L. S., 394(157), *428*
Vanotti, A., 212, *220*
Van Zoeren, G. J., 404(145), *427*
Varma, D. R., 214(17), *216*, 381, *385*, 464(169), *486*
Varnauskas, E., 182(81), 183(82), *188*
Vaughan-Williams, E. M., 380(84), 381, *387*, *390*, *391*
Vazakas, A. J., 202, *220*
Veale, A. M. O., 13(262, 287), 14(262), 15(262), 18(287), 19(263), *64*, *65*
Vejdělek, Z. J., 196(46), 198(195), 200(139), 201(141), *216*, *219*, *220*, 317(52), 319, 320, *329*, 432(155), 436(155, 156), *457*
Veldkamp, W., 144(83), *147*
Velluz, L., 197(197, 198, 199), *220*
Venning, E. H., 90(51), *110*
Verbruggen, F. J., 342(185), *390*
Verney, E. B., 23(288), 45, 46, *65*
Vernier, V. G., 478(170), *486*
Verschuer, O., 18(289), *65*
Vestre, N. D., 354(123), *388*
Veyrat, R., 25, 26(92), 31(92), *60*, *65*, 76(14), 81(14), *109*
Vick, J., 252(196), *262*
Vidrio, H., 355(206), *391*
Vigran, I. M., 471(171), *486*
Villarreal, J., 415(144), *427*
Vogel, J., 380, *392*
Vogin, E. E., 228(57), 232(57), *259*, 362(122), *388*
Vogt, M., 23(288), 45, 46, *65*, 205(200), 208(120), 209, 213(153), 214, *217*, *218*, *219*, *220*, 402(79), 415(146, 147), *426*, *428*
Volhard, F., 51, *65*, 263, *277*
Volle, R. L., 290(54), *293*, *294*, 441(66), *455*
von Bezold, A., 444, *457*
von Euler, U. S., 47(26), *59*, 152(113), *189*
Vormittag, E., 360(87a), *387*
Voskian, J., 452(158), *457*

W

Waal, H. J., 465(146), 467(146), 470(155), 475(155), 476(155), 477(155), 479(155, 172, 173), 480(155), *485*, *486*
Wagle, G. L., 211, *220*
Wagner, H. H., 415(87), *426*
Wahlgren, N., 86(61), *111*
Wakerlin, G. E., 32, *61*, 73, *114*
Wakim, K. G., 224(2), 225(2), 255(2), *257*, 377(108), *387*
Waldeck, B., 119(30), *146*, 208(33), 209(33), *216*, 420, *424*
Walk, R. A., 403(70), *425*
Walker, E. F., 196(164), *220*
Walker, H. A., 250(197), *262*, 373(250), 374(203), *390*, *392*, 446(130), 448(130), *457*
Wallace, A. G., 382, *392*
Wallis, A. T., 13(264), 35(78), *60*, *64*
Walsh, J. J., 462(159), *486*
Walter, C. R., Jr., 404(31), *424*
Walters, M. B., 10(174), 11(174), *62*
Walton, A., 399(18), *424*
Walton, E., 140(17), 141(140), *145*, *149*
Walz, D., 236(198, 199), *262*
Wang, C. C., 130(33), *146*
Wang, C. Y., 379(106), *387*
Wang, H.-H., 210, *220*
Wang, S. C., 210, *220*, 445(159), *457*
Wangh, J. M., 373(211), *391*
Ward, L. E., 224(2), 225(2), 255(2), *257*
Ward-McQuaid, J. N., 23(49), *59*
Warner, R. R. P., 402(148), *428*
Warren, M. R., 374(241), *392*
Warthin, T. A., 46, *65*
Watanabe, N., 226(99), 227(99), 232(99), 233(99), *260*
Watkin, D. M., 8(293), *65*
Watson, L. S., 106(191), *114*, 175(78), 177(78), 178(78), 179(78), 181(78), *188*
Watts, J., 478(165), *486*
Weaver, L. C., 437(90, 94), 438(86, 160), 446(1), 447, *453*, *455*, *456*, *457*
Weber, A., 415(19), *424*
Webster, R. A., 476(174), *486*
Weinberg, M. S., 198, *218*
Weiner, M., 479(19), *482*
Weinstein, P., 422(54), *425*
Weisbach, M. J., 127(102), *148*, 227(131b), *260*

Weise, V. K., 420(90), *426*
Weisenborn, F. L., 436, *457*
Weissbach, H., 168(47), 169(47), 186, *187*
189, 398(143), 402(142), 418(94), *426*,
427
Weissler, A. M., 382(102), *387*
Wells, J., 415(72), *425*
Welsh, A. L., 476(175), *486*
Welt, L. G., 465(80), *484*
Wendel, H., 405(136), *427*
Wenger, H. C., 184(107), *189*
Wenis, E., 398(56–58), *425*
Wenner, W., 135, *149*, 361, *392*
Wenstrand, D. E. W., 38, 39, 41, 42, *60*
Werle, E., 185(115), *189*, 236, 237, *262*
Werkö, L., 29(294), *65*, 182(81), 183(82),
188
Werner, G., 158(116), *189*
Werner, H., 159(38), *187*
Wescoe, W. C., 352, *386*
Wesley-Hadžija, B., 235(201), *262*
West, J. W., 246(202), *262*
West, T. C., 380, *392*
Westermann, E., 153(117), 184(117), *189*
Wezler, K., 244(203), *262*
Whalen, R. E., 381, *392*
Wheatley, W. B., 349, *392*
Wheeler, T. S., 164(118), *189*
Whelan, R. F., 211, *221*
Wheland, G. W., 126(143), 128(143),
149
Whitby, L. G., 117(63), *147*
White, A. G., 478(176), *486*
White, C. A., 446(13), *454*
White, F. N., 92, *111*
White, H. L., 432(38), *454*
White, J. B., 100(190), 105, 106, *114*
White, J. P., 91(94), *112*
White, P. D., 430(21), 452(21), *454*
Whitlock, R. T., 182(13), *187*
Whitman, E. N., 137(1), *145*
Wicker, T. H., 353, *390*
Wiegand, R. G., 107, *113*, 405(50), 407,
409(50, 100), 410(100), 411(124), 413
(50), 415, *425*, *426,427*
Wiemeler, L. H., 145(125), *148*
Wien, R., 284, *294*
Wilcoxon, F., 449, *456*
Wilhelm, M., 232(167), *261*
Wilkens, R. W., 414(78), *426*

Wilkins, R. W., 29(86), 40(134, 135), *60*, *61*,
93, 105(87), *111*, *114*, 264(30), 265(30),
266(30), 268(31), *277*, 378(74), *386*,
414(78), 418(131), *426*, *427*, 452(36),
454, 460(78), 462(79, 177, 179), 463(78),
465(77, 79), 467(77, 79), 477(178), *484*,
486
Willey, G. L., 137(55), 138(6), *145*, *146*,
343(13), 344(13), *385*
Williams, D. E., 162(108), *189*
Williams, H. W. R., 398(48), *425*
Williams, J. R., 246, *262*
Williams, R. E., 195(85, 86), *217*
Williams, T. F., 465(80), *484*
Williamson, H. E., 479(82), *484*
Willkens, R. F., 255(205), *262*
Willoughby, D. A., 33(185), *63*, 402(133)*427*,
Wills, S. H., 255(4), *257*
Wilms, H., 134(144), *149*
Wilske, K. R., 255(205), *262*
Wilson, A., 318(50), *329*
Wilson, B. N., 480(181), *486*
Wilson, C., 9, 22, 32, *65*, 68, 77, 78, *114*,
342(65), *386*
Wilson, C. W., 80, *114*
Wilson, C. W. M., 290, *294*
Wilson, G. M., 465(48), *483*
Wilson, I. M., 264, *276*, 326(19), *328*
Wilson, R., 475(180), *486*
Wilson, S., 250(197), *262*, 373(250), *392*
Wilson, W. R., 271, *277*, 467(115), *485*
Wimberley, N. A., Jr., 480(181), *486*
Windesheim, J. H., 39, *65*
Winer, B. M., 437(163, 164), 453(163, 164),
458
Winfield, M. E., 383(148), *389*
Winkler, E. G., 453(165), *458*
Winkler, G., 287(35), *294*
Winsor, T., 413, *428*, 472(182), *486*
Winters, R. W., 465(80), *484*
Winters, W. D., 185(49), *187*
Wintersteiner, O., 432(38), *454*
Wirth, W., 319(25), 321(25), *328*
Wirz, E., 211(185), 212(185), *220*, 244(192,
193, 194), 245(194), 251(195), *262*
Withrington, P., 212, *221*
Witkop, B., 398(143), *427*
Witt, I. H., 348(64), 349(64), *386*
Witt, P. N., 439(166), *458*
Witzleb, E., 440, *458*

Wolf, M., 360(91a), *387*
Wolf, R. I., 271(42), *277*
Wolf, R. L., 33(178), 34(179), *62*, 412(107), 416(107), *426*, 460(183), *486*
Wolff, H. G., 34, *63*, 378(255), *392*
Wolff, H. P., 30(58), *60*
Wolkerstorfer, H., 255(206), *262*
Wollweber, H., 134(144), *149*, 319(25), 321(25), *328*
Wood, J. E., 39, *65*
Woodbury, R. A., 374(4, 6, 241), 375(4), *384*, *392*
Woods, E. F., 212(6, 7), *215*
Woods, J. W., 249(207), *262*
Woodson, R. E., 193(205), *221*
Woodward, R. B., 193(206, 207), *221*
Woolley, D. W., 402(151, 152), 403(153), *428*
Worthing, C. R., 138(5), *145*
Worthington, J. W., 224(2), 225(2), 255(2), *257*
Wragg, W. R., 132(76), *147*, 296(31), 299(17), 300(17, 32), 301(17), 302(17), 307(31), 309(33), 310(30), 312(7), 315(6, 8), 319(7), *328*, *329*
Wright, E. B., 439(168), *458*
Wright, S., 84(99), *112*
Wrigley, T. I., 138(5), *145*
Wrong, O., 31(100), *61*
Wu, Y. H., 367(87), *387*
Wykes, A. A., 405(137, 138), 407, 410(137), 412(139), *427*, *428*
Wylie, D. W., 355(8, 256), 356(8), *384*, *392*
Wyngaarden, J. B., 479(137, 184), *485*, *486*
Wynne, N. A., 471(83), *484*
Wyso, E. M., 131(120), *148*
Wyss, E., 253, *261*, 395, *427*
Wyss, S., 437(169), 451(169), 452(141), 453(169), *457*, *458*

Y

Yagi, A., 432(153, 170, 171), 433(171), *457*, *458*
Yagi, S., 93(88), *111*
Yamamoto, K., 226(99), 227(99), 232(99), 233(99), *260*

Yard, A. S., 235(110), *260*
Yates, M. R., 39, *65*
Yeakel, E. H., 23(71), *60*, *65*
Yeary, R. A., 228, *262*
Yelnosky, J., 362, *392*
Yiengst, M. J., 42(195), *63*
Yonkman, F. F., 223, *258*, 357(49, 160), 372(160), 375(48, 258), *386*, *389*, *392*, 394(40), *425*
Yost, W., 354(174), 355(174), 356(174), *390*, 403, 404(30), *424*
Young, A. A., 327(13), *328*
Young, D. S., 274(14), *276*, 466(42), *483*
Young, E. H. P., 102(189), *114*, 132(134), 144(38), *146*, *148*, 296, 305(59), 319(59), 324(59), *329*
Young, J. A., 183, 186(119), *189*
Youngken, K. W., 193(205), *221*
Yu, I. C., 130(33), *146*
Yu, M., 105(169), *114*
Yu, P. N., 29(301), *65*, 465(27), *482*
Yunice, A., 239(141), *261*
Yuwiler, A., 173, *189*

Z

Zaimis, E., 68, *113*, 212, *221*, 280, 298, *293*, *294*, 323(4), *328*, 461(185), *486*
Zaltman-Nirenberg, P., 156(112), 182(111), 184(111), 185(111), *189*
Zaltzman, P., 413(129), *427*
Zarowitz, H., 466(66), *483*
Zbinden, G., 395, 397, 412, 413(156), 415, *428*
Zeller, E. A., 394, *428*
Zeller, P., 393(120), 398(158), 415(72), *425*, *427*, *428*
Zempler, G., 160(30), *187*
Zenno, H., 226(99), 227(99), 232(99), 233(99), *260*
Zerngibl, L., 403(85), *426*
Ziegler, M., 25(107), *61*
Ziegler, W. H., 182(86), 184(83), *188*
Zielinska, M., 184(101), *189*
Zimmer, J. G., 186(22), *187*
Zimmerman, J., 119(130), *148*
Zimmerman, J. H., 430(95), *456*
Zipperlen, V., 18(289), *65*
Zirkle, C. L., 403(85), 404, *426*, *428*

Zizine, L., 48(285), *65*
Zohman, B. L., 38, 39, *64*
Zollinger, H. U., 21(302), *65*
Zonis, R. D., 432(92), *456*

Zotti, E. F., 382(251), *392*
Zsolnai, T., 252(209), *262*
Zugravescu, I., 128(145), *149*, 226(210), *262*
Zweifach, B., 211(152), *219*

SUBJECT INDEX

A

Acetamidine hydrochloride, 126
Acetazolamide, 275
Acetazolamide, as antihypertensive agent, 267–268
Acetylcholine, 279
ACTH, reserpine and, 213–214
Adrenal regeneration hypertension, 89–91
Adrenal system, reserpine, effect of on, 213
   Veratrum alkaloids, effect of on, 441
Adrenergic blockade, 99–100
Adrenergic blocking agents, 99, 331 ff.
   α-receptors, 473–474s
   β-receptors, 364–368, 379–384
   monoamine oxidase inhibitors, 415
Adrenergic neuronal blockade, 100–101
   central nervous system, effect on, 119–120
   circulation, effect on, 119
   gastrointestinal tract, effect on, 120
   genitourinary system, effect on, 120
   tolerance to, 122
Adrenergic neuronal blocking agents, chemistry of 123 ff.
   metabolism of, 122
   pharmacology of, 116–123
   side effects of, 122
   therapeutic uses of, 122–123
Adrenocorticotropic hormone. *See* ACTH
Aldosterone
   hypertension induced by, 30–31, 87–89
   renal hypertension and, 74
Alkaloids
   clavine, 363
   ergot, 362–364, 376–379
   harmala, 398–399
   Rauwolfia, 191 ff.
   Veratrum, 429 ff.
N-Alkylhydrazinophthalazines, 229
Alpha-receptors, 332
Amanozine, 268
Amidines, 126
   as adrenergic neuronal blocking agents, 127–128

Amidoximes, 125, 126
   as adrenergic neuronal blocking agents, 126–128
Amines
   as ganglionic blocking agents, 297 ff.
   methyldopa and, 183–185
   reserpine and, 210
   tertiary, 307
3-Aminochromane, 138
Aminoguanidine, 234
Amino isocamphanes, as ganglionic blocking agents, 298–305
2-Aminomethyl dihydrobenzofurans, 342
2-Aminomethylimidazoline derivatives, synthesis of, 360
1-Aminomethyl-1-phenylcyclopropane, 404
α-Amino-α-methylphenylpropionic acid, 179
Amino-oxazolines, 358
α-Amino-β-phenylpropionic acids, 161
Amisometradine, 275
   as antihypertensive agent, 266–267
Amitriptyline, 478
Amphetamines, 121
   antihypertensive drugs and, 475
Angina pectoris, β-adrenergic blocking drugs and, 383
Angiotensin, 46, 72
   bilateral nephrectomy and, 50
   hypertension and, 26 ff.
   hydralazine and, 238
   in renal hypertension in dogs, 72–75
Angiotensin I, 72
Angiotensin II, 26, 30, 72. See Angiotensin
Angiotensinase, 28
Angiotensin-renin system. *See* Renin-angiotensin system
Angiotonin, 72
Antazoline, 357
Antianginal drugs, antihypertensive agents, use with, 479
Antiarrhythmic drugs, antihypertensive agents, use with, 480
Antidecarboxylases, 153–154
   in vivo, 179–182
   synthetic, 157–167

Antidepressants, antihypertensive drugs, use
  with, 477–479
Antihistamines, antihypertensive drugs, use
  with, 476
Antihypertensive agents
  acting on vascular smooth muscle, 104–
  105
  amphetamines, use with, 475
  antianginal drugs, use with, 479
  antiarrhythmic drugs, use with, 480
  antidepressants, use with, 478
  antihistamines, use with, 476
  bronchodilator drugs, use with, 475
  cardiac glycosides, use with, 480
  cholesterol-lowering agents, use with, 480
  cold remedies, use with, 475–476
  development of, 93–107
  diuretic agents, use with, 464–468
  gout treatment and, 479
  monoamine oxidase inhibitors, use with,
  471–473
  phenylbutazone, use with, 479
  Rauwolfia alkaloids, use with, 462–464
  suppressing the sympathetic nervous
  system, 98–104
  tranquilizers and sedatives, use with,
  476–477
  use in combinations, 459 ff.
Antirenin, 32
Aralkoxy guanidines, 144
Arterial clamping, 46
  in the dog, 69–70
  in the rabbit, 81
  in the rat, 77–78
Atheromatosis, hydralazine for, 237
Atherosclerosis, 57
Atropine methylnitrate, 288
Audiogenic hypertension, in the rat, 85
Autonomic ganglia, *Veratrum* alkaloids,
  effect of on, 441
Azabicyclononanes, as adrenergic neuronal
  blocking agents, 139, 140
Azabicyclooctanes, as adrenergic neuronal
  blocking agents, 139–140
Azamethonium, 282–284, 291
  dosage of, 292
Azapetine, 361
  pharmacological activity of, 375–376
Azaspiroalkanes, as adrenergic neuronal
  blocking agents, 134–135

B

Barbiturates, 477, effects on the blood pressure, of
Barium chloride, bilateral nephrectomy and,
  49
Baroceptor denervation, 82–86
Baroceptors, 83
  hypertension and, 50, 452
  in renal hypertension in dogs, 73
Basal blood pressure, 13–14, 15–16
Benzodiazepines, 477
Benzodioxan derivatives, 138
  as adrenergic blocking agents, 334 ff.
  pharmacological effects of, 368–369
1,3-Benzodioxoles, 138
Benzyl guanidine, as monoamine oxidase
  inhibitors, 399
Benzyl guanidine derivatives, as adrenergic
  neuronal blocking agents, 140–141
N-Benzyl-*N*-methyl-2-propynylamine. *See*
  Pargyline
Benzyloxyamines, 164
N^2-Benzylpivalic acid hydrazide, 395
Beta-receptors, 332
  blocking agents, 364 ff.
Bethanidine, 118, 121, 122–123, 141, 400,
  402, 461
  guanethidine, use with, 470
  methyldopa, use with, 471
  pargyline, use with, 473
  reserpine, use with, 463
  tolerance to, 122
Bicyclic compounds, as adrenergic neuronal
  blocking agents, 135–140
Bicyclo(3,2,1)azaoctanes, 310
Blood pressure, 2, 4 ff. 52 ff.
  angiotensin and, 28
  basal. *See* Basal blood pressure
  casual. *See* Casual blood pressure
  chlorothiazide and dihydrochlorothiazide
  and, 265, 266
  diastolic, 82
  elevation of, hypertension and, 7 ff.
  ganglionic blocking agents and, 322
  hydralazine and, 241
  hypertension, pathogenesis of, 2 ff.
  supplemental. *See* Supplemental blood
  pressure
  systolic, 82

Blood vessels, reactivity of, 33–34
Botulinum toxin, 290
Bradycardia, *Veratrum* alkaloids and, 441
Breath-holding, hypertension and, 41–42
Bretylium, 101, 115–116, 118, 120, 121, 123–125, 297, 461
  absorption of, 122
  metabolism of, 122
  as monoamine oxidase inhibitor, 399, 401
  tolerance to, 122
Bretylium tosylate, 287
o-Bromobenzylethyldimethylammonium *p*-toluene sulfonate. *See* Bretylium
Bronchodilator drugs, antihypertensive agents and, 475
Butoxamine, 368

C

Caffeic acid, 169, 170
Carbon dioxide, hypertension and, 40–41
Carcinoid syndrome, methyldopa and, 185
Cardiac muscle, *Veratrum* alkaloids, effect of on, 441
Casual blood pressure, 11, 12–16, 52
Catalase inhibition, hydralazine and, 237
Catapresan, 359–360
Catecholamines
  biosynthesis of, 154–156
  monoamine oxidase inhibitors and, 415, 418
  reserpine and, 208 ff.
Central nervous system
  adrenergic neuronal blocking agents and, 119–120
  reserpine, effect of on, 206–207
  Veratrum alkaloids, effect of on, 441
Cevadine, 436, 439
Ceveratrum alkamines, 430, 431
Chalcones
  as decarboxylase inhibitors, 172, 173
  synthesis of, 164
Cheeses, tranylcypromine therapy and, 422–423
Chelation, hydralazine and, 236
Chlorazinil, 268, 275
Chlorisondamine, 285
  dosage of, 292
N-*o*-Chlorobenzyl-*N′N″*-dimethylguanidine sulfate, 402

N-(2-Chloroethyl)dibenzylamine hydrochloride. *See* Dibenamine
2-Chloromethyl-8-alkoxy-1,4-benzodioxan, 335
2-Chloromethylimidazoline, 360
Chlorothiazide
  as antihypertensive agent, 264
  synthesis of, 264
Chlorpheniramine, antihypertensive drugs, use with, 476
Chlorthalidone, as antihypertensive agent, 271–273
Cholesterol, hydralazine and, 237
Cholesterol-lowering agents, antihypertensive agents, use with, 480
Cinnamic acid, 169, 170
Cinnamic acid derivatives, as decarboxylase inhibitors, 169–172
Cinnamyl guanidines, as adrenergic neuronal blocking agents, 141–142
Circulatory system
  adrenergic neuronal blocking and, 119
  hydralazine and, 241
  reserpine, effect of on, 210–212
Clavine alkaloids, 363
Clofibrate, 480
Clopamide, methyldopa use with, 467–468
Cocaine, 290
Cold pressor test, 38–40, 46
Cold tablets, antihypertensive agents and, 475–476
Compound 6084, 230
Copper ions, hydralazine and, 236
Coronary blood vessels, hydralazine and, 241
Cough preparations, antihypertensive agents and, 475–476
Cushing's syndrome, 3
N-Cyanoethyldopa, 168
Cycloalkylamines, 317–319
Cyclobutylamines, 318–319
Cyclohexylamines, 317–318
Cyclopropylamines, as monoamine oxidase inhibitors, 403–405
Cyclopropylbenzylamine, 409

D

DCA. *See* Deoxycorticosterone acetate
DCI. *See* Dichloroisoproterenol

Debrisoquin, 118, 120, 121, 135
Decamethonium, 280, 282
Decamethylenediguanidine dihydro-
  chloride. *See* Synthalin
Decarboxylase inhibition, *in vivo*, 176–182
Decarboxylase inhibitors. *See* Antidecarb-
  oxylases
Deoxycorticosterone acetate (DCA), 9
  hypertension induced by, 85–87
Depression, in hypertensive patients, 477–
  478
Desatrine, 438
Deserpideine, 196
Deserpidine, 103–104, 194, 195, 196
3,4-Diacetoxycinnamic acid, 169, 171
N,N'-Dialkyl-N''-(2-thenyl)guanidines, 134
Diamine oxidase inhibition, hydralazine and,
  253
Diamine oxidase inhibitors, 236
Diamonal, 284
Dibenamine, 344, 348, 370
Dibenzazepines, 361
Dibozane, 341, 344
Di-*tert*-butylamine, 305, 316
Di-*tert*-butylamine congeners, 321
Dichloroisoproterenol, 365
  pharmacological activity of, 379
2,3-Dichloro-4-(2-methylene-butyl)-phen-
  oxyacetic acid. *See* Ethacrynic acid
Dietary hypertension, 92
1-(2-(Diethylamino)ethyl)-reserpine, 197
2-(Diethylaminomethyl)-1,4-benzodioxan.
  See Prosympal
Dihydralazine, 104, 223–224
  properties of, 235
  synthesis of, 225
1,4-Dihydrazinophthalazine. *See* Dihydralazine
Dihydrazinopyrimidines, 231
Dihydrazinotriazines, 231–232
6,7-Dihydro-5-H-dibenz[c,e]-azepines, 361
Dihydroergocornine, 363
  pharmacological activity of, 377–378
Dihydroergocristine, 363
Dihydroergocryptine, 363
3,4-Dihydroxybenzylguanidine, 129
2,6-Dihydroxycinnamic acid, 169, 170
3,4-Dihydroxycinnamic acid, 169, 170
3,4-Dihydroxyphenylacetic acid, 168
3,4-Dihydroxyphenylalanine. *See* Dopa

Dihydroxyphenylalanine decarboxylase. *See*
  Dopa decarboxylase
3,4-Dihydroxyphenylpropionic acid, 166, 168
N^2-p-Dimethylaminobenzyl-[5-methyl-
  isoxazolyl-3]-carbonyl hydrazide, 398
trans-3-Dimethylamino-2,2,4,4-tetramethyl-
  cyclobutanol, 318
N,N-Dimethyl-β-chlorophenethylamine, 352
3,3-Dimethylpyrrolidine, 3,4-dimethylpyr-
  rolidine, 3,3,4-trimethylpyrrolidine,
  134
2,6-Dimethylphenoxyethylguanidine, 143
cis-Dimethylpiperidine, 134
2,6-Dimethylpiperidine, 306
Diphenylmethyl atropinium bromide, 288
Diuretics, 105–106, 107, 264 ff.
  ganglionic blocking agent and reserpine,
    use with, 468–469
  reserpine, use with, 462–463
  therapeutic use of, 464–468
  use in combination, 466–468
Dog
  hypertension in, 23
  neurogenic hypertension in, 84
  renal hypertension in, 69–77, 82
  testing procedure using, 99
Dopa, 152, 154
Dopa decarboxylase, 156–157
  hydrazines and, 237
Dopa decarboxylase inhibition, 152 ff.
  hydralazine and, 253
Dopamine, 154
Droperidol, 362

E

Eclampsia, hydralazine and, 255
Emotion, hypertension and, 41
Endrocrine-induced hypertension, 85 ff.
  adrenal regeneration, 89–91
  aldosterone, 87–89
  deoxycorticosterone, 85–87
  glucocorticoids, 91
Endrocrine kidney, 79
Endocrine system, reserpine, effect of on,
  212–214
Endotoxin shock, hydralazine and, 252
16-Epi-17-epireserpine, 194
18-Epi-3-isoreserpine, 194
Epinephrine, 332
  bilateral nephrectomy and, 48

Epinephrine—*continued*
  biosynthesis of, 154–155
  hypertension and, 40, 45
  reactivity of blood vessels and, 33
16-Epireserpine, 194
18-Epireserpine, 194
16,17,18-Epireserpine, 194
Ergoline, 363
Ergonovine, 362, 378
Ergot alkaloids
  as adrenergic blocking agents, 362–364
  pharmacological activity of, 376–379
Ergotamine, 362, 378
Essential hypertension, 2 ff., 53 ff.
Ethacrynic acid, 274, 275
  as antihypertensive agent, 273–274
  as diuretic, 466
  thiazides, use with, 467
Ethiquinium, 287
Ethyl-*N*-benzyl-*N*-cyclopropylcarbamate.
  See MO1255
17α-Ethyl 17-demothoxyreserpine, 197
α-Ethyltryptamine. *See* Etryptamine
Etryptamine, in cats, 403

F

Ferric ion, hydralazine and, 236
Ferrous ion, hydralazine and, 236
Flavones
  as decarboxylase inhibitors, 172, 174
  synthesis of, 164
3-Formamidoisocamphane, 298
Furosemide, 274, 275
  as antihypertensive agent, 273
  as diuretic, 467

G

Gallamine triethiodide, 280
Ganglionic blockade, 101–102
Ganglionic blocking agents, 102, 223
  in the cat, 322
  monoamine oxidase inhibitors, 415
  Rauwolfia alkaloids, use with, 462
  reserpine and a diuretic, use with, 468–469
  use in combinations, 468–469
Ganglionic blocking agents, nonquaternary,
  295 ff.
  excretion of, 324–326

Ganglion blocking agents, nonquaternary—
  continued
  mode of action of, 323–324
  test methods for, 322–323
  side effects of, 296–297
  therapeutic use of, 326–328
Ganglionic blocking agents, quaternary
  chemistry of, 279–289
  mechanism of action, 290–291
  side effects of, 295–296
  therapeutic use of, 291–292
Gastrointestinal tract, adrenergic neuronal
  blocking agents and, 120
Genetics, of hypertension, 16–20
Genitourinary system, adrenergic neuronal
  blocking and, 120
Germidine, metabolism of, 450
Germine, 431, 434, 435
Germine esters, 435, 436, 437, 439
Glucocorticoid hypertension, 91
Glyceryl trinitrate, antihypertensive agents,
  use with, 479
Glycosides, cardiac, antihypertensive drugs,
  use with, 480
Goldblatt hypertension, 46–47
Gossypin, 172, 174
Gout, antihypertensive therapy and, 479
Guanethidine, 100–101, 115, 118, 120, 121,
  129–131, 252, 297, 461
  amphetamines, use with, 475
  bethanidine, use with, 470
  hydrochlorothiazide, use with, 270–271
  metabolism of, 122
  methyldopa, use with, 471
  as monoamine oxidase inhibitor, 399, 401
  pargyline, use with, 473
  pempidine, use with, 469
  reserpine, use with, 463
  tolerance to, 122
Guanidine, 129
Guanidine derivatives, 129–131
  aliphatic, 144–145
  aromatic, 140–144
  heterocyclic, 131–140
  as monoamine oxidase inhibitors, 399–402
Guanidine salts, 128 ff.
N-(2-Guanidinoethyl)hexahydrobenzo[*d*]-
  azocine sulfate, 137
2-Guanidinomethyl-1,4-benzodioxan. *See*
  Guanoxan

Guanisoquin, 118, 121, 137
Guanoclor, 118, 120, 121, 144
Guanoxan, 118, 120, 121, 123, 139

H

Haloanisone, 355
  pharmacological effect of, 371
β-Haloethylamines
  as adrenergic blocking agents, 344–352
  pharmacological effects of, 369–372
  side effects of, 371
Harmala alkaloids, as monoamine oxidase
  inhibitors, 398–399
Harmaline, 398–399
Hereditary hypertension, 92–93
3 - (Hexahydro - 1 - azepinyl)propionamid -
  oxime, 126–127, 129
Hexamethonium, 15, 44, 68
  dosage of, 292
  mode of action of, 322
Histidine decarboxylase, hydralazine and,
  237
Huntington's chorea, methyldopa and, 185
Hydralazine (1-hydrazinophthalazine), 9–10,
  90, 104–105, 223 ff.
  anti-inflammatory effect of, 252
  biochemistry of, 236–238
  cardiovascular activity of, 239–251
  metabolism of, 238–239
  pharmacodynamic properties of, 252–254
  properties of, 235
  side effects of, 255–256
  synthesis of, 224–225
  therapeutic use in man, 254–256
Hydralazine derivatives, 225 ff.
  side effects of, 255–256
Hydralazine syndrome, 255
Hydrazine derivatives
  as decarboxylase inhibitors, 172, 175, 179
  as monoamine oxidase inhibitors, 394–398
  synthesis of, 164–165
Hydrazinoisoquinoline, 231
α-Hydrazino-α-methylphenylpropionic acid,
  172, 175
Hydrazinophenylpropane, 232
1-Hydrazinophthalazine. See Hydralazine
Hydrazinopyridazines, 230–231
Hydrochlorothiazide, 105–106, 232
  guanethidine, use with, 270–271

Hydrochlorothiazide—continued
  α-methyldopa, use with, 271
  spironolactone, use with, 268–270
  synthesis of, 264
  therapeutic use of, 264 ff.
2-Hydroxybenzalacetone, 169, 170
3-Hydroxybenzalacetone, 169, 171
N-(3-Hydroxybenzyl)-N-methylhydrazine,
  172, 175
3-Hydroxybenzyloxyamine, 172, 175
2-Hydroxycinnamic acid, 169, 170
3-Hydroxycinnamic acid, 169, 170, 172
5-(3-Hydroxycinnamoyl)-salicylic acid, 179,
  180
Hydroxylamine derivatives
  as decarboxylase inhibitors, 172, 175, 179
  synthesis of, 164–165
α-Hydroxyphenylpropionic acid, 166, 168
4-Hydroxyphenylpyruvic acid, 169
3-Hydroxy-ω-styrene, 172
5-Hydroxytryptamine. See Serotonin
Hyperaldosteronism, 88
Hypertensin, 72
Hypertensinase, 72
Hypertensinogen, 71
Hypertension
  adrenal regeneration-induced. See Adre-
    nal regeneration hypertension
  audiogenic. See Audiogenic hypertension
  blood-pressure elevation and, 7 ff.
  blood vessel reactivity and, 33 ff.
  cold pressor test, 38–40
  dietary. See Dietary hypertension
  endocrine-induced. See Endocrine-
    induced hypertension
  experimental, 69 ff.
  genetics of, 16–20
  glucorticoid-induced. See Glucorticoid
    hypertension
  hereditary. See Hereditary hypertension
  induction of, 246 ff.
  by intercranial tension elevation, 85
  metacorticoid, 86
  neurogenic. See Neurogenic hypertension
  pathogenesis of, 2 ff.
  renal. See Renal hypertension
  salt-induced. See Salt hypertension
Hyperuricemia, with diuretic therapy, 465–
  466
Hypokalemia, with diuretic therapy, 465

Hypotensive agents. *See* Antihypertensive agents
Hypovolemia, 370

I

Imidazolines, substituted
  as adrenergic blocking agents, 357–360
  pharmacological effect of, 372–376
Imidazolinylalkylindoles, 357
Imipramine, 478
Indole, 355
Intercranial tension, hypertension by elevation of, 85
Iproniazid, 394, 396
Iron ions, hydralazine and, 236
Ischemic kidney, in the rat, 79
Isoamylamine, 46
Isocarboxazid, 396, 413
Isoniazid, 397
N^2-Isopropyl-DL-serine hydrazide, 395
Isoraunescine, 195
3-Isoreserpine, 194

J

Jerveratrum alkamines, 430
Juxtaglomerular cells, as renin source, 74–75

L

Lysergic acid diethylamide, 363

M

Man, hypertension, genetics of, 16–18
MAO. *See* Monamine oxidase
Mebutamate, 476–477
Mecamylamine, 296, 298–299
  excretion of, 324–325
  isomers of, 304
  mode of action of, 323–324
  side effects of, 326
  therapeutic use of, 326–327
Mecamylamine congeners, 299–305
Mental disease
  methyldopa and, 185
  serotonin and, 402
3-Mercaptocinnamic acid, 169, 171
Mercaptophthalazine, 233
Metacorticoid hypertension, 86

Methindethyrium, 286, 287
10-Methoxydeserpidine, 197, 205
12-Methoxydeserpidine, 197
3-Methylamino isocamphane. *See* Mecamylamine
Methylchlothiazide, pargyline, use with, 271
α-Methyl-β-(3,4-dihydroxyphenyl)-alanine. *See* α-Methyldopa
1-Methyl-3(4-dimethylaminobutyl)piperidine, 296, 297
Methyldopa, 106, 107, 465
  amines (biogenic) and, 183–185
  bethanidine, use with, 471
  cardiovascular effects of, 182–183
  clopamide, use with, 467–468
  guanethidine, use with, 471
  metabolic effects of, 183
  metabolism of, 186
  pargyline, use with, 473
  reserpine, use with, 463–464
  side effects of, 183
α-Methyldopa, 153, 181, 297
  hydrochlorothiazide, use with, 271
  mechanism of action of, 168–169
  synthesis of, 161–162
N-Methyldopa, 167, 168
Methylergonovine, 362, 378
α-Methyl-3-hydroxy-4-methoxyphenylalanine, 168
N-Methyl-4-hydroxy-3-methoxyphenylalanine, 168
α-Methyl-5-hydroxytryptophan, 169, 181
12-Methylmercaptodeserpidine, 197
α-Methyl norepinephrine, 464
β-Methylphenylalanine, 168
N-Methyl-1-phenylcyclopropylamine, 404
1-Methyl-4-phenylpiperazine, 353
2-(4-Methylpiperazine)ethylguanidine, 134
3-Methylpyrrolidine, 134
Methyl reserpate, 214
17α-Methyl 17-demethoxyreserpine, 197
α-Methyltyrosine, 167, 168
α-Methyl-*m*-tyrosine, 167, 168, 181
α-Methyl-*p*-tyrosine, 156
Methysergide, 362
MJ-1999, pharmacological activity of, 380
MO936, 409, 413
MO1255, 409, 413
Monkey, renal hypertension in, 82
Monoamine oxidase (MAO), 393

Monoamine oxidase inhibition, hydralazine and, 236, 253
Monamine oxidase inhibitors, 106–107, 232, 393 ff.
  mode of action of, 412–420
  side effects of, 420–424, 471–472
  use in combinations, 471–473
Monoamines, as ganglionic blocking agents, 319–322
Monomethylpiperidine, 132–133
Myocardial infarction, β-adrenergic blocking agents, treatment with, 383–384

N

Nasal decongestants, antihypertensive agents, use of with, 475–476
Neoreserpine, 194
Nephrectomy, bilateral, response to pressor stimuli after, 48–50
Nephritis, hydralazine and, 255
Nephrotic syndrome, hydralazine and, 255
Nethalide. *See* Pronethalol
Neurochemical transducer, 418
Neurogenic hypertension, 82–85
Nialamide, 397, 419
Nicotinic acid, 480
Norepinephrine
  adrenergic neuronal blocking agents and, 117, 119, 120–121
  bilateral nephrectomy and, 49
  hypertension and, 40, 45
  methyldopa and, 184–185
  monoamine oxidase inhibitors and, 415, 418
  reactivity of blood vessels and, 33
  reserpine and, 207 ff.

O

tert-Octylguanidines, 144–145
α-Oxophenylpropionic acid, 168

P

Parasympathetic nervous system, 98
Pargyline, 107, 394, 405–407
  bethanidine, use with, 473
  guanethidine, use with, 473
  methylchlothiazide, use with, 271
  methyldopa, use with, 473

Pargyline—*continued*
  pharmacological activity of, 409–412
  reserpine, use with, 473
  side effects of, 472
Parkinson's disease
  β-adrenergic blocking agents, treatment with, 384
  methyldopa and, 185
Pempidine (1,2,2,6,6-pentamethylpiperidine), 132, 296, 305, 307
  excretion and distribution of, 325–326
  guanethidine, use with, 469
  mode of action of, 324
  side effects of, 328
  therapeutic use of, 327–328
Pempidine congeners, 312 ff.
Pentacynium, 286
Pentamethonium, pharmacological effects of, 290
1,2,2,6,6-Pentamethylpiperidine.
  See Pempidine
Pentolinium, dosage of, 292
Pentolinium tartrate, 284
Peripheral nervous system, *Veratrum* alkaloids, effect of on, 440
Phaecromocytoma, 4, 54, 120
Phenelzine, 397
Phenethylamine derivatives, as adrenergic blocking agents, 333–334
Phenethylguanidine, as monamine oxidase inhibitors, 399
Pheniprazine (PIH), 395, 396, 402
Phenothiazines, 476, 477
Phenoxybenzamine, 364
  pharmacological activity of, 369–370
  use in combination, 474
Phenoxyethylguanidine, 129
Phenoxy guanidines, as adrenergic neuronal blocking agents, 143–144
Phentolamine, 100, 357, 364
  pharmacological effect of, 372–374
Phenylalkylamines, 121
Phenylbutazone, antihypertensive drugs, use with, 479
2-Phenylcycloheptylamine, 404
2-Phenylcyclopentylamine, 404
trans-2-Phenylcyclopropylamine.
  See Tranylcypromine
2-Phenylcyclopropylamine derivatives, 404
Phenylethylamine, 46

Phenylisopropylhydrazine. *See* Pheniprazine
β-Phenyllactic acids, 160
N-Phenylpiperazine, 353
Phenylpiperazine derivatives
  as adrenergic blocking agents, 353–357
  pharmacological effect of, 372
Phenylpropionic acid derivatives
  as decarboxylase inhibitors, 166–169
  synthesis of, 158–164
Phenylpyruvic acid, 159
Pherentasin, hydralazine and, 238
Δ³-Piperidinoethylguanidine, 134
Piperoxan, 344
  pharmacological effects of, 369
Pitressin, bilateral nephrectomy and, 49
Polyalkylpiperidines, as antihypertensive
  agents, 305–317
Postcorticoid hypertension, 86
Posterior pituitary hormone, hypertension
  and, 40, 45
Postural hypotension, 295
Potassium, supplemental, with diuretics,
  274, 276
Pre-eclampsia, hydralazine and, 255
Prenylamine, antihypertensive agents, use
  with, 479
Primary hypertension, 2
Probenecid, 479
Procainamide, 480
Pronethalol, 251, 366
  pharmacological activity of, 379
Propanolol, 366, 480
  pharmacological activity of, 379 ff.
Propynylamines, as monoamine oxidase
  inhibitors, 405–412
Prosympal, 335, 344
Protoveratrine A, 437–438
Protoveratrine B, 437–438
Protoverine, 430, 431, 434, 435
Protoverine esters, 435, 437
Pseudoreserpine, 195

Q

Quiloflex, 340
Quinidine, 480

R

Rabbit
  high blood pressure in, 23

Rabbit—*continued*
  neurogenic hypertension in, 84
  renal hypertension in, 81–82
Radiation, hydralazine and, 252
Rat
  audiogenic hypertension in, 85
  blood vessel perfusion in, 35
  dietary hypertension in, 92
  high blood pressure in, 22–23
  neurogenic hypertension in, 84
  renal hypertension in, 77–81, 82, 248–249
  salt hypertension in, 91
Raugustine, 195
Raujemidine, 196
Raunescine, 195
Rauwolfia alkaloids
  ganglionic blocking agents, use with,
    462
  hypotensive drugs from, 191 ff.
Renal hypertension, 28–29
  experimental, 69 ff.
  hydralazines and, 246 ff.
  in the dog, 69–77, 82
  in the rabbit, 81–82
  in the rat, 77–81, 82
  pathogenesis of, 21 ff.
  renoprival studies, 82
Renin, 46, 71
  antirenin, 32
  bilateral nephrectomy and, 50
  juxtaglomerular apparatus and, 26 ff.
  liberation of, 24–26
  renal hypertension in dogs, 69 ff.
Renin-angiotensin system, 28, 72
  in the dog, 72 ff.
  in the rat, 78 ff.
Renin substrate, 71
Renoprival hypertension, 47–48
Renoxidine, 194
Rescidine, 195, 196
Rescinnamine, 103–104, 194, 195
Reserpine, 9, 10, 90, 91, 102–103, 108, 194,
    196, 205 ff., 461
  bethanidine, use with, 463
  central nervous system, effect of on,
    206–207
  circulatory system, effect of on, 210–212
  diuretics, use with, 462–463
  endocrine system, effect of on, 212–214
  furosemide, use with, 273

Reserpine—*continued*
 ganglionic blocking agents and a diuretic, use with, 468–469
 guanethidine, use with, 463
 interference with action of, 214–215
 methyldopa, use with, 463–464
 pargyline, use with, 473
 sympathetic nervous system, effect of on, 207–210
Reserpine derivatives, 196 ff., 205
Reserpine-type alkaloids, 193, 194–196
 chemistry of, 193–194
Respiration, *Veratrum* alkaloids and, 441–442
Rhesus monkey, renal hypertension in, 82
RO4-1038. *See* 1-DL-Seryl-2-isopropylhydrazide
Rutin, 172, 174

S

Salt hypertension, 20, 91–92
 diuretics for, 264 ff.
Schizophrenia, methyldopa and, 185
Scopolamine butylbromide, 288
Sedatives, antihypertensive drugs, use with, 476–477
Serotonin, 5-Hydroxytryptamine
 bilateral nephrectomy and, 49
 in mental disease, 402
Serum cholesterol, hydralazine and, 237
1-DL-Seryl-2-isopropylhydrazide (RO4-1038), 410
N-Seryl-N'-(2,3,4-trihydroxybenzyl)-hydrazine, 172, 175
Shock, hydralazine and, 252
Skeletal muscle, *Veratrum* alkaloids, effect of on, 440–441, 449–450
Smoking, hypertension and, 41
Smooth muscle, *Veratrum* alkaloids, effect of on, 442
Sodium azide, 16
Sodium nitroprusside, 16
Spironolactone, 467
 as antihypertensive agent, 268–270
Supplemental blood pressure, 13, 14–15, 52
Sympathetic nervous system
 adrenergic blockade, 99–100
 antihypertensive agents suppressing, 98–104

Sympathetic nervous system—*continued*
 blood pressure-regulatory function of, 95–98
 ganglionic blockade, 101–102
 reserpine, effect of on, 207–210
Sympatholytic drugs
 tricyclic antidepressants, use with, 478–479
 use in combinations, 469–471
Synthalin, 129
Syrosingopine, 90, 104, 197, 205

T

Tachycardia, β-adrenergic blocking agents and, 383
Tenseness, hypertension and, 41
Tersavid, 395
Tetraethylammonium bromide, 281
Tetraethylammonium chloride, 280
Tetrahydroisoquinolines, 362
Tetrahydronaphthalines, 361
2,2,6,6-Tetramethylpiperidine, 132, 306
3,3,4,4-Tetramethylpyrrolidine, 134
Tetramines, 296
 as ganglionic blocking agents, 297–298
Tetrazole, 355
Thiazide derivatives
 ethacrynic acid, use with, 467
 pargyline, use with, 472
 side effects of, 465 ff.
 sympatholytic drugs, use with, 470
α-Thiophenylpropionic acid, 168
Thiophenylpyruvic acids, 159–160
Tolazoline, 357, 360
 pharmacological effects of, 374–375
Tranquilizers, antihypertensive drugs, use with, 476–477
Tranylcypromine, 403, 404–405
 cheese in diet and, 422–423
Triamterene, thiazides, use with, 467
s-Triazolo[3,4-a]phthalazines, 229–230
N-(2,3,4-Trihydroxybenzyl)-hydrazine, 172, 175
Trihydroxybenzylhydrazine, as decarboxylase inhibitor, 179
Trimetaphane, dosage of, 292
Trimetaphane camphorsulfonate, 287
Trimethidinium, dosage of, 292
Trimethidinium methosulfate, 285
2,2,6-Trimethylpiperidine, 317

Trinitrin, 16
Tropenzylium, 288
Tryptamine, bilateral nephrectomy and, 49
Tryptamine derivatives, as monoamine oxidase inhibitors, 402–403
Tubocurarine, 280
Tyramine, 121
  hypertension and, 46
  methyldopa and, 184
Tyrosine hydroxylase, 154

V

Veracevine, 431, 434, 435
Veratric acid esters, 435
Veratridine, 436, 439, 450
Veratrum alkaloids, 429 ff.
  chemistry of, 430–435
  clinical uses of, 451–453

Veratrum alkaloids—*continued*
  distribution, *in vivo*, 450–452
  emetic activity of, 446–448, 449, 453
  hypotensive activity of, 444–446, 447–448
  pharmacological action of, 439 ff.
  side effects and toxicity of, 452–453
Veratrum viride, 106

X

Xylocholine, 115–116, 123

Y

Yohimbanes, synthetic, 199

Z

Zygadenilic acid δ-lactone, 431, 434-435
Zygadenine, 431, 434, 435

47533